USEFUL REFERENCE SERIES, NO. 99

CLASSIFIED LIST OF PERIODICALS

FOR

THE COLLEGE LIBRARY

Fifth Edition

Classified List of Periodicals for the College Library

By

EVAN IRA FARBER
Librarian, Earlham College

*

with the assistance of

THOMAS G. KIRK, JR.
Science Librarian, Earlham College

and

JAMES R. KENNEDY, JR.
Reference Librarian, Earlham College

*

FIFTH EDITION
Revised and Enlarged

*

WESTWOOD, MASS.
THE F. W. FAXON COMPANY, INC.
1972

COPYRIGHT BY

F. W. FAXON COMPANY, INC.

1972

*

No material in this book may be
used for commercial purposes
without the author's permission.

*

International Standard Book Number 0-87305-099-1
Library of Congress Card Number 72-76264

PRINTED IN THE UNITED STATES OF AMERICA

For Hope

CONTENTS

A NOTE ON THE NEW EDITION

Only titles that began publication before 1969 are included in this list. This fundamental limitation was necessitated by the fact that most of the work on individual periodicals was done in 1969 and 1970 (though I have tried to make revisions up to 1972) and I felt it was impossible to evaluate adequately titles that had only recently started, even if I could have become aware of the existence of all those new ones that deserved evaluation. This decision was made reluctantly; I realize that librarians find it more difficult to select new journals than older, established ones, but I did not see how I could make a responsible contribution toward relieving that difficulty. Of course there were some titles that began in 1969 or 1970 which I would have had no hesitation in recommending but I felt that by including these I would create an invidious distinction between them and those I did not know or those of which I was not quite as certain. So I chose what I considered the lesser disadvantage, a cut-off date of 1968, and, as a partial response to objections, hope to update the present listing with periodic supplements. What the format of these will be is not yet clear, and suggestions from users would be appreciated.

The *Classified List of Periodicals* appeared originally in the *Wilson Library Bulletin,* October, 1931 to June, 1932, and was first published in book form in 1934; there was a second edition in 1938, which was revised and enlarged in 1940; a third edition came out in 1946, and a fourth in 1957.

The purpose of the present edition, like the earlier ones, is to provide an effective aid in selecting journals for: (1) supplying reading collateral to students' courses; (2) keeping the faculty informed of developments in their fields; (3) affording good general and recreational reading; (4) providing in some measure for the research needs of advanced students and faculty. When in doubt, the ultimate criterion for inclusion was "Is this periodical *important* for a four-year liberal arts college library?" Admittedly, such a criterion is not the most precise one and, frequently, the selection came down to a matter of personal taste or prejudice.

In the previous edition, the selection was much less personal as I felt somewhat constrained by the choices of the original editors — Guy Lyle and Virginia Trumper — and by my lack of experience. But I no longer feel that constraint (though my appreciation to those two for their trust remains unabated); during the intervening years I have been working closely with periodicals in many ways — as a university serials librarian, as a college library administrator and reference librarian, and as a teacher of courses on periodicals — and my knowledge of periodicals and their place in a college library is, I hope, sound enough to advise librarians for whom the world of periodicals is not as central to their interests as it is to me.

In selecting titles for inclusion, the first step was to examine the titles in the previous edition. It seemed sensible for several reasons to drop titles that are still extant for very good reasons only, and just a few have been dropped. The second step was to examine the lists of current subscriptions and of holdings of about fifty libraries of colleges which I felt represent a range of programs, geographical areas and sizes, though focusing on those with enrollments of less than 2000 students and recognized for their academic quality. The examination of these lists helped in two ways: they suggested titles that I had considered but which appeared on the lists only rarely. Then I searched the bibliographical literature — critical, descriptive and inventorial — all of which appears in the Bibliography. (Here I must acknowledge my debt to Bill Katz's *Magazines for Libraries*. Although our points of reference differed, and I disagreed with a number of his evaluations, his admirable book was extremely helpful in checking my bibliographical information and qualitative estimates.) In the next place, individual subject areas were discussed with various faculty members chosen for their professional competence and their congeniality with the purpose of the list, and two members of Earlham's library staff helped particularly with the selection and annotation of titles in the sections in which they are especially competent — Tom Kirk in the various Science sections and Jim Kennedy in the Religion and General sections. But after all of these, perhaps the most important criterion consisted of my personal preferences and biases, and since they have affected the choices much more than in previous editions, some elaboration seems appropriate.

Two aspects of my experience at Earlham College have led to the inclusion of a number of titles which might otherwise have been overlooked, or perhaps noted but not included. One of these has been an involvement with area studies which has convinced me that materials on the non-Western world must be given a larger place in most academic libraries than they have been. (The use of the term "non-Western" is perhaps misleading, since it includes Latin America and East Europe, as well as Asia, Africa, the Middle East and Oceania. It is, however, as good a term as has been suggested to encompass those geographical areas that have generally been neglected in most colleges and universities, and the term has received the respectable, if unofficial, imprimatur of the American Universities Field Staff, whose *A Select Bibliography: Asia, Africa, Eastern Europe, Latin America* helped define the term.) Though my conviction came about quite fortuitously — merely because I happened to be at a college where there was a strong and growing emphasis on the non-Western world — it is no less sincere, and like many converts, I became a proselytizer, working through a variety of means to encourage other institutions to increase the size and use of their collections of non-Western materials. I am more convinced than ever of this need, and it is manifested in this list by the new section "Area Studies" and the substantial number of recommended periodicals which are from or about the non-Western world.

My experience as a Reference Librarian has led me to list and describe many of the features of individual titles, particularly those features that have some bibliographical use. I have come to realize that periodicals are not used as much as they might be for reference purposes and I assume this is because reference librarians are not always familiar with their contents. Hence, I've tried to call attention to such features.

The other aspect of experience at Earlham has been my working with, at one time or another, almost every part of the College's administration and academic program. This involvement has made me much more aware of the literature on higher education and the crucial role the library can have in acquiring and keeping this material and, no less important, in informing administrators and faculty of items of interest. So few libraries do much to act as information centers for the most fundamental concerns of their own institutions, yet the problems all liberal arts colleges face today — problems that are causing them to work on educational reform and administrative efficiency — mean that libraries should be playing a much more important role.

The annotations in this edition are, on the average, much longer than those in previous editions. Some of this additional length is due to the historical information on many of the titles as well as to the more detailed descriptions of individual features. I must confess to an uncertainty as to whether these historical comments derive from my long-standing interest in the history of periodicals or from my belief that such comments would be helpful for deciding on the purpose of backfiles and for some reference purposes. I suspect the former, but I hope the latter is sufficient justification. The length and depth of these historical comments varies greatly from title to title, according to the availability of information, to the importance of such information for considering the purchase of backfiles, and to whether or not the history seemed interesting. Most of the increase in length of annotations, however, is the result of the more detailed description of features and departments, and the more specific data about the length and number of book reviews. (Users of the list will quickly realize that the phrase "signed and critical reviews" has been repeated mercilessly. I apologize for this and other repetitions, but that was one of the most troublesome aspects of writing the annotations: to try to give them some variety, to make them a bit more readable. But, after all, how many ways can one describe briefly the average length of articles in a periodical? Or, note that they are "scholarly", or "written for the intelligent layman"? Roget can carry one just so far.)

Some comments on the change in classifications are appropriate. "Area Studies" and its subdivisions is new; the reason for adding it was alluded to above. "Modern Languages" combines the previous edition's separate sections devoted to German and the Romance Languages; this was done to permit the single listing of the several periodicals which cover many modern languages as well as to provide a place for Russian; it also reflected a fairly common development among college departmental structures — that is, the consolidation of several languages into one department. The greatly increased interest in films and film-making led me to remove journals on these from the "General" category and include them with the other performing arts under "Music, Drama, Film, Dance." During the past ten or fifteen years, the tremendous growth of interdisciplinary studies and the many important journals reflecting this growth have made much more difficult what used to be an easy classification of subjects and assignment of titles to those subjects. My partial solution for the latter has been to assign the periodicals with their annotations to the subjects under which they seemed most important, and to simply note them under other subjects, with *see* references to the more important ones.

The number of annotated titles is distributed as follows: Area Studies 62; Art 24; Astronomy 6; Biology 50; Book Reviews and Book Selection 16; Chemistry 24; Classics and Archeology 20; Economics and Business Administration 65; Education 78; English 59; General 108; Geography 15; Geology 19; History 34; Home Economics 16; Indexes 26; Library Science 18; Mathematics 17; Modern Languages 39; Music, Drame, Film, Dance 25; Philosophy 24; Physical Education and Health 9; Physics 9; Political Science 50; Psychology 43; Religion 18; Science 19; Sociology and Anthropology 35. These total 939; another 111 titles are listed in the descriptive notes or in footnotes. The total 1048 titles are all included in the alphabetical list at the end which serves as an index.

For comparison's sake, the previous edition had a total of 601 titles — 544 fully annotated, with 57 in the notes. Another comparison: in this edition 367 titles are recommended for first purchase; the previous edition 197 were. It would have been interesting to compare cost figures — the percentage increase over the previous edition would have been, I'm afraid, appalling, and I'll be happy to have others play with such figures.

I should like to acknowledge the assistance of individuals, especially members of the Earlham faculty, whose formal and informal comments and advice helped in the selection and evaluation of journals. Thanks are due the many libraries whose collections were made available to me — in particular those of Antioch College, Miami University, Indiana University and Columbia University. I am grateful to Earlham College for a summer's sabbatical to work on the book and for the administration's continuing interest, moral support and patience. Leo Chang, of Earlham's library staff, generously helped in finding fugitive LC card numbers. Jim Kennedy and Tom Kirk used their knowledge, energy and time to research, discuss and evaluate many of the titles in the list; for their good sense and assistance I am most appreciative. Finally, to Hope, my wife and secretary, my indebtedness could not be sufficiently expressed in words. Not only did she do all the typing, but her extraordinarily efficient and orderly mind caught a multitude of inconsistencies and errors, and her acute literary sensibility smoothed many an awkward sentence. Moreover, her patience and encouragement (and prodding, when necessary) were things every author or editor needs, especially when the task seems endless. Without her assistance and advice, this book would neer have been done.

BIBLIOGRAPHY

This bibliography includes only the references used since the last edition, and only those relating to an entire field or at least to a group of journals. Originally I intended to list the articles, editorial notes, anniversary announcements, historical studies, etc., treating individual journals, but the number grew too rapidly. Some time in the future I would like to compile a bibliography of such items relating to the periodicals in this book, and would be happy to receive contributions from readers.

Association of American Geographers. Commission on College Geography. *A Basic Geographical Library: A Selected and Annotated Book List for American Colleges.* Comp. and ed. by Martha Church, Robert E. Huke, Wilbur Zelinsky. (Commission on College Geography, Publication No. 2) Washington, D.C.: The Association, 1966.

Baumgardt, David. *Philosophical Periodicals: An Annotated World List.* Washington, D.C.: Library of Congress, 1952.

Berton, Peter and Eugene Wu. *Contemporary China; A Research Guide.* (Hoover Institution Bibliographical Series: XXXI) Stanford, Calif.: The Hoover Institution on War, Revolution and Peace, Stanford University, 1967.

Billott, Mary M. "French Language and Literature Periodicals: An Annotated Select List of Current Serial Publications." *International Library Review* 1:283-304 (1969).

Bleznick, Donald W. "A Guide to Journals in the Hispanic Field: A Selected Annotated List of Journals Central to the Study of Spanish and Spanish American Language and Literature." *Hispania* 52:723-37 (November, 1969).

Boehm, Eric H., ed. *Bibliographies on International Relations and World Affairs, An Annotated Directory.* (Bibliography and Reference Series, No. 2) Santa Barbara, Calif.: Clio Press, for the American Bibliographical Center, 1965.

Bowen, Jean and Paul T. Jackson. "A Study of Periodicals Indexed in [MLA] *Notes'* Index of Record Reviews." *MLA Notes* 22:945-55 (Winter, 1965-66).

Bowen, Willis H. "Selective Critical Bibliography of Interest to Students of French and Spanish." *Bulletin of Bibliography* 27:29-33, 41 (April-June, 1970).

Brock, Clifton. *The Literature of Political Science; A Guide for Students, Librarians and Teachers.* New York: R.R. Bowker Co., 1969.

Bryant, E.T. *Music Librarianship; A Practical Guide.* London: James Clarke & Co., 1959. Esp. ch. 2, "Reference Books and Periodicals."

Byrd, Milton Bruce and Arnold L. Goldsmith. *Publication Guide for Literary and Linguistic Scholars.* (Wayne State University Studies, No. 4) Detroit, Mich.: Wayne State University Press, 1958.

Camp, William L. *Guide to Periodicals in Education.* Metuchen, N.J.: The Scarecrow Press, 1968.

Chamberlin, Mary W. *Guide to Art Reference Books.* Chicago: American Library Association, 1959. Chapter 18, "Periodicals."

Chicago. University. Press. *The University of Chicago Press, 1891-1965: Catalogue of Books & Journals.* Chicago, Ill.: The University of Chicago Press, 1966.

Coats, A. W. "The American Economic Association's Publications: An Historical Perspective." *Journal of Economic Literature,* 7:57-68 (March, 1969).

Creager, Jean, C., ed. *Guidelines and Suggested Titles for Library Holdings in Undergraduate Biology.* Commission on Undergraduate Education in the Biological Sciences, Publication No. 32. Washington, D.C.: The Commission, 1971.

Duckles, Vincent, comp. *Music Reference and Research Materials: An Annotated Bibliography.* 2d ed. New York: The Free Press, 1967.

Foreman, Milton E. "Publication Trends in Counseling Journals." *Journal of Counseling Psychology,* 13:481-85 (Winter, 1966).

Gerber, William. "Philosophical Journals." *Encyclopedia of Philosophy,* 1967, VI, pp. 199-216.

Gerstenberger, Donna and George Hendrick. *Second Directory of Periodicals Publishing Articles in English and American Literature and Language.* Denver, Colo.: Alan Swallow, 1965.

Gillin, Donald et al., eds. *East Asia: A Bibliography for Undergraduate Libraries.* (Foreign Area Materials Center, Occasional Publication No. 10) Williamsport, Pa.: Bro-Dart Publishing Co., 1970.

Harmon, Robert B. *Political Science: A Bibliographical Guide to the Literature.* Metuchen, N.J.: The Scarecrow Press, 1965.

———. ———.*Supplement, 1968.* Metuchen, N.J.: The Scarecrow Press, 1968.

Harris, Chauncey D. *Annotated List of Selected Current Geographical Serials of the Americas and the Iberian Peninsula.* Chicago, Ill.: Center for International Studies, University of Chicago, 1967.

Horecky, Paul L., ed. *East Central Europe; a Guide to Basic Publications.* Chicago, Ill.: University of Chicago Press, 1969.

———. *Russia and the Soviet Union; a Bibliographic Guide to Western-Language Publications.* Chicago, Ill.: University of Chicago Press, 1965.

Jacob, Louis A., Stephen N. Hay et al., eds. *South Asia: A Bibliography for Undergraduate Libraries.* (Foreign Area Materials Center, Occasional Publication No. 11) Williamsport, Pa.: Bro-Dart Publishing Co., 1970.

Jakobovitz, Leon A. and Charles E. Osgood. "Connotations of Twenty Psychological Journals to their Professional Readers." *American Psychologist* 22:792-800 (September, 1967).

Johnson, D. Kay. "German Language and Literature Serials: An Annotated Select List of Journals Dealing with German Language and Literature." *International Library Review,* 1:143-65 (Jan., 1969).

Johnson, Donald Clay et al., eds. *Southeast Asia: A Bibliography for Undergraduate Studies*. (Foreign Area Materials Center. Occasional Publication No. 13) Williamsport, Pa.: Bro-Dart Publishing Co., 1970.

Katz, William A. and Berry Gargal. *Magazines for Libraries*. New York: R. R. Bowker Co., 1969.

Keenan, Stella and Pauline Atherton. The Journal Literature of Physics; A Comprehensive Study Based on Physics Abstracts (Science Abstracts, Section A, 1961 issues). New York: American Institute of Physics, 1964.

King, A. Hyatt. "Periodicals." *Grove's Dictionary of Music and Musicians* (5th ed.) VI, pp. 637-72.

Koster, Donald. "Abstracting Services and American Studies." *American Quarterly* 17:421-27 (Summer, 1965).

Langlois, Pierre et André Mareuil. *Guide Bibliographique des Études Littéraires*. 3d ed., rev. et cor. Paris: Hachette, 1965. [c.1958]

Library of Congress. *Children's Literature: A Guide to Reference Sources*. Prepared under the direction of Virginia Haviland. Washington, D.C.: Library of Congress, 1966.

Lins, Joseph L. and Robert A. Rees. *Scholars' Guide to Journals of Education and Educational Psychology*. Madison, Wis.: Dembar Educational Research Service, 1965.

Lock, C.B. Muriel. *Geography: A Reference Handbook*. Hamden, Conn. and London: Archon Books & Clive Bingley, 1968.

McGowan, John P. "Science Magazines for Laymen." *RQ* 8:3-12 (Fall, 1968).

Mandelbaum, David G., et al. *Resources for the Teaching of Anthropology, with a Basic List of Books and Periodicals for College Libraries*. Berkeley, Calif.: University of California Press, 1963.

Marquardt, D.N., ed. *Guidelines and Suggested Title List for Undergraduate Chemistry Libraries*. (Advisory Council on College Chemistry, Serial Publication Number 44) Stanford, Calif.: Advisory Council on College Chemistry, Department of Chemistry, Stanford University, Sept., 1969.

Mason, John Brown. *Research Resources; Annotated Guide to the Social Sciences. Volume 1, International Relations & Recent History; Indexes, Abstracts and Periodicals*. Santa Barbara, Calif.: American Bibliographical Center - Clio Press, 1968.

Mathematical Association of America. Committee on the Undergraduate Program in Mathematics. Basic Library List. First ed., Feb., 1963. (Mimeographed)

——. ——. Teacher Training Supplement to Basic Library List. April 4, 1965. (Mimeographed)

Merritt, LeRoy C., Martha Boaz, and Kenneth S. Tisdel. *Reviews in Library Book Selection*. Detroit, Mich.: Wayne State University Press, 1958.

Mott, Frank Luther. *A History of American Magazines*. 5 vols. Cambridge, Mass.: Harvard University Press, 1930-68.

Muller, Robert H., Theodore J. Spahn, and Janet M. Spahn. *From Radical Left to Extreme Right; Current Periodicals of Protest, Controversy, or Dissent—USA*. 2d ed. rev. and enl. Ann Arbor, Mich.: Campus Publishers, 1970.

New Catholic Encyclopedia. New York: McGraw-Hill, 1967. Passim.

"Periodicals, Dance (U.S.) " *in* Chujoy, Anatole and P. W. Manchester, comp. & ed., *The Dance Encyclopedia*, rev. and enl. edition. New York: Simon & Schuster, 1967.

Pittsburgh. University. Department of Economics. *International Economics Selections Bibliography*. Series II, Basic Lists in Special Fields: Section A, Selected Bibliography of Economics Reference Works and Professional Journals; Section B, Citizenship Reference Library. Pittsburgh, Pa.: Department of Economics, University of Pittsburgh, December, 1965.

Sable, Martin H. *A Guide to Latin American Studies*. 2 vols. (Reference Series No. 4) Los Angeles, Calif.: Latin American Center, University of California, 1967.

Schwab-Felisch, Hans. "Quality Periodicals [in Germany Today]" *American-German Review* 31:26-9 (April-May, 1965).

Somit, Albert and Joseph Tanenhaus. *American Political Science: A Profile of a Discipline*. New York: Atherton Press, 1964.

——. *The Development of American Political Science: From Burgess to Behavioralism*. Boston, Mass.: Allyn and Bacon, 1967.

Sutherland, Zena. "Current Reviewing of Children's Books." *Library Quarterly* 37:110-18 (January, 1967).

Tompkins, Margaret and Norma Shirley, comp. *A Checklist of Serials in Psychology and Allied Fields*. Troy, N.Y.: Whitston Publishing Co., 1969.

UNESCO. *Liste mondiale des periodiques specialises dans les sciences sociales. World List of Social Science Periodicals*. 3 ed., rev. et augm. Paris: Unesco, 1966.

U.S. Superintendent of Documents. *Government Periodicals and Subscription Services*. Washington, D.C.: Government Printing Office, 1967.

Varet, Gilbert and Paul Kurtz, eds. *International Directory of Philosophy and Philosophers*. New York: Humanities Press, 1965.

Watanabe, Ruth. "Current Periodicals for Music Libraries." *MLA Notes* 23: 225-35 (December, 1966).

White, Cynthia L. *Women's Magazines, 1693-1968*. London: Michael Joseph Ltd., 1970. Esp. ch. 8, "The Women's Press in America."

Winckler, Paul A. *Library Periodicals Directory: A Selected List of Periodicals Currently Publishing Throughout the World Relating to Library Work*. Brookville, N.Y.: Graduate Library School of Long Island University, Merriweather Campus, 1963.

ABBREVIATIONS

Art I.	Art Index
Alt.Pr.I.	Alternative Press Index
A.S.T.I.	Applied Science & Technology Index
Bio.Ag.I.	Biological & Agricultural Index
Br.Hum.I.	British Humanities Index
Bus.Per.I.	Business Periodicals Index
B.R.D.	Book Review Digest
Ed.I.	Education Index
In.Ltl.Mag.	Index to Little Magazines
In.Per.Negroes	Index to Periodicals By and About Negroes
In.Rel.Per.Lit.	Index to Religious Periodical Literature
Lib.Lit.	Library Literature
Ment.Hlth.B.R.I.	Mental Health Book Review Index
Music I.	Music Index
P.A.I.S.	Public Affairs Information Service
R.G.	Readers Guide to Periodical Literature
S.S.H.I.	Social Sciences & Humanities Index

*An asterisk before a title indicates that the title is recommended for first purchase. (See "Introduction", p. xii.)

AREA STUDIES/GENERAL

AMERICAN ORIENTAL SOCIETY.   JOURNAL.   v. 1, 1843/49-

Quarterly.   New Haven, Conn. $10.00

The Society "was founded in 1842 for the promotion of research and publication in Oriental languages, literatures, history and art. Its field embraces the entire Orient from the Mediterranean to the Pacific." Until 1896, the *Journal* was issued in parts or whole numbers issued irregularly; from 1897 to 1907, semi-annually; then an annual, and in 1910 it became a quarterly.

The articles, which are very scholarly, and contributed by Orientalists from universities and institutes here and abroad, are almost never on current or even recent topics, but aside from this, they range over all geographical areas of the Orient and all chronological periods, and vary in length from just a few pages to an entire issue. 17 supplements were issued between 1935 and 1954, but now most longer pieces appear in the Society's other series. Review articles appear frequently. The number of book reviews per issue varies considerably, from none to 70; they are all signed and critical, and average about 1000 words, though often are several times that.

An important journal for ancient history, Old Testament studies, Islamic studies, Oriental language, literature and thought, and Oriental history up to about 1800.

Indexed in: S.S.H.I.   12-32032

JOURNAL OF ASIAN AND AFRICAN STUDIES.   v. 1, 1966-

Quarterly.   Leiden, Netherlands. $12.00

"Presents a scholarly account of studies of man and society in the developing nations of Asia and Africa. It endeavours to fill a need in the field in that it invites contributions from anthropology, sociology, history, and related social sciences into a concerted emphasis upon building up systematic knowledge and using the knowledge derived from pure research for the reconstruction of societies entering a phase of advanced technology."

Edited in Canada, with an international editorial board, its articles, which are generally of moderate length, are mostly by younger scholars from different countries, and are in all areas of the social sciences, with an emphasis on sociology, anthropology and political science. Notes and news of activities, conferences, new programs, etc. The book reviews, signed and critical are mostly 400-750 words long. Also list of books received. The journal was founded to publish articles "of a scientific nature which would be neither too abstract for the undergraduate student, nor too popular to be of scientific value," so that it is especially appropriate for college libraries.

75-1539

JOURNAL OF COMMONWEALTH LITERATURE.   no. 1, 1965-

Semi-annually.   London. $5.00

Published by a commercial firm along with the University of Leeds, its aim "is to provide information to writers and scholars throughout the world about creative writing in English from all Commonwealth countries (except Great Britain, which is already adequately covered)." Issues contain articles of criticism and historical studies on all aspects of Commonwealth literature, contributed by eminent British and Commonwealth scholars. The geographical coverage can be shown best by listing the sections of the *Annual Bibliography of Commonwealth Literature,* an extensive listing of books and articles arranged under these areas: Commonwealth-General; Africa-General; East and Central Africa; Southern Africa; West Africa; Australia; Canada; Ceylon; India, Malaysia and Singapore; New Zealand; Pakistan; the West Indies. Each section is compiled by an authority on that area who also contributes a short introductory essay commenting on some of the more significant or interesting developments. Each section also includes translations and a listing of the more important literary journals. Up to 10 signed and critical reviews of novels, poetry and critical works, mostly at least 1000 words, and often much longer.

An important journal for institutions with much interest in comparative literature, or for institutions with strong area studies programs, and essential for those doing much with African literature.

65-9987

JOURNAL OF DEVELOPING AREAS.   v. 1, 1966-

Quarterly.   Macomb, Ill. $8.00

Concerned with all aspects of area studies, and especially with the interaction of phenomena in the process of development. Issues contain 4 or 5 scholarly articles of moderate length, the coverage fairly evenly divided among politics, economics and sociology, and among the various geographical areas. Contributors include professors and officials from both this country and abroad. An extensive "News and Notes" section of research in progress, fellowships, grants, conferences, new publications relating to development study. 15-20 book reviews per issue, signed and critical, usually 500-1000 words, but occasionally longer. List of publications received. Each issue carries an extensive *Bibliography of Periodicals and Monographs,* organized by geographical area. Covering a large number of periodicals, foreign and domestic, and documentary sources, it is an important current bibliography on the subject. A very useful journal for courses in development economics and comparative politics and sociology.

70-1323

LONDON.   UNIVERSITY.   SCHOOL OF ORIENTAL AND AFRICAN STUDIES.   BULLETIN.   v. 1, 1917-

3 nos./yr.   London. $33.15

Contains rather specialized articles—generally between 6 and 12 an issue—of varied length, on the languages, cultures, history or society of Asia, the Near East and Africa, with least attention to Africa. Though Biblical stud-

ies are not included, the articles do treat subjects as early as the ancient
Near East, or even prehistoric archaeology; almost never do they treat anything more recent than the 19th century. There are a large number of book
reviews—usually more than 50 longer ones, mostly 500-1000 words but
often up to several thousand, plus a smaller number of short notices. These
are all signed and critical, and cover the more specialized works in African
and Oriental studies. Also a list of books received.

For advanced students and faculty.

Indexed in: Br.Hum.I.   26-23015

*ASIA.   v. 1, 1964-

Quarterly.   N.Y. $6.00

A major activity of the Asia Society, which publishes this journal, is providing "a wide range of information on Asia by means of lectures and conferences focused on various Asian countries." The lectures and papers given serve as the major source for *Asia's* contents, which are "selected to provide representative geographical and topical coverage." Authors are scholars, journalists, U.S., U.N. and foreign government officials, and writers and artists. Issues contain from 4 to 6 articles, varying in degrees of scholarliness, but readable and reliable, on all aspects of Asian life, politics and culture, with an almost perfect topical balance in each issue, though in some issues 2 or 3 articles may treat aspects of a single topic. No reviews.

64-9388

ASIAN AFFAIRS.   v. 1, 1914-

3 nos./yr.   London. $12.00

Subtitled "Journal of the Royal Central Asian Society," that was its full title until 1970. The present title reflects much more accurately the journal's content, since it does cover all of Asia. The Society was founded to fill a geographical gap—at the time, there was no society devoted to the study of Central Asia. Its interests gradually widened, and since 1945 at least, it has covered the entire continent, from the Middle East to Japan.

Each issue contains 4 or 5 articles or lectures on all aspects of politics, history, economics, geography, religion, etc., of Asia and the Middle East, by scholars, former government officials, military officers and others who have spent long periods in the areas covered. The contributions are somewhat uneven in quality and a number are simply descriptive, but for the most part they are interesting and useful because of the personal involvement of the authors. Also carries news of the Society and reports of its meetings and officers. Occasional review articles, about 35-50 individual reviews in each issue, signed and critical, varying greatly in length, but averaging 500-750 words. A useful journal, but not of primary importance.

Indexed in: P.A.I.S.   59-33349

*ASIAN SURVEY.   v. 1, 1961-

Monthly.   Berkeley, Calif. $10.00

"A monthly review of contemporary Asian affairs," it is published by the University of California (by its Institute of International Studies to 1969), but its contributors, among whom are some of the leading authorities in Asian affairs, are from many universities and institutes, both domestic and foreign. Usually 5 or 6 articles per issue, mostly of moderate length, on all areas of Asia, covering politics, economics and sociology, but with great emphasis on political affairs. Issues are occasionally devoted to a single topic, e.g., Agricultural Prospects, Higher Education in India, and since 1963, the first two issues of each year contain "A Survey of Asia in 19--," a country-by-country survey of internal and foreign politics during the preceding year. It is perhaps the best scholarly source for a background analysis of the current Asian scene. There are no book reviews, but an occasional brief section, "Recent Books on Asia," critically annotates a few titles.

Indexed in: S.S.H.I.   64-44237

*FAR EASTERN ECONOMIC REVIEW.   v. 1, 1946-

Weekly.   Hong Kong. $30 air freight ($56 air mail)

"A Weekly Journal of Trade, Industry, Finance, Transport and Public Affairs in South and East Asia." Three characteristics of the *Review* should be pointed out: 1) it covers all Asia, from the Philippines to Pakistan; 2) its comments on political and social matters make it of much wider interest than its title might indicate—one might regard it as the Asian counterpart of the *Economist;* 3) it is generally reliable and objective. Regular features include: "Far Eastern Round-Up," a weekly summary of events; "Regional Affairs," a country-by-country survey of political affairs especially; "Business Reviews," comments on specific industries or economic developments and financial and stock market figures; "Economic Indicators," the latest monthly figures for the chief countries. Each number also carries a few feature articles; special surveys, reporting in depth on a country, an industry, or an important issue—e.g., Banking in Asia, Australia in Asia—appear fairly often (one or two a month, now). The section "Bookshelf," in almost every issue, contains only one or two reviews usually, mostly just 500-600 words long, but they are good. Overall, the *Review* is an excellent source of well-balanced information and interpretation on current events, providing an expert and different viewpoint from many Western sources. An important publication for students in economics and international affairs, and essential where there is much interest in Asian affairs.

Indexed in: P.A.I.S.   51-33412

*JOURNAL OF ASIAN STUDIES.   v. 1, 1941-

Quarterly (5 nos.)   Ann Arbor, Mich. $30.00

Formerly (until 1956) the *Far Eastern Quarterly,* it is the official publication of the Association for Asian Studies (called through February, 1957 the Far Eastern Association). The leading scholarly journal in the field of Asian studies, it covers all disciplines of the social sciences and humanities relating to East, Southeast, and South Asia, from Japan to Pakistan. Each regular number carries 5 to 10 research articles, some shorter articles carried as "Notes," and frequently one or several review articles. The signed book reviews occupy from 50 to 90 pages, with as many as 100 titles reviewed; these reviews are all signed and critical, averaging about 800 words; also some shorter "Book Notes," and a list of books received. The fifth number of each volume (dated September, but recently published 6 months or more late) is the invaluable *Bibliography of Asian Studies,* the most comprehensive current American bibliography in the field. It is a classified listing of almost all Western-language books and articles in scholarly periodicals that appeared during the previous calendar year. The 1969 number contains over 13,000 items.

An essential journal where there is any serious work done in Asian studies, and because the journal is not primarily concerned with current developments, a back file is also important.

Indexed in: P.A.I.S.   43-14717
              S.S.H.I.

MODERN ASIAN STUDIES.   v. 1, 1967-

Quarterly.   London. $9.50

Established on the initiative of several British schools and departments of Asian studies, "its concern is with modern Asian societies as seen from the standpoints of the several social sciences (including human geography and modern history)," covering Asia from West Pakistan to Japan. Each issue carries 3 to 5 articles, from 2000 to 6000 words in length, by scholars from universities throughout the world. Occasional issues devoted to a single topic—e.g., the Meiji Restoration, Gandhi. Generally between 5 and 10 book reviews per issue, all signed and critical, mostly 500-1000 words in length; also an occasional review article. An important journal for advanced undergraduates and faculty in Asian studies.

73-200129

*PACIFIC AFFAIRS.   v. 1, 1926-

Quarterly.   Vancouver, B.C. $7.00

Pacific Affairs was for many years the organ of the Institute of Pacific Relations (in its first two years it was known as the Institute's *News Bulletin*), though it did not necessarily reflect its sponsor's views. With the disappearance of the I.P.R. in 1960, the journal was taken over by the University of British Columbia. Each issue contains 4 or 5 scholarly articles, of medium length, on Asia and the Pacific area, mostly concerned with current or recent political matters, though with some attention to the social and economic events that impinge on politics. "Notes and Comments" contain briefer articles or reports, and responses to or comments on previously published articles. Contributors are professors and government officials from many areas. Almost every issue has at least one review article in addition to a large number of book reviews—as many as 90, averaging 500-600 words, plus 20 "Briefly Noted," of 300-400. All are signed and critical. An excellent journal for undergraduate study of Asian affairs. The articles are reliable, not too long, and, though scholarly, not so specialized as to be useful only to scholars. Should be in every library for courses in Asian and international affairs.

Indexed in: B.R.D.   39-1202
          P.A.I.S.
          S.S.H.I.

*CHINA QUARTERLY.   v. 1, 1960-

Quarterly.   London. $7.50

Its claim that it is "the only western journal specializing in all aspects of contemporary China" is probably true, but it is important also because of the quality of the articles: its contributors are the world's foremost scholars on China. While they obviously do not all write from the same viewpoint, it may fairly be said that in general their theoretical frame of reference balances the "Kremlinologist" approach of so many American writers on China. The articles of course stress politics; the other social sciences are frequently represented, but the humanities only rarely. The format of the issues varies; usually it consists of a number of articles, all on different, or perhaps on several subjects, though sometimes most of an issue will be devoted to a single topic—e.g., "Special Survey of Chinese Communist Literature," "Formosa." Regular features include "Comment" on previous articles; "Quarterly Chronicle and Documentation"—a "narrative, backed by documentation, of the major events of the preceding three months," though avoiding comment. The number of book reviews varies from just a few to more than 20—they are signed and critical and mostly 750-1000 words in length. As the leading journal of analysis of China, it is important for the library of any institution that studies international affairs.

Indexed in: P.A.I.S.   62-248

JAPAN INTERPRETER.   v. 1, 1963-

3 times/yr.   Tokyo. $12.00

Published by the Center for Japanese Social and Political Studies which was founded in 1962 "to promote mutual understanding between Japanese and people in other parts of the world." The journal, which until 1970 was titled the *Journal of Social and Political Ideas in Japan,* attempts to aid in this purpose by not only presenting "Japanese thinking, but also to relate it to the traditions out of which it has evolved, and to do so by offering translations which can stand as polished, integrated English essays in themselves." The first 5 volumes stressed recent and contemporary Japanese history; the new emphasis will be more on current events—youth, urban problems, ecology and environment, changing values, politics, business, foreign affairs, etc.—and contributions by non-Japanese will also be included. 5 or 6 articles in most issues, between 5000 and 15,000 words each, translated from leading academic and general journals and parts of books. Themes in the past have included: Education in Japan, 1943-1963; the Left-Wing Movement in Japan, 1945-1964; University and Society; 'Modern' Man and Modernization. Some issues have included an assortment of articles. Among the contributors are Japanese scholars and writers; the lengthy biography for each of them is one of the journal's useful features. To become a quarterly in 1971; hopefully, its new emphasis and face will enable it to keep on schedule, because it provides valuable insights into Japan and is useful for comparative government and sociology, as well as for Japanese studies.

66-84872

*JAPAN QUARTERLY.   v. 1, 1954-

Quarterly.   Tokyo. $7.00

Published by Asahi Shimbun, the publishers of Japan's largest newspaper, *Japan Quarterly* contains well-written, reliable articles on all aspects of Japanese life, history and culture, past and present. Contributors include staff members of the newspaper, Japanese and U.S. scholars, and other writers. The contents of each issue generally contain a number of short articles and essays on a variety of topics, including current affairs, literature, and reproductions of art or photographs of architecture. The Book Section consists of a regular column, "In the Magazines," which usually surveys attitudes on a current issue as reflected in various popular journals; from 3 to 6 signed and critical book reviews of western and Japanese books on Japan (according to one authority, the reviews are either very good or very bad—fortunately, the former predominate); a listing of "Recent Japanese Publications on Japan" that also includes documents. Finally, "Chronology" covers the quarter day-by-day in some detail. All articles have been written in or have been well translated into English. Because of the quality and breadth of the contributions, the *Japan Quarterly* is essential where there is much interest in Japan.

Indexed in: P.A.I.S.   56-34321

*PEKING REVIEW.   v. 1, 1958-

Weekly.   Peking. $4.00

Successor to *People's China,* which lasted from 1950 to 1957, the *Peking Review* is generally regarded as the most important English-language periodical published in mainland China. It contains mostly short articles and news items on current developments in China and in international affairs, and also translations of editorials, articles and documents from the major party organs. Also published in French, German, Spanish and Japanese editions. As an interpreter for the outside world of official Chinese viewpoints, it should be in every library where any work is done on contemporary China.

61-4993

Libraries with a special interest in this area should also consider several other mainland publications: (1) *Chinese Literature* (v. 1, 1951- $3.00), with its short stories, poetry, essays, literary criticism and art work, is an excellent instance of art in the service of the revolutionary state—e.g., a poem, "Pneumatic Drill So Militant," or a story, "An Old Couple Vie As Revolutionaries." (2) *China Pictorial* (no. 1, 1951- $3.00) and *China Reconstructs* (v. 1, 1951- $3.00) are both monthlies and both cover various aspects of contemporary China, but especially point up developments in science, technology, industry, and agriculture, profiles of individuals who have made some small but special contribution to the revolutionary effort, and contain articles on specific events and places. *China Pictorial* consists mostly of illustrations, a large portion of which are in color, and very well reproduced; *China Reconstructs* is mostly text, but includes many illustrations. Both are also published in a number of other languages.

An inexpensive and useful periodical is *China Notes* (v. 1, 1962 – $1.50). A quarterly, in newsletter format, it is sponsored by the China Committee of the National Council of the Churches of Christ, and is the successor to the NCCC's *China Bulletin*. Though especially concerned with religion in China, it is really much more eclectic, and contains many items, including those from official publications, on the general Chinese political, social and cultural scene.

CALCUTTA REVIEW.   v. 1, 1844;   n.s.v. 1, 1913;   ser. 3, v. 1, 1921; n.s.v. 1, 1969-

Quarterly.   Calcutta.   20s. $3.35

A general quarterly, containing articles mostly by faculty members at various Indian universities, with the largest number from Calcutta University, which publishes the journal. The articles cover all areas of "intellectual and educational interest," including politics, literature, history, philosophy, religion, etc., mostly of interest to the educated general reader, but some that are primarily for scholars. Its backfile is especially useful for examining in their historical context the ideas of the Anglo-Indian press, as the *Review* was long regarded as the most distinguished organ of the cultured English society in India. Today it represents a segment of Indian intelligentsia that is still very much in the British tradition: there are, for example, almost as many articles on English literature as on Indian.

SA 64-761

ECONOMIC AND POLITICAL WEEKLY.   v. 1, 1966-

Weekly.   Bombay, India. $10.00

Superseded (though really continuing) the *Economic Weekly*, which had begun in 1949. It is similar to the London *Economist* in purpose, in that it emphasizes matters of special concern to businessmen and others especially interested in the economy, as well as discussing political developments related to the economy and, to a lesser extent, social and cultural matters. Thus, there are articles on the caste system, on "Freedom of Speech and Contempt of Court," on urbanization, on "Hindu Conservatism in the Nineteenth Century," etc. With its own corps of correspondents, it carries many articles on the political, economic and social affairs of other countries. Four numbers a year have special sections devoted to a Review of Agriculture, and four others to a Review of Management. The initial number each year (2 or 3 numbers combined, actually) summarizes or surveys developments and prospects in many areas of the Indian economy. Usually 1 or 2 book reviews per issue, on mostly political or economic topics; these are all signed, and generally 1000-1500 words long.

Provides probably the best current coverage on Indian political and economic affairs.

Indexed in: P.A.I.S.   S A 67-2009

INDIA QUARTERLY.   v. 1, 1945-

Quarterly.   New Delhi. $5.00

"A Journal of International Affairs," it is published by the Indian Council of World Affairs, a non-government, non-partisan organization. Each issue contains usually 3 or 4 articles, averaging 7-8000 words, with a strong emphasis on Indian and Asian politics, economic and international relations, though occasionally treating matters such as the United Nations or even "Land and Labor Policy in Brazil." Contributors include Indian scholars, government officials and politicians, some with international reputations. Most issues contain 15-30 signed and critical reviews, primarily of Indian, but also of British and American books; these vary from 100 to over 1000 words in length, averaging about 500 words.

"Indian Books of the Quarter" contains a listing of current Indian publications—books, pamphlets and documents—in the social sciences. Some are briefly annotated.

An important journal for the study of Asian politics and foreign affairs.

47-29726

INDIAN LITERATURE.   v. 1, 1957-

Quarterly.   New Delhi. $3.65

Published by the Sahitya Akademi, India's national academy of letters, it consists of mostly short articles of literary criticism and history, poetry, stories and reviews. Most of the articles are, of course, on modern Indian writers and writing, but writers in the Western tradition, from Dante to Wallace Stevens, are frequently treated, and the Indian interpretations of these writers is often interesting. All contributions are in English, though many have been translated. One issue a year is devoted to useful reviews of Indian writing, surveying the trends in each of 15 or so major languages, including English, writing by Indians. Issues contain at the most 3 book reviews (often none); these are signed and critical, and vary greatly in length. The survey articles in particular make this a useful journal for the study of Indian culture or comparative literature.

SA 63-1678

JOURNAL OF SOUTHEAST ASIA STUDIES.   v. 1, 1970-

2 nos./yr.   Singapore.   S$17.00

The *Journal of Southeast Asian History,* published by the University of Singapore's Department of History, lasted from 1960 through 1969. In 1970, McGraw-Hill Far Eastern Publishers Ltd. took it over, though keeping the same editorial staff, and changed the title. Even under its original title, however, the journal increasingly had covered more than history, so that the change has been one of form rather than content. Its "main emphasis . . . is on the peoples and governments of Southeast Asia: how societies, cultures and institutions have evolved in the past and are evolving in the present; how indigenous forces have interacted with exogenous elements in shaping developmental patterns; how East and West are contending to determine the destinies of nations in the region; how the conflicts between the traditional and modernizing forces are being resolved; and how the problem of economic development are being solved."

Contributors include the foremost authorities on the area, from universities all over the world, with some preponderance of those from the area itself, their articles are "preferably" between 4000 and 8000 words. Issues are occasionally devoted to single topics; most issues contain about 15 reviews, signed and critical, averaging about 600-700 words.

Now that the lack of knowledge of this area has become notorious, increased attention will undoubtedly be given to it, and this journal is basic to any course that treats Southeast Asian history, politics or society.

Indexed in: S.S.H.I.

MODERN REVIEW.   v. 1, 1907-

Monthly.   Calcutta. $6.50

Founded at a vital junction of India's history, the journal played an important part in reflecting and stimulating thought about Indian nationalism, national culture and political institutions, and for a long period was by far the most influential Indian periodical. Between the two World Wars, its major role was interpreting India to the world and the world to the Indians; since then it has remained one of the more significant general English-language periodicals in the non-Western world. Its character is similar to that of the traditional British general journals such as *Blackwood's* or the *Contemporary Review,* with a balanced mixture of articles on economics, history, religion, politics, and art and literature. The articles are mostly fairly brief and aimed at the intelligent layman; in general, those on Indian or Asian matters are much more useful than the others which, for the Western reader, seem fairly pedestrian. Regular features include comments on current affairs and summaries of a few articles from other periodicals. Unfortunately, the quality of paper, printing, and illustrations is very poor. Still, to represent the thought of this large and important area of the non-Western world, it is perhaps the best single title.

Indexed in: P.A.I.S.

25-4740

PAKISTAN QUARTERLY.   v. 1, 1951-

Quarterly.   Karachi. $4.00

An attractive publication, featuring articles on all aspects of the country— social and cultural life, history, geography, art and literature, flora and fauna, etc. —with frequent short stories, poems and reproductions of paintings and other art works. Issues are occasionally devoted to a single topic—education, Pakistan's 20th anniversary, etc. There is nothing even faintly critical of the country or its rulers, and the magazine is hardly useful for any incisive analysis. It is, however, valuable for its descriptive articles, especially on the arts, literature and religion, and the many illustrations, often in color, enhance its usefulness here and make it popular browsing material.

56-33237

QUEST.   no. 1, 1955-

Bi-monthly.   Bombay. $4.00

An intellectual and literary journal, it appeared quarterly until 1971, when it incorporated the *Humanist Review,* another general periodical. Sponsored by the Indian Committee for Cultural Freedom, it takes no specific political position, but is most interested in the revitalization of Indian culture. To that end, it publishes articles by recognized Indian scholars and commentators treating various aspects of social, political and cultural affairs; each issue also contains some poetry and fiction, and occasionally a play. Usually about 10 book reviews, of both Indian and British publications, including non-fiction and creative literature. These are signed and critical, mostly 500-1000 words in length, but often much longer.

Patterned after *Encounter, Quest* is one of the better Indian journals, and represents well the outlook of the modern, cosmopolitan Indian intellectual.

SA 62-656

AFRICA.   v. 1, 1928-

Quarterly.   London. $12.30

Published by the International Africa Institute, which is concerned primarily with African ethnology, sociology and linguistics and related subjects, it is considered by many the leading journal in its field. Usually 3 or 4 articles per issue, very scholarly but rarely more than 8,000 words, in the areas of interest. In its earliest years, a number of the articles were in German or French, as well as English, but today there are almost none in German, and infrequent ones in French. English or French summaries are provided for all articles. "Notes and News" covers information on current research projects, news of meetings and conferences, new journals and other important publishing news, new academic programs, news of the Institute, etc. Carried through 1970 the extensive "Bibliography of Current Publications" covering books, pamphlets, government publications and articles in many languages. Because of its size (about 3000 items in 1970), it became a separate publication in 1971. Signed, critical reviews of 20 to 30 books per issue, averaging about 700 words. An important periodical, but for advanced students and research primarily.

Indexed in: Br.Hum.I.   29-10790
P.A.I.S.

*AFRICA REPORT.   v. 1, 1956-

Monthly (except July-Sept.)   Washington, D.C. $9.00

Known as *Africa Special Report* from 1956 to 1961, it is published by the African-American Institute, New York. Probably the leading American publication on contemporary Africa, it contains informed and clearly presented news and comment on all aspects of Africa, with political affairs greatly emphasized. In November, 1969, it changed its character. The news summaries, a country-by-country chronicle of events of the preceding month, were dropped and replaced by "firsthand coverage   of African events and developments." It also dropped its role of impartial observer, and though still independent, now carries controversial articles and takes positions, though these are clearly so marked. The book reviews are now longer and fewer (5-7 per issue, mostly over 1000 words), and "examine the basic questions raised by the books" rather than merely commenting on the books themselves. The useful music section, in which a leading ethnomusicologist reviewed recent records, was dropped. The charts, diagrams and compilations of statistics have been cut, and the journal, "without being doctrinaire or propagating any particular line, is committed to commitment." The back files, then, are certainly useful; the new, different *Africa Report* serves another function, but one just as important to the academic library.

Indexed in: P.A.I.S.   59-15428
S.S.H.I.

AFRICA TODAY.   v. 1, 1954-

Quarterly.   Denver, Colo. $6.50

Published in association with the Center on International Race Relations, University of Denver, it emphasizes the cultural and political aspects of contemporary Africa, and the relationship to them of African and Afro-

American studies in this country. The articles are relatively short, and
are didactic (even polemic) or descriptive rather than scholarly. Nevertheless, they are almost always solid and worth reading. Issues frequently
take a single subject—e.g., African Studies and the Black Protest, First
Pan-African Cultural Festival—and treat it from several viewpoints. Most
issues include some regular features: "Washington Letter" contains news
of official actions of U.S. and other nations; "Afro-Americana" has news
of programs, institutes, meetings and other news; "Research Notes" lists
publications, projects and miscellaneous items. The number and length
of book reviews varies considerably—4 or 5 per issue, 500-600 words
each is about the average. They are, however, all signed and critical. The
appearance of the journal is hardly commendable—extra-small type, offset,
on poor paper. But the contributions, while not of major importance, are
worthwhile and the journal should be in libraries where Africa receives
much attention.

Indexed in: P.A.I.S.   61-46302

AFRICAN AFFAIRS.   v. 1, 1901-

Quarterly.   London. $9.00

"The Journal of the Royal African Society," a non-political organization,
it is the oldest English-language journal on Africa now being published.
Until the 1950's, it was concerned almost solely with British Africa, but
in recent years has expanded its coverage to include the entire continent,
though there is still more attention to the areas that were British Africa
than to North or French West Africa. Each issue contains usually 2 or 3
scholarly articles, primarily on current or recent political problems, plus
a somewhat larger number of "Talks, Notes, Short Articles." The contributors are mostly faculty members at British or African universities,
though authors from other areas and from the government are frequently
represented. Each issue contains two bibliographies: one, an international
listing of books, pamphlets and government publications; the other, *A
Select List of Articles on Africa Appearing in Non-Africanist Periodicals,*
that covers about 150 leading international scholarly and intellectual
journals. Includes announcements, reports and other news of the Society.
20-30 book reviews per issue, signed and critical, mostly 350-750 words,
but occasionally much longer. An important scholarly journal, essential
where there is much work on Africa.

Indexed in: Br.Hum.I.   61-6176
            S.S.H.I.

AFRICAN STUDIES REVIEW.   v. 1, 1958-

3 times/yr.   East Lansing, Mich. $20.00

The official journal of the African Studies Association, the major American
scholarly organization devoted to the study of Africa, past and present, it
was titled the *African Studies Bulletin* through 1969. According to the
Editor's Note (April, 1970) the change in title "reflects the opinion of

many of us in the Association that African studies have progressed beyond the bibliographic stage. . . . Almost exclusively the *Bulletin* tended to reflect the very important early stages of research associated with the gathering of bibliography and the dissemination of data." The *Bulletin* was of primary interest to scholars in the area who profited by the excellent bibliographical articles, descriptions of collections and archives, directories of information about new programs, courses, journals, etc., and various items about the A.S.A. and other professional news. It was of course essential for librarians working with African materials, but for most undergraduate libraries, was not very useful. Now, because of its changed policy and its connection with the A.S.A., it will undoubtedly become one of the leading scholarly journals in the field. Also, the *Review* now has book reviews, which the *Bulletin* did not. In the first 4 issues, the number of reviews varied from 7 to 23; signed and critical, they range from 500 to 2500 words. Its high price may discourage many libraries from subscribing and it is really necessary only where there is a strong interest in African studies.

65-4459

BLACK ORPHEUS. v. 1, 1957-

Quarterly. Lagos, Nigeria.

The dean of African literary magazines, the original was founded in Nigeria by two Europeans, Ulli Beier and Janheinz Jahn. It played an exceptionally important part in introducing African writers to other Africans and to the world, and the members of its editorial board included the leading African writers and critics—Aimé Césaire, Léopold Senghor, J.A. Ramsaran, Wole Soyinka, Ezekial Mphalele, J.P. Clark, Chinua Achebe, Christopher Okigbo—all of whom, at one time or another, contributed. Subtitled "A Journal of African and Afro-American Literature," it included contributions by Black Americans and West Indians, and in addition to the poetry, fiction and criticism, contained art work and lengthy book reviews.

Because of the Nigerian civil war, the emigration of Ulli Beier, and the flight of many Ibo writers, it appeared the journal would collapse and, indeed, publication was delayed in 1967-68. However, Nigerian writers, especially J.P. Clark and Abiola Irele began it again in 1968. The main difference is the source of contributions: formerly, contributors were from many parts of Africa and the outside world; now, they are mostly from West Africa and the material is mostly about its art and literature. Aside from this, however, it is just as interesting in content and appearance, and every library interested in African literature or culture should receive it and attempt to get the backfile.

CURRENT BIBLIOGRAPHY ON AFRICAN AFFAIRS. n.s.v. 1, 1968-

Monthly. Westport, Conn. $25.00

Published for the African Bibliographic Center, Washington, D.C., it is arranged in 4 main parts: 1) Original bibliographic essays (e.g., Medicine in Africa, Blacks and Arabs: Past and Present) or bibliographic contributions (African Population Problems and Trends, Rewriting Black History in America and Africa); 2) a brief listing of forthcoming books; 3) a selection of short reviews of books of special interest; 4) Bibliographical Section, arranged by subject and by geography, listing with brief descriptions" a selection of references to a considerable diversity of materials—scholarly books, documents published by governments and international organizations, and articles appearing in the usual periodicals specializing in African studies, as well as selections from lesser known magazines and journals which frequently or occasionally include pertinent resources for the Africanist." While by no means exhaustive, it is fairly comprehensive (about 2500 items in 1970) and up-to-date. There is an author index to the bibliographical section. This listing, plus the useful subject bibliographies and essays, make this an important reference tool for the undergraduate library.

65-81645

JEUNE AFRIQUE.   v. 1, 1960-

Weekly.   Paris. $30.00

A profusely illustrated popular journal, covering all of Africa, but with a special emphasis on the former French colonies (it is entirely in French). Thus, it is most valuable for its coverage of North Africa (indeed, it was originally published in Tunis) and West Africa, but by no means slights other areas and frequently treats countries outside Africa which have substantial black populations, such as those of the Caribbean or Brazil, and it has paid increasing attention to other Third World nations. Treats all aspects of contemporary African life, with special emphasis on political and social affairs. Its articles are incisively written, often in the form of interviews (these are particularly valuable), and without pretense to objectivity. More or less regular columns on meetings, art exhibits, stamps; usually a few signed book reviews, of varying length, of fiction and non-fiction, published in Africa or in France.

Frequent supplements, on a great variety of subjects: recent ones have been on soccer, Lenin, women in Africa, and African agriculture. The subscription cost includes an annual, *Afrique '70* (or whatever the year is) providing much statistical and descriptive information about each country, the continent as a whole, and relations with the rest of the world. It is a useful reference work.

Written by Africans, and read by a large, but fairly select audience of Africans, it is one of the best sources for insight into African opinion; if it were in English and indexed, it would be recommended as an essential purchase for all college libraries. As it is, it should be in any library where there is much interest in contemporary Africa.

70-8039

JOURNAL OF MODERN AFRICAN STUDIES.   v. 1, 1963-

Quarterly.   London. $6.50

With its emphasis "upon the people and policies, the problems and progress" of Africa, it is concerned primarily with political and economic aspects rather than the sociological or historical. Edited from Africa, it is contributed to by eminent scholars from African universities, but also by scholars from many other institutions. From 5 to 7 scholarly articles, usually bibliographical in content. A section, "Africana," contains notes on the work of institutes and centers of African studies, reports on conferences, and other items of professional interest. 15 to 20 books are re-

viewed in each issue, mostly 650-800 words each, by authorities in their
respective fields. An essential journal where there is much interest in recent and contemporary Africa.

Indexed in: Br.Hum.I.   65-5452
            S.S.H.I.

JOURNAL OF THE NEW AFRICAN LITERATURE AND THE ARTS.
   v. 1, 1966-

Quarterly.   N.Y. $7.50

Founded and still edited by Joseph Okpaku, a Nigerian who is not only a
playwright and author, but also a New York publisher, who founded it "to
encourage writers to give expression to their own inclinations, no matter
the straightness or waywardness of their works."

Publishes "creative works of art, including plays, essays, short stories, poetry, and reproductions of art work as well as critiques, criticisms, reviews,
and other scholarly articles on African literature, music, fine art, dance,
and other aspects of African culture."

The contributions, which are brief and of high quality, do range over all
the areas and genres enunciated in the editorial policy quoted above, and
are by Africans and whites, some of whom are recognized authorities or
well-known authors. Occasional contributions in French. Some drawings
and photographs. Several good book reviews, of both fiction and non-
fiction, in most issues, usually 500-700 words in length.

Publication in the first few years has been slow, and there have been but
two issues a year, usually combined, but even these have appeared very
late. (Quarterly publication is announced for 1971.) Nevertheless, it has
an outstanding group of editorial consultants, and some important creative and critical writing, and the *Journal* should be in any library where
there is serious interest in contemporary African culture.

*PRÉSENCE AFRICAINE.   no. 1, 1947-

Quarterly.   Paris. $5.10

A "Cultural Review of the Negro World," it is especially concerned with
literature and cultural history, and to a lesser (but quite important extent) pan-Africanism and Negritude. Beginning as the voice of West African intellectuals in particular, it has broadened to include all areas, and
has carried contributions from the leading writers and scholars from
Africa and from Europe and America, both black and white. Contains
poetry and short stories, but it is most valuable for its articles and criticisms relating to all aspects of Africa's past and present cultural history
(and, frequently, Black culture outside Africa) and on political matters
as they interact with this culture. It is also important for the documents,
often those emanating from a congress of writers or scholars.

It originally appeared only in French, but about 1959 an English edition
was also published; unfortunately, due to rising costs, it was dropped in
1967, and now there is only one edition with contributions in both
French and English, with the former predominating. A few book reviews
in each issue, some of them quite long, and a list of books received
(French and English).

With its wide range of interests and eminent contributors, it is probably the most important journal for the study of contemporary African thought and culture, its antecedents and ramifications. Should be in every library where there is an interest in Black and/or African culture.

51-31032

*TRANSITION.   v. 1, 1961-

Bi-monthly.   Accra, Ghana. $6.50

Beginning as a handset publication with a run of 2000, in its first 7 years (when it was published in Uganda) it became one of the best and perhaps the most important English-language journal in Africa. Contents included short stories, poetry, literary criticism, art work and articles on social, cultural and political matters, with contributions by many of the most eminent African literary and political figures who wrote in English.

In 1967, several articles appeared criticizing the proposed Ugandan constitution, and governmental displeasure, which had occasionally been hinted at, now became explicit. Action was finally taken in October, 1968: an issue featuring 3 articles on the Nigerian Civil War led to the banning of the magazine and the arrest of its staff; the editor, Rajat Neogy, though acquitted was banished from Uganda. (An account is given in the June-July, 1971 issue). After a hiatus of 2½ years, publication was resumed in Ghana, with the same excellent quality and variety of contributions from African and western writers, critics and journalists.

In its new home, with the continuing financial support of the International Association for Cultural Freedom, *Transition* should resume its place as a most important periodical for keeping up with intellectual and cultural developments in Africa.

Lively, informative and creative, it belongs in every college library, and a complete backfile is desirable.

ISLAMIC STUDIES. v. 1, 1962-

Quarterly. Islamabad, Pakistan. $5.00

The journal of the Islamic Research Institute, its purpose is "to uncover the worthy ideas in our Islamic tradition, but with a view to re-evaluating them." Each issue contains usually 4 or 5 articles of 5,000-10,000 words, on all aspects of Islamic history, philosophy and practices. While many articles are fairly specialized, and of interest only to Islamic scholars ("Prophetology of Shah Wali Allah," for example), a large number are on more general aspects of Muslim life and theology and on political and social affairs (e.g., "The Impact of Modernity on Islam," "The Sources of Islamic Law"). Contributors include many of the most eminent Islamic scholars from Asia, Europe and America; all articles are in English. Usually just one lengthy book review per issue, generally on a highly specialized work, often one published in Arabic.

Primarily for advanced students or faculty, it is an important journal for the study of Islamic history and traditions, and also useful for courses in comparative religion.

SA 63-1336

*MIDDLE EAST JOURNAL. v. 1, 1946-

Quarterly. Washington, D.C. $9.00

Published by the Middle East Institute, an organization founded "to develop among the American people an interest in the Middle East and an appreciation of its history, culture, and political and economic affairs." Issues contain 3 or 4 scholarly articles, mostly on recent and contemporary events, and on developments in the culture, institutions, and politics of the Middle East since the rise of Islam. The area covered includes North Africa, the Arab World, Ethiopia, Israel, Turkey, the Transcaucasian states of the Soviet Union, Iran, Afghanistan, Pakistan, Turkistan and Muslim Spain. The ancient Near East and Byzantium are excluded. "Chronology," compiled from a large number of domestic and foreign sources, lists important events and developments in each country during the recent quarter, and appears in every issue. The *Bibliography of Periodical Literature* in each issue attempts "to survey all periodicals of importance" and is arranged by general topic rather than area and includes book reviews; more than 2500 items have been listed annually in recent years. Each issue contains usually 12 to 15 longer reviews (500 to 1000 words), plus a number of shorter (100-200 words) ones; all are signed and critical. Also an extensive and detailed listing of other recent publications, including documents, plus a brief list of some forthcoming books. The basic scholarly journal for this area, it is important for all libraries, and essential where any work is done on the Middle East.

Indexed in: P.A.I.S.   48-2240*
           S.S.H.I.

MIDDLE EASTERN STUDIES. v. 1, 1964-

3 nos./yr. London. $9.80

Published as a quarterly until 1969, each volume contains about 15 articles, on all aspects of the modern Middle East since the end of the 18th century, but especially on 20th-century developments, in particular recent and contemporary politics and international affairs, including of course the Arab-Israeli conflict and its background. The articles are moderately long to lengthy, and are contributed by leading scholars from many countries, especially Great Britain and the U.S. The number of reviews per issue varies from just a few up to 10; they are all excellent, and mostly 1000-2000 words. "Other Publications Reviewed" includes some brief reviews, plus usually a listing of books received.

An important scholarly journal where there is a special interest in the area.

65-9869

MUSLIM WORLD.   v. 1, 1911-

Quarterly.   Hartford, Conn. $6.00

Published by the Hartford Seminary Foundation, it was originally *Moslem World,* adopting the modern spelling in 1948. Each issue consists of 5 or 6 scholarly articles on Islam and the Middle East by recognized authorities from both Western and Middle Eastern universities. These articles treat all aspects of Islamic culture and civilization—from investigations of esoteric segments of Islamic philosophy or minor figures in history to political and sociological analyses of the current Middle East situation. Even such topics as the Persian short story or a description of "Some Useful French Depositories for the Study of the Algerian Revolution" are treated, so that the journal is of much broader interest than it used to be when it was primarily concerned with Islam as a religion and with missionary work among the Muslims.

The "Survey of Periodicals" in each issue, covering a large number of international periodicals, lists articles over a wide variety of topics relating to Islamic history, theology, and philosophy, but generally excludes the current political scene. "Notes of the Quarter" includes news of programs, of seminars and conferences, exhibits, new journals or special publishing projects. Usually 7 to 10 excellent reviews per issue, mostly 500-800 words, but often much longer. An important journal for the study of Islam as a religious, social or historical phenomenon.

Indexed in: In.Rel.Per.Lit.   SA 65-2358

*NEW MIDDLE EAST.   v. 1, 1968-

Monthly.   London. $16.00

Contains thoughtful, non-partisan articles on the political, economic, social and cultural aspects of the present day Middle East. Though edited by English Jews who have had long associations with Israel, it is not at all wedded to the Israeli viewpoint, yet it is regarded suspiciously by many Arabs. Contributors are recognized scholars and journalists, mostly from Britain and the U.S., but also from other European countries and from other European countries and from both sides of the Arab-Israeli conflict. Reports or translations from the press of the Arab states, the Soviet Union or other countries are frequently carried. Regular departments include a chronology of the month, texts of important documents and speeches, and an extensive book section, the latter consisting of short, critical annotations of a large number of books, plus longer reviews (up to 1000 words) of several more important works. A useful journal that gives an intelligent, balanced presentation.

Indexed in: P.A.I.S.   77-3685

There are a number of journals and newsletters on the Middle East, expressing various shades of political views. For libraries where there is much interest in the area, a few of the less ephemeral ones include:

ARAB WORLD (v. 1, 1954- $2.00) is published monthly (occasionally appears bi-monthly) by the Arab Information Center in New York. It contains an average of about 6 articles on Middle Eastern culture, history, or politics, with an emphasis on the Arab-Israeli situation or the Palestinian refugees. The articles are well written and illustrated with, as one would expect, a strong predisposition toward the Arab cause and the virtues of the Arab heritage. Occasional poetry. Usually one or two book reviews per issue, mostly 300-600 words in length. It is indexed in *P.A.I.S.*

The MIDDLE EAST NEWSLETTER (v. 1, 1967- $10.00) is published in Beirut by Americans for Justice in the Middle East, an organization of Americans who have had long associations with the Middle East, and are highly sympathetic to the Arab cause. Appearing somewhat irregularly— 5 or 6 times a year—it is quite polemic, presenting forcefully the plight of the Palestinian Arabs and opposing Israeli "expansionism." It contains texts of speeches, reprints of magazine and newspaper articles and editorials, and contributions by its officers and members on the Arab-Israeli situation, with only occasional attention to other matters.

NEAR EAST REPORT (v. 1, 1956- $7.00), a weekly (bi-weekly until October, 1970) "Washington letter on American policy in the Near East," is manifestly pro-Israel, and might even be called a semi-official spokesman for the Israeli government's viewpoint. Each issue is usually 4 pages, and often treats the situation of Jews in other countries (especially the Soviet Union) as well as the Middle East. An annual volume containing all issues for the previous year is distributed to many libraries by the American Israel Friendship Committee. Indexed in *P.A.I.S.*

NEW OUTLOOK (v. 1, 1957- $7.50), published in Tel Aviv, is the voice of Israeli dissenters, who are Middle East moderates. It intends to serve as "a medium for the clarification of problems concerning peace and cooperation among all the peoples of the Middle East." The Editorial Board is comprised of both Jews and Arabs in Israel, many of the former who have long been associated with Mapam, the left-socialist party. It carries articles on many aspects of life in the area, with an emphasis, of course, on Arab-Israeli relations and on topics within Israel. As a medium of reconciliation, a forum for "mutual understanding, justice and the essential rights of both sides," it is frequently criticized—by both sides—but also carries some weight. Occasional lengthy, thoughtful book reviews. Indexed in *P.A.I.S.*

AMERICAS. *see* HISTORY.

*AMÉRICAS.   v. 1, 1949-

Monthly.   Washington, D.C. $6.00

Published by the Pan American Union, it contains popularly written, extensively and attractively illustrated articles on all aspects of Latin American (and U.S.) life, history, geography and culture, though with controversial topics de-emphasized. Stories and poetry used to appear frequently, but rarely now; art work is often reproduced. There is usually a book review section with signed, critical and often quite lengthy reviews of fiction, poetry and scholarly works by Latin-American and U.S. authors. The section "Hemisphere" contains miscellaneous items—news of the OAS, of inter-American development activities, of art and music activities. Before 1969, these topics were covered in special sections, and those on music and the visual arts were especially useful. Published in separate editions— English, Spanish and Portuguese. For college libraries the Spanish edition is perhaps more appropriate: since the journal's usefulness for the social scientist is greatly limited by its lack of candor and incisiveness, the cultural and historical articles used most often by those with a reading knowledge of Spanish comprise the magazine's real value.

Indexed in: R.G.   52-24809

CUADERNOS AMERICANOS.   v. 1, 1942-

Bi-monthly.   Mexico, D.F. $13.50

A generaı review, carrying literary, historical, philosophical, and political articles mostly relating to Latin America, it is regarded by many as the best single quality journal on the area. Each issue is divided into 4 sections: Nuestro Tiempo, Aventura del Pensamiento, Presencia del Pasado, and Dimension Imaginaria. The articles, or stories or poems, are contributed by the leading writers, critics and scholars from the countries of Latin America. The journal has no political affiliation, but it has been devoted to humanitarian causes, and is highly regarded by literal intellectuals throughout the hemisphere. The book review editor, Mauricio de la Selva, reviews at length 5 or 6 recent books, on a variety of topics, and also lists the contents of recent issues of other Latin American reviews. An important journal where there is much interest in Latin American culture.

45-1784

There are a few other general reviews that are highly regarded. *Cuadernos Hispanoamericanos* (v. 1, 1950- $10.00) is published bi-monthly in Madrid by the Instituto de Cultura Hispanica. *Sur* (v. 1, 1931- $12.00), published bi-monthly in Buenos Aires, was founded by Waldo Frank, J. Ortega y Gasset and Alfonso Reyes, and is mostly concerned with literature, and carries a good bit of original prose and poetry.* *Revista Ibero-americana* (v. 1, 1939- $8.00), the publication of the Instituto Internacional de Literatura Iberoamericana at the University of Pittsburgh, is concerned with literary history and criticism, especially as manifested through the Spanish influence. It contains articles in both English and Spanish, whereas the others are entirely in Spanish.

*According to the Spring, 1971 *Books Abroad,* "*Sur,* the most important literary journal of Argentina, and one of the most representative of all Latin America, has suspended publication after 326 issues during forty years (1931-70)."

INTER-AMERICAN ECONOMIC AFFAIRS.   v. 1, 1964-

Quarterly.   Washington, D.C. $10.00

Despite the title, the journal is almost as much concerned with the history, politics and government of Latin America as it is with economics, and the articles on economics frequently focus on the social or political implications. Usually 5 to 7 articles, of brief to moderate length, per issue, mostly by U.S. scholars. Government documents, or portions thereof, relating to the area, are occasionally reproduced. A useful journal for undergraduates, it is important where Latin American studies are emphasized. No book reviews.

Indexed in: P.A.I.S.   50-1412
          S.S.H.I.

INTERAMERICAN REVIEW OF BIBLIOGRAPHY; REVISTA INTERAMERICANA DE BIBLIOGRAFÍA.   v. 1, 1951-

Quarterly.   Washington, D.C. $3.00

Official organ of the Inter-American Committee on Bibliography, and published by the Division of Philosophy and Letters, Department of Cultural Affairs, Pan American Union, it is devoted to information about new and old publications, authors and libraries of a Latin American, or inter-American character. Issues are comprised of critical, bibliographical and review articles, book reviews, news and notes, listings of recent books, and an annual listing of new journals. The articles (usually 3 or 4 per issue) are on all aspects of Latin American literature and bibliography; the bibliographical articles and the review articles (which may be on any aspects of Latin American history or culture) are especially useful for building collections. The book reviews (usually about 15 an issue) are mostly 500-1000 words, occasionally much longer. They are all signed and critical. The "News and Notes" contains a variety of items from individual countries and international groups. The section "Recent Books," containing a classified listing of important works on Latin America published throughout the world, is selective but lengthy (over 1000 titles a year in recent years). An important journal for courses dealing with Latin American history or culture, it is essential for libraries that do much buying in this area. Articles and reviews are in English, Spanish or Portuguese.

51-8429 rev.

JOURNAL OF INTER-AMERICAN STUDIES.   v. 1, 1959-

Quarterly.   Coral Gables, Fla. $8.00

Published for the Center for Advanced International Studies of the University of Miami, it contains scholarly articles on all aspects of the Americas, with special emphasis on the social sciences—in particular, recent history and contemporary developments. Each issue carries about 10 articles, mostly of moderate length, by professors at U.S. and Latin American universities, and occasionally by government officials. Some book reviews appeared in the early volumes; they were then dropped only to be resumed in 1967, and there are now a few (4 or 5) per issue, signed and critical, averaging about 1000 words. List of books received. Articles and reviews may be in English, Spanish or Portuguese, with the majority—by far—in English.

Indexed in: S.S.H.I.   A 59-9349

MUNDO NUEVO.   *see* MODERN LANGUAGES/SPANISH

VISIÓN.   v. 1, 1950-

Bi-weekly.   Mexico, D.F. $15.00

A newsmagazine of world events, with special attention to Latin American affairs. All in Spanish, it is financed and largely controlled by U.S. businessmen, and though reliable, cosmopolitan, and thorough, it is identified with American business interests. Emphasizes economic and business matters, though it includes much material of general interest.

Each issue includes a feature article, on a current political, economic or social question, treated in some depth, and it is for these—since the topics are mostly related to Latin America or at least discuss the implications for the area—that the journal is especially useful. There are many other items of news, personalities and developments, both straight reporting and some interpretation, plus regular sections on business affairs, on art, theater, television, the cinema, and books. Usually 2 or 3 long signed reviews per issue, covering both fiction and non-fiction, published in various countries. A widely read publication, with a circulation of over 175,000, it provides excellent coverage of current Latin American affairs, and should be in libraries where there is much interest in the topic. (For institutions concentrating on Brazil, a Portuguese edition, *Visão*, is available.)

Institutions with a strong interest in Latin America should consider the bi-weekly *Economist para America Latina* (v. 1, 1967- $15.00) which is published by the London *Economist* and has very much the same format, style and features, even including some of the same book reviews. Like its parent publication, it has an emphasis (in this case, Latin American economics and politics, and Latin American relations with Europe), but it also contains news and analysis of the rest of the world. Occasional special supplements (also available separately) treat individual countries or major topics. Its reliability and incisive reporting make the journal an important one for students of the area; for other students, such as those in international affairs or comparative economics, the language barrier may limit its usefulness.

56-21856

CURRENT DIGEST OF THE SOVIET PRESS.   v. 1, 1949-

Weekly.   Columbus, Ohio. $250.00

Published by the American Association for the Advancement of Slavic Studies, it "presents a selection of the contents of the Soviet press, carefully translated in full into English, or objectively condensed by competent editors, and arranged by subject matter. The translations are presented as documentary materials without elaboration or comment." These claims are adhered to carefully. The translations are from about 60 different periodicals and newspapers, from all parts of Russia and in all fields, but especially they are from *Pravda* and *Izvestia*; each issue also contains complete weekly indexes to the contents of the latter two, which are, of course, the leading Soviet dailies. Texts of all major speeches and documents are included, condensed where appropriate, and statistical tables for various matters often appear.

From 1968 into late 1970 the same publisher issued a monthly *Current Abstracts of the Soviet Press* which covered articles from the specialized journals in the social sciences, arts and humanities, from popular weeklies and Party organs, literary monthlies, and from major newspapers in the various Union republics. Beginning in late 1970 the *Current Digest* included those items that would have appeared in the *Current Abstracts,* increasing the usefulness of the former.

Expensive to subscribe to and to bind (microfilm, $50.00 per year for subscribers to the printed issues, and $75.00 for non-subscribers, may be an answer for many libraries), it is nevertheless perhaps the most important primary source in English for studying contemporary Russia and should be available wherever students do serious work in the area.

Indexed in: P.A.I.S.   50-3493

EAST EUROPE.   v. 1, 1952-

Monthly.   N.Y. $10.00

"A monthly review of East European affairs," it was published until 1970 by Free Europe, Inc., an organization that supports the right of East European nations to achieve, by peaceful means, free and independent governments, and which is also responsible for Radio Free Europe. Under its original title, *News From Behind the Iron Curtain,* it appeared as a newsletter, taking its present title in 1957. In 1970, it suspended publication between January and November; the new publisher is a private firm with no connections to the previous one. Contains articles and news on all aspects of recent political, economic, social and intellectual trends in East Europe, from Bulgaria and Albania in the South, to Estonia in the North. In addition to news items and the 4 or 5 articles, which are fairly brief, well illustrated, and written by scholars and journalists, it has several features: "From East European Sources" gives the translated texts of significant broadcasts, newspaper and magazine editorials and articles that appeared in the area; "Current Developments" surveys country by country important events and trends. Frequently carries signed and critical book reviews that are mostly quite long. Despite the purposes of the journal, under its original sponsor it was rarely polemical or didactic, but gave a well balanced and fair coverage of the area. The new publisher, Robert Speller & Sons, is a trade book publisher, one of whose specialities is books written by emigrés from Russia and East Europe, and the articles have taken on a somewhat less objective tone.

Useful for courses stressing Russia and East Europe, a backfile is particularly important.

54-23061 rev

NEW HUNGARIAN QUARTERLY.   v. 1, 1960-

Quarterly.   Budapest. $6.00

A general cultural quarterly, written by Hungarians for English-language
circulation abroad. Contains articles on various aspects of Hungarian life,
history and culture, translations of short stories, poetry and portions of
novels, news of important social developments, reproductions of paintings
and drawings (some in color), reviews of books, theater and films.

Contributors include some of the most eminent writers, artists and scholars
in Hungary and the contributions, though rarely scholarly, are on a very
high level, comparable to those in *Encounter* in Britain or the *Yale Review*
in this country. Even the political articles are informative rather than polemical.

As a representation of the best in Hungarian culture, a means of introducing the intelligent reader to Hungary, it does a superb job. Even apart
from this, the quality of the contents makes it one of the better general
quarterlies published anywhere, and because Hungary is so pivotal between
Eastern and Western Europe, and because it has produced so many eminent
scientists, writers and artists (to whom many articles, even portions of issues,
have been devoted), the *Quarterly* deserves a place in a good academic
library. Surely, it is one of the best buys—the format is excellent and each
issue contains over 200 pages.

Indexed in: Music I.   63-36282

RUSSIAN REVIEW.   v. 1, 1941-

Quarterly.   Stanford, Calif. $9.00

Sponsored (since 1966) by the Hoover Institution on War, Revolution and
Peace, its purpose "is to interpret the real aims and aspirations of the
Russian people, as distinguished from and contrasted with Soviet Communism, and to advance general knowledge of Russian culture, history and
civilization." Some indication of the journal's point of view may be inferred from the careful distinction between "Russian" and "Soviet" (a
distinction that was not declared openly before 1954) and from the frequency of contributors and editors who are Russian émigrés. On the other
hand, many of the best known experts on Soviet Russia have also been contributors, and a major proportion of its articles have dealt with aspects of
Soviet rather than Czarist Russia. There are usually 5 or 6 articles, most of
them brief to moderate length, frequently a review article, occasionally
notes on or the text of important documents, and usually 10 to 15 signed
and critical reviews, mostly around 600-700 words, but often much longer.
Through 1959 it carried the annual *Bibliography: Books and Articles on
Russia Published in the Year 19--*. An important and readable journal for
Russian studies.

Indexed in: P.A.I.S.   43-16148 rev. 2*

*SLAVIC REVIEW.   v. 1, 1941-

Quarterly.   Columbus, Ohio $15.00

Published by the American Association for the Advancement of Slavic
Studies since 1948, its first three volumes were published as volumes 20
to 22 of the *Slavonic and East European Review* (American Series). With
volume 4, in 1945, it became the *American Slavic and East European
Review*; the AAASS was formed in 1948 and took over its publication,
and its present title began in 1961. The leading American scholarly journal
in this area, it covers all fields of interest—history, politics, literature, economics, sociology, etc.—with most attention, by far, to Russia rather than
other East European areas. In the first part of the 1960's, the format of
most issues included: first, a Discussion, or Symposium on a single subject;
then 5 or so scholarly articles, normally 7500 words or less. This format
grew less common toward the end of the decade, and issues contained 5 or
6 unrelated articles. In 1970, the Editor announced the intention of reviving the Discussion section, in 2 or 3 of the 4 issues. Other regular sections,
include: "Notes and Comment," normally briefer articles of 3000 words or
less; "News of the Profession"; and signed, critical book reviews (sometimes
in the form of review articles) of about 50 books, mostly 700-1000 words
in length, covering books in all western languages. There is also a list of
books received. The listing of *Doctoral Dissertations on Russia, the Soviet
Union, and Eastern Europe Accepted by American, Canadian and British
Universities* has been carried since 1964; the first listing covered 1960-64,
since then it has appeared annually. A very important journal for all areas
of Russian studies.

Indexed in: S.S.H.I.   47-6565 rev

SLAVONIC AND EAST EUROPEAN REVIEW.   v. 1, 1922-

Twice a year.   London. $8.40

Organ of the School of Slavonic and East European Studies in the University of London, it was originally the *Slavonic Review,* changing to the
present title in 1942. Started by Bernard Pares and Alan Seton-Watson,
it was for many years the most important journal in the field of Russian
studies, and still is one of the most important in all Slavic studies. During
the Second World War, 3 volumes were also called American Series I-III;
these were then continued in the U.S. as the *Slavic Review* (q.v.) Contains
scholarly articles, generally limited to 8000 words, on all aspects of Russian
and Slavic studies—language, literature, history, culture—with little attention to current, or even recent events. Also includes texts of recently
discovered documents of historical importance. It is, then, especially useful for the history and culture of the area, but not especially for courses
on politics or international affairs. Contains usually 35 or 40 book reviews, signed and critical, mostly 750-1000 words in length, which also
emphasize history and culture.

Indexed in: Br.Hum.I.   26-18203 (rev '38)
               S.S.H.I.

SOVIET LIFE.   no. 1, 1956-

Monthly.   Moscow. $3.95

Until 1964 known as *USSR*, it is published and circulated under a recip-
rocal agreement between the governments of the U.S. and the Soviet
Union—*Soviet Life* is distributed here and *America,* published by the U.S.
government, distributed in the Soviet Union. Rather sumptuous in appearance, replete with photographs and art work in color as well as black-and-
white, it covers all aspects of Russian society, culture, history and technology. While one hardly reads the articles for their incisive interpretation or keen analysis, the sheer size of the magazine, the variety of its
contents, and the attractiveness of their presentation compensates for its
lack of depth.

Not for courses in Soviet government (though a few articles might be
useful) nor for the study of Marxian economics, but primarily for browsing purposes. An extensive backfile is not necessary.

Similar in purpose is *Soviet Union* (no. 1, 1950- $4.50) which was
founded in 1930 as *U.S.S.R. in Construction* by Maxim Gorky. Available
in 14 languages, it serves as a world-wide public relations organ. It is
somewhat more extensive than *Soviet Life,* but the subject matter and
method of presentation are essentially the same.

Indexed in: Music I.   58-45996 rev.

SOVIET LITERATURE.   1931-

Monthly.   Moscow. $4.50

Under the title *International Literature,* which it had through 1945, when
it was published by the International Union of Revolutionary Writers, it
was devoted to proletarian literature of all countries (including Dos Passos,
Dreiser and Upton Sinclair) and to promoting Marxist aesthetics. Since
1946, in a new format, and published by the Writers Union of the U.S.S.R.,
it has not been nearly so didactic; rather it carries the latest works of
Soviet writers, poets and critics, including portions of recent novels, or
even entire short novels (or occasionally entire longer novels, run over
several issues). Also film, theatre, and art reviews, and reproductions, in
color and black-and-white, of paintings and photographs. "New Books"
contains long signed reviews of new fiction and poetry, or sometimes
literary history or criticism. News of Soviet authors and books.

Because of its official status, reflecting official attitudes, it is an important journal for the study of contemporary Soviet culture. Its creative
writing and literary criticism also make it useful for the study of
comparative literature, and it is essential where there is any serious interest
in the U.S.S.R.

SOVIET REVIEW.   v. 1, 1960-

Quarterly.   White Plains, N.Y. $12.00

Its purpose is to provide "a cross-section of significant articles published in Soviet periodicals in the social sciences and the field of literary criticism." Each issue contains 4 to 7 translated articles selected mostly from a regular list of 10 important Soviet scholarly journals in the field of economics, political science, education, philosophy, history, literature and psychology, and one general journal (16 journals were regularly covered up to 1970), but also including articles from other journals when considered of sufficient interest. Issues of the first three volumes appeared monthly, but as the publisher began other journals of translations in subject areas, the coverage and content was reduced. For example, whereas between one quarter and one third of earlier volumes was devoted to literature and the arts, recent volumes have almost ignored them. Despite the reduction in size, it is still an interesting and useful journal for keeping up with developments in Soviet scholarship. Where there are exceptionally strong programs of Soviet studies, this publisher's other journals of translations should also be examined.

Indexed in: S.S.H.I.   62-58109

SOVIET STUDIES.   v. 1, 1949-

Quarterly.   Glasgow, Scotland. $10.00

Edited at the University of Glasgow, it was originally subtitled "A Quarterly Review of Social and Economic Institutions of the U.S.S.R.," and though the subtitle has been dropped, the emphasis remains the same. Each issue contains usually 7 to 10 articles of brief to moderate length, by scholars from many countries. The reviewing policy has changed from reviewing more non-English language titles to reviewing mostly those in English; the high quality of the reviews, however, has remained unchanged, and many run to several thousand words, the average being 600-700. There is also a list of books received. From 1963 to 1970 a separate *Information Supplement* was published, and was received along with *Soviet Studies,* or subscribed to separately. Its purpose was "to provide the research worker with material [i.e., abstracts of articles] from a wide range of current Soviet newspapers and journals and brief notes on new Soviet books." In 1970, with the July issue, the *Supplement* was replaced by a new service, *Soviet and East European Abstracts,* which cost $12 per year separately, or jointly with *Soviet Studies* $17.00. It proposes to publish "several times the present volume of material" and give "coverage to East European periodicals and books, in addition to more comprehensive coverage of Soviet publications." Supported by a Ford Foundation grant, this new service sounds as though—at the price, certainly—it should be, along with *Soviet Studies,* in every library where there is much interest in current and recent developments in the Soviet.

Indexed in: Br.Hum.I.   51-27967
                P.A.I.S.
                S.S.H.I.

*SPUTNIK.   1967-

Monthly.   London. $5.00

Edited and compiled by the Novosti Press Agency, Moscow, a nominally
non-governmental agency, it contains some original articles but mostly
translations culled and condensed from Russian periodicals and newspapers. One might consider it a Russian version of the *Reader's Digest;*
however, not only is there the obvious contrast in political outlook, but
Sputnik is profusely illustrated with photographs and art work in color
and black-and-white, and cartoons. Its content is meant for universal
appeal: articles on science, literature and the arts (which are stressed),
history, geography, technology, social life, even recipes, with surprisingly
little on politics or Marxist doctrine; there was even a series of lessons for
learning Russian. Though its purpose is obviously to portray Russian in the
most favorable light and to attract tourists, it is readable, attractive and
interesting, and provides a handy means for acquainting students with
Russian society and culture.

70-265113

STUDIES ON THE SOVIET UNION.   v. 1, 1957; n.s.v. 1, 1961-

Quarterly.   Munich, Germany. $12.00

Published by the Institute for the Study of the U.S.S.R., located in Munich, one of the leading research organizations on the Soviet Union. Each
issue consists of 5 to 10 scholarly articles, mostly of moderate length,
contributed by members of the Institute or, more often, by eminent Sov-
ietologists from many countries. Issues usually focus on a single topic—
e.g., Lenin's Centenary, The Soviet Union and Latin America, Religion
in the U.S.S.R., the Soviet Moslem World, Soviet Literature, etc.— often
resulting from a conference or symposium. Book' reviews rarely appear.

An important journal for the study of contemporary Russia.

64-2663

*SURVEY.   no. 1, 1956-

Quarterly.   London. $8.00

Presently subtitled "A Journal of Soviet and East European Studies,"
Survey was first published as a mimeographed review and entitled *Soviet
Survey.* In its early years it was primarily concerned with the social and
cultural trends in the Soviet bloc—indeed, its subtitle then was "A Quarterly Review of Cultural Trends"—but it now pays most attention to political
matters, with much less to the other social sciences and to cultural affairs.
Its viewpoint is professedly dispassionate; its contributors, most of whom
are well known, are professors at American and foreign universities, former
government officials, staff members of research institutes, and include a
number who were formerly Russian or East European subjects.

Frequently issues are devoted to a single subject—e.g., Report on Soviet
Science, Germany: Today and Tomorrow, Polycentrism, Religion in the
U.S.S.R.—a number of which have later appeared in book format. The
section "Views and Reviews" contains shorter items. A few book reviews,

some of which are quite long, and occasional documents. Supported by the International Association (formerly the Congress) for Cultural Freedom, it is not an academic journal in the parochial sense, but attempts to provide material both for the specialist and for the general student of international affairs. The quality of its contributions is high, and it uses a variety of approaches to understanding political and social developments in and relating to the Soviet Union; it is generally regarded as the most perceptive interpreter of all journals in this area, and it should be in every academic library.

Indexed in: P.A.I.S.   59-54578 rev

*AFRICAN ARTS.   v. 1, 1967-

Quarterly.   Los Angeles, Calif. $10.00

Published at the African Studies Center, University of California, Los Angeles, it is "devoted to the graphic, plastic, performing, and literary arts of Africa." Includes all regions of Africa. During its first three years, its title was *African Arts/Arts d'Afrique,* and articles were published in either English or French, and sometimes both; if they were in only one of the languages, there was a summary in the other. Beginning with the Summer, 1970 issue, the French-language aspect of the journal was dropped. Contributions have emphasized (as one would expect) the visual arts—sculpture, painting, engraving, handicrafts, etc.—but there have also been a substantial number of articles on music, dance, literature, aesthetics, and the sociology of art. The articles, by scholars, devotees of African art, collectors, and others, are well written and well illustrated, with many color plates as well as black-and-white photographs. Contains some original poetry. No book reviews. It is especially important because of the growing interest in African art and the relative lack of coverage in other journals; because of its wide subject coverage, it is useful in all libraries where there is any interest in Africa.

Indexed in: Art I.

AMERICAN ARTIST.   v. 1, 1937-

Monthly (except July-Aug.)   Cincinnati, Ohio $11.00

Intended for the practicing artist, the art student, and the teacher of studio art rather than for the art critic or historian. The articles are mostly on living artists—painters, primarily, though also on sculptors, illustrators, graphic artists, etc.—and their works and techniques, along with a number of illustrations in color and black-and-white. Articles are frequently autobiographical, but rarely is an avant-garde figure treated. There are a number of features."Bulletin Board" lists forthcoming shows and competitions which artists may enter."MuseumCalendar" indicates exhibits across the country. "Ralph Mayer's Technical Page" answers readers' questions on paints, equipment, special effects, and other technical matters. For many years Frederic Taubes wrote on this and other matters. In 1964, an annual oil school directory was begun in the March issues. The annual Travelogue, begun in April, 1959, describes all sorts of summer opportunities, both domestic and foreign. "The Art Mart," describing new products and equipment for the artist, appears frequently. The January issue has since 1955 carried the annual "Buyer's Guide of Art Materials," a listing of many types of materials and their suppliers. Several books, mostly on techniques or individual artists, are reviewed in each issue. The reviews are of short to moderate length, mostly unsigned, and tend to be descriptive rather than critical. In colleges where studio art is taught, this is an important periodical.

Indexed in: Art.I.   40-12135 Rev
            R.G.

AMERICAN Fabrics. *see* HOME ECONOMICS

APOLLO. v. 1, 1925-

Monthly.   London. $32.00

A somewhat pedestrian art journal for most of its life, it seemed close to
demise in 1962 when its present editor took it over. Now it is a sumptuous publication devoted to art and antiques. While it has treated, at
one time or another, many different periods and locales, its emphasis has
always been on European art in all its forms, covering from the Renaissance through the 19th century. Complete issues are often devoted
to single museums (including American ones) and collections owned by individuals are often featured in articles. Articles by scholars, curators, collectors and others, are thoroughly illustrated with color and black-and-
white plates. The advertisement pages comprise at least half of each issue;
they are also beautifully illustrated, often showing some of the finest
examples of art and antiques. "Reports on London Galleries," in two
parts, reviews exhibitions of traditional works in one section, and contemporary works in the other. Also reports from New York galleries and
exhibitions. Book reviews, of varying length, are signed and critical. Because of its expense, its bulk, and its emphasis, it is important only for
those institutions with strong art history programs.

Indexed in: Art I.   28-50
            Br. Hum. I.

ARCHITECTURAL FORUM.   v. 1, 1892-

10 nos./yr. (Jan./Feb. and July/Aug. combined)   N.Y. $12.00

Founded as a "medium of exchange between brick manufacturers and
architects," it was titled during its first 25 years *The Brickbuilder,*
"devoted to the advancement of brick architecture," and in 1919 assumed
its present title. Time, Inc. took it over in 1932, but dropped it in October
1964; in April, 1965 it resumed publication under the sponsorship of Urban America, Inc. (formerly American Planning and Civic Association),
a non-profit organization. From the 1930's to 1964 it was similar in appearance to the *Architectural Record,* its major competitor, but was not as
professionally oriented, and though its circulation was much larger than
the *Record,* it was not as popular with architects and engineers—though,
for the same reason, was more useful to libraries and to the general public.
Since 1965, under its new sponsorship, its emphasis is on the building, design, transportation, and other planning problems of cities, with fairly
long and well illustrated articles. Regular sections include "Forum," a
review of events and ideas, and "Focus," a review of notable new buildings. Book reviews appear frequently; sometimes just one long review
of an important new book; other times, shorter reviews of several works.

Indexed in: A.S.T.I.   43-10759
            Art I.
            P.A.I.S.
            R.G.

*ARCHITECTURAL RECORD.   v. 1, 1891-

Monthly (semi-monthly, May).   N.Y. $7.50

Each issue features a Building Types study, showing recent outstanding examples of one type of building—hospitals, college buildings, hotels, shoping centers, etc.—with explanatory text and fully illustrated with plans and interior or exterior views. There are also a few other recent architectural projects, also with plans and views, but much of the rest of each issue is given to trends in construction costs, to methods and design, new products, etc.—items, in other words, primarily of interest to the practicing architect. News of the profession; "Required Reading" reviews briefly a few new books and lists others received. The extra mid-May number is devoted to outstanding houses of the year and news of developments in housing design and products.

An insert, "Personal Business," in each issue, began in 1971. Similar to those in other McGraw-Hill publications, it contains a variety of items on vacations, travel, family advice, investments, entertainment tips, clothing, etc. Although a professional journal, its non-technical presentation and readable articles on the history, aesthetics, and sociology of architecture make it useful for students; furthermore, the fairly frequent articles on college and university buildings, including libraries, also make it useful for campus planning. Since much of the journal consists of advertising, librarians should consider the binding problem carefully.

Indexed in: A.S.T.I.   12-17303 rev 2
         Art I.
         R.G.

*ART BULLETIN.   v. 1, 1913-

Quarterly.   N.Y. $15.00

It is now a very scholarly journal published by the College Art Association of America, but for its first few years, as the bulletin of the Association, it was mostly concerned with discussions of new courses, bibliographical suggestions, and teaching methods. After the first World War, when it was sponsored only by Harvard, Princeton and the University of Chicago, it carried some historical articles, primarily on medieval art and archaeology. With the growth of art courses in the thirties, and the changing nature of the College Art Association, its sponsorship widened and its coverage began to include American and more recent art, and since the second World War it has had a number of foreign contributors.

Its articles, notes and book reviews are still primarily on the Baroque, Medieval and Renaissance periods, with only occasional attention to modern or non-Western art. It is an elegantly printed journal, a case study in typographical excellence. Thoroughly illustrated, of course. 10 to 15 book reviews per issue, varying in length from just a few paragraphs to 5000 or more words. They are all signed and many are extremely thorough, with footnotes and illustrations. Where there is any serious study of art history, this is an essential journal.

Indexed in: A.S.T.I.   29-12891 rev 2
         B.R.D.

ART Education. *see* EDUCATION

*ART IN AMERICA.   v. 1, 1913-

Bi-monthly.   Des Moines, Ia. $15.00

From its founding until 1949, the title belied its contents: it was not devoted to American art, but rather to articles on all periods, types and
schools of art, with, perhaps, just a bit more attention to American art
than the traditional art periodicals gave it. The articles were scholarly
and reliable, but unexciting, even though it contained some of the first
serious studies of American artists. In 1949, it began to concentrate on
American artists, and in 1951 its cover was subtitled "Dedicated to Promoting the Study of American Art" and its format was improved. While
this subtitle was short-lived, the new emphasis of the journal remained. In
1958 it became a quarterly, each issue hard-bound; in 1963 it became a
bi-monthly, but the hard covers gave way to soft, but of heavy enameled
stock. Beautifully illustrated, it covers the entire world of art—sculpture,
graphics, architecture, and especially painting—with attention to the entire
world of art, but with great emphasis on this country and on the contemporary. Beginning in 1969, Russell Lynes has a regular column, "The
State of Taste." The book reviews are all by Jay Jacobs; he covers usually
15-20 titles, from popular to scholarly works, over all periods and genres,
in anywhere from a short paragraph to 1000 or so words, and writes in a
personal style with his biases open to all. A readable, handsome journal,
probably the single most useful one for college libraries in the field of
contemporary art.

Indexed in: Art I.   14-11738
          R.G.

ART Index. *see* INDEXES

ART INTERNATIONAL.   v. 1, 1956-

Monthly (except one number, June-Aug.)   Lugano, Switzerland. $22.95

The title for its first volume was *European Art This Month.* It is only
slightly concerned with art history, and its art criticism pertains
mostly to contemporary artists. A sumptuous publication, oversize
and on (for the most part) glossy paper, it contains a large number of photographs of paintings and sculpture, mostly in black and white. The early
volumes were almost solely concerned with events in the European art
world—indeed, it was compiled from "the announcements and catalogs"
of museums and galleries—but its emphasis now is on the works of individual artists (mostly still alive and exhibiting) and on contemporary
trends, and it now covers American artists almost as much as Europeans
in its articles and interviews. The "Chronicles" section has always been
important, covering shows, exhibits and discussing other news from various cities; as the number of articles has increased, the number of chronicles have decreased. It is now almost all in English, though occasional
articles and chronicles are in French, German or Italian. No book reviews.
An important journal where there is strong interest in contemporary, and
especially avant-garde, art.

Indexed in: Art I.   62-3686

*ART JOURNAL.   v. 1, 1941-

Quarterly.   N.Y. $5.00

A publication of the College Art Association of America, it was titled
College Art Journal through volume 19 (1959/60) when its title was
changed to encourage wider circulation. Contains articles on artists
and their works, on art theory and history; most are scholarly, but the
subject matter and style are of more popular interest than the Association's *Art Bulletin,* and there is some emphasis on art of the twentieth century. Also carries professional articles on art education, techniques and media, collections, buildings and major exhibits, as well as news
of the Association and its members' activities. Since 1957, a section has
been devoted to college and university museum notes, including acquisitions, exhibits, gifts, etc., and an occasional feature article; news of personnel appointments, honors, etc., and of departmental activities.
A compilation of doctoral dissertations in art history completed since
1960 appeared in the Summer, 1968 issue, and is occasionally supple-
mented. There are 10 or so book reviews in each issue, fairly long and
critical, and a list of books received.

Indexed in: Art I.   45-50467 rev

*ART NEWS.   v. 1, 1902-

Monthly (except July-Aug.)   N.Y. $13.00

The oldest continuously published art periodical, it began as *Hyde's Weekly
Art News,* then in 1904 became *American Art News* and in 1923 took its
present title. In 1936 Alfred Frankfurter, the noted art historian and critic
assumed the editorship, and kept it until his death in 1965. Under him it
became an important and influential journal, reporting on painters and
painting throughout the world. It is concerned primarily with contemporary art, though there are a few articles on earlier artists and art, particularly
in connection with current exhibitions. Brief reviews of all new shows in
New York, and of some in other cities; thorough listing of exhibitions to
come here and abroad. Useful listings of summer art schools, of competitions and scholarships. All articles are fairly brief, but thoroughly illustrated in color and black-and-white. *Art News* is most useful where there is
much interest in what is now going on in the world of art.

Indexed in: Art I.   6-12267 rev. 2
        R.G.

ARTFORUM.   v. 1, 1962-

Monthly (except July-Aug.)   N.Y. $15.00

First published in San Francisco, it emphasized Western art activity, though
it did not exclude other areas; contained well illustrated articles, mostly on
contemporary painters, sculptors and other artists and their works, and on
Western museum exhibitions and collections. These early issues carried reviews of shows and exhibitions at Western galleries and museums; also a
calendar of shows in the West. This emphasis on the West gradually diminished until, in 1965, the editorial offices moved from California to New

York. It has now no regional emphasis, and almost totally ignores any art but recent or contemporary; interviews with artists are almost a regular feature. Frequent articles on art criticism. The contributions, by artists, scholars and critics, are well written and well illustrated. Reviews of shows and exhibitions in New York and other art centers; reviews of photography shows and books; long reviews of some new films, and comments on film history and festivals; occasional book reviews that are signed and critical.

Indexed in: Art I.   65-8747

ARTS IN SOCIETY.   v. 1, 1958-

3 nos./yr.   Madison, Wis. $5.50

"*Arts in Society* exists to discuss, interpret, and illustrate the various functions of the arts in contemporary civilization. Its purpose is to present the insights of experience, research and theory in support of educational and organizational efforts to enhance the position of the arts in America. In general, four areas are dealt with: the teaching and learning of the arts; aesthetics and philosophy; social analysis; and significant examples of creative expression in a media which may be served by the printing process." The first 4 numbers were general in nature, but since then each issue has been devoted to a single topic, with contributions by leading writers, artists, scholars and others. The subjects for topics have ranged widely—e.g., Government in Art, The Avant-Garde Today, The University as Cultural Leader in Society, Happenings and Intermedia, The Arts and the Black Revolution—but all are intelligently and attractively presented, with a large number of illustrations and an interesting format. The space given to poetry, essays and criticism has steadily increased, so that the journal is of much wider interest than just to art departments. An excitingly creative journal, important where there is much interest in the relationships among the arts and between the arts and society, particularly the avant-garde of these areas.

Indexed in: In.Ltl.Mag.   67-115032

*ARTS MAGAZINE.   v. 1, 1926-

8 nos./yr.   N.Y. $11.20

Starting as the *Art Digest,* it changed to *Arts Digest* in 1954, to *Arts* in 1955, and to its current title in 1961. Most articles are not scholarly, but many are by noted writers and critics. It is concerned primarily with painting, and mostly with recent and contemporary painting, and interviews with practicing artists appear frequently. Much of it is devoted to what is going on in the world of art: regular features include a calendar of auctions, a listing of forthcoming shows for artists who want to exhibit, reports from art centers here and abroad, and a thorough coverage of exhibitions in museums and galleries of the New York area. These reviews, however, run from only a few words to a few paragraphs. There are usually 5 to 10 book reviews an issue. They vary greatly in length, from a paragraph or two to 1000 words, but they are signed and critical. An important journal, widely read by those in the art world.

Indexed in: Art I.   29-15619 rev. 3

BURLINGTON MAGAZINE.   v. 1, 1903-

Monthly.   London. $32.00

Covers all the plastic and graphic arts, of all periods and countries, though the traditional art of Western Europe is emphasized. When it began it paid very little attention to recent developments, but after a few years, under the editorship of Roger Fry it began to notice contemporary trends in European art; presently, however, it is not known for its treatment of modern art—indeed, scholarly articles on any twentieth-century artist are rare. However, the articles are excellent and well-illustrated, though mostly in black-and-white. Useful regular features are the extensive notes—frequently article-length—on recent acquisitions by museums, or descriptions of current and forthcoming exhibitions. The book review section is excellent with generally 6 or 7 reviews, almost all at least 1000 words and frequently several times that, on books in all areas and all periods. Also list of publications received. The advertisements, illustrating paintings, drawings and *objets d'art* for sale, are also useful. An important art journal, especially where art history is emphasized.

Indexed in: Art I.   8-15095
         Br.Hum.I.

CONNOISSEUR.   v. 1, 1901-

Monthly.   London. $30.00

A sumptuous journal, intended primarily for the collector. Articles on all types of works of art—architecture, armour, books and manuscripts, enamels, furniture, glass, jewelry, pottery and porcelain, textiles, etc., as well as paintings, drawings, and sculpture. The articles emphasize the physical and historical aspects of works, rather than their theoretical or aesthetic attributes; very little attention to modern work. Had given some attention to American works of art, collectors and collections for many years in the section American Notes; in 1935 this section was expanded and retitled Connoisseur in America; then, as the American Connoisseur, it expanded further. The journal still, however, caters mainly to a British audience. It is thoroughly illustrated in superb color and black-and-white. Features include: "In the Galleries," descriptions of current exhibits in London galleries; "Paris Dispatch," containing news of shows; "International Saleroom," illustrations of important sales at galleries and auctions. The number of reviews varies; they are, however, good—signed and critical, mostly 500-600 words long, and frequently on books that are difficult to find reviews of elsewhere. Also a list of books received. In addition to all these, there are a large number of advertisements by galleries and exhibitors, with useful illustrations.

Indexed in: Art I.   8-15088-9
         Br.Hum.I.

*CRAFT HORIZONS.   v. 1, 1941-

Bi-monthly.   N.Y. $10.00

Published by the American Craftsmen's Council, it contains articles on the work and technique of individual designers and craftsmen in contemporary handicrafts—ceramics, jewelry, weaving, carving, bookbinding, etc. Thoroughly illustrated. Regular features include news of the Council and of various activities around the world; rather careful reviews of exhibits; a calendar of events, including a section "Where to Show." The May/June issue contains the annual "Travel and Study Directory," published since 1958, which lists "complete information on craft summer study and school year craft curricula," both here and abroad. Most issues contain one or a few book reviews; these are signed and critical, but vary greatly in length from a paragraph to over 1000 words. An important journal where there is interest in handicrafts, and since that is just about everywhere now, it should be in all libraries.

Indexed in: Art I.   52-17216
         R.G.

DESIGN QUARTERLY.   v. 1, 1946-

Irregular.   Minneapolis, Minn. $5.00 for 4 issues

Published by the Walker Art Center, Minneapolis. Each issue is devoted to a single topic—product and industrial design, architecture, the graphic arts, but not painting or sculpture. Typical subjects are: Industrial Design in Germany, Japan—Book Design, Signs and Symbols in Graphic Communication, Form Follows Fiction, Tradition in Good Design. Each topic is treated by abundant use of photographs and drawings and interesting layout, with supplementary text. Though termed a quarterly, for the last few years there have been just two single numbers, or one single and one double number per year. No book reviews. A handsome publication, important where there is interest in graphics and contemporary design.

Indexed in: Art I.   50-57011

GRAPHIS.   v. 1, 1944-

Bi-monthly.   Zurich, Switzerland. $23.50

An "international journal of graphic art and applied art" containing articles on all forms of these arts, with some emphasis on advertising and poster art. Since the text must be repeated three times (English, French and German), there is not much space for long discussions, and the articles, mostly by practicing artists, consist primarily of illustrations, which are exceptionally well done, with a little explanatory text. Brief book reviews. A good journal just for browsing, it is important where there is much interest in the graphic arts, especially for keeping up with European developments. For an art journal, margins are small, and may cause some problem in binding.

Indexed in Art I.   49-25759*

INTERIORS. *see* HOME ECONOMICS

JOURNAL of Aesthetic Education. *see* EDUCATION

JOURNAL of Aesthetics and Art Criticism. *see* PHILOSOPHY

METROPOLITAN MUSEUM OF ART BULLETIN. v. 1, 1905; n.s.v. 1, 1942-

Monthly (except 1 issue July-Sept.)   N.Y. $7.50

Devoted primarily to the Museum's accessions and exhibits and to articles on items in its collection, though there are occasional general articles on art theory or history. It started as primarily a listing of new accessions; as the descriptions of these grew longer, more detailed and set in their historical or aesthetic context, the need for a new format was seen, and so the new series began. Most contributors are members of the Museum's staff; outside experts are sometimes called upon, and occasionally artists themselves comment. Like the Museum's collection, though with more attention to the contemporary scene, the *Bulletin* covers all periods and geographical areas. The October issue is devoted to the Museum's Annual Report, which includes reports by departments. Replete with illustrations, but unfortunately these are rarely in color.

Similar in nature and also recommended are such bulletins as the *Boston Museum Bulletin* (v. 1, 1903- $4.00), the *Cleveland Museum of Art. Bulletin* (v. 1, 1914- $5.00), the *Detroit Institute of Arts. Bulletin* (v. 1, 1919- $3.00), the *Minneapolis Institute of Arts. Bulletin* (v. 1, 1905- $3.00), and the *Philadelphia Museum of Art. Bulletin* (v. 1, 1903- $4.00), all of which are covered in the *Art Index*. Individual libraries may want some of these as well as the lesser-known but useful (and often very good) bulletins of nearby museums and galleries.

Indexed in: Art I.   8-18253

ORIENTAL ART. v. 1, 1948; n.s.v. 1, 1955-

Quarterly.   London. $12.00

The first series ended with volume 3 in 1951; after a lapse of a few years the journal was revived under the editorship of Peter C. Swann, who remained as editor until 1971. The articles are specialized, but readable and illustrated; it is true, as the periodical claims, that they are on "all forms of Oriental art," but no attention is given to contemporary arts, and many more articles by far are concerned with China than with any other area. The affiliations or positions of the contributors are not given, but most of them and the reviewers are eminent in the field. From 5 to 9 books are reviewed in each issue; the reviews vary in length, but they are all critical. Each issue also has a bibliography of recent books and articles; news from museums and of exhibitions from all over; reports on dealers' sales; and other news and reports from the field. The text, and the dealers' advertisements, have good illustrations, but almost none are in color. Because it is aimed at collectors as much as scholars, and because it is limited in scope, it is important only where courses on Oriental art specifically are given.

Libraries that need to support such courses should also receive *Artibus Asiae* (v. 1, 1925- $15.00), published in Switzerland by the Institute of Fine Arts of New York University. Devoted to illustrations (in black-and-white) of previously unpublished art objects and documents, and to descriptions of recent discoveries, it is a very scholarly journal on the traditional arts of Asia. It also has excellent book reviews, about 6 an issue, often quite long and detailed.

Indexed in: Art I.   51-23285

PRINT.   v. 1, 1940-

Bi-monthly.   Washington, D.C. $14.00

Its early volumes—the first ten years or so—are almost impossible to get,
but are especially important in the study of the history and theory of
graphic arts and for insights into the work and personality of individual
artists. It treated book design, print making, type design, etc.—in other
words, fine craftsmanship—in creative, attractive and interesting ways, and
included many tipped-in examples. More and more it has become concerned with items of interest to the advertising profession, though it is
still a well-produced periodical. Carries articles, interviews and features
on design, printing, paper, advertising art, typography, techniques, products and trends, and on outstanding individuals in the graphic arts, with
increasing attention to film and electronic media. Issues treating a single
subject appear frequently. Examples: "Great Graphic Designers of the
20th Century," "Where the Graphic Arts are Going," "The Creative Uses
of Photography." There are a number of departments. "Top Drawer"
features graphic ideas, techniques, innovations. "Paper and Design" emphasizes the "creative use of paper." Others include: "Letterhead Design," "Corporate Design," "Events of Interest" reporting shows, competitions, meetings, etc. "Materials and Methods" describes new products
and services, listing a variety of swatch books, type display booklets, and
other free material. "The Production Clinic" "deals with the how-to, technical aspect of graphic design." A regular feature appearing in alternate
issues is "New Developments in the Graphic Arts," treating materials and
technology. It began in mid-1967; in 1970 it extended its coverage to
television and film. The book review section contains usually 6 to 10 fairly
brief (50-150 words) reviews. Few of these features appear in every issue,
but all of them appear frequently. Not as important for college libraries
as it used to be, but still good to have where there is an interest in
graphic art.

Indexed in: Art I.   42-18861

PROGRESSIVE ARCHITECTURE.   v. 1, 1920-

Monthly.   Stamford, Conn. $12.00

Originally titled *Pencil Points,* with the subtitle, *Progressive Architecture*
added in 1944; in 1945 the two were reversed; "Pencil Points" then became parenthetical and was dropped entirely in 1949. A professional architects' journal, it covers all types of buildings. Issues are often devoted
to a single architectural topic—e.g., Schools, Dwellings, Performance Design, Earth—which is treated from its theoretical, practical and historical
aspects, including its implications for architects' work. Thoroughly illustrated, of course. The Annual Design Awards issue (the 17th in 1970)
features the highly-coveted awards and citations in the magazine's content. Contains a number of features on news of the profession, of important new construction projects, technical data, etc. A few book reviews,
varying greatly in length.

Indexed in: Art I.   22-21759 rev

SCHOOL ARTS.   v. 1, 1901-

Monthly. (except July-Aug.)   Worcester, Mass. $8.00

"The art education magazine for teachers," it is devoted to brief, well illustrated articles on all aspects of teaching art to students from kindergarten through high school. Some of the articles are on the theory of art education, but most suggest creative ways of using materials, of making instruction more interesting and effective, or introduce teachers to new materials or techniques. A number of regular features: the May or June issue features a "Showcase of Student Art"; in each issue, news of people, events, descriptions of new products and teaching aids; a listing, usually with brief descriptions, of new books. Important where there are courses in art education, it is also of some interest to the student artist.

Similar to it is *Arts and Activities* (v. 1, 1937- $7.00), which is also published monthly, except July and August. *Design* (v. 1, 1899- $7.00),· published bi-monthly, does not focus on art education as much as either of the others, but the level of presentation, the discussions of art history or interpretation, for instance, makes it appropriate for the elementary or high school art teacher.

Indexed in: Ed.I.   14-15843 rev. 3*
            R.G.

*STUDIO INTERNATIONAL.   v. 1, 1893-

Monthly (bi-monthly, July-Aug.)   London. $23.00

Its bibliographical history is a fairly complicated one, having changed title and/or subtitle several times and including, for most of its life, an American edition as part of each issue or as a separate concurrent publication. For many years it was perhaps the most distinguished English-language art journal and, as the only one dealing with contemporary art, was an important influence in the history of modern art. It has remained a standard source of information on recent developments in art, especially those in Great Britain. Its present enlarged format and increased use of color help make it one of the leading journals in the world of modern art. While a major portion of the contents relate to the British art scene, there is extensive coverage of events in other art centers. Frequent interviews with artists. Seasonal supplements contain about 15 or 20 signed and critical reviews of varying length, with a listing of other recently published and forthcoming titles. Because of the excellent articles, the breadth of coverage, and the number and quality of reproductions, it is an important journal for any art department concerned with contemporary developments.

Indexed in: Art I.   8-15092 rev 2
            Br.Hum.I.

ASTRONOMICAL JOURNAL.   v. 1, 1849-

Monthly (except Jan. and July)   New York $40.00

Published by the American Institute of Physics for the American Astronomical Society, it publishes "articles reporting original research in all
branches of astronomy." Articles on celestial mechanics—that is, dealing
with the motion of both natural and artificial planets and satellites—are
published; those dealing with astronautics—on the motion of self-propelled
or actively navigated vehicles—are not. Articles, which vary greatly from
just a page or two to the very lengthy, are quite technical, and are contributed by astronomers from observatories all over the world. Proceedings of conferences are frequently carried. "Reports of Observations,"
"Abstracts of Meetings" of the AAS, and miscellaneous news and reports
had been carried regularly, but in 1969 were removed to the Association's
new *Bulletin*, available separately.

Perhaps the most important professional journal in the field, it is useful
only for advanced students and faculty.

65-7885/CD

ASTRONOMICAL SOCIETY OF THE PACIFIC.   PUBLICATIONS.   v. 1, 1889-

Bi-monthly.   San Francisco, Calif. $16.50

Contains short technical articles on current astronomical research, including
discoveries, methods and equipment. Articles, all preceded by abstracts,
are by astronomers associated with observatories or universities, both U.S.
and abroad. Until about 1960 it carried non-technical and historical articles,
but these appear rarely now. Also includes technical "Notes from Observatories," a regular section "Comet Notes," other news and notes of individual and observatory activities, plus activities of the Society. Occasional
book reviews, mostly 400-500 words.

Included in the subscription price is the Society's monthly *Leaflet* (v. 1,
1925-   ), designed primarily for the non-technical reader, which usually
provides in about 1500 words a statement by a noted authority on some
recent development or special aspect of astronomy, such as "Stellar Evolution," "The Composition of the Interstellar Dust," or "Magnetic Fields
and the Solar Cycle"; occasionally, these leaflets contain tables of astronomical data.

29-19168

ASTROPHYSICAL JOURNAL.   v. 1, 1895-

Semi-monthly.   Chicago, Ill. $65.00

Published in collaboration with the American Astronomical Society, it is
the medium for the publication of research conducted at the Mount Wilson

and Palomar, Yerkes, Harvard and numerous other observatories and at government, university and industrial research laboratories. Articles of various lengths on improved methods of observation, new astronomical theories, tables, discoveries, the application of physics to astronomy, etc. Each article is preceded by an abstract. Notes contain shorter reports of research and comments on other articles. The "Letters to the Editor" section has always been an important part of the journal; beginning in April 1967 it has been separately published as Part 2 of each issue, thus permitting more immediate appearance. Contains abstracts of the *Astrophysical Journal Supplement Series* (v. 1, 1954- $12.00), which appears monthly, and is the "medium for the publication of extensive investigations, such as wavelength lists of stars of special interest, photometric data, results of numerical integrations pertaining to stellar interiors, model stellar atmosphere calculations, and original memoirs," Normally, each memoir consists of a single paper, anywhere from 20 to 50 pages in length.

Both are of basic importance—many of the great astronomical discoveries since 1895 have appeared first in the *Journal's* pages—but they are too technical for most undergraduates, and are really useful only for advanced courses and research.

17-24351 rev

ROYAL ASTRONOMICAL SOCIETY OF CANADA. JOURNAL. v. 1, 1907-

Bi-monthly.   Toronto. $12.00

Contains some reports of original astronomical observations, but more important for its general and review articles, covering topics of current and historical interest. Also articles of more general interest to astronomers: education, equipment and techniques, on particular planetaria. Regular features include: "About Our Authors" (who are primarily Canadians, but often from the U.S. and other countries); "Advances in Astronomy," reporting on developments in theory, equipment or techniques; "Notes from Observatories" and "Notes from Planetaria"; "Variable Star Notes," with monthly observations charted. One or two brief signed book reviews per issue. Also contains reports of international meetings and minutes of the annual R.A.S.C. meeting. Subscription includes the annual *Observer's Handbook,* which contains a variety of charts, maps, tables and other data useful to astronomers.

A useful publication, especially where there is an observatory, and because of its locational information, particularly in Canada and northern U.S.

11-23485

ROYAL ASTRONOMICAL SOCIETY OF LONDON.   QUARTERLY JOURNAL.   v. 1, 1960-

Quarterly.   London. $12.00

The *Journal* began when the Society felt that its *Monthly Notices* (see below) were becoming so technical that they were becoming less and less suitable as a link among the members. Everything except the technical papers was shifted to the *Journal*, so that it includes reports of meetings and of officers, Presidential addresses, obituary notices, annual proceedings of Commonwealth observatories, some non-technical (but authoritative) articles on recent developments in a particular area, or on a topic of more general interest (e.g., "The Education of Astronomers") and a list of the Society's library accessions.

The Society's *Monthly Notices* (v. 1, 1827- $120 for 4 volumes) now contains lengthy technical articles reporting original research in "positional and dynamical astronomy, astrophysics, radio astronomy, cosmology, space research and the design of astronomical instruments." The individual numbers appear irregularly, but there are now 16 or 20 a year—that is, 4 or 5 volumes. It is appropriate only for very advanced students and faculty. Subscribers to it automatically receive the *Quarterly Journal* (also available separately—see above) and the Society's *Memoirs* (v. 1, 1821-   not available separately) which appear irregularly but often, and contain those technical papers with a higher proportion of tabular or mathematical material so that the format is larger.

64-50164

*SKY AND TELESCOPE.   v. 1, 1941-

Monthly.   Cambridge, Mass. $8.00

Intended for the amateur and student, it contains well written and profusely illustrated articles by experts. Articles and news on all areas of astronomy: stars, planets and satellites, observatories and planetariums, their designers and directors, telescopes and telescope making, radio and radar astronomy, comets, meteorites, artificial satellites and spacecraft, history of astronomy, celestial navigation, cosmological theory, etc. A number of regular features: "Amateur Astronomers" covers meetings and activities of local and regional societies; "Astronomical Scrapbook," in alternate issues (or less frequently), is mostly on aspects of the history of astronomy; "News Notes," of personnel, programs, minor findings, new periodicals, etc.; "Gleanings for ATM's (Amateur Telescope Makers), with descriptions of telescopes and telescopic equipment built by individuals: "Observer's Page," observations with photographs from readers, including regular reports on Deep-Sky Wonders and on Sunspot Numbers; "Celestial Calendar," describing the movements of the sun, moon, planets and stars for the coming month, with a star map for the month. "Books and the Sky" contains 3 or 4 excellent signed book reviews. Almost all are at least 500 words long—and often several times that; they are authoritative and frank. Also a listing of "New Books Received," briefly annotated. An essential item where there are any courses in astronomy, it is a worthwhile addition to every library.

Indexed in: R.G.   44-30805

BIOLOGY

47

AMERICAN BIOLOGY TEACHER.   v. 1, 1938-

Monthly (except June-Aug.)   Washington, D.C. $10.00

Official journal of the National Association of Biology Teachers, which is composed of biology teachers at all levels and those who teach biology teachers. Each issue usually contains 10-12 brief articles on the content and method of biological instruction at the elementary, secondary and college levels, especially descriptions of particular demonstrations, experiments and exercises. Occasional articles on the history of biology, and on the purposes and objectives of biology teaching. "A-V News," appearing in several issues a year, contains a few brief reviews of films, but mostly is devoted to descriptions of new materials and sources. Usually 20-30 signed book reviews per issue, mostly 150-300 words in length and almost never over 500.

Though the emphasis is on biology for elementary and secondary schools, there is enough on college biology to make the journal useful for many college libraries. It is, however, essential for those institutions that give courses in science education or prepare many biology teachers.

Indexed in: Ed.I.   E 41-383

*AMERICAN FORESTS.   v. 1, 1895-

Monthly.   Washington, D.C. $7.50

The first 35 volumes were published under 6 different titles by a number of different organizations. It was taken over by the American Forestry Association shortly after the turn of the century and was given its present title in 1930. The magazine is devoted to popular material on forests, soil, water, and wildlife conservation, and outdoor recreation. In addition to news columns, there are staff-written and contributed articles, almost all rather brief, on all aspects of conservation but especially forest conservation. In recent years it has become a more attractive magazine with a handsome format and use of color photographs. Since the American Forestry Association is supported primarily by members of the wood and wood pulp industry, the journal has a point of view that contrasts with, say, that of the Audubon Society or the Conservation Foundation. One long review and a few shorter ones in the column "Reading About Resources." Useful for browsing and for introductory material.

Indexed in: R.G.   10-18571 (rev. '35)

*AMERICAN JOURNAL OF BOTANY.   v. 1, 1914-

Monthly (bi-monthly, May-June, Nov.-Dec.)   N.Y. $21.50

Official publication of the Botanical Society of America, it is the foremost botanical journal in this country. Publishes the results of research in all branches of the plant sciences, each issue now containing usually 12-15 technical articles of short to moderate length, well-illustrated and each preceded by an abstract. Occasional "Special Papers" serve as review articles or discuss techniques or methodology. Part 2 of the July issue carries the program and abstracts of most papers presented at the annual meeting of the Botanical Society and certain affiliated groups. Essential for every library supporting courses in botany.

Indexed in: Bio.Ag.I.   17-5518

AMERICAN JOURNAL OF PHYSIOLOGY.   v. 1, 1898-

Monthly.   Bethesda, Md. $60.00

Published by the American Physiological Society, it is devoted to the publication "of significant new research findings in some area of physiology.
The area is immaterial, but the emphasis and point of view must be on
physiological mechanism or action." Each issue contains about 35 articles,
of short to moderate length, well-illustrated, and each preceded by an abstract. One of the pioneer publications in the bio-medical sciences, with
emphasis on vertebrate physiology, its increasing attention in recent years
to the results of medical research has made it of lesser importance to
undergraduate institutions than it used to be.

Indexed in: Bio. Ag.I.   A43-3158

AMERICAN MEDICAL ASSOCIATION.   JOURNAL.   v. 1, 1883-

Weekly.   Chicago, Ill. $23

Official journal of the A.M.A. Contains the proceedings of the A.M.A.,
papers read at meetings, editorials, research papers covering the whole
field of general medicine, often including articles of historical interest and
reflecting social concerns, plus many other features and departments of
interest to those in the medical field. There are a number of special issues;
one of particular interest to college libraries is the one treating Medical
Education in the United States. Published usually in November, it covers
trends and developments in the field, plus a great amount of data and
statistical information on individual schools and programs as well as on
the national scene. Usually about 5 signed book reviews per issue, mostly
200-400 words, plus some very brief notices, and a substantial listing of
new books. The regular section "References and Reviews" provides abstracts of articles appearing in recent issues of the world's major medical
journals. Of interest to prospective medical students, it is useful for some
areas of biology, but is necessary only for those undergraduate libraries
which are supporting wide-ranging biology programs with some emphasis
on research.

Indexed in: P.A.I.S.   7-37314

AMERICAN MICROSCOPICAL SOCIETY.   TRANSACTIONS.   v. 1, 1880-

Quarterly.   Lawrence, Kans. $11.00

The Society has a long history, beginning in 1878. In its early years the
journal and the Society dealt with the microscope *per se*; later, as it began
to publish the results of research which used the microscope, it became an
important interdisciplinary journal in the general field of biology. Besides the 10 or 12 6 to 10-page research articles, there is a "Shorter Communications" section containing 1 to 3-page reports on topics similar to
the longer articles or on specific techniques. All are well illustrated with
micrographs and drawings. One number annually contains a Directory of
Members, Abstracts of Papers Presented at the Annual Meeting, and Proceedings of the Annual Meeting. Beginning in 1968, the April issue number carries a large number of reviews. They are all signed, but only a few
are lengthy; most are 150-300 words.

56-45586

AMERICAN MIDLAND NATURALIST. v. 1, 1909-

Quarterly. Notre Dame, Ind. $15.00

"A general biological journal published quarterly by the University of Notre Dame." Each issue contains 15 to 20 articles of varying length, but averaging about 15 pages, plus a few shorter "Notes and Discussions." In its earlier years, the journal was limited to the natural and physical features of middle America, but it has expanded to cover all phases of field biology—botany, zoology and entomology, and especially the ecology and life histories of organisms—throughout the U.S. and occasionally Canada and Mexico. The number of book reviews varies; many issues contain none, and rarely are there more than just a few. They are signed and critical, and vary greatly in length. Almost every number contains a listing of 15-20 books received with short critical annotations. An important research journal for field biology.

Indexed in: Bio.Ag.I.   13-3548

*AMERICAN NATURALIST. v. 1, 1867-

Bi-monthly. Chicago, Ill. $18.00

Published for the American Society of Naturalists, whose objectives are the "discussion, advancement and diffusion of knowledge concerning the broader biological problems, including organic evolution, thus serving to correlate the various biological sciences into a common philosophy of biology." The oldest continuously published American biological journal, its backfile is especially important between 1900 and 1940, when it was contributed to by so many important biologists, especially in genetics. Now there are usually 6 or 7 articles, mostly 10-15 pages, in many areas of biology, but with a heavy emphasis on population ecology, followed by evolution and population genetics. Also contains reports of the Society and its Presidential Addresses. Articles do not contain abstracts, but each concludes with a summary. Brief, 1 or 2-page research reports are included in "Letters to the Editor." Book reviews have not been carried since 1947. Contributed to by biologists from universities and laboratories in many countries, it is an important journal for all students, but especially for advanced undergraduates working in population genetics, evolution, or ecology.

Indexed in: Bio.Ag.I.   12-30247

*AMERICAN ZOOLOGIST. v. 1, 1961-

Quarterly. Thousand Oaks, Cal. $15.00

The Official journal of the American Society of Zoologists. Most of the papers, which usually combine reviews and original research, originate in symposia of the Society and its annual refresher course. Of the four issues per year, "ordinarily two issues of about 130 pages each contain original papers. The other two issues contain the programs of the Society and abstracts of the papers to be presented at the meetings. Previously these had been published as Supplements to the *Anatomical Record*." Issues devoted to the Society's program include a list of members, the Presidential address and other official reports, but primarily they contain the papers presented at symposia and are frequently significant. Most are well illustrated with photographs and drawings. An essential journal where zoology is of any interest.

Indexed in: Bio.Ag.I.   63-6324

ANATOMICAL RECORD.   v. 1, 1906-

Monthly.   Philadelphia, Pa. $45.00

Official journal of the American Association of Anatomists and published by the Wistar Institute of Anatomy and Biology. "Intended primarily for prompt publication of concise, original articles dealing with descriptive or experimental vertebrate anatomy." Papers are of moderate length (approximately 20 pages) and handsomely illustrated. In addition it contains the proceedings and abstracts of papers and demonstrations of the Society's annual meeting. An important title for institutions where zoology or vertebrate biology is emphasized, but others, even with strong biology departments, need not have it.

ANIMAL BEHAVIOUR.   v. 1, 1953-

Quarterly.   London. $28.00

The relatively new field of animal behavior, bridging psychology and biology, has developed rapidly in the past few years, and libraries supporting strong biology departments should be aware of the basic sources. *Animal Behaviour* (which was titled *British Journal of Animal Behaviour* before 1958), published jointly by the Association for the Study of Animal Behaviour (U.K.) and the newer Animal Behavior Society (U.S.), is probably the leading journal in the field. It carries mostly brief (averaging 5-6 pages) technical articles reporting the results of experimental work on all aspects of animal behavior; also proceedings of both societies' meetings, and usually 5 or 6 critical, signed book reviews, mostly 200-600 words in length.

In 1968 the same groups began *Animal Behaviour Monographs* (v. 1, 1968- $13.00), published 3 times a year, covering the same field but carrying review papers or research reports from 30-80,000 words in length. Its cost is $10.00 for those who also subscribe to *Animal Behaviour*.

Indexed in: Ment.Hlth.B.R.I.   56-2267 rev. 3

ANNALS OF BOTANY.   v. 1, 1887-

Quarterly.   London. $25.00

The most important British journal in the field, containing medium length articles reporting research in the various areas of botany. The emphasis is on Britain, but though American contributors are few, there are a number from other countries. Necessary only where there are strong biology departments and especially where there is much work done in botany.

Indexed in: Bio.Ag.I.   23-15643-4

*AUDUBON.   v. 1, 1899-

Bi-monthly.   N.Y. $9.00

Originally entitled *Bird-Lore*, and devoted to the study and protection of birds, its title was changed to the *Audubon Magazine* in 1941 to reflect its expanded coverage from birdlife to the whole field of the conservation of wildlife resources. In 1966, "Magazine" was dropped from the title, and reflecting an even broader coverage, it became "Dedicated to the conservation and appreciation of wildlife and wilderness, natural resources and natural beauty." It is, then, a periodical covering many aspects of natural history and conservation, though there is still some emphasis on bird life that one would expect from the National Audubon Society (whose official publication this is) and which distinguishes it from other journals in conservation and natural history. The articles are frequently by well-known naturalists, well written and profusely—often breathtakingly—illustrated, and range over the subjects mentioned above. The beauty and technique of the photographs should really receive special mention, and some libraries may want the journal primarily for them. The section "National Outlook" tells about federal activities and legislation affecting wildlife and natural resources. The "Naturalist's Bookshelf" contains reviews of usually 6 or 7 books; the reviews are signed and critical, seldom more than a few hundred words, but frequently much less. In the November/December issue, this section is devoted to recommendations of nature books for children. A beautiful, well edited, interesting periodical, now of interest to photographers as well as naturalists and conservationists.

Some libraries may also want the bi-monthly *American Birds* (formerly *Audubon Field Notes*) (v. 1, 1947- $5.00). Published originally as section 2 of the Regular Edition of *Audubon Magazine* from 1942 through 1946, it is now published in collaboration with the U.S. Fish and Wildlife Service. It contains an occasional article, but mostly it is "devoted to reporting the distribution, migration and abundance of birds" in four seasonal issues and issues devoted to the annual Breeding Bird Census and to the annual comprehensive and detailed Christmas Bird Count covering the United States and Canada.

Indexed in: R.G.   38-5885 rev 2

*BACTERIOLOGICAL REVIEWS.   v. 1, 1937-

Quarterly.   Baltimore, Md. $12.00

Published by the American Society for Microbiology, it is intended "to provide authoritative critical surveys on the current status of subjects and problems in the diverse fields of microbiology and cognate disciplines, such as immunology and genetics. This scope includes the occasional short monographs, incorporating and summating original investigations of such breadth and significance that they would lose cogency if published as a series of research papers." In these contributions, the expert can "interpret his special knowledge for the benefit of the main body of microbiologists." Also carries the Society's annual Presidential Address. Issues, or portions of them, frequently consists of papers presented at a conference or symposium.

Indexed in: Bio. Ag.I.   40-10088

BIOCHEMICAL Journal. *see* CHEMISTRY

BIOCHEMISTRY. *see* CHEMISTRY

*BIOLOGICAL ABSTRACTS.   v. 1, 1926-

Semi-monthly.   Philadelphia, Pa. $800.00

Published by BioSciences Information Service, it is the most important abstracting/indexing service in the biological sciences. Abstracts are arranged under 85 subject sections, each of which is subdivided into more specific subjects. Abstracts appear for the biological literature identified in some 7500 serials, and books from about 750 publishers. Abstracts are usually those of the author which appear at the heads of published articles, others are done by a staff of abstractors. A regular feature is the section "New Books and Periodicals Received."

The abstracts are indexed in each issue in the key word index, author index, bio-systematic index, and cross index. (A detailed explanation of these is given in A.T. Bottle's *The Use of Biological Literature*, London, 1967.) All indexes are cumulated at the end of the year.

A related publication is *BioResearch Index* (1965-$1,000.00), previously called *BioResearch Titles*. It was started to provide indexing for materials that could not be included in *Biological Abstracts* because of their highly specialized nature, or the form of publication. It has become increasingly important as more and more material is moved into it from *Biological Abstracts*. Such things as books containing collections of papers, and abstracts of papers appearing in society publications are covered in *BioResearch Index*. The increased importance has necessitated annual cumulative indexes, the first of which appeared in 1970.

Biological Abstracts is a must for any school which has an active life sciences program. *BioResearch Index* is needed only when complete coverage of the literature in this area is needed.

31-13663

BIOLOGICAL & Agricultural Index. *see* INDEXES

*BIOLOGICAL BULLETIN.   v. 1, 1898-

Bi-monthly.   Lancaster, Pa. $28.00

Published by the Marine Biological Laboratory, Woods Hole, Massachusetts, one of the country's leading biological research centers. Contains usually 10 to 15 articles, mostly of moderate length, reporting the results of research in a variety of biological areas. Well illustrated. No abstracts, but every article concludes with a summary. Contributors are from research laboratories and universities both here and abroad. Does not publish review articles, "very short papers, preliminary notes, and papers which describe only a new technique or method." Contains the MBL's Annual Report, and abstracts of papers and other reports presented at the Laboratory. Provides a good cross section of modern biological problems and approaches, even though most articles relate to marine life forms. A basic journal for all biology departments.

Indexed in: Bio.Ag.I.   A38-518 (rev. '43)

*BIOLOGICAL REVIEWS OF THE CAMBRIDGE PHILOSOPHICAL SOCIETY. v. 1, 1923-

Quarterly.   London. $26.50

Each number contains 3 or 4 articles which are critical and authoritative summaries of particular areas of research. Those are preferred in which a new theory or point of view is embodied, in addition to a review of the literature. Articles are addressed both to research workers in the particular subjects and to non-specialist biologists; they are written in a straight — forward, comprehensible style and each contains a general introduction, a summary and conclusion(s). The long list of references for each article provides a useful bibliographical guide to the subject. Covers all aspects of biology except those of primarily medical interest or those which require a good deal of pictorial matter.

A basic journal for all biology collections.

Indexed in: Bio.Ag.I.   27-4191

*BIOSCIENCE.   v. 1, 1951-

Semi-monthly.   Washington, D.C. $24.00

Official publication of the American Institute of Biological Sciences, it was titled *AIBS Newsletter* until 1963 when it assumed its current title. Intended primarily to keep biologists in all areas informed of general developments in biology and other fields affecting biology. Therefore, sections such as "People and Places," "BIAC" (Bio-Instrumentation Advisory Council), "Capitol Comment," "Calendar," "Institute News," "Meeting Reports" occupy a substantial number of pages. But as the journal developed, more space has been given to material that is of more than just ephemeral interest. Each issue leads off with a few articles which review topics both in specific research areas (e.g., Plant Taxonomy and Modern Systematics) and also more general areas of interest (e.g., Some Issues in Biology Teaching; The Scientist and the UFO) with many relating to research methodology and techniques including those relating to biological bibliography. Several short "Research Reports" and an article or two on "Education" are also included. The "Books" department contains fairly lengthy, signed reviews of books of general interest to biologists, brief reviews of technical books, and lists of new titles arranged by subject. Frequently, annotated bibliographies on areas of biology (e.g., Ornithology, Developmental Biology, Animal Ecology) are published. These are excellent selection aids as they are prepared by experts and cover the best in the field—not just the most recent—including texts and reference works, laboratory and field manuals, and sometimes periodicals.

Because of the many articles of interest to college instructors and the useful bibliographical features, *BioScience* should be in every library where biology is taught.

54-37606

BOTANICAL GAZETTE.   v. 1, 1875-

Quarterly.   Chicago, Ill. $15.00

With the exception of an occasional review article, it is devoted to reporting the results of original research. In its early years it was more a pamphlet that dealt with natural history, but it constantly expanded along with
the science itself to cover morphology, physiology and ecology. Usually
10 to 12 articles per issue, mostly 6 to 8 pages in length, illustrated with
photographs, charts and diagrams. Contributors include research workers
of government agencies, commercial and industrial laboratories, and foreign and American universities; reports of work on domestic species are
prevalent by far.

Indexed in: Bio.Ag.I.   19-16845

BOTANICAL REVIEW.   v. 1, 1935-

Quarterly.   New York. $14.00

Published by the New York Botanical Garden, its purpose is "interpreting botanical progress." Devoted to review articles—most quite long—that
collate, summarize and evaluate all recent and important work on a subject. Subjects may be a particular plant, or part of one, a plant disease,
or botanical concept or process, even nomenclature. No reports of original
research. Contributors are botanists from foreign and domestic universities,
industrial and government research laboratories. The long bibliographies for
all articles make the journal especially useful.

The 25-year index, which is very detailed, permits the *Review* to be used
almost like an encyclopedia, so that a backfile is especially useful. A basic
journal where there is substantial interest in botany.

Indexed in: Bio.Ag.I.   Agr. 36-330 rev. 4

DEVELOPMENTAL BIOLOGY.   v. 1, 1959-

Monthly (except bi-monthly, Jan./Feb.)   N.Y. $90.00

An international research journal published under the auspices of the Society
for Developmental Biology. It is evidence of the merging of the common aspects of the fields concerned with growth and development (e.g., embryology, genetics, plant growth, biochemistry) and as such reflects the modern
concern of biologists working in this area. While many journals contain
research reports on various aspects of development, this is the major one
emphasizing the unity of the field. In its "Information for Authors," it
states that "the principal criterion of acceptability will be the degree of
focus on developmental problems. Articles based on the incidental use
of developing systems for other purposes will not be accepted."

The size (and cost) of the journal has increased rapidly, again reflecting
the growth of the field. Just 5 years ago the volume for 1966 consisted
of 511 pages; in 1970, the issues for the first 6 months contained 1027
pages. The articles themselves, however, have remained about 15-20 pages
in length. No book reviews.

An important research journal, with contributions from members of the leading universities, medical schools and institutes, mostly in the U.S., but often from abroad.

Indexed in: Bio.Ag.I. A61-440

*ECOLOGY. v. 1, 1920-

6 nos./yr. Durham, N.C. $24.00

An official publication of the Ecological Society of America, whose purpose is to give "unity to the study of organisms in relation to environment as a means of furthering intercourse between persons who are approaching widely different groups of organisms from closely related points of view." An average of 15 articles per issue, of moderate length (5-20 pages), are devoted to all phases of basic (as opposed to applied) ecological biology. Illustrated. Also contains "Reports," which are briefer (1-5 pages) and appear more quickly. Usually 5-10 signed and critical reviews. These vary greatly in length, but many are several thousand words in length. A list of "Books and Monographs Received for Review" appears in alternate issues.

The basic journal in the field. Libraries taking it will also want the Society's quarterly *Ecological Monographs* (v. 1, 1939- $9.00) which covers the same subject but carries papers of 20 pages or more.

Indexed in: Bio. Ag.I. 21-17038

ENTOMOLOGICAL SOCIETY OF AMERICA. ANNALS. v. 1, 1908-

Bi-monthly. Baltimore, Md. $25.00

"Devoted to the following basic subdivisions of entomology: biology, biochemistry, ecology, genetics, morphology, pathology, physiology, and systematics. Contributions should not have economic application or chemical control as their primary objective. However, research on economically important arthropods and studies involving the use of chemicals as metabolic inhibitors are within the scope. . . ." Each issue now contains 25 to 50 technical articles, mostly brief (averaging about 6 pages), plus a small number of "Scientific Notes," usually less than a page in length. All are well illustrated with photographs and diagrams.

Institutions taking the *Annals* will also want the Society's quarterly *Bulletin* (v. 1, 1955- $6.00), which contains news of the Society and its branches as well as items of interest to the profession in general—meetings, descriptions of programs at various universities, personnel news, lists of members and officers, texts of addresses, publication notices, etc. Articles of more general interest—often given as addresses—such as those on the development or impact of entomology, often appear. Of particular interest to libraries are the frequent bibliographies of single genera or species, and the book reviews—usually from 6 to 12 an issue, ranging from a paragraph to a page in length, but mostly 350-700 words.

Indexed in: Bio.Ag.I. 8-18807

EVOLUTION.   v. 1, 1947-

Quarterly.   Lawrence, Kans. $17.00

Subtitled the "International Journal of Organic Evolution," it is published
by the Society for the Study of Evolution, the object of which "is the
promotion of the study of organic evolution and the integration of the
various fields of science concerned with evolution." About 15 articles
per issue (limited, with rare exceptions, to 20 pages), in all areas of the
sciences concerned with organic evolution, especially zoology, entomology,
ecology, genetics and botany, with occasional articles in geology, geography and paleontology. Mostly they report results of experimentation, but
often they consist of theoretical explorations. Also a few lengthy signed
book reviews in each issue. Institutions offering both geology and biology
will find this title useful; where there is some emphasis on genetics (especially Drosophila) or vertebrate evolution, the journal is especially important.

Indexed in: Bio.Ag.I.   51-4882

EXPERIMENTAL CELL RESEARCH.   v. 1, 1950-

Monthly.   N.Y. $192.00

Published under the auspices of the International Society for Cell Biology,
it carries "experimental studies on the general organization and operation
of cells," including "all aspects of cell biology, from the molecular level
to the level of cell-interactions and differentiation." It does not include
papers whose results are of more "morphological, histological, pathological,
pharmacological, and microbiological interest." Articles average about 10
pages, are well illustrated with micrographs, diagrams and graphs, and are
contributed by scientists from university and institute laboratories all over
the world. Articles occasionally appear in French or German; English summaries are provided for these. A smaller section of "Preliminary Notes"
provides for rapid publication of items limited to 1900 words. Abstracts
of papers presented at meetings are occasionally published.

An important journal for advanced students and research, it should be available where there is a strong program in biology.

                                                                  54-1254

*GENETICS.   v. 1, 1916-

Monthly.   Austin, Texas. $29.00

Published by the Genetics Society of America as "a periodical record of investigations bearing on heredity and variation," it carries reports of research
in genetics and related fields—cytology, taxonomy, and embryology. Each
issue contains usually about 15 articles, ranging from just a few to 30
pages in length. Occasional supplements carry the proceedings of important, usually international, symposia. Part 2 of the February issue is the
Annual Report Issue of the Society. It carries abstracts of papers presented at the Society's meetings, a directory of members and officers,
reports from committees and offices, the program of the annual meeting
and obituaries of notable members. Since 1967, each issue contains a
section "Genetics Literature," which reproduces the contents pages of
some 50 journals in which geneticists might be interested—a very useful
feature.

The basic journal in the field, it should be in every college library where biology is taught.

(Subscriptions for bound volumes per year are available for $25.00. The 3 volumes are sent at 4-month intervals and libraries with limited binding budgets, where having the latest issues available immediately is not essential, might consider this.)

Indexed in: Bio.Ag.I.   A38-521*

HUMAN BIOLOGY.   v. 1, 1929-

Quarterly.   Detroit, Mich. $8.00

Since 1963 the official publication of the Society for the Study of Human Biology. It publishes research articles on the "biology of past and present human populations—with the nature, extent and processes of human variation, adaptation and affinity, and with the underlying genetic and environmental factors" emphasized. The articles are, for the most part, lengthy papers which follow the traditional organization: introduction, methods, results, and conclusions. Contributors are primarily American university natural scientists and social scientists. Beginning in December, 1965, there are Notes on International Activities in Human Biology which report on meetings, government operations and large research projects. The book section contains, in each issue, one long review and several shorter ones which are generally descriptive. Primarily for colleges that do much work on population studies, it is just as useful for the sociologist in that area as for the biologist.

                                                                       31-29123
Indexed in: Bio.Ag.I.
            Ment.Hlth.B.R.I.

*JOURNAL OF BACTERIOLOGY.   v. 1, 1916-

Monthly.   Baltimore, Md. $52.00

Official organ of the American Society for Microbiology, it "is devoted to the advancement and dissemination of fundamental knowledge concerning bacteria and other microorganisms." Issues usually contain between 40 and 50 research reports, averaging about 7 pages, which are divided into areas: 1) taxonomy and ecology; 2) morphology and ultra structure; 3) genetics and molecular biology; 4) physiology and metabolism; 5) enzymology. The third and fourth areas contain a large majority of the contributions. Contributions from laboratories in universities, hospitals, government agencies, institutes, etc., both here and abroad.

The most important journal in an area that is basic to biological research, it should be in all libraries where there is a major in biology.

Indexed in: Bio.Ag.I.   SG 16-91 rev. 3

*JOURNAL OF BIOLOGICAL CHEMISTRY.   v. 1, 1905-

Semi-monthly.   Baltimore, Md. $120.00

Published by the American Society of Biological Chemists, it is the most important American biochemical journal. Each issue contains anywhere from 20 to 50 articles, most fairly short, arranged under these general subjects: Chemistry and Metabolism of Macromolecules; Chemistry and Metabolism of Substances of Low Molecular Weight; Oxidation-Reduction and Bioenergetics; Enzymology; Control Mechanisms and Biochemical Genetics. Every article is preceded (before 1966, followed) by a summary. Contributors are from universities, governmental and private research laboratories, and medical schools, mostly American, but with some foreign representation. In addition to the articles, "Communications" report experimental data of immediate importance.

Essential where there are courses in biochemistry.

6-46735

JOURNAL of Biological Psychology/Worm Runner's Digest. *see* PSYCHOLOGY

JOURNAL OF CELL BIOLOGY.   v. 1, 1955-

Monthly.   N.Y. $90.00

Formerly the *Journal of Biophysical and Biochemical Cytology,* this journal has, since the early and mid-sixties, been one of the most important journals in cell biology, with contributors from the major universities and research institutes all over the world. It publishes "reports of original observations on the behavior, structure, and function of cells and cell products. It is especially interested in bringing to the attention of readers discoveries arising from the application of modern techniques," and in correlating "the findings of the biophysical and biochemical disciplines with physiological and morphological information." Usually 10-15 articles per issue, mostly 10-15 pages in length (articles are limited to 20 pages, with occasional exceptions). Also some "Brief Notes," from 2 to 7 pages in length. A supplement to one number is devoted to abstracts of papers presented at the annual meeting of the American Society for Cell Biology, which cooperates in the journal's editing. All contributions are profusely illustrated, especially with electron micrographs. An essential journal where there is any advanced work in the area.

56-58208 rev.

JOURNAL OF CELLULAR PHYSIOLOGY.   v. 1, 1932-

Bi-monthly.   Philadelphia, Pa. $18.00

A Wistar Institute publication, formerly titled the *Journal of Cellular and Comparative Physiology.* 8 to 16 research articles appear in each issue "concerned with physiology at the cellular level: the biochemical and biophysical mechanisms concerned in the regulation of cellular growth, function and reproduction." A section, "Comments and Communications," appearing frequently but irregularly, contains shorter (2 pages) but complete, papers. Occasional supplements contain the papers presented at symposia, primarily the annual ones sponsored by the Biological Division of Oak Ridge National Laboratories.

SG 33-116*

JOURNAL OF ECOLOGY.   v. 1, 1913-

3 nos./yr.   Oxford, Eng. $47.00

Published by the British Ecological Society, it contains a wide range of research reports and reviews on all aspects of ecology. Studies with geographical import are usually concerned with Great Britain. The *Journal* also contains Short Notices, which are brief communications, and reports on the activities of the Society and summaries of papers presented at its meetings. Many critical, signed book reviews make this one of the most important book reviewing media in ecology. The section Biological Flora of the British Isles (begun in 1941), a regular feature of the *Journal,* provides complete information on the biology of individual British plant species. The emphasis on British ecology makes this title less useful for American colleges than *Ecology* and *Ecological Monographs,* though for larger collections, it is still important.

Indexed in: Bio.Ag.I.   A 42-1872

*JOURNAL OF EXPERIMENTAL BIOLOGY.   v. 1, 1923-

Bi-monthly.   London. $39.00

Before 1930 titled *British Journal of Experimental Biology.* The "Biology" in the title is misleading as the subject matter is entirely zoological; the editors, as a matter of fact, are at the Zoological Laboratory of Cambridge University. The 15 to 20 articles, mostly 10-15 pages in length, are well illustrated and cover a wide range of topics in experimental zoology—marine biology, neurophysiology, entomology, morphology and animal behavior. Though vertebrates are frequently discussed, the preponderance of articles are concerned with invertebrate zoology. It is, in a sense, the British counterpart of *Biological Bulletin,* but contains contributions from many countries.

Indexed in: Bio.Ag.I.   49-24583*

*JOURNAL OF EXPERIMENTAL ZOOLOGY.   v. 1, 1904-

Monthly.   Philadelphia, Pa. $64.00

Published under the auspices of the American Society of Zoologists by the Wistar Institute of Anatomy and Biology, it contains "articles in zoology which embody the results of original research of an experimental or analytical nature, including investigations of all levels of biological organization from the molecular to the organismal." The 10 or so articles per issue are mostly 10-15 pages in length and—with only rare exceptions—are limited to 26 pages; all are profusely illustrated.

One of the basic journals where biology is taught.

Indexed in: Bio.Ag.I.   5-40843 rev.

JOURNAL OF GENERAL PHYSIOLOGY.   v. 1, 1918-

Monthly.   N.Y. $50.00

Official organ of the Society of General Physiologists, it publishes articles on original research in all fields of physiology but stresses cellular physiology. Letters commenting on articles previously published are also included. Occasional special numbers containing the proceedings of important meetings on physiology, such as the issue on Cell Membrane Biophysics, resulting from a symposium held in Caracas. These special numbers may also be purchased separately. Important only where there are strong biology departments emphasizing physiology.

Indexed in: Bio.Ag.I.   19-20041

JOURNAL OF MAMMALOGY.   v. 1, 1919-

Quarterly.   Stillwater, Okla. $11.00

Published by the American Society of Mammalogists and covering all phases of mammalian biology, but stressing American mammalian ecology. Each issue contains a dozen or so articles, well illustrated and averaging about 10 pages in length, reporting research from both field and laboratory work on basic mammalian biology. The "General Notes" are 1 to 3-page research papers. The 3 to 5 signed book reviews are mostly 300-500 words, but often longer. The section "Recent Literature" is an extensive listing of recently published books and journal articles; though it covers all languages, articles in languages other than English, French, German or Spanish are given with their titles translated into English. (Beginning in 1968, each citation carries a citation number; these are indexed and incorporated in a Citation Retrieval System, permitting literature searches to be made. These are available on a subscription basis or by a special charge. Beginning in 1970, the "Recent Literature" sections are published as separate supplements to the *Journal*. In 1970 there were about 1500 items in each number.) "Comments and News" is a catch-all for news of the Society and personal notices of items to be sold or wanted. Also carries the program and proceedings of the annual meeting of the Society.

A 42-1146

*JOURNAL OF HEREDITY.   v. 1, 1910-

Bi-monthly.   Washington, D.C. $15.00

Official journal of the American Genetic Association which is "devoted to promoting a knowledge of the laws of heredity and their application to the improvement of plants, animals, and human racial stocks." The brief, technical articles are well illustrated and are mostly on animal and plant breeding and genetics. Occasional signed reviews of moderate length.

Indexed in: Bio.Ag.I.   11-19964 rev. 2

JOURNAL OF MOLECULAR BIOLOGY.   v. 1, 1959-

Semi-monthly.   London. $254.00

"Publishes papers on the nature, production and replication of biological structure at the molecular level, and its relation to function. Suitable subjects are sub-cellular organization: molecular genetics, structure and replication of viruses: molecular structure of muscle, nerve and other tissues, structure of proteins, nucleic acids, carbohydrates, liquids, etc. and their synthetic analogues, as investigated by X-rays, light absorption and other methods: problems of inter- and intra-molecular transfer." Each issue now usually consists of 10-20 articles of varying length, illustrated with micrographs and drawings, plus several shorter letters, all contributed by scientists from the leading universities, institutes and other research organizations throughout the world.

It is perhaps the leading journal in this rapidly expanding field (the issues for 1960 contained just 451 pages; for 1970, over 10 times that), with a distinguished list of editors and contributors, representing many countries. Because of its expense and technical nature, it is only appropriate for libraries supporting strong biology programs, for use by advanced undergraduates and faculty.

61-19997

JOURNAL OF MORPHOLOGY.   v. 1, 1887-

Monthly.   Philadelphia, Pa. $60.00

Published by the Wistar Institute of Anatomy and Biology, it is "devoted to the publication of original research on animal morphology, including cytology, protozoology, and the embryology of vertebrates and invertebrates." Known as the *Journal of Morphology and Physiology* from 1924 through 1931. Consists entirely of research papers ranging from moderate length (8 pages) to lengthy (20 pages). All are thoroughly illustrated, especially with photomicrographs and electron photomicrographs. A journal of longstanding, it is one of the most important journals in the field. However, since morphology is no longer common to most undergraduate curricula, it is needed only by colleges having especially strong biology departments that emphasize morphology and are involved in research.

11-8011 (rev. '43)

JOURNAL OF PARASITOLOGY.   v. 1, 1914-

Bi-monthly.   Lawrence, Kans. $25.00

Official organ of the American Society of Parasitologists. Publishes technical articles which report results of research in the field of animal parasitology. Now 30-40 articles per issue, averaging about 6 pages each, but ranging from 2 to 30 pages in length. "Research Notes" are even briefer— at the most 2 pages, but there are fewer of these. Both articles and notes are illustrated. Reports of the Society's meetings; announcements of other meetings. A few book reviews, usually 3 to 5, in most issues; they are signed and critical, and mostly 400-600 words in length.

Indexed in: Bio.Ag.I.   64-36489

*PHYSIOLOGICAL REVIEWS.   v. 1, 1921-

Quarterly.   Bethesda, Md. $20.00

Published by the American Physiological Society, it contains papers in all areas of physiology—human, animal, comparative, cell, physiological psychology—plus biochemistry and nutrition. The papers are lengthy (20 to 50 pages), comprehensive, analytical, critical reviews of the topic, written by authorities, both American and foreign, in their fields. Articles are especially important for advanced students and faculty in biology and psychology.

22-18915 rev. 2

PHYSIOLOGICAL ZOOLOGY.   v. 1, 1928-

Quarterly.   Chicago, Ill. $16.00

"A quarterly journal of zoological research," it is devoted to articles that are experimental and/or analytical in character on the following subjects: "the physiology of development and of relation to environment in general; physiology of the cell and of protoplasm; physiology of the nervous system and behavior in the stricter sense; physiology of populations; hormones and other features of chemical correlation that are of general biological interest; sex in its physiological aspects; the physiological phases of genetics." Usually 7 to 13 articles per issue, averaging about 10 pages each. Book reviews now appear in about half the issues; sometimes just one, and never more than 4 reviews—they are signed and critical and mostly 500-750 words in length.

Indexed in: Bio.Ag.I.   Agr. 29-827 rev. 2

PHYTOPATHOLOGY.   v. 1, 1911-

Monthly.   St. Paul, Minn. $40.00

Official organ of the American Phytopathological Society. The 20-35 articles per issue are brief (averaging about 5 pages each) and mostly report the results of original research on some phase of plant disease. Occasionally, a review paper appears, "developing a new concept, hypothesis, theory, or other integration of plant pathology." Also a few even briefer "Phytopathological Notes," which are "accounts of techniques, original research, or phytopathological history." The articles are by academic, governmental and other research scientists both here and abroad, though domestic interests predominate by far, since many of the authors are connected with the USDA or state experimental stations. Abstracts of papers delivered at the Society's regional divisions are published. Useful for advanced botany courses and research.

Indexed in: Bio.Ag.I.   A 41-4856 rev*

PLANT PHYSIOLOGY.   v. 1, 1926-

Monthly.   Washington, D.C. $70.00

Published by the American Society of Plant Physiologists, each issue now
contains from 20 to 40 research articles, averaging about 4 pages each, in
all areas of plant physiology. The number of pages has increased greatly
in recent years (from less than 700 in 1959 to about 1800 in 1969) so
that it went from 6 to 10 issues a year in 1966, to a monthly in 1967, and
to two volumes a year in 1970. Articles are well illustrated, with micrographs, drawings and diagrams, and are contributed by scientists in universities, research institutes and government laboratories all over the world.
Supplements containing the programs and abstracts of papers delivered at
the annual or sectional meetings. A journal of basic importance where
there is much work done in botany, but primarily for advanced students
and research.

Indexed in: Bio.Ag.I.   Agr. 28-1636

*QUARTERLY REVIEW OF BIOLOGY.   v. 1, 1926-

Quarterly.   Baltimore, Md. $10.00

Sponsored by the American Society of Naturalists, and published for the
State University of New York at Stony Brook, it "publishes critical reviews of recent researches in all of the special fields of biological science.
Contributions should present a synthesis or digest of researches and a
critical evaluation of them," not a mere synopsis. "Theoretical papers
are published occasionally, especially when such papers 1) include a critical
synthesis of the literature bearing on the theory and 2) are likely to promote further research in a given field." Issues carry from 1 to 3 contributions plus, on occasion, the papers given at a specialized symposium.
The section "New Biological Books" is an important bibliographical feature. It carries an occasional long review of an especially significant work,
but most of it is devoted to a classified arrangement of shorter signed reviews and brief notices of a large number of books (well over 100 in recent issues). These range from mere listings to reviews of 500-700 words.

Because of its breadth, its basic nature, the eminence of its contributors
and the useful reviewing function, it is an essential journal for every academic library.

Indexed in: Bio.Ag.I.   29-4102

**SOCIETY FOR EXPERIMENTAL BIOLOGY AND MEDICINE.   PROCEED-
INGS.   1903-**

Monthly (except Aug.)   N.Y. $25.00

Originally contained papers presented at the Society's and its sections'
meetings, along with the business of the Society. Currently it consists of
brief contributed papers which are reports of research, primarily by members of the Society who include scientists from universities, government
research bureaus, and laboratories all over the world. Topics are in most
areas of biology and medicine—physiology, nutrition, pharmacology, biochemistry, endocrinology, pathology, enzymology, microbiology, radio-
biology, etc. One of the oldest biological-medical journals in English, it has
greater breadth than many others, making it especially useful for libraries
where the biologists emphasize medical aspects of biology.

6-41460

STAIN TECHNOLOGY.   v. 1, 1926-

Bi-monthly.   Baltimore, Md. $10.00

"A journal for microtechnic and histochemistry," it is the official organ of the Biological Stain Commission. Each issue contains about 7 original short articles (averaging 5-6 pages) on the "nature and use of dyes and other staining agents; histological technics, including autoradiography and electron microscopy; histochemistry." Also a few 1 or 2-page "Notes on Technic," reporting new techniques in the subject area covered. Each issue also carries a list of "Stains Recently Certified." One or two book reviews now appear in most issues, signed and critical, 500-1000 words in length.

28-6915

TORREY BOTANICAL CLUB.   BULLETIN.   v. 1, 1870-

Bi-monthly.   Bronx, N.Y. $12.00

The oldest botanical serial in America, it includes reports of research on all aspects of botany with emphasis on taxonomic and morphological studies. While earlier volumes emphasized New York and northeast American botany, it no longer has that restriction but covers American botany in general. "Torreya" a regular section of each issue, may include obituaries, briefer papers, field trip reports, and book reviews. There are a few critical signed reviews in each issue. An *Index to American Botanical Literature*, a regular feature since 1886, provides a classified list of scholarly articles on American botany. The list is useful in keeping faculty abreast of new work but is not useful for retrospective searching, since there are no indexes to it.

The *Bulletin* is important for colleges with strong biology departments emphasizing botany. Its earlier northeastern orientation makes it more useful for colleges in that area. Though the earlier volumes contain many landmark articles in botany, they will rarely be needed unless there is serious interest in the history of the natural sciences or in field botany.

Indexed in: Bio.Ag.I.   61-45242

WILDLIFE REVIEW.   no. 1, 1935-

Quarterly.   Laurel, Md.   Free.

An abstracting service issued at the Patuxent Wildlife Center by the Bureau of Sport Fisheries and Wildlife of the Fish and Wildlife Service, U.S. Department of Interior, it was originally published in mimeographed form, irregularly. Its present format began in 1955. Devoted to all aspects of wildlife management, including appropriate areas of conservation, it covers books, articles, pamphlets, reports and documents from all over the world. Recent numbers have listed 700-800 items, each giving complete bibliographical (and frequently ordering) information; abstracts or summaries from the source or done by the *Review's* editors are given for many of the items, with others having just a few words of description or no comment at all. The arrangement is classified by subject, with an author index in each number.

An important reference source where there is much interest in animal biology or natural history, it is useful as a buying guide as well. Available as a depository item or from the issuing office.

53-17432

*AMERICAN BOOK PUBLISHING RECORD.   v. 1, 1960-

Monthly.   N.Y. $19.00

Each issue cumulates all listings contained during the previous month in the Weekly Record section of *Publishers' Weekly* (q.v.) and arranges them by subject (Dewey decimal arrangement), with separate sections for juvenile, fiction, and talking books. The listings are exactly the same as in the Weekly Record; only the arrangement is different. There is an author index plus a subject and title index in each issue. Annual indexes for 1962, 1963 and 1964 were available separately; in 1965 they were succeeded by the *BPR Annual Cumulative* (available separately) which cumulates the listings for the entire year in the same form as the monthly issues, with an author and a title index. The subject arrangement makes this title a very useful reference and book selection tool but the annual cumulative volume should be purchased for permanent use, and the monthly issues discarded.

62-53533

*BOOK REVIEW DIGEST.   v. 1, 1905-

Monthly (except Feb. and July)   N.Y. $30.00

An index to, and digest of book reviews appearing in a selected list of some 75 American, Canadian and British periodicals and newspapers. These sources range from the mass media, such as *Time* and *Newsweek*, to the scholarly journals, such as the *English Historical Review* or *Modern Philology,* and include most of the standard professional library periodicals– *Choice, Library Journal, Horn Book,* etc. The list of periodicals covered varies every few years to reflect the changing needs of subscribers, new periodicals, changes in reviewing practices, etc., but the general policy has been to keep the emphasis "on books and reviews for the general user rather than the specialist who has other sources of information."

To be included, a book must be published in the U.S., works of non-fiction must have at least two reviews and fiction at least four in the sources used, the only exception being books reviewed in the *Subscription Books Bulletin.* While for most fiction titles listed three reviews are excerpted and for most non-fiction, four, controversial books or works of special importance are represented by more reviews. However, all reviews of a particular title that are found in the sources used are at least cited. Approximately 4000 titles a year are included.

Books are alphabetically listed by author; each entry gives full bibliographical information and price, Dewey classification, subject headings (based on the *Sears List),* LC card number. This is followed by a descriptive annotation, taken from one of the reviews, from the book itself, or from the publisher's note, and then by quoted passages from the reviews with full references to their sources, including the name of the reviewer (if known) and the length of the review. The excerpts range from just a few lines up to 150 or 200 words, with an average of 80-90 words. Up to 1963 a + or - indicated the favorableness of the review, but this was dropped because it seemed to be misleading. The index is by subject and title only, with a cumulated subject and title index every fifth year. Quarterly cumulations, with an annual bound volume.

While the books listed are mostly of general interest, a large number of scholarly works are also included. Its many uses—for book selection, reference, bibliography, etc.—make it essential for even the smallest library.

6-9994 rev

*BOOK WORLD. v. 1, 1967-

Weekly. N.Y. $10.00

A successor to the *New York Herald Tribune Book Review* and to *Book Week*, which was published by that newspaper until its demise in 1966, it is available either on a separate subscription or as a supplement to the Sunday editions of the *Chicago Tribune* or the *Washington Post*. Generally superior to its earlier predecessor in format, quality of newsprint, style, and eminence of contributors, it contains reviews that are lively and authoritative, with seemingly little or no attempt to soft-pedal negative criticism. Usually, less than a dozen titles are reviewed in depth; briefer reviews of children's books, of mysteries, and of other fiction appear sometimes in groups. Other features include a tabulation of bestsellers, or annotated listing of new paperbacks, and an occasional interview or guest essay. There are two supplements a year: on children's books, and an annual paperback issue.

Indexed in: B.R.D.

*BOOKLIST. v. 1, 1905-

Semi-monthly (monthly, Aug.) Chicago, Ill. $12.00

Published by the American Library Association. In September, 1956 the semi-monthly *Booklist* and the quarterly *Subscription Books Bulletin* were merged, though kept as two distinct sections under the one cover, and continuing the numbering of the *Booklist*. The *Subscription Books Bulletin* section, prepared by the Subscription Books Committee of ALA, describes and evaluates sets of books or single works usually sold by agents or by mail on extended payment plan. However, it is mainly important to librarians for reviews of important reference works available through the regular book trade channels, although these reviews usually appear rather late for selection purposes of most libraries. Each review provides a thorough, critical evaluation based on the work's authority, content, binding, format and cost, and states whether it is recommended or not, and if so, for what kind of library. Gives complete bibliographical and buying information.

The *Booklist* section selects, describes and evaluates (though the evaluations are not very critical) adult, young people's and children's books, providing complete buying information, Dewey classification number, subject headings, and LC card number. Also lists, with brief annotations, series and new editions, free or inexpensive material, government publications, occasional bibliographies in fields of current interest. Author, title and subject index in each number with semi-annual and annual cumulations.

Aimed primarily at public libraries, the *Booklist* section is useful for the college library in rounding out its general book collection; the combination of the two services makes this publication essential for every library.

Indexed in: B.R.D. 5-18642 rev 2

*BOOKS ABROAD. v. 1, 1927-

Quarterly. Norman, Okla. $15.00

"An international literary quarterly," it contains articles, reviews and features about the literatures of the world. The articles, mostly brief, are on specific authors and their works, on trends in the literature of one country or just one type of literature, with occasional issues devoted to a single subject with several contributors. Most attention is devoted to contemporary or recent writers and writing, with personal interpretations emphasized rather than scholarly analysis. There are a number of briefer pieces similar in nature to the feature articles, also interviews with authors, and news of the world of publishing.

More than half of each issue is devoted to book reviews. First, the Headlines, in all languages, then the others: arranged by language (but rarely a non-Western one) and then by genre, the reviews vary in length from 100 to 500 words, with most around 200; the number of reviews has steadily increased to some 200 per issue currently. The reviews are done by specialists, and though brief, they are critical and incisive. In recent years also, there have been annual literary surveys of particular countries, and lists of outstanding books of the year. From 1952 to 1961 a section "Periodicals at Large" listed the contents of current issues of a large number of scholarly and literary journals, domestic and foreign. An important and unique journal, useful not only for literary research but for book selection, since so many of the books reviewed here are not reviewed in other readily accessible journals.

Indexed in: S.S.H.I.   52-34205

CENTER FOR CHILDREN'S BOOKS. BULLETIN. v. 1, 1947-

Monthly (except Aug.) Chicago, Ill. $4.50

A publication of the Graduate Library School of the University of Chicago. Each issue consists of 70 to 80 brief (60-250 words) reviews of recent books for children and young people, from kindergarten through high school. The reviews are designed to point out each title's content, usefulness, reading level, and strong and weak points; symbols indicate whether it is recommended, acceptable, marginal, or not recommended; or, occasionally, whether it is just for special collections or will appeal only to the unusual reader. Each issue also contains a one-page listing of recent books and articles on children's books and reading. The December issue carries a list of books recommended during the year. Generally recognized as one of the most reliable reviewing media for children's books, it is important where there are courses in the area.

67-1426

*CHOICE. v. 1, 1964-

Monthly (except bi-monthly, July-Aug.) Chicago, Ill. $20.00

Published by the Association of College and Research Libraries, it is a book selection guide for colleges, junior colleges, universities and other libraries interested in scholarly publications. It consists mostly of reviews, usually 100-200 words in length, of books either published or distributed in this country; arranged by subject, there are about 500 titles per issue, with complete bibliographical and ordering information given for each title. Though the reviews are anonymous, a list of all reviewers is in each issue; almost all are faculty members working with undergraduates, and their reviews are keyed to the books' suitability for college libraries. The number of books reviewed has been steadily increasing—in 1969-70, some 6500 titles. In addition to the brief reviews which comprise the bulk of each issue, there are a number of other features, the number and type varying from issue to issue. There may be a lead article on a problem relating to college libraries, usually some aspect of book selection. Almost every issue now contains at least one selective (though usually lengthy) bibliography, in list or essay form, on a special subject or geographical area—e.g., France Since 1919, Early History of Medicine, Criminology, Advertising. These are most useful for checking one's collection. The May issue has carried since 1966 the feature "Outstanding Academic Books," titles selected from those listed during the previous year. Author and title index in each issue, with annual cumulative indexes.

The most useful single reviewing medium for college libraries, many libraries will want multiple copies. Some may want to subscribe also to Choice Reviews-on-Cards ($80.00 per year) which permits distribution of the reviews to individual faculty and staff members.

Indexed in: B.R.D.   64-9413
           Lib.Lit.

ECONOMICS Selections: An International Bibliography. *see* ECONOMICS

*FORTHCOMING BOOKS. v. 1, 1966-

Bi-monthly.   N.Y. $24.00

Lists books of all American publishers scheduled for publication during the coming five months, plus a continuing cumulative index to books published since the appearance of the most recent *Books in Print*. Each issue "overlaps, updates, and expands the previous one and includes all categories: adult trade books, technical and scientific books, juveniles, el-hi and college texts, paperbacks, imports, and revised and new editions." The author and title sections are separate; entries in both sections include author, title, price, publisher and actual or planned month of publication. The bi-monthly *Subject Guide to Forthcoming Books* (v. 1, 1967- $8.95, or $7.00 in combination with *Forthcoming Books*) presents under almost 200 subject categories the forthcoming titles listed in corresponding numbers of *Forthcoming Books*. For libraries that need to keep absolutely current in specific areas, both titles are essential; most libraries will need only *Forthcoming Books*, which is very helpful in acquisitions and reference work.

67-1000/CD

HORN Book Magazine. *see* LIBRARY SCIENCE

INTERAMERICAN Review of Bibliography; Revista Interamericana de Bibliografia. *see* AREA STUDIES/LATIN AMERICA

JOURNAL of Economic Literature. *see* ECONOMICS

NEW TECHNICAL BOOKS.   v. 1, 1915-

Monthly (except Aug.-Sept.)   N.Y. $7.50

"A selective list of noteworthy English language imprints compiled from the many titles submitted for the monthly exhibits of new technical books in the Science and Technology Division, The Research Libraries, The New York Public Library. Noteworthy foreign works . . . may also be included from time to time."

In recent years, some 1200-1300 books have been listed. Issues are arranged by broad Dewey decimal classes, with each entry giving full bibliographical information, plus price and LC card number. The annotations for the entries contain a listing of their contents (sometimes abridged) or descriptive notes by members of the Division's staff, or sometimes both. The descriptive notes usually indicate something about the author or the audience for whom the books are useful and appropriate.

Subjects include "the pure and applied physical sciences, mathematics, engineering, industrial psychology, and related disciplines," and the levels range from "technician and introductory-college level to highly specialized advanced graduate and research level."

A useful listing, important for libraries with strong science collections.

15-24011

*NEW YORK REVIEW OF BOOKS.   v. 1, 1963-

Bi-weekly (monthly, July-Aug.)   N.Y. $10.00

Begun when two national weekly book-reviewing sources were not being published because of a newspaper strike, it quickly became a leading medium for book reviews. The reviews are long, never less than 1500 words, usually between 2000 and 3000, and often even longer, so that in many cases the reviews turn into significant essays on the subject or author under review. The books range over all areas, from current fiction to fairly specialized works in the social sciences, the humanities, and the history and philosophy of science, though none are so technical as to be beyond the interest of the intelligent general reader. Books of only ephemeral interest are rarely reviewed. The reviewers, who are almost always authoritative (which is not the same as objective), are drawn from British and American universities or intellectual circles, and write extremely well. In its early days, the review was sometimes referred to as "*The New York Review* of each others' books" because of the frequency with which some names appeared.

There have been an increasing number of significant contributions on current political, social, racial and educational matters, mostly from a fairly radical position, written by eminent intellectuals of the New Left—Noam

Chomsky, Paul Goodman, George Wald, Christopher Lasch, et al. Often these turn into debates, and with their proliferation, the number of book reviews has necessarily decreased, so that the *NYRB* has assumed importance as a political-literary journal perhaps even more than as a book reviewing medium. The caricatures by David Levine have become famous; other drawings also add greatly to its interest. Its tabloid size and newsprint stock handicap its binding. Because of the eminence of its contributors and the authority of its reviews, it has become a periodical of real intellectual significance and should be in every academic library.

Indexed in: Alt.Pr.I.   68-6716
          B.R.D.

NOTE: In 1972, I.F. Stone was added as a regular contributor after he discontinued his *Weekly*. It makes the *Review* even more important.

*NEW YORK TIMES BOOK REVIEW. v. 1, 1896-

Weekly.   N.Y. $13.00

Founded as the *Saturday Review of Books and Art,* it only became a Sunday supplement in 1911. Its original idea was to keep it strictly a publication of news about books, but opinion gradually was added, the reviews became longer, and features on publishing trends, on foreign developments, on particular authors, and individual columns on types of books, along with readers' departments, became more prevalent.

Today it is perhaps the most widely read reviewing medium, going to all the Sunday *Times* readers plus the many libraries which subscribe to it separately. Most issues contain 20-30 reviews, ranging from a few hundred to a few thousand words, with the lead reviews quite long. Reviewers are usually well known authors, scholars or men in public affairs, and the *Review* has been criticized for sacrificing incisive reviewers for names. The quality of the reviews has improved in recent years, perhaps as a result of stinging comments that reviewers were catering to the publishers and not being sufficiently critical. To a much lesser extent, this is still true, but on the other hand, many of the reviews are excellent, and the eminence and ability of many of the reviewers more than balances the weaknesses.

There are several special numbers each year, on science books, paperbacks, religious books, children's books, summer reading, education, Christmas books. Regular features include: "Criminals at Large," brief but expert reviews of mystery fiction; the Best Seller list, based on reports from bookstores around the country; "Queries and Answers," in which readers submit and answer questions of literary interest, especially sources of quotations. Though its value for book selection is limited, particularly for academic libraries, because of the relatively small number of titles reviewed, every library should receive it and keep it, and librarians themselves should read it—not just for the reviews but also for the other features that are of interest to anyone concerned with the current publishing scene.

Indexed in: B.R.D.

*PAPERBOUND BOOKS IN PRINT. v. 1, 1955-

Monthly.   N.Y. $32.50

Most useful are the 3 cumulative issues (now containing over 90,000 titles) that appear in October, February, and June, listing the paperbacks currently available from U.S. publishers or distributors. These are contained in 3 separate indexes: title index; author index, which gives the complete ordering information; subject index, listing all title under about 80 general subjects. The 9 other monthly issues contain a cumulating title list of paperbacks published in the interim months between the 3 large cumulative numbers. The section "The Month Ahead," in all issues, contains previews of titles to be published, with some bibliographic information and brief descriptive notes; there are also articles and news of interest to publishers and retailers of paperbacks—the role of paperbacks in education, announcements of new series, paperback reading lists on subjects of current interest (many of which are extremely useful), display suggestions, histories or profiles of concerns and individuals. Because of the constantly increasing importance of paperbacks (to libraries as well as to students and teachers), and because they are not covered thoroughly in other current listings, *Paperbound Books in Print* shou d be in all libraries.

55-9561 rev.

NOTE: The monthly numbers of *PBIP* were discontinued in March, 1971. At that time it was announced that beginning in 1972 *PBIP* will be published semi-annually, with "a durable hard binding" and at an annual subscription cost of $32.50.

*PUBLISHERS' WEEKLY.   v. 1, 1872-

Weekly (except one issue covering last two weeks of the year)   N.Y. $18.50

Contains articles, talks, notes, departments and features on all aspects of the book trade: on authors and their works, legislation and censorship, promotions, typography and production, dealers, publishers and other matters of prime importance to the knowledgeable librarian. The many features and departments include: "Media," items about newspapers, periodicals, radio and television that affect book reviewing or promotions; a "Calendar" of meetings, conferences, workshops, institutes, etc., for sections of the industry itself or of professional groups that are concerned with the use and purchase of books; "Retailing," news and reports from bookstores; "Rights and Permissions," items on the sale of books to movies, television, reprint houses, etc.; People, news of personnel changes; "Tips" on forthcoming promotions, special discounts, new series, publications of special interest, etc. Beginning in the late 1920's there was a monthly section devoted to the design and production of books; beginning in 1970, book production here has been integrated with the body of the weekly issues, with specialness in a Bookbinding department. A monthly report on publishers' and allied industry stock prices.

The Annual Summary Number (around February) contains the year's statistics on total sales, title output by subject and publisher, price averages, roundup of literary awards, and trends in the industry. Other special issues include Spring and Fall Children's Book Numbers, Reference Book Issue, Paperback Book Issue, Religious Book Number, Scientific and Technical Books Number; also Spring, Summer and Fall Announcement issues. All these special issues contain indexes to books appearing in the advertisements.

For book selection there are, in addition to the advertisements, a number of helpful features. The special subject numbers describe many of the books to be published in these subjects, with brief descriptions, promotion plans, etc.

Forecasts provide capsule reviews, weeks or even months before publication, of fiction and non-fiction, children's books and paperbacks, that the editors consider important. These reviews, in length up to 250 words, are usually critical and fairly reliable, though not by any means authoritative. The "Weekly Record" is "a conscientious listing of current American book publication." Almost all entries are represented by full Library of Congress cataloging, including full bibliographical description, LC and Dewey classifications, LC card number and tracings, and frequently a listing of the contents, plus the price. Very brief annotations are helpful in describing the book. Does not include government publications, subscription books, dissertations, periodicals, pamphlets under 49 pages, specialized publications such as catalogs, telephone books, or catalogs of a transitory nature or intended as advertising. A few books printed abroad are included. The listings in the Weekly Record are cumulated in the *American Book Publishing Record* (q.v.).

Many libraries will want to take several copies of *Publishers' Weekly*—for circulating to the staff, for reference, acquisitions, etc. (extra- subscriptions are $13.00 each), but every library should receive at least one copy.

Indexed in: Bus.Per.I.   1-15589
            Lib.Lit.
            P.A.I.S.
            R.G.

SATURDAY Review. *see* GENERAL

*SCIENCE BOOKS.   v. 1, 1965-

Quarterly.   Washington, D.C. $6.50

Published by the American Association for the Advancement of Science. "It reviews trade books, textbooks, and reference works in the pure and applied sciences for students in the elementary schools, in secondary school and in the first two years of college, including selected advanced and professional books useful for reference by students and faculty members. . . . Each book is reviewed by a qualified specialist, and then published annotations are prepared by the editorial staff based on annotations and comments of the professional reviewers." About 300 books, arranged by Dewey classification, are reviewed in each number; the reviews, which are critical and evaluative, not just descriptive, range from 100 to 500 words, with most of them around 250. Symbols indicate the level(s) for which the book is suitable (from "Elementary, very simple" to "Professional") and whether it is "highly recommended," "recommended," "acceptable" or "not recommended." Complete ordering information is given, including LC card numbers and publishers' book numbers. A most useful aid in book selection for undergraduate collections.

65-9914

TECHNICAL BOOK REVIEW INDEX.   v. 1, 1935-

Monthly (except July-Aug.)   Pittsburgh, Pa. $16.00

Compiled and edited in the Science and Technology Department, Carnegie Library of Pittsburgh, it is published by the Special Libraries Association. Its purpose "is to identify reviews in current scientific, technical and trade journals and to quote from these reviews. . . . Each quotation immediately follows the name of the journal from which it is taken."

Gives basic bibliographic information, price, and length of review (in columns and pages, or fractions of them, only) and LC card numbers where available. About 1200 titles per year have been listed recently; a minority of these receive more than one review. Nevertheless, it provides the only clues to reviews for most of the books listed, so that for any library doing much buying in science and technology, it is an essential item, and useful for all libraries of any size where there is some attention to science.

37-9385

*TIMES LITERARY SUPPLEMENT.   v. 1, 1902-

Weekly.   London. $21.00

Considered by many to be the English-speaking world's leading book reviewing medium. Covers all subject areas and books from all countries, though of course emphasizing British and Commonwealth publications. All reviewers are anonymous, thus permitting a freedom reviewers in other journals might envy. Usually 40 to 50 books are reviewed in each issue; these range from 200 words to 3-4,000 word review-essays for front page titles. It is for the reviews—gracefully written, thoughtful, and frequently authoritative—that *TLS* is most useful, but there are many other features that enhance its value to librarians, scholars, and general readers. The "Letters to the Editor" section provides a forum for lively, frequently acid remarks between reviewers and the reviewed; the "Appointments Vacant" notices for librarians and teaching faculty in Britain and the Commonwealth are interesting; the back page always contains news of book exhibits, book sales, and reviews of bibliographical resources and works on bookmaking, printing and collecting. In 1968 there began a more or less regular series of articles on learned literary journals and little magazines in different countries and areas. These treat older, standard journals as well as newer ones, and they are helpful to serials librarians in keeping up with the field. Each year there are four or five special numbers, often quite large (some of them have been reprinted in book form) on, for example, a survey of major literary developments in a country or area, trends in historical writing and scholarship. Occasional numbers are devoted to religious books and children's books. *TLS* is essential for keeping up with the world of books, especially for these published outside the United States, and it should be in every scholarly library, though many librarians will want to subscribe to it themselves.

Indexed in: B.R.D.   8-7193
            Br.Hum.I.
            S.S.H.I.

ACCOUNTS OF CHEMICAL RESEARCH.   v. 1, 1968-

Monthly.   Washington, D.C. $15.00

Published by the American Chemical Society, it contains "concise, critical reviews of research areas currently under active investigation." The articles, which are aimed at "a general audience of research-minded chemists," are almost all between 5 and 10 pages long, and about half are "directed mainly to the general audience, providing background and orientation as well as discussions of terms or concepts of special value in the field of the article." The authors, who are usually directly involved in research in the area treated, are from universities and research laboratories.

Though the topics treated are specialized, because they range over all areas of chemistry and are so clearly presented, they are especially useful for advanced undergraduates. The journal should be available wherever there is a major in chemistry.

70-8300

*AMERICAN CHEMICAL SOCIETY.   JOURNAL.   v. 1, 1879-

Bi-weekly.   Washington, D.C. $66.00

Contains original papers dealing with any phase of "pure" or "fundamental" chemistry; articles are arranged by general type: physical, inorganic, organic and biological. A 1968 count of the contributions showed that 59% were in organic chemistry, 18% physical, 17% inorganic, and 6% biological. Usually 35 to 50 articles, plus up to 40 shorter (not over 1000 words) "Communications to the Editor" that list preliminary reports "of unusual urgency, significance and interest," also in pure chemistry. Usually one to three signed, critical book reviews, mostly about 500 words; also a monthly listing, rather brief, of books received. Widely recognized as one of the most important journals in the field, with contributors from all over the world, it is indispensable to chemistry departments.

Indexed in: A.S.T.I.   9-4698

ANALYST.   v. 1, 1876-

Monthly.   Cambridge, Eng. $87.10

Subtitled "Journal of the Society for Analytical Chemistry," it is the British counterpart of *Analytical Chemistry*. "Papers on all aspects of the theory and practice of analytical chemistry, fundamental and applied, inorganic and organic, including chemical, physical and biological methods." Besides the regular articles, several short papers (1-2 pages) are published. These cover the same areas but usually give very specific information on a method or technique, or data on a particular analytical problem. A number of signed book reviews (200-400 words) are published in each issue. Since analytical chemistry is no longer a separate branch of chemistry but a basic technique used in all of chemistry, most articles on the field are scattered throughout the literature thus making this less useful.

Since 1964 the *Proceedings* of the Society have been published separately under its own title and are received with a subscription to the *Analyst*.

17-735-7

*ANALYTICAL CHEMISTRY.   v. 1, 1929-

Monthly.   Washington, D.C. $7.00

Published by the American Chemical Society, it covers all branches of analytical chemistry. It started as the Analytical Edition of *Industrial and Engineering Chemistry*, assuming its present title in 1948. "Its pages are devoted principally to publication of original research papers which are either entirely theoretical with regard to analysis or which are reports of laboratory experiments that support, argue, refute, or extend established theory.

"Research papers may contribute to any of the phases of analytical operations, such as sampling, preliminary chemical reactions, separations, instrumentation, measurements and data processing. They need not necessarily refer to existing or even potential analytical methods in themselves, but may be confined to the principles and methodology underlying such methods."

There are usually from 35 to 45 of these contributions, a majority in the form of articles and shorter notes, but also in correspondence, and in the section "Aids for Analytical Chemists" which describes new devices and methods. Only articles are preceded by abstracts, but the "Notes" are briefly summarized in the section "AC Briefs." Contributors include analytical chemists in industry, educational institutions, research foundations, government laboratories, including some in other countries.

In addition to the scientific papers, there are many pages of advertisements and a number of special features. The monthly "Report for Analytical Chemists" describes some current development of special interest, e.g., "New Dimensions in Medical Diagnosis," "Chemical Instrumentation in Europe," "Extraterrestrial Neutron Activation Analysis," "New Horizons in Education." Another regular feature is "Laboratory of the Month," illustrated stories of laboratories around the world, emphasizing their special methods or equipment. The monthly column "Instrumentation," is on developments in this area. Other regular features include a "Calendar of Events," descriptions of new products and new chemicals, and a news section covering exhibits and meetings, industry news, programs of special meetings, etc.; in 1966 it began carrying a listing of short courses in analytical techniques. The number of book reviews has increased; now usually 7 to 10 signed, critical reviews, varying in length from 200 to over 1000 words. Other new books and government publications are briefly described or noted.

Two supplementary issues each year. In April, a separate *Annual Reviews* issue consists of articles with extensive bibliographies, reviewing and interpreting the significant developments in a large number of specific areas in fundamentals or applied developments, alternating between the two each year. The July issue also contains an annual supplement, the *Laboratory Guide to Instruments, Equipment and Research Chemicals*, a useful buyers' guide.

Indexed in: A.S.T.I.   31-21682* rev. 2

ANGEWANDTE CHEMIE.   International edition in English.   v. 1, 1962-

Monthly.   Weinheim/Bergstrasse, Germany and New York. $53.25

Published under the auspices of Gesellschaft Deutscher Chemiker, it is a translation of the German periodical which began in 1888 and was considered Germany's most important industrial chemical journal until World War II. Its interests are much broader now, and it ranges over all areas of chemistry, and contributors are international. Issues may contain just a few lengthy articles, plus a large number of "Communications," which are brief research reports. "Conference Reports" summarizes reports and discussions at conferences or symposia, or significant lectures which had appeared in the German edition. "Selected Abstracts" of especially important articles in other journals. From 4 to 12 book reviews, mostly from 300 to 500 words, but occasionally somewhat longer.

64-1757

BIOCHEMICAL JOURNAL.   v. 1, 1906-

Monthly.   London. $112.00

The official journal of the Biochemical Society (London). Presents results of original research in the chemical aspects of plant and animal physiology, excluding special bacteriology. Carries Proceedings of the Society, consisting of abstracts of papers read and brief descriptions of demonstrations; also "Short Communications." The most important British biochemical journal but even strong collections need not have more than the last 20 years.

Indexed in: Bio.Ag.I.   26-11128 rev*

*BIOCHEMISTRY.   v. 1, 1962-

Bi-weekly.   Washington, D.C. $60.00

Published by the American Chemical Society, its aim "is to publish the results of original research in all areas of fundamental biochemistry. . . . investigations that generate new concepts and experimental approaches. It is not intended to be solely a depository of scientific data." Reflecting the rapid growth of this field, it began as a bi-monthly with the first volume containing some 1200 pages, became a monthly in 1964, and a bi-weekly in 1970, with over 5000 pages. Issues now usually contain 20 to 35 articles, of short to moderate length, contributed from laboratories all over the world, with most, of course, from this country. An essential journal where there is any work done in biochemistry.

A 63-602 rev.

*CHEMICAL ABSTRACTS.   v. 1, 1907-

Weekly. Columbus, Ohio. $1900.00 Teaching Institutions $2400.00 Others

Published by the American Chemical Society, it is perhaps the most comprehensive abstracting medium in any field. In 1970, it carried over ¼-million abstracts from some 12,000 American and foreign serials, plus books, dissertations, government publications, and patents in all areas of chemistry and related branches of other sciences. These are divided into

80 subfields which make up the sections under which the abstracts are arranged. The first 34 sections (covering biochemistry and organic chemistry) are published every other week, alternating with the latter 46 sections (macromolecular, physical, analytic and applied chemistry, and chemical engineering). Each issue has an author and keyword index. Words in the index are drawn from the title of the article as well as the text of the abstract. Since 1962 *CA* has published two volumes per year resulting in semi-annual author, subject, formula, patent indexes, patent concordances (since 1963) and an HAIC (Hetero-Atom-in-Context) Index (since 1967). These semi-annual indexes, like the earlier annual ones, are eventually cumulated into collective indexes. Through 1956 these were decennial; since 1957 they have been issued at 5-year intervals. (The subscription cost does not include these collective indexes which are usually essential if *CA* is used very much. The seventh collective index, 1962-66, is priced at $2,000; the eighth, covering 1967-1971, will be $2700.)

A *List of Periodicals Abstracted* was last published in 1961; there are annual and semi-annual supplements to it through 1965. This list, with cross-references, bibliographical information, and locations of individual journals in libraries throughout the U.S. and Canada, includes not only chemical journals, but scientific journals in all fields that have any relation to chemistry. An exceptionally useful bibliographic tool, it is no longer being revised; instead Chemical Abstracts Service published separately in October, 1969 *Access* ($100 for 1969 edition, $75/year for supplements) which covers all current and discontinued serials in chemistry and chemical engineering. Libraries doing extensive work with interlibrary loans should have *Access* since it is the most complete and accurate union list of chemistry and other science periodicals available.

CA should be in every library where there is a major in chemistry. It is terribly expensive, but no serious work can be done without it.

Chemical Titles (v. 1, 1961- $60.00), another Chemical Abstracts Service publication, provides a current bi-weekly listing of the contents of approximately 650 journals in pure and applied chemistry and chemical engineering. In addition to the tables of contents, there is a key-word-in-context index and an author index. *CT* is strictly a current awareness tool. It has no retrospective value since there are no cumulative indexes and all periodicals indexed are also covered in *Chemical Abstracts. CT* is needed only by larger institutions doing extensive research which demands access to the literature as soon as it is published.

Chemical Titles serves the same purpose as *Current Contents: Chemical Sciences,* one of the by-products of *Science Citation Index* (q.v.). If either of these two is to be purchased the library staff and faculty should compare them and select the one that best suits their needs.

9-4698 rev. 2

*CHEMICAL AND ENGINEERING NEWS.   v. 1, 1923-

Weekly.   Washington, D.C. $8.00

Published by the American Chemical Society, it provides all kinds of information for chemists in industry, education, and research. It is not a technical trade journal, but rather a newsmagazine, containing a variety of news items and articles: research developments, the industry, new products and equipment, economic conditions especially relating to the industry, personnel, products, etc. Articles frequently treat in some depth matters relating to social, political, economic or educational concerns that are of interest to the chemical profession or industry and often to scientists in general. A breakdown of the journal's articles and features showed that about one-third of the content was industrial, 12.3 per cent research and education, 16.3 per cent technology, slightly over one-quarter of professional interest—book reviews, ACS news, meetings, personnel, etc.—and 11.8 per cent service and miscellaneous. A substantial part of each issue is devoted to reports of new research developments of special interest; also much attention is given to statistical information of interest to the chemical industry. Two special issues appearing each year are: *Facts & Figures for the Chemical Process Industries* (September); *Career Opportunities* (March). The latter is of special interest to chemistry majors, but the journal as a whole, because of its readability, timeliness and special concerns, should be in libraries of all colleges where chemistry is a major.

Since 1967 quarterly indexes and an annual cumulative index have been published. All are available at $20 per year; the annual alone is $15.00.

Indexed in: A.S.T.I.   A-41-2413 (rev. '43)

CHEMICAL ENGINEERING (with Chemical & Metallurgical Engineering).
v. 1, 1902-

Bi-weekly.   N.Y. $20.00

Subtitled "Chemical technology for the profit-minded engineer," it is an important trade and technical journal for those in the industry rather than the student or academic chemist. Briskly written, thoroughly reported, authoritative articles and notes on current developments, new equipment, materials, techniques and processes, and on the economic and managerial aspects of the chemical industry. Many regular features: news notes, convention calendar, employment opportunities, economic indicators for the industry, etc. Three extra issues a year (in February, June and October), called "Deskbooks," each focuses on a particular area of chemical engineering—Environmental Engineering, Solids Separations, Engineering Materials, etc.—including articles on the subject, a review of the technology, a listing of literature and a directory of suppliers and services.

Not important for most academic libraries—except where chemical engineering is emphasized—it is an interesting journal for prospective chemists' browsing.

Of like interest, though a much more modest publication, is the monthly *Chemical Engineering Progress* (v. 1, 1908- $25.00), which is published by the American Institute of Chemical Engineers. It is concerned with Institute affairs and meetings, as well as matters of management and engineering, and also devotes some attention to education—an annual feature, for example, is a listing of dissertations pertinent to the field.

Indexed in: A.S.T.I.   11-12192 rev. 2

*CHEMICAL REVIEWS.   v. 1, 1924-

Bi-monthly.   Washington, D.C. $39.00

Published by the American Chemical Society, its purpose is to provide "authoritative critical reviews and comprehensive summaries of recent research in theoretical chemistry." Topics are those with a considerable literature that have generally not been the subjects of review articles for five years. From 3 to 6 articles per issue, ranging from less than 10 to almost 100 pages, averaging 30 or 35. Beginning in 1969, single issues from time to time may be devoted to a single topic—"a symposium in print."

Written in an easily-comprehended style, with lengthy bibliographic lists, the journal provides invaluable introductions to the subjects treated and should be in all libraries where chemistry is taught.

25-15032

*CHEMICAL SOCIETY, LONDON.   JOURNAL.   v. 1, 1847-

Sections A & B, Monthly. Sections C & D, Semi-monthly.   London. (see NOTE below)

The oldest chemical society journal in existence, it actually began in 1811 as the *Proceedings of the Chemical Society*. In 1847 it merged with the *Memoirs and Proceedings* and became the *Quarterly Journal of the Chemical Society;* in 1862 it became a monthly and assumed its present title. For many years it was perhaps *the* most important journal in the entire chemical field, and still is one of the most important. It contains the results of original work in pure chemistry; organic chemistry has long predominated, with the remainder divided between physical and inorganic.

From 1871 to 1926 (when *British Abstracts* was formed) it carried abstracts from other journals on pure and theoretical chemistry. Until 1957 it also carried news and activities of the Society; these were then taken over by the Society's *Proceedings* (distributed along with the *Journal*) which also began to publish abstracts of papers read at meetings of the Society and accounts of the ensuing discussions, plus a number of other items, including a list of additions to the library and "Communications" dealing with original work meriting publicity prior to full publication. The *Proceedings* was discontinued at the end of 1964; news of the Society was carried in *Chemistry in Britain* (see below); the "Communications" in a separate journal, *Chemical Communications*.

In 1966 the *Journal* divided into three sections, each of which is available separately: Section A, Inorganic, Physical and Theoretical Chemistry ($52.80); Section B, Physical Organic Chemistry ($27.60); Section C, Organic Chemistry ($57.60). In 1969 *Chemical Communications* became Section D ($30.00). The overall subscription price for the four sections, $172.80, includes a subscription to the monthly *Chemistry in Britain* (v. 1, 1965- $16.80) which was formed by incorporating the *Journal of the Royal Institute of Chemistry* and the *Proceedings of the Chemical Society*. It carries news and activities of these organizations and of individuals, articles on the profession, on government activities, on chemical education, news and notes of all sorts of professional events and a few general technical articles. Since 1965 each issue has carried at least one authoritative, short review article. Usually 15 to 20 book reviews per issue; they are signed and critical, but rarely more than 300-400 words, and usually less. Also brief list of other publications received.

As one of the world's leading professional organizations, its journals should be available wherever chemistry is studied seriously.

Section A: 68-51868
Section C: 68-40613

NOTE: In 1971 the Faraday Society and the Chemical Society amalgamated and, beginning in 1972, have combined, respectively, their *Transactions* and Journal under *Chemical Society, London. Journal,* published in 6 parts. The arrangement of these parts is to be somewhat different from the previous arrangement, and the price is to be $455.00. For details, see inside front cover of late 1971 issues.

*CHEMICAL SOCIETY, LONDON.   QUARTERLY REVIEWS.   v. 1, 1947-

Quarterly.   London. $20.80

Published by the Chemical Society, it "contains articles by recognised authorities on selected topics from general, physical, inorganic and organic chemistry." Designed for a wide range of readers, it "is intended that each review article shall be of interest to chemists generally and not only to workers in the particular field being reviewed." Most issues contain 6 or 7 articles, varying greatly in length—from 10 to almost 100 pages, with an average of about 20. Through volume 20 (1966) each volume contained cumulative author and title indexes for articles published since the journal began; the cumulation began over again with volume 21. Because the articles are written in a fairly informal style and are aimed at the general chemist, they make excellent material for the undergraduate, even though they are contributed by leading chemists from many countries. Given the modest cost, it should be in every library where chemistry is taught.

52-30086

CHEMISCHE BERICHTE.   v. 1, 1868-

Monthly.   Weinheim/Bergstrasse, Germany. $150.00

Published since 1868, except for 1945 and 1946, it was titled *Berichte der deutschen chemischen Gesellschaft* until 1947. For years it was perhaps the world's leading chemical journal; though other journals now surpass it in prestige, it is still one of the more highly regarded. Before World War II, most papers were short communications; today papers are longer and provide thorough reports of original research. The contributions are divided into three sections: physical, inorganic, and organic chemistry, with the organic section predominating. Most contributors are from Germany and all contributions are in German.

13-24569 rev.

*CHEMISTRY.   v. 1, 1927-

Monthly (bi-monthly, July-Aug.)   Washington, D.C. $6.00

Published by the American Chemical Society since 1963, it is aimed primarily at the beginning student of high school or college chemistry and his teacher. Its editorial board includes chemists from the high school, junior college, college and university levels, as well as from industry. Articles, by research chemists and teachers of chemistry from both colleges and high schools, are well written and exceptionally well illustrated, so that the periodical is eminently readable. Subjects covered include all areas of chemistry: history, methodology, industrial and consumer applications, chemical theories, chemistry in the news, relationships of other sciences to chemistry, etc. Regular features include: "Research Reporter," reporting recent developments involving chemistry; "Lab Bench," describing experiments, lecture material and other presentations used in the teaching of chemistry; "Walrus," a miscellany of general science news throughout the world; "Library at

Large," in most issues, reviews 1 to 3 books in brief (300-500 words) but signed and critical reviews. Also a noting of selected other books and films. A very useful journal for the beginning chemistry student, but a file before 1964 (when it became a more lively journal) is not necessary.

Indexed in: R.G.   30-8009 rev.

FARADAY SOCIETY.   TRANSACTIONS.   v. 1, 1905-

Monthly.   London. $78.00

The original purpose of the Society, which is one of the world's foremost physico-chemical societies, was to promote the study of electrochemistry, electrometallurgy, physical chemistry and metallography. Its interests have broadened to include related topics, though its great emphasis is still physical chemistry, with most attention to reaction kinetics, spectra and spectroscopy, and thermodynamics.

Each issue consists of 30 to 40 reports of original research, varying in length, averaging about 10 pages, contributed by chemists of many nationalities, but mostly British and American. Most issues contain some book reviews (totaling about 100 a year). These range from 100 to 1000 words, with most 300-400; all are signed and critical. The Society also publishes its *Discussions* (normally appearing twice a year) which consist of papers read at meetings along with the ensuing discussions, and *Symposia* (published annually), which contain several papers on a single major topic and the discussions. Both publications are available separately or along with the *Transactions*. Because of the Society's eminence, departments with much work in physical chemistry should take them all.

                                                              17-12280

NOTE: See NOTE under *Chemical Society, London. Journal*.

*INORGANIC CHEMISTRY.   v. 1, 1962-

Quarterly.   Washington, D.C. $54.00

A publication of the American Chemical Society, it contains "fundamental studies, both experimental and theoretical, in all phases of inorganic chemistry. These include synthesis and properties of new compounds, quantitative studies regarding structure, and thermodynamics and kinetics of inorganic reactions." Each issue contains from 25 to 50 articles, of short to moderate length, plus a number of shorter (less than 1500 words) notes; contributors are from university, industrial and research institute laboratories, both domestic and foreign. The correspondence section provides "a medium for effective exchange of ideas and views outside of the usual formalities of regular Articles and Notes, but not preliminary communications of results." Book reviews, which were short and infrequent anyway, were discontinued in 1967. The basic journal in the field, its articles range widely, even to organic chemistry and theoretical physics, and it should be available wherever chemistry is taught.

                                                              63-25878

JOURNAL OF APPLIED CHEMISTRY AND TECHNOLOGY.   v. 1, 1951-

Monthly.   London. $52.00

Published by the Society of Chemical Industry, it superceded the Society's *Journal* and was titled until 1969 the *Journal of Applied Chemistry*. Contains research reports in applied chemistry (excluding food and agriculture chemistry) and biotechnology—fermentation technology, enzymic and biochemical processes, biodeterioration, and biodegradation. Part 2, the abstracts section, replaces Part B of *British Chemical Abstracts,* which was discontinued in 1953. It covers chemical engineering, safety and hygiene, fuel and fuel products, industrial inorganic and organic chemistry, biological products, detergents, fibers, polymers, paints, laboratory techniques, analysis, miscellaneous, and recent books and journals. Each issue contains an author index and there are annual author and subject indexes. Needed only in institutions with courses in chemical engineering or where the chemistry department emphasizes applied chemistry.

52-2921

JOURNAL OF CHEMICAL AND ENGINEERING DATA.   v. 1, 1956-

Quarterly.   Washington, D.C. $45.00

An American Chemical Society publication, it is "directed to the publication of experimental or, in some cases, derived data in sufficient detail to form a working basis for applying the information to scientific or engineering objectives." The contributions, which are mostly just a few pages in length, from chemists both here and abroad, are not at all concerned with theoretical matters. Each issue also contains a listing, with annotations, of New Data compilations.

Primarily for advanced research, it is important where there are strong departments of chemistry, and especially an emphasis on chemical engineering.

60-4857

*JOURNAL OF CHEMICAL EDUCATION.   v. 1, 1924-

Monthly.   Easton, Pa. $6.00

Official journal of the Division of Chemical Education of the American Chemical Society, it is not intended for research, but for chemistry teachers, especially on the college level. Contains articles and features on recent chemical advances, on historical and biographical aspects of chemistry, on classroom techniques and procedures, on the chemistry curriculum, and on the purposes, methods and apparatus of laboratory experiments. Regular features include: "Textbook Errors," a column to prevent the spread and continuation of errors found in standard texts; "Topics in Chemical Instrumentation," describing new developments or explanations of topics useful to users or teachers of instrumentation; "Safety in the Chemical Laboratory"; "Tested Overhead Projection Series," describing simple demonstrations and new equipment for demonstrations. The section "Out of the Editor's Basket" notes and describes new apparatus and equipment, books and pamphlets of special interest, new chemicals, and miscellaneous items on conferences, seminars, and other news of professional interest.

The book reviews (generally 10 to 15 per issue) are most useful. Though most are not detailed they are all signed and critical and usually examine the books for their worth to the student or as additions to the library. The September issue contains the annual *Book Buyers' Guide,* a classified listing of chemistry books selected by their publishers for display at the Division's annual meeting. The April issue contains a similar listing of paperback books. In addition to all these features, the advertisements for equipment and supplies are useful. An essential journal for every college library where chemistry is taught.

Indexed in: Ed.I.   26-5777

JOURNAL of Chemical Physics. *see* PHYSICS

JOURNAL OF INORGANIC AND NUCLEAR CHEMISTRY.   1955-

Monthly.   Elmsford, N.Y. $190.00

Publishes research papers in all areas of inorganic and nuclear chemistry. Each issue also contains one signed critical book review of moderate length. International both in contributors and readership, it is regarded as one of the more prestigious journals in the field of inorganic chemistry, but is less important for undergraduates than the *Journal of Inorganic Chemistry.* Because of its expense, it is necessary only where there are strong chemistry departments which emphasize inorganic chemistry.

57-59242

*JOURNAL OF ORGANIC CHEMISTRY.   v. 1, 1936-

Bi-Weekly.   Washington, D.C. $60.00

Published by the American Chemical Society, it is one of the few journals devoted exclusively to organic chemistry. "The areas emphasized are the many facets of organic reactions (including synthetic, exploratory, degradative, photochemical, organometallic), natural products, studies of mechanisms, theoretical organic chemistry, and the various aspects of spectroscopy related to organic chemistry." Contributions from industrial, governmental and academic laboratories, domestic and foreign, reporting accounts of original work or interpreting existing data in a new light. Now about 70 articles per issue; the format of almost all includes a narrative section of the problem, method and result with tables and diagrams, a detailed description of the experiment, and an abstract. Also contains "Notes," "Brief, concise accounts or studies of smaller scope." "Communications to the Editor," which had been used "for printing significant advances in the field which warrant immediate publication," were transferred to the ACS's *Journal* in 1964. Even so, its growth in the last 10 years has been great: the 1960 volume contained some 2200 pages; the 1970 volume, just about double that.

38-5884

*JOURNAL OF PHYSICAL CHEMISTRY.   v. 1, 1896-

Bi-weekly.   Washington, D.C. $60.00

Published by the American Chemical Society, it is the only basic journal published in this country devoted to general physical chemistry and the second oldest such journal in the world. From volume 51 (1947) through 56 (1951) it was titled the *Journal of Physical and Colloid Chemistry*. Up to the early 1960's only technical papers were published; now, preference "is given to papers dealing with fundamental concepts, atomic and molecular phenomena, and systems in which clearly defined models are applicable." There are usually about 50 articles, most fairly short, but some quite long; presentations given at symposia or conferences are often published. Many contributors are from abroad; an arrangement with the Faraday Society, London, provides for screening foreign contributions. In addition to the articles, shorter "Notes" (under 1500 words) treat limited subjects; there are also two types of "Communications to the Editor": Letters, reporting preliminary results of immediate interest; and Comments, remarks on the work of others. In late 1970 it began reproducing the tables of contents of the most recent issue of the *Journal of Chemical and Engineering Data.*

The basic journal in the field, it has increased greatly in size, from less than 2000 pages in 1960 to almost 5000 in 1970. Still, it should be in every library where chemistry is taught.

34-23847*

TETRAHEDRON.   v. 1, 1957-

Semi-monthly.   Oxford, Eng. $240.00

"The international journal of organic chemistry," it is published by Pergamon Press. Contains articles on "all aspects of organic chemistry, whether theoretical or practical, analytical or synthetic, physical or biological." Most papers report the results of original work, but reviews of work appear as part of many contributions, so that the articles vary greatly in length, from a few to perhaps 50 pages. The number of articles per issue likewise varies widely—from less than 20 to over 50. Contributors are from all countries, but almost all articles are in English; occasional ones in French or German. A number of separately issued Supplements have appeared, comprised of either proceedings, symposia or *Festschriften.* It has expanded enormously, from about 1200 pages in 1960 to over 6000 in 1969 (its cost in 1960 was only $17.00), and it is a journal important where there is some emphasis on research, but its cost is prohibitive for most college libraries.

57-3385

NOTE: Institutions with strong departments in chemistry should consider subscribing to some of the other leading foreign journals. Among the more important ones are: *Acta Chemica Scandinavica* (v. 1, 1947- $96.81); *Canadian Journal of Chemistry* (v. 29, 1951- $48.00); *Chemical Society of Japan, Bulletin* (v. 1, 1926- $54.00); *Helvetica Chimica Acta* (v. 1, 1918- $49.00); *Journal of General Chemistry of the USSR* (v. 19, 1949- $55.00); *Recueil des Travaux Chimiques des Pays-Bas et de la Belgique* (v. 1, 1882- $58.00); *Russian Chemical Reviews* (v. 29, 1960- $101.40); *Société Chimique de France. Bulletin* (v. 1, 1858- $127.25); *Zeitschrift fur anorganische und allgemeine Chemie* (V. 1, 1892- $57.70).

AMERICAN ANTIQUITY. v. 1, 1935-

Quarterly. Salt Lake City, Utah. $20.00

Published by the Society for American Archaeology, it contains "original papers on the archaeology of the New World and closely related subjects." Occasional articles on Oceania and Asia. Usually about 10 articles an issue, mostly from short to moderate length, treating techniques, reporting new finds, and on theory. Each article is preceded by an abstract and most are liberally illustrated with photographs and diagrams. Briefer items (though also containing abstracts and illustrations) are in the section "Facts and Comments." The reviews number 10-15 an issue, are signed and critical, and of varying length, with some running to several thousand words, and rarely to less than 600-700. Also occasional brief "Book Notices." "Current Research" primarily reports on field work being carried on in specific areas of North and South America, and occasionally carries news of conferences of important local or regional publications. Reports and announcements of the Society and its programs. *Memoirs* of the Society, published occasionally (there have been 21 so far) are issued as Supplements, but may also be purchased separately. Many libraries treat them as a separate series.

Indexed in: S.S.H.I.   46-36122

AMERICAN JOURNAL OF ARCHAEOLOGY.   Ser. 2, v. 1, 1897-

Quarterly.   N.Y. $15.00

The journal actually began in 1885, but did not assume much significance or regularity until 1897 when it became the official organ of the Archaeological Institute of America. Through volume 12 it contained various reports and supplements relating to the Institute, and to the American Schools in Athens, in Rome and in Palestine. These were taken over by the Institute's *Bulletin* in 1909. Its very scholarly articles and notes, with many plates appended, initially pertained to both the Old and New Worlds, but they are now almost solely concerned with classical archaeology. The excellent signed book reviews, a number of which are long and detailed, also reflect this primary concern, though not quite so exclusively. Additional features are the annual newsletters from Asia Minor, Greece and Rome, reporting archaeological developments in those areas, and a report on the Institute's annual meeting, with summaries of the papers delivered.

Indexed in: Art I.   12-30242
          S.S.H.I.

AMERICAN JOURNAL OF PHILOLOGY.   v. 1, 1880-

Quarterly.   Baltimore, Md. $15.00

"Publishes original contributions in the field of Greco-Roman antiquity, especially in the areas of philology, literature, history and philosophy." At first, because of the scarcity of any philological journals in this country, it published articles on the language and literature of many areas and periods (though with an emphasis on Greece and Rome), but as the number of outlets for articles increased, it concentrated more and more on classical antiquity, and since the 1930's has published only in that area. At the same time, the nature of the articles on classics shifted from an emphasis on textual criticism to the philosophical, historical and literary. The articles, all very scholarly, vary widely in length; there are generally about 5 per issue. The book reviews (which have been slowly increasing in number—there are usually 12-15 per issue) also are very scholarly and though there are a few fairly brief ones, almost all are at least over 1000 words, and many run to several thousand. List of books received. For advanced students and research.

Indexed in: S.S.H.I.

5-31891

AMERICAN SCHOOLS OF ORIENTAL RESEARCH. BULLETIN. v. 1, 1919-

Quarterly.   Cambridge, Mass. $6.00

The ASOR is the research arm in Near Eastern antiquity for some 140 colleges and universities in the United States and Canada, carrying on active research and excavation programs in various parts of the ancient Near East. The *Bulletin* carries reports and notes deriving from these various projects, other brief, scholarly articles, and official reports of the ASOR. Articles and reports, dealing with both epigraphic and non-epigraphic discoveries, are illustrated with photographs and diagrams. Review articles, covering recent publications on a particular area or major topic—e.g., "Books on the Archaeology of Palestine, Syria and Phoenicia," "Some Recently Received Books About the Dead Sea Scrolls"—appear fairly often. Useful for advanced students and faculty in Near Eastern archaeology, ancient history, and Old Testament studies.

Indexed in: S.S.H.I.

59-4636

*ANTIQUITY.   v. 1, 1927-

Quarterly.   Cambridge, Eng. $8.40

Articles, mostly fairly brief and well illustrated with photographs, maps and diagrams, are written in a non-technical style but by recognized authorities. These, and the much briefer notes and news, cover all aspects of the field—news of excavations and discoveries, problems of method or theory, archaeological relationships to other disciplines, etc.—in all geographical areas, though with some emphasis on British digs and diggers. Surveys of present work in specific sites are a frequent feature. Editorial comments on current events and developments; other news of professional interest. Usually 15 to 20 signed and critical reviews per issue, mostly 500-1000 words in length. Listing of a few other books. Admirably fulfilling its purpose to serve as a link between specialists and the general public, it is a useful journal for undergraduates.

Indexed in: Art I.
          Br.Hum.I.

29-21740

*ARCHAEOLOGY.   v. 1, 1948-

Quarterly.   N.Y. $8.50

Published by the Archaeological Institute of America, it contains articles—usually 5 or 6 per issue—by prominent archaeologists, classicists, anthropologists, historians and biblical scholars on all geographical and subject areas of the ancient world. Contains both general articles on aspects of ancient civilizations as well as more specialized reports on recent explorations and discoveries; occasional articles on new museums or exhibitions of special significance; also occasional review articles of important new publications. The articles, which are exceptionally well illustrated—occasionally with color photographs—are written in a non-pedantic style to appeal to beginning as well as to advanced students. "Archaeological News" contains news of personnel, scholarships, new programs, and other activities of interest, including brief reports on projects and discoveries. The book reviews, of both foreign and English-language publications, now number usually 20-30 per issue; they are signed and critical but not very long—seldom over 1000 words, and usually less than 500. Also a few even briefer book notes.

Indexed in: Art I.   50-37022

*ARION.   v. 1, 1962-

Quarterly.   Austin, Texas. $5.00

"A journal of the humanities and the classics," it is published at the University of Texas and edited primarily by the members of its Classics Department. A scholarly journal whose main purpose is to apply the critical imagination to classical culture generally, but especially to its literature. This it accomplishes by essays on and interpretations of classical writers and their works, by modern translations of standard and new works, by articles on approaches to classics, and on individual classicists. Brief articles on methods and materials of teaching the classics appear frequently. Occasional long review articles; shorter reviews appear even less occasionally. An attractive, well-edited journal.

Indexed in: S.S.H.I.   64-28291

*CLASSICAL JOURNAL.   v. 1, 1905-

Bi-monthly (except June-Sept.)   Lawrence, Kans. $8.00

Published by the Classical Association of the Middle West and South, with the cooperation of the Classical Associations of the Pacific States and of the Atlantic States. Each issue contains usually one scholarly article on classical archaeology, history, literature or study, plus shorter notes in these same areas and a reader's forum commenting on articles and containing miscellaneous items, news and developments of interest to scholars and teachers. "From Other Journals," a listing, with summaries, of articles relating to classical studies in non-classical journals, appeared annually, but beginning in the 1969-70 volume appears twice a year. About 8 to 10 signed, thorough book reviews per issue, varying in length from a few hundred to more than 2000 words; also a list of books received. The journal's appearance and size is slight, but it is an important journal in the field, with much worthwhile material for undergraduates.

Indexed in: Ed.I.   8-6753 rev. 2

CLASSICAL QUARTERLY.   v. 1,1907-

Semi-annual.   Oxford, Eng. $6.75

Published by the Classical Association, it is devoted solely to scholarly articles, of brief to moderate length, on all aspects of classical Rome and Greece. While the early years treated philology almost exclusively, history and culture have been receiving increased attention. There are no book reviews; a section "Summaries of Periodicals," carried from the beginning of the journal, was discontinued in 1940. The Classical Association, whose objects are "to promote the development and maintain the well-being of classical studies," also publishes the *Classical Review.* Members may receive both publications for $13.00; since the Association intends the two journals to be mutually complementary, colleges with strong programs in classics should certainly take both.

Indexed in: Br.Hum.I.   8-19521 (rev. '19)

CLASSICAL REVIEW.   v. 1, 1887-

Three times a year.   Oxford, Eng. $7.25

Published for the Classical Association, it contains brief, scholarly notes primarily relating to the interpretation of the texts of Greek and Roman classics. A major part of each issue is devoted to reviews. Usually there are 30 or 40 long reviews, generally about 1000-1200 words (but some much larger), plus a large number of shorter (though by no means skimpy) ones. Both types are signed and critical. Also a list of books received. A regular feature, "Summaries of Periodicals," listed the articles and briefly summarized some, in selected classics journals, but this was discontinued after 1962. A "Notes and News" section, containing reports on meetings, special publications, etc.

Indexed in: Br.Hum.I.   10-32843
            S.S.H.I.

*CLASSICAL WORLD.   v. 1,1907-

Monthly (September through May)   Newark, Del. $5.25

Published by the Classical Association of the Atlantic States, its title through volume 50 (1956/57) was the Classical Weekly. Although it contains some scholarly articles, most of it is concerned with bibliography, review articles, and items relating to the teaching of classics. It is a most helpful tool in book selection, since the book reviews and the review articles are written from the instructor's rather than the research scholar's point of view, and because of the review articles, such as "A Survey of Publications on Greek Lyric Poetry Since 1952," and "Some Books on Greece." There are a number of useful lists: "Historical Fiction on Classical Themes" appeared *first* in 1963 and was revised, most recently, in 1967; "Inexpensive Books for Teaching the Classics" has appeared annually since 1949; an annual listing of "Textbooks in Greek and Latin;" a roster of members of college classical departments appears every few years; figures on enrollments in classics courses, etc.

Indexed in: B.R.D.   10-2751 rev.*

DIDASKALOS.   v. 1, 1963-

1 no./yr.   Oxford, Eng.   ₤3.15

"The Journal of the Joint Association of Classical Teachers," it is devoted to articles, comments and reviews relating to materials, courses and teaching methods of Latin and Greek languages and culture in secondary and higher education, and to discussion of the place of classics in the modern curriculum. There are only occasional research articles but even these tend to be on subjects (e.g., "Two Strands on Greek Influence in Architecture") that are useful for teachers of Latin or Greek rather than for the traditional classicist scholar. Though most of the discussions of course relate to British experience and matters of concern, the difference in interest or emphasis is very slight, and most present and prospective teachers of classics should profit from the journal, especially since it is exceptionally well edited. There are only a few book reviews, but each number contains a list of publications received.

63-25640

GREECE AND ROME.   v. 1, 1931-

2 nos./yr.   Oxford, Eng. $5.45

Published for the Classical Association, it is intended for those who want to keep up with the field of classics, but whose interests are not as detailed or as deep as the scholar's. Articles such as "Professional Musicians in Ancient Greece," or "On Reading Plutarch's *Lives,*" etc., some of which are illustrated, make it useful for undergraduates. Covers all aspects of Greek and Roman life, history and literature, and also treats education in the classics. A few supplementary numbers have been published. The book review section is especially useful for undergraduate libraries. Though the reviews are not long—they are done in groups—they are informative, and symbols indicate that specific titles are appropriate for school libraries, for advanced students, or for the non-Greek reader. Also a list of books and journals received.

Indexed in: Br.Hum.I.   34-30109

JOURNAL OF HELLENIC STUDIES.   v. 1, 1880-

Annual.   London. $16.00

Published by the Society for the Promotion of Hellenic Studies, it was originally a semi-annual, but due to the problem of costs during World War II was only published annually, and has stayed that way. Each issue contains 15 or 20 articles, varying greatly in length from just a few pages to many, on all aspects of Greek language, literature, history and art; contributors are among the leading figures in the field. Many of the articles are illustrated with drawings and/or photographs. There are a large number of reviews (150-200 in each of the latest volumes) of books in many languages. The reviews, all signed and critical, range greatly in length, but most are between 700 and 1000 words. Also a list of books received. Subscribers also receive the annual *Archaeological Reports,* a fully illustrated account of fresh discoveries in Greece and Greek lands, with bulletins announcing important new acquisitions by museums in Britain. The *Journal* is perhaps the leading English-language publication in the field of Greek scholarship, but is important for libraries only where there is advanced undergraduate work in classics or Greek archaeology.

Indexed in: Art I.   9-20515
            Br.Hum.I.

JOURNAL OF NEAR EASTERN STUDIES. v. 1, 1942-

Quarterly,   Chicago, Ill. $8.00

"The Journal of the Department of Near Eastern Languages and Civilizations of the University of Chicago," it is successor to the *American Journal of Semitic Languages and Literatures,* which, though it had a strong Biblical emphasis, was a scholarly, highly respectable journal in the entire area of Near Eastern studies; its editor from 1884 to 1906 was William Rainey Harper; also connected with it for many years was James Henry Breasted, the noted Egyptologist and founder of the University of Chicago's Oriental Institute.

Its articles, generally 5 or so an issue, of short to moderate length, are concerned with all areas of the ancient Near · East, including Biblical scholarship, archaeology, art, history, linguistics, history of science, etc. Translations of ancient texts and newly discovered works often are published. Usually 5 to 10 book reviews, signed and critical, mostly 750-1000 words, though books of outstanding importance receive more attention. Important for Old Testament studies, ancient history, and archaeology, it is primarily for advanced undergraduates and research.

Indexed in: S.S.H.I.   47-34083 rev*

JOURNAL OF ROMAN STUDIES. v. 1, 1911-

Semi-annual.   London. $9.95

Published by the Society for the Promotion of Roman Studies, whose scope "embraces the history, art, archaeology and literature of Rome, Italy and the Roman Empire, down to about A.D. 700." Issues contain very scholarly articles, varying greatly in length, and many illustrated with photographs and drawings. "Roman Britain in 19--" reports on the findings in Great Britain during the year; reports and proceedings of the Society. Book reviewing is an important feature: several long review-discussions, often article length, plus a number of other reviews, usually about 1000 words, of books on all aspects of ancient Rome. In recent years, the journal has appeared in a single annual volume. Useful only where there is strong interest in Roman history and/or archaeology.

Indexed in: Br. Hum.I.   26-2981
            S.S.H.I.

PHOENIX. v. 1, 1946-

Quarterly.   Toronto, Canada. $10.00

"The Journal of the Classical Association of Canada," it is devoted to scholarly articles of varying length on all aspects of Greek and Roman civilization and culture. The journal's early volumes emphasized philological studies, but that emphasis decreased and more attention has been paid to history and culture. Contributors are mostly Canadian, but there are a large number of Americans and British also. About 10 book reviews per issue, signed and critical, that range from brief to very long. List of books received. Articles and reviews are sometimes in French. An important journal where there is much interest in classical studies.

52-15373

*ACCOUNTING REVIEW. v. 1, 1926-

Quarterly. Menasha, Wis. $15.00

Publication of the American Accounting Association, an organization comprised primarily of teachers of accounting. Each issue contains about 15 articles, of varying length, on the theory, methods, and materials of accounting itself, and on the profession—standards, ethics, etc. Reflecting the professional trend, in recent years articles have used more and more mathematics. Regular features include: "The Teachers' Clinic," brief articles and notes on the teaching of accounting and "on pedagogical aspects of the developments occurring in business and in accounting today"; "CPA Examinations," containing selected problems from recent examinations in accounting practice, auditing and the theory of accounts; "News Notes" of individuals and programs; announcements and reports of its Association; and book reviews. The reviews—generally 15 to 20 per issue—are signed and critical, from 500 to 1000 words in length.

Indexed in: Bus.Per.I.   29-8222 rev. 2

ADMINISTRATIVE MANAGEMENT. v. 1, 1940-

Monthly. N.Y. $7.00

Although it changed in 1961 from *Office Management and American Business* (it had various earlier titles) to its present title, it has very much the same emphasis as formerly—that is, on the functions of the business office: communications, information processing, personnel, systems management, selection and maintenance of equipment and facilities. It does not, in other words, cover the fundamental activities of sales, production and finance, except as these relate to office administration. The articles are brief, well illustrated and usually very practical (e.g., "Maintaining the Company Washroom") though there is some attention to management theory. The news of furniture, equipment and supplies is given much space; a frequent feature is the thorough comparative listing of equipment—copiers, calculators, filing systems, etc.—which of course are useful for almost any organization. Only really useful where there are courses concerned with office management and equipment.

Indexed in: Bus.Per.I.   46-38214*

ADMINISTRATIVE Science Quarterly. *see* POLITICAL SCIENCE

ADVERTISING AGE. v. 1, 1930-

Weekly. Chicago, Ill. $10.00

"The national newspaper of marketing," it is primarily devoted to news of the advertising world—personnel changes, new accounts and campaigns, media news, government action, etc.—but there are also a number of feature articles on the theory and practice of advertising and marketing. Often publishes tables of figures of interest to the field: program ratings, linages, billings, etc. A trade publication in the strictest sense, only useful in academic libraries where there are courses in advertising and/or marketing.

Indexed in: Bus.Per.I.   42-47059

*AMERICAN ECONOMIC REVIEW.   v. 1, 1911-

5 times/yr.   Evanston, Ill. $30.00

Published by the American Economic Association, it now consists of four quarterly numbers, plus a number carrying the complete *Papers and Proceedings* of the A.E.A.'s annual meeting, plus the *Handbook* number which includes a roster of members, officers, committees, awards, etc. Other supplements, usually of a monographic nature, appear occasionally, perhaps once or twice a year, and are included in the subscription. The quarterly numbers contain about 10 articles plus a larger number of communications which are either shorter original contributions or comments on previous articles, often with replies by the original author; also occasional review articles. While all aspects of economics are covered, there is an emphasis on theory. Through 1968, the *Review* carried authoritative book reviews (about 50 per issue in 1968) averaging almost two pages in length, plus a listing, by subject, of other new books. In 1969 these were transferred to the new *Journal of Economic Literature* (q.v.) which is included in the subscription cost. The quarterly issues carry "Notes" of personnel and professional activities. The September issue carries the annual *List of Doctoral Dissertations in Political Economy in American Universities and Colleges*; through 1965, this included dissertations in progress as well, but was simply a listing by subject; since then, only completed dissertations are listed but each one is briefly described.

Under its first editor, who remained until 1940, the *Review* was a fairly stodgy journal, not in the same league with the other major economics journals, and its early files are not as useful to today's student. Since 1940, however, it has almost steadily improved so that it now enjoys the reputation of being one of the, if not *the* most important journal in the field. A current subscription and partial backfile are essential for all college libraries.

Indexed in: B.R.D.   11-7619
     Bus.Per.I.
     P.A.I.S.
     S.S.H.I.

AMERICAN FEDERATIONIST.   v. 1, 1894-

Monthly.   Washington, D.C. $2.00

"Official monthly magazine of the American Federation of Labor and Congress of Industrial Organizations." Each issue contains 4 or 5 short articles, mostly on matters of interest to labor in general, or to labor unions in particular: collective bargaining, present or proposed legislation, aspects of the economic situation, problems of health or retirement, occupational trends, etc. Also many articles on other current political and social issues, most written by staff members of the AFL-CIO's Department of Research or Department of Education, or by a union official. Needless to say, the viewpoints expressed represent, as far as possible, an official labor viewpoint, and the value of the periodical for academic libraries is the expression of this viewpoint. Book reviews, 750-1000 words in length, appear in about half the issues; like the articles, they are on topics relating specifically to labor or to political and economic issues of general interest to labor. Also descriptions of "New Pamphlets," from union, governmental and other sources.

Indexed in: Bus.Per.I.   8-10669
     P.A.I.S.

AMERICAN JOURNAL OF ECONOMICS AND SOCIOLOGY.   v. 1, 1941-

Quarterly.   Lancaster, Pa. $5.00

Published "in the interest of constructive synthesis in the social sciences," it contains mostly brief scholarly and semi-scholarly articles, primarily on economic questions and their relationship to sociology, political science, history and education. Its founders were devoted to the work of Henry George, so that social reform and especially the implications of land reform, have always been major concerns of contributors. Only one or two reviews per issue; these tend to be review essays and are fairly long. Not of first importance, but useful in strong undergraduate programs.

Indexed in: P.A.I.S.   45-42294
            S.S.H.I.

AMERICAN LABOR.   v. 1, 1968-

Monthly.   N.Y. $15.00

"The magazine of labor news," it is independently published and devoted to issues, personalities, trends and developments on the current labor scene. Each issue contains just a few articles, one of them usually a profile in depth (sometimes in the form of an interview) of an important labor leader or a government official in the labor area. The other articles range over all areas of labor: history, trends in employment, reports on meetings, economic or technical developments in particular industries that may affect labor, etc. These are well-illustrated articles, popularly written, with a pro-labor viewpoint in controversial issues. The rest of the periodical contains regular features covering a calendar of events, developments in Washington and the states, summaries of NLRB decisions, international news, news of pension and welfare funds, economic indicators.

A useful journal where there is much interest in current developments affecting organized labor.

Indexed in: P.A.I.S.

BANKING.   v. 1, 1908-

Monthly.   N. Y. $8.00

Journal of the American Bankers Association. Usually about 10 feature articles in each issue, well illustrated, covering all phases of banking—operations, personnel, public relations, governmental regulations and policy, investments, trust funds, etc.—as well as some general articles on economics and finance. A number of regular features and sections, including: "Bonds—Government and Municipal," "Business Development" which describes new ideas and programs for expanding banking services, "Operations Bulletin" which discusses equipment, systems, facilities, products, methods and buildings, "News for the Country Banker," a "Calendar" of meetings of the A.B.A., state associations and related organizations. News and notes of national and international developments, of the members and activities of the Association, and reports of the annual convention. A few brief book reviews.

Indexed in: Bus.Per.I.   38-7912
            P.A.I.S.

BARRON'S.   v. 1, 1921-

Weekly.   Chicopee, Mass. $21.00

Subtitled "National Business and Financial Weekly" it is published by Dow Jones and provides many features relating to the general investment situation. The first half of each issue is devoted to articles and departments on national and international events, trends in particular industries or areas, actions of individual companies, news of the investment world, and detailed analyses of the current financial position and potential of 4 or 5 corporations. The latter half is devoted to the Statistical Section, covering prices, earnings and dividends of all stocks on the New York and American Stock Exchanges as well as quotations from other regional exchanges, and a listing of price movements and other economic and financial indicators. An important journal for the study of corporation finance.

Indexed in: Bus.Per.I.   23-18506 rev.*

*BUSINESS HISTORY REVIEW.   v. 1, 1926-

Quarterly.   Boston, Mass. $10.00

Formerly the *Bulletin of the Business Historical Society*, it is now published by the Harvard Graduate School of Business Administration. Each issue contains 4 to 6 scholarly articles on the history of industries and of individual firms, on important episodes in business history, biographies of significant figures, on the history of business methods and theory, and on the uses and methods of business and economic history. The emphasis is, of course, on American business, but there are many articles on foreign companies. Occasional issues are devoted to a single topic. Between 1959 and 1964 there was an annual bibliography, *Studies in Enterprise*, listing the most significant books, pamphlets and articles on American and Canadian company histories and biographies of businessmen. "Lagniappe," a regular section since 1963, contains "documents illustrative of the evolution of business enterprise, from "A Thirteenth-Century Castilian Sumptuary Law" to "Uniform Containerization of Freight: Early Steps in the Evolution of an Idea." "The Editor's Corner" includes news and notes of meetings, new programs, awards, personnel and publications of special interest. About 20 signed, critical book reviews per issue, most about 750-1000 words.

Indexed in: Bus.Per.I.   30-8718 rev. 2
              P.A.I.S.

BUSINESS Periodicals Index. *see* INDEXES

*BUSINESS WEEK.   no. 1, 1929-

Weekly.   N.Y. $12.00

A widely read, heavily used periodical that is devoted to extensive, objective coverage of today's business world—especially as that world affects and is affected by current political, social, economic and financial events and developments. Contains briskly written and thoroughly illustrated reports and stories on activities and people in all aspects of business, international trade, labor, technology and politics. Frequent comprehensive "Special Reports" treat major problems or developments that should concern business, and these often have social or political implications— e.g., "The Trade-Offs for a Better Environment," "Japan's Remarkable

Industrial Machine." Regular features include "Figures of the Week," containing the latest and comparative statistical data of U.S. production, trade, prices and finance; the newsletters—"Washington Outlook," International Outlook," and "Personal Business," the last containing a variety of items for individuals, from tax hints to vacation spots to recommended night clubs; an editorial page that is moderate in tone. In March, 1970 a weekly "Books Department" began; it carries one or two reviews, by both staff writers and guest experts, of books mostly in the area of politics, business and economics, but often on social problems. They are good critical reviews, often 1000 words in length. Reliable, readable, and profusely illustrated with photographs, diagrams and charts, it is recommended for all libraries.

Indexed in: Bus.Per.I.   31-6225
            P.A.I.S.
            R.G.

CANADIAN JOURNAL OF ECONOMICS. REVUE CANADIENNE D'ECONOMIQUE. v. 1, 1968-

Quarterly.   Toronto. $15.00

Sponsored by the Canadian Economics Association, it continues the economics portion of the *Canadian Journal of Economics and Political Science* (1935-1967), which had become one of the more important social science journals. From 5 to 10 articles per issue, mostly of moderate length, plus a number of shorter Notes. While the articles are concerned with the entire field of economics, there is special emphasis on Canadian problems. Most of the contributors are from Canadian universities, with some from the U.S. News of the Association, other professional news, and listing of staff changes. The number of book reviews per issue varies widely—about 40 were reviewed altogether in 1970. These are of books either—of special interest to Canadians, or important books of interest to economists generally, with most of the reviews 600-1000 words.

Contributions are in either English or French, the great majority in English. Articles in English are summarized in French, and vice-versa. An important journal for all strong economics collections, it is essential where there is much interest in Canada.

Indexed in: P.A.I.S.   75-11454
            S.S.H.I.

*COLUMBIA JOURNAL OF WORLD BUSINESS.   v. 1, 1965-

Bi-monthly.   N. Y. $20.00

Published under the auspices of the Graduate School of Business, Columbia University, its purpose is "to serve as a means of communication for members of the global business community and university scholars; to deepen understanding of significant developments of concern to business wherever they occur; to keep executives and students of business abreast of important advances in business thinking throughout the world; to provide a platform from which authorities can speak freely on business and related issues of our time." Usually about 10 articles of moderate length per issue, written by professors of economics and business, and by consultants, government officials, and executives concerned with foreign trade and development; authors include some very well known names, often from abroad. Book reviews appear sporadically; they are signed and critical, usually 700 - 1000 words long. An important journal for students of international economics, it is useful to others interested in world affairs.

Indexed in: P.A.I.S.   65-9951

*COMMERCIAL AND FINANCIAL CHRONICLE.   v. 1, 1865-

Semi-weekly.   N. Y. $95.00

The oldest American business publication in existence, it has been and still is one of the most important, providing complete coverage of the business and financial world. The Monday issue contains stock and bond quotations (for the week on the New York exchanges and the week's high and low on eight other American and two Canadian exchanges), including over-the-counter and municipal bond quotations, brief notes on individual companies, bank clearings, foreign exchange rates, Federal Reserve Bank statements, and general news for investors. The Thursday issue contains news, commentary, and expert articles on finance, business, economics, and governmental affairs. Contributors are from the academic world as well as from business and government, and the articles are authoritative and well written. Because of its frequency and size, the cost of binding may be prohibitive, but for some libraries the earlier volumes are more important than recent ones, as the *Chronicle* is generally recognized as one of the best sources of information for the student of American business history.

Indexed in: Bus.Per.I.   8-15431 (rev. '17)

DATA PROCESSING MAGAZINE.   v. 1, 1958-

Monthly.   Philadelphia, Pa. $10.00

Originally titled *Machine Accounting and Data Processing,* and concerned with automated office procedures, it changed several times (*Punched Card Data Processing, Data Processing for Management*) and in 1964 adopted the present title. These title changes reflected changing trends in the field of data processing use: merely a way of speeding up certain office procedures at first, it quickly expanded to a total systems approach, and the magazine's coverage thus includes now the uses of data processing in research, engineering, science and manufacturing, as well as education for the field. Contains articles and features in these various areas, including news and notes of the industry, trends and developments in the field, calendar of meetings, seminars and courses, news of personnel, descriptions of new products and services, etc. The section "Bookshelf" contains annotated, uncritical listings of recently published books and pamphlets. Primarily a trade journal, it is useful where there are courses in EDP and especially where EDP equipment is used for business and/or teaching purposes.

Similar in nature is the semi-monthly *Datamation* (v. 1, 1957- $25.00). It is probably even more widely read by those in the field.

Computers and Automation (v. 1, 1951- $18.50) published monthly, is the oldest of the trade journals in the EDP field. It contains both technical and semi-technical articles, as well as features similar to those described above, but has two especially worth noting—the monthly computer census of the United States and the annual extensive *Computer Directory and Buyers' Guide* in the June issue.

All three journals are indexed in the *Business Perodicals Index,* and libraries where there are strong programs in EDP, either in training or application, should probably take all. They are useful for browsing and keeping up with the field, but just because the field is changing so quickly, extensive backfiles are not necessary.

Indexed in: A.S.T.I.   65-73750
        Bus.Per.I.

DUN'S REVIEW.   v. 1, 1893-

Monthly. N.Y. $7.00

Founded under its present title, it went through several title changes, and was known as *Dun's Review and Modern Industry* from 1953 through 1966. Written primarily for the business executive, it contains articles, interviews and essays on the general situation and trends in business, foreign developments, particular firms and businessmen, industries, executive management, etc. These are all popularly written and well illustrated. There are a number of regular features including: "Washington Desk," which reports on rules, regulations, policies and pending legislation affecting business; "The Executive Investor" contains analyses of particular firms and reports investment news in general; "Business Failures" includes statistics and discussion; "Sales and Marketing" covers trends in selling, distribution and advertising; "Executive Bookshelf" reviews briefly (180-300 words, usually) a few books of interest to businessmen, including government documents, and scholarly and popular non-fiction. Published by Dun and Bradstreet, it is readable and knowledgeable, but a lengthy back file is not essential for most college libraries.

Indexed in: Bus.Per.I.   8-10651*
             R.G.

ECONOMETRICA.   v. 1, 1933-

Bi-monthly. New Haven, Conn. $35.00

Published by the Econometric Society, "an international society for the advancement of economic theory in its relation to statistics and mathematics. . . . Its main object shall be to promote studies that aim at the unification of the theoretical-quantitative and the empirical-quantitative approach to economic problems." Each volume contains 30 to 40 technical articles of varying length, by authors from many countries. The number of articles per issue varies, since publication of single issues is often delayed and double numbers result. Each article is preceded by an abstract. Also briefer notes and comments on earlier articles. Usually 10-15 book reviews per issue; signed and critical, they are mostly about 750 words in length, though varying frequently for books of greater or lesser importance. A Supplementary Number, containing the programs and abstracts of papers given at various national and international meetings, has been issued beginning with the 1967 volume. That number also includes a listing of the Society's membership. An important journal for very advanced students and research.

Indexed in: S.S.H.I.   34-16980

ECONOMIC BULLETIN FOR ASIA AND THE FAR EAST.   v. 1, 1950-

Quarterly. N.Y. Bill Later

A United Nations publication, it is prepared by the secretariat of the Economic Commission for Asia and the Far East (now located in Bangkok). Contains articles, reports, papers and statistics on all aspects of the area's economy, including related topics such as population and social trends. The March issue comprises the annual *Economic Survey of Asia and the Far East,* an important reference source which, in addition to reviewing the current situation by tables and charts, contains (since 1957) a lengthy study on some major aspect or problem of Asian economy—e.g., Aspects of the Finance of Development, Asia's Trade With Western Europe. (The *Economic Survey* is also available separately.) The June and September issues contain articles and notes on subjects related to the Asian economy. The December issue features special studies and reports relating to economic development and planning.

An important publication for the study of comparative economic systems and the economics of developing areas, it is essential where there is any emphasis on the economy of Asia. A backfile is also useful for tracing the recent development of the area.

Also published by the United Nations are: the *Economic Bulletin for Europe* (v. 1, 1949- $), the *Economic Bulletin for Africa* (v. 1, 1961-   ), and the *Economic Bulletin for Latin America* (v. 1, 1956-   ). Each of these is issued by the Economic Commission for that area, appears twice a year (though the one for Africa somewhat less regularly), and each consists of articles, some regular surveys and a large number of statistical tables. None includes the. annual *Economic Survey* for the area, as does the one for Asia, and for this reason, as well their infrequency, they are somewhat less valuable. But if there is a strong interest in any of the areas, the appropriate *Economic Bulletin* should be received, and libraries with extensive economics holdings should probably receive all of them. All are indexed in *P.A.I.S.*

Indexed in: P.A.I.S.   56-16233

ECONOMIC DEVELOPMENT AND CULTURAL CHANGE.   v. 1, 1952-

Quarterly.   Chicago, Ill. $12.00

Edited at the Research Center for Economic Development and Cultural Change at the University of Chicago, "it is designed for exploratory discussion of the problems of economic development and cultural change." Its emphasis is, of course, on economics, but it is also concerned with the political, social and cultural implications of economic growth, especially as related to the developing areas. Usually 5 to 10 articles per issue; occasionally issues deal with various aspects of a single topic. Almost every volume has had a special supplement of a monographic nature. In addition to the frequent review articles, there are from 3 to 10 reviews per issue; signed and critical, they are all long, and many of them several thousand words long. List of books received.

Indexed in: P.A.I.S.   56-15874

ECONOMIC Geography. *see* GEOGRAPHY

ECONOMIC HISTORY REVIEW.   v. 1, 1927;   n.s.v. 1, 1948-

Quarterly.   Hartfordshire, Eng. $15.00

A publication of the Economic History Society, it carries scholarly articles "on economic and social history and articles dealing with the borderlands between those subjects and other aspects of history and economics." Each issue now contains about 7 articles, rarely more than 8000 words long, on all aspects of economic history and its implications, but primarily related to Britain. The bibliographical contributions of the journal are significant. First, there are the annual listings and surveys of periodical literature on the economic history of European countries and the United States, the thorough "List of Publications on the Economic History of Great Britain and Ireland Published During 19   ," a feature that covers all types of materials and has appeared since the journal began. Second, there are a large number of signed and critical reviews—over 100 in some issues— that range in length from a few hundred to perhaps 1500 words, with most about 500-750 words long. Finally, there are the "Essays in Bibliography and Criticism" that are lengthy reviews of important recent works, often surveying much of the literature on the subject under review; several of these may appear in a single issue. An important journal for serious work in economic history and English history.

Indexed in: Br.Hum.I.   29-11002 rev. 2
            P.A.I.S.
            S.S.H.I.

*ECONOMIC INDICATORS.   1948-

Monthly.   Washington, D.C. $3.00

"Prepared for the Joint Economic Committee by the Council of Economic Advisors." Originally intended just to provide the Joint Economic Commit- tee with information on prices, wages, production, business activity, pur- chasing power, credit, money, and Federal finance "in a concise and graphic form," its monthly publication for a wider audience was later authorized. While it contains almost no textual material, a *Historical and Descriptive Supplement,* published every few years, contains historical data and a description of each series dating back to 1947 in all cases, and in some, to 1929. This explanatory text, which cannot be repeated in each month's issue, "is essential for understanding and interpreting the signifi- cance of the current data." In non-technical language it explains "how the data are obtained and the series derived, its relation to other series, and its principal uses and limitations." References to related statistical sources and for more background information are also given. Because it contains in such handy form the raw data for the study of the current economic scene, it is an essential item for academic libraries, but since the data is eventually collected in more permanent form in other publi- cations, binding is not necessary. A depository item.

48-46615

ECONOMIC JOURNAL.   v. 1, 1891-

Quarterly.   London. $16.25

Founded as the British Economic Association's *Journal,* it took its pre- sent title in 1902 when the Association became the Royal Economic Society. It "is intended to represent the various shades of economic opin- ion, and to be the organ, not of one school of economists, but of all." Among its early contributors were Marshall, Pigou and Keynes, the last serving as editor or co-editor from 1911 to 1945. Noted economists from all over the world have been contributors and many important advances in the field were first presented on its pages. Covers all subject areas of economics, with some emphasis on theory and on matters relating to Great Britain. Each issue contains an average of 7 or 8 articles, a number of "Notes and Memoranda," and a "Current Topics" section which is devoted to news of the Society and its members. The number of books reviewed varies greatly from issue to issue, from a dozen or so to more than 70; all of the reviews are signed and average 600-700 words. An important bibliographical feature is the listing of the contents of recent issues of economics journals from all over the world (some 130 titles in recent issues), in the section "Recent Periodicals and New Books"; this section also lists and annotates a large number of recent books from various countries. An important journal for departments strong in economic theory.

Indexed in: Br.Hum.I.   7-41368
P.A.I.S.
S.S.H.I.

ECONOMICA.   v. 1, 1921;   n.s.v. 1, 1934-

Quarterly.   London. $9.00

Published by the London School of Economics and Political Science, it originally covered all the social sciences, but with the beginning of the New Series, it has been "devoted to Economics, Economic History, Statistics, and closely related problems." An average of 8 or 9 articles per issue, varying greatly in length, but fairly evenly divided between applied economics and economic theory. Some 20 to 25 signed, critical book reviews per issue of the more important works in the field; a few shorter notices and a list of books received. Important for research, especially in economic theory and history.

Indexed in: Br.Hum.I.   22-23854 Revised
P.A.I.S.
S.S.H.I.

*ECONOMICS SELECTIONS: AN INTERNATIONAL BIBLIOGRAPHY.   1954-

Quarterly.   Pittsburgh, Pa. $15.00

Originally *Economics Library Selections,* it changed to *International Economics Selections Bibliography* in 1966, and to its present title in 1967. From 1954 to 1962 it was published at Johns Hopkins University, then was taken over by the Economics Department and the University Libraries of the University of Pittsburgh. It appears in two series. Series I: *New Books in Economics,* provides annotations of all books on economics published in English and selected titles in other languages, especially German, French and Spanish. A letter after each annotation indicates the size of the library (in terms of annual expenditure for books in economics: A, for under $500; B, $500-1300; C, $1300-2400; D, $2400-$3000) for which the book is recommended, but the intrinsic merits of the book are not evaluated. All necessary acquisitions information is given, including LC card and standard book numbers. Series II, which is included in the subscription cost, is a supplementary publication, scheduled to appear once a year (but not having kept to that schedule), containing annotations of books in a special field or subdiscipline of economics. Series II makes an excellent retrospective buying guide, and Series I is a convenient and reliable way of fitting a library's purchases to its budget—at least in one field. The economics departments as well as the library staff should go through it systematically. Recent issues have appeared late.

65-16720

*ECONOMIST.   v. 1, 1843-

Weekly.   London. $33.60 (surface mail); $48.00 (air mail)

Since its beginning, the *Economist* has been one of the most respected observers of the current political and economic scene, closely followed by statesmen around the world. Though specially concerned with matters relating to Britain and the Commonwealth (and this of course was especially true in the 19th and early 20th centuries), it is of primary interest now for its reports and articles on other areas, and this accounts for the fact that half its readership is outside Britain. Its lead articles are mostly on British affairs, but a large portion of the journal is devoted to "International Report," "American Survey," and (not every week) "Communist Affairs" carrying items and articles on social, political and economic events. Special surveys, treating areas or topics of current interest more or less in depth, appear frequently. Usually 6 or 7 book reviews per issue (more in the Spring and Fall Book Numbers), averaging around 500 words. Though unsigned, these are perceptive, and they cover many subjects— art, literature, travel, etc.—in addition to politics and economics. Throughout its history, leading English economists have written for the *Economist*, and a back file is important for the study of economic history as well as for the history of Britain and the Commonwealth. Because of its coverage, its influence and political acuteness, it is useful for current events, and the air mail edition may be worthwhile. In any case, it should be in every academic library.

Indexed in: B.R.D.   8-17464
            Br.Hum.I.
            Bus.Per.I.
            P.A.I.S.
            S.S.H.I.

FAR EasternEconomic Review. *see* AREA STUDIES/ASIA

*FEDERAL RESERVE BULLETIN.   v. 1, 1915-

Monthly.   Washington, D.C. $6.00

Published by the Board of Governors of the Federal Reserve System. Each issue contains from one to several articles on current general economic matters or on specific activities or policies of the Federal Reserve Board. Regular departments include: "Law Department," carrying administrative interpretations, new regulations, statutes and decisions; "Announcements" of personnel and institutions connected with the system; "National Summary of Business Conditions"; listings of Federal Reserve Banks and branches and Board publications. Half or more of each issue consists of "Financial and Business Statistics," with current data on banking, credit, money, public finance, the stock market, industrial production, employment and earnings, prices, national product and income, and flow of funds, with an index to the statistical tables. Useful for reference and essential for any research into the current financial or economic scene, it should be in all libraries with economics majors. (A library that subscribes to this will probably also want the releases of the Federal Reserve bank for its particular district; these are usually available for the asking.)

Supplementing the *Bulletin* and also published by the Federal Reserve Board is the *Federal Reserve Monthly Chart Book* (v. 1, 1947- $6.00) which presents in graphic form economic and financial data, much of which is given in tabular form in the *Bulletin*, but also additional data. Subscription to it includes the annual supplement, the *Historical Chart Book*, which contains long-range charts of data covered in the monthly issues plus some additional series. Useful for advanced students and research. A depository item.

Indexed in: Bus.Per.I.   15-26318
          P.A.I.S.

*FINANCE AND DEVELOPMENT.   v. 1, 1964-

Quarterly.   Washington, D.C.   Free

Originally titled the *Fund and Bank Review: Finance and Development,* it is published by the International Monetary Fund and the International Bank for Reconstruction and Development (the World Bank) to explain to students and to the general public the work of these two organizations. Contains articles of moderate length, not just on the organizations, but on economic and financial problems and analyses of situations relating to their work—e.g., "Stabilizing An Economy—Spain"; "Interest Rate Policies in Developing Countries?"; "Science and World Animal Production: Achievement and Failure." Contributors are either staff members of one of the organizations or specialists who have, in one capacity or other, been associated with them. A few signed reviews; however, they are fairly brief and descriptive rather than critical. Regular sections summarize recent work of each of the organizations. Well illustrated and edited, it is a useful journal for students, especially those working in the fields of international finance or development economics.

Indexed in: Bus.Per.I.   66-3101
          P.A.I.S.

FORBES.   v. 1, 1917-

Bi-monthly.   N. Y. $9.50

Founded by B.C. Forbes, a well known financial columinst and editor for Hearst newspapers, and edited by him until his death in 1954. One of the most important business periodicals in the 1920's, it failed to see that the public's attitude toward business was changing; it was eclipsed by newer publications in the 30's and 40's, and not until the 1950's did it again become important. One of the few independently owned business journals, its underlying philosophy—that business is people—has not changed. Intended primarily for the corporate investor, the articles, which are briskly written and mostly brief, treat single corporations, emphasizing trends, developments and problems. There are a number of other features on business, the stock market, and the economy in general. Since 1949, the January 1st issue has been devoted to the Annual Report on American Industry, a ranking of the largest stockholder-owned corporations, plus an industry-by-industry survey; beginning in 1969, the May 15th issue carries a listing of the top 500 corporations in revenue, market, value, assets and net profits. Both these annual issues are useful reference tools. Another useful feature is the index (located next to the table of contents) of all companies mentioned in an issue. An important journal where there are courses related to corporation finance, it will be used wherever there is much interest in business affairs.

Indexed in: Bus. Per.I.   CA 19-172 unrev'd
              R.G.

*FORTUNE.   v. 1, 1930-

Monthly.   Chicago, Ill. $10.50

This deluxe monthly of business contains thorough and well written articles on industrial and commercial enterprises, here and abroad, on key figures in government, business, labor and technology, on political or social trends or scientific developments, usually with their implications for business. The May issue contains a directory of the 500 largest U.S. industrial corporations, with figures for sales assets, net income, capital, employees, and earnings; it also contains directories of the 50 largest commercial banks, life-insurance companies, retailing companies, transportation companies, and utilities, with appropriate data for each list. The June issue (beginning in 1970) has similar information for the second 500 largest U.S. corporations, and the August issue, the 200 largest foreign industrial corporations. Monthly features include: "Business Roundup," a monthly report on the economic outlook; "Businessmen in the News," concise, personal biographies of businessmen, along with photographs; "Report from ——————," trade or investment news from a city, country or area abroad; "Personal Investing," news and trends of the securities markets. "Books and Ideas," appearing in almost every issue since 1967, discusses a recent important book, not always in economics or business; these are fairly long reviews, written by guest experts, and they are always thoughtful and often controversial.

Beautifully produced, with many illustrations, diagrams and charts, a large portion of them in color, *Fortune* is an outstanding example of magazine production. Although generally thought of as a business magazine, the growing number of articles on social and political issues, not necessarily related to business, make it of much more general interest and essential for every library.

Indexed in: Bus.Per.I.   31-7716 rev.2
              P.A.I.S.
              R.G.

*HARVARD BUSINESS REVIEW.   v. 1, 1922-

Bi-monthly.   Boston, Mass. $12.00

Contains contributions relating to all aspects of business by professors, private consultants, businessmen, and specialists connected with public organizations. About 10 articles per issue, mostly of moderate length. Stresses practical matters on the managerial level, such as public and personnel relations and communications, long-range planning, etc., but the articles are by no means "how-to-do-it" ones. Rather, in keeping with the journal's appeal to "thoughtful businessmen," they almost always discuss the theory behind the approach, and are well written and attractively presented. Also frequent articles on public affairs and social concerns that affect or can be affected by businessmen. Published by the Graduate School of Business Administration at Harvard, but operationally independent of it, the journal is intended as "a bridge between the academic and research world and the practical, operating businessman's world," and enjoys a wide readership among business leaders (its circulation is over 120,000). There are no regular book reviews as such, but the section "Keeping Informed" usually discusses a current problem or issue in terms of its recent literature.

Indexed in: Bus.Per.I. 25-10769 rev
           P.A.I.S.
           R.G.

*INDUSTRIAL AND LABOR RELATIONS REVIEW. v. 1, 1947-

Quarterly. Ithaca, N.Y. $8.00

Published by the New York State School of Industrial and Labor Relations at Cornell University. Contains scholarly articles, discussions and shorter communications on labor organizations, collective bargaining, labor economics, labor-management relations, government and labor, and other labor and social security problems, both domestic and foreign. "Research Notes" of projects and activities of universities, institutes and official bodies, here and abroad. Occasionally carries texts of important documents; excellent signed, critical book reviews, about 20-25 per issue, mostly 600-1000 words in length. *Recent Publications,* in each issue, is a lengthy classified bibliography of books, articles, pamphlets and documents.

Indexed in: Bus.Per.I. 50-3249
           P.A.I.S.

INTERNATIONAL FINANCIAL STATISTICS. v. 1, 1948-

Monthly. Washington, D.C. $10.00

Prepared by the Statistics Bureau of the International Monetary Fund, it is devoted almost entirely to tables of statistics. The first section consists of tables relating to the International Monetary Fund and to international liquidity, exchange rates, prices, interest rates, changes in money supply and international trade. Statistical tables for the International Bank for Reconstruction and Development were carried until 1964. A much more extensive portion of each issue consists of country-by-country tables on money, banking and trade for Fund members. A regular annual supplement provides time series tables consistent with the current figures; there are special supplements on the seasonal adjustment of selected data. Important for research in international finance and trade, but most college libraries need keep only a few years' backfile, since the statistics are eventually compiled in other reference sources.

49-22514*

INTERNATIONAL LABOUR REVIEW.   1921-

Monthly.   Geneva, Switzerland $8.50

Published by the International Labour Office, each issue contains usually 3 to 5 articles, by staff members of the ILO and by outside experts, on social and economic policy, labor law and labor relations, manpower and training, social security, working conditions, labor unions, etc., and also accounts of conferences on these topics. "Current Information" contains news items from various countries. "Bibliography" contains descriptions of new ILO publications, about 10 reviews, varying greatly in length up to a few thousand words, of recent books and documentary publications, plus, frequently, a lengthy review article, plus briefer descriptions of other books received. "Automation Abstracts," which notes books, articles, speeches, etc., dealing with the social and economic aspects of automation, has appeared semi-annually beginning in 1966.

Through 1964, each issue included a *Statistical Supplement* which updated much of the information in the ILO's important *Yearbook of Labour Statistics*. Since then that information has been carried in its quarterly *Bulletin of Labour Statistics* (v. 1, 1965- $4.00) which is important for institutions where there is much work done on international economics. To keep the quarterly numbers of the *Bulletin* even more current, a processed *Supplement* with some updated figures is published in the off-months. Information in the *Bulletin*, except for some monthly, quarterly or half-yearly data, is eventually gathered in the *Yearbook*, so binding, or even permanent keeping of the *Bulletin* may not be necessary for most libraries.

Indexed in: P.A.I.S.   21-18897 rev.*
             S.S.H.I.

INTERNATIONAL MONETARY FUND.   STAFF PAPERS.   v. 1, 1950-

3 nos./yr.   Washington, D.C. $6.00

From the Foreword to the first issue: "Through the publication of *Staff Papers*, the Fund is making available some of the work of members of its staff. The Fund believes that these papers will be found helpful by government officials, by professional economists, and by others concerned with monetary and financial problems. Much of what is now presented is quite provisional. On some international monetary problems, final and definitive views are scarcely to be expected in the near future, and several alternatives, or even conflicting approaches, may profitably be explored . The views presented in these papers are not, therefore, to be interpreted as necessarily indicating the position of the Executive Board or the officials of the Fund." About 6 articles per issue, on all aspects of the Fund's work, international trade and finance, studies of national economics and financial policies and monetary systems, etc.—from general subjects ("The Effect of Inflation on Economic Development") to very specific studies ("The Mexican Balance of Payments, 1947-50"). Resumes of each article in French and Spanish. Important for courses in international economics. The International Monetary Fund also publishes a weekly *International Financial News Survey* (v. 1, 1948-   Free) which concisely reports on national and international situations and developments in fields of interest to the Fund. Though written by staff members, items are based on material in newspapers, periodicals, documents and other publications which are cited. Handy for keeping up with developments, but for college libraries binding and permanent addition is probably not necessary, especially since it's not indexed, and most information in it will be available elsewhere.

Indexed in: Bus.Per.I.   53-35483
              P.A.I.S.

JOURNAL OF ACCOUNTANCY.   v. 1, 1905-

Monthly.   N.Y. $10.00

Published by the American Institute of Certified Public Accountants, it is an influential journal, widely read by accountants and businessmen concerned with accounting. Articles, mostly by practicing accountants, on theory, but especially on the problems and practices of accounting and other matters of interest to accountants. There are a number of regular features and departments: news notes—government activities, professional news, meetings, etc.; "Statements in Quotes," addresses by accountants, government officials, and business leaders, or texts of reports; "Accounting and Auditing Problems," "Tax Clinic" and "Practitioners Forum"—all give advice and answers to problems or matters of practical concern; "Management Services," discussions of various management services technical areas; "Education & Professional Training"—on teaching, recruiting, accounting curriculum, etc., intended not only for teachers and students of accounting, but others interested in personnel preparation and postgraduate training. This section began in 1961; at the same time the journal discontinued the semi-annual CPA examination questions and answers. "Current Reading" carries from one to six signed book reviews, a number of them quite long; also summaries of articles in other periodicals.

Indexed in: Bus.Per.I.   7-39524 rev.*
              P.A.I.S.

*JOURNAL OF BUSINESS.   v. 1, 1928-

Quarterly.   Chicago, Ill. $12.00

"A quarterly devoted to professional and academic thinking and research in business." Edited by the Faculty of the Graduate School of Business of the University of Chicago, and reflecting, in large part, the views of the faculty, it contains an average of 6 or 7 scholarly articles on all aspects of business, both theoretical and applied. In general, its approach to research is quantitative or analytic rather than descriptive. Beginning with 1963, the January issue contains a few articles on "The Business Outlook" for the year. Each issue includes a section of news of personnel at university schools of business in the U.S., and the January issue contains a classified list of doctoral dissertations accepted by the schools. About 10 books are reviewed; the reviews, averaging a page in length, are signed and critical. There is also a classified listing of books received.

Indexed in: Bus.Per.I.   29-15410 Revised
              P.A.I.S.

JOURNAL of Developing Areas. *see* AREA STUDIES/GENERAL

JOURNAL OF ECONOMIC HISTORY.   v. 1, 1941-

Quarterly.   N.Y. $15.00

Published for the Economic History Association by the New York University School of Business Administration. Contains medium-length to lengthy scholarly articles and shorter notes on economic history and related aspects of history or economics. Frequent review-articles; each of three numbers contains a list of books received and an average of 50 or so signed, critical book reviews, mostly 500-750 words in length. One number of each volume, subtitled *Tasks of Economic History*, contains the papers read at the annual meeting of the Association (through 1952, this was issued as a supplement). One session at the meeting is devoted to presentations of "Summaries of Doctoral Dissertations" in the field, each 2 to 5 pages long. An important journal for social and economic historians.

Indexed in: P.A.I.S.   43-6024 rev.
                 S.S.H.I.

*JOURNAL OF ECONOMIC LITERATURE.   v. 1, 1963-

Quarterly.   Evanston, Ill. $30.00

Originally, as the *Journal of Economic Abstracts*, it contained abstracts of articles appearing in 37 of the world's leading economic journals. In 1969, its title and nature changed and its functions expanded considerably. Its basic purpose is to help economists keep abreast of the vast literature, some 1500 books and 5000 major articles published each year. To do this it is organized into three sections. The first consists of articles, essays and communications that review the literature in a subfield of economics, or that give the reactions of a leading economist to his recent reading, or that review at length an outstanding book or other significant materials. Often the original author's response is included. The second section provides a classified, annotated listing of new books (some 1100 were so listed in 1970), and signed, critical reviews, 40-50 per issue, mostly 750-1000 words in length. The third section covers periodicals: it first lists the tables of contents of 250 titles in economics and business, or in other fields of related interest; then it arranges the articles by subject; finally, it provides abstracts—some quite lengthy—of several hundred of the more important articles.

A journal of unusual coverage for an entire field, it is of obvious bibliographic importance to economists and librarians and should be in every academic library where economics is studied.

Indexed in: P.A.I.S.   64-54734

JOURNAL OF FINANCE.   v. 1, 1946-

5 nos./yr.   Worcester, Mass. $15.00

Official journal of the American Finance Association. Contains authoritative articles on the theory and practice of finance, with special emphasis on business finance and investments and on money and banking, and with lesser emphasis on international and consumer finance. Reflecting developments in the field itself, there have been an increasing number of contributions based on mathematical analyses and model building. The second number of each volume is devoted to the *Papers and Proceedings* of the Association's annual meeting. The number of contributions to the other issues has expanded considerably in the past few years, reflecting the *Journal's* growing reputation as one of the leading specialized periodicals for economists. In 1966, 20 articles were published, whereas 49 appeared in 1970; the average length remained at 12-15 pages. Over the same period the number of reviews increased from 47 to 96 annually; these average about 1000 words, though with considerable variation. Each regular issue also now contains a section of full-length *Abstracts of Doctoral Dissertations* in the field, totalling 40 for both 1969 and 1970. Occasional review articles. The "Notes and Communications" section was replaced in 1967 with a "Comments" section; it includes now just responses to articles, and what were once published as "Notes" now appear as short articles. The basic journal in the field.

Indexed in: Bus. Per.I.   49-22513*
              P.A.I.S.

JOURNAL OF MARKETING.   v. 1, 1936-

Quarterly.   Chicago, Ill. $30.00

Published by the American Marketing Association, it contains about 15 articles (limited to 4000 words each) per issue on all phases of marketing: advertising and sales promotion, consumer analysis, foreign marketing, governmental relationships to marketing, industrial marketing, marketing education, management, research and research techniques, retailing, sales management, and marketing theory. Regular sections are "Legal Developments in Marketing," presenting and discussing judicial and administrative decisions relevant to marketing; "Marketing Abstracts," covering a wide variety of periodical articles, government documents, bulletins, reports, etc.; "Book Reviews," about 15 per issue, ranging up to 1000, but mostly 600-700, words in length; they are signed and critical. The fourth issue of each volume contains an organizational directory of the divisions, chapters, and officers of the AMA.

Institutions which emphasize this area of business administration should also consider the *Journal of Retailing* (v. 1, 1925- $3.50), a quarterly published by the New York University Institute of Retail Management, and devoted to studies of retailing practices and problems, especially as they affect or are affected by theory. There are usually several book reviews per issue; they are signed, but mostly just a few hundred words in length.

Indexed in: Bus.Per.I.   38-24264 rev.
              P.A.I.S.

*JOURNAL OF POLITICAL ECONOMY.   v. 1, 1892-

Bi-monthly.   Chicago, Ill. $20.00

Edited in cooperation with members of the Economics Department of the University of Chicago, it publishes important empirical, theoretical and historical research. The "political" in its title is misleading, since it now deals almost solely with economics, but in this general area, it treats all aspects—economic history and theory, labor economics, money, international trade, etc.—with 10 to 15 articles per issue, mostly short to moderate length. Many well known economists, especially those associated with the University of Chicago, have contributed to it throughout its history, and its backfile is significant. Occasional supplementary numbers, usually a symposium or papers given at a conference. "Puzzles and Problems," a feature appearing occasionally, began in 1968. The number of book reviews varies greatly—from none or just a few to more than 20 per issue; they are signed and critical, but rarely more than a page long. List of recent publications in most issues. A basic journal in the field.

Indexed in: B.R.D.   8-1721
             S.S.H.I.

KYKLOS.   v. 1, 1948-

Quarterly.   Basel, Switzerland. $13.00

Subtitled an "International review for social sciences," it is published for the List Society, an organization of economists and businessmen interested in the practical applications of economic theory. Each issue contains usually 7 or 8 articles, plus a few notes, almost strictly in economics, both theoretical and applied. Contributors are from the major universities and research institutes in North America and Western Europe, with a majority of articles in English, though many are in German and a few in French. A summary of each article appears in all 3 languages. 25-30 book reviews per issue, about the same proportion in English, German or French as the articles, mostly 600-750 words in length. Also list of books received.

For advanced students and faculty, it is an important journal in the fields of international economics and economic theory.

Indexed in: P.A.I.S.   50-17368

LABOR History. *see* HISTORY

*LAND ECONOMICS.   v. 1, 1925-

Quarterly.   Madison, Wis. $15.00

Edited by Richard Ely, the eminent economist, from its founding until 1943, it was known through 1947 as the *Journal of Land and Public Utility Economics*. Its coverage has steadily broadened, so that its subtitle now declares it is "devoted to the study of economics and public institutions" and its statement of purpose indicates that it "reflects the growing emphasis on planning for the wise use of urban and rural land to meet the needs of an expanding population. Housing, air and water use, and land reform are within its scope. It views land economics in the broadest sense with particular emphasis on public action to achieve the best use of resources in the public interest." It is, then, of interest to those in political science, sociology, and urban studies, etc., as well as economists. Now generally about 10 scholarly articles in these subject areas, plus a number of briefer reports and comments. There have been no book reviews since 1963. An important journal for many years, it has become even more significant because of the growing interest in the problems of urban growth and land use in this and other countries, and the problem of land reform in underdeveloped areas.

Indexed in: Bus.Per.I.   26-19201 rev*
        P.A.I.S.

MANAGEMENT REVIEW. v. 1, 1914-

Monthly. N.Y. $15.00

Published by the American Management Association, whose aim is increased efficiency through the improvement of management practices, it contains some original articles but mostly a selection of articles digested from other business and general publications, all on various aspects of managerial responsibility. Each issue also contains brief annotations of recent books of interest to managers; a longer review of a single book appears occasionally. Intended for the busy executive, it is not a significant journal for research; rather, it provides browsing material for those interested in the business world.

Indexed in: Bus.Per.I.   15-8562

MANAGEMENT SCIENCE. v. 1, 1954-

Monthly. Baltimore, Md. $25.00

Published by the Institute of Management Sciences, "an international society to identify, extend and unify scientific knowledge pertaining to management." The rapid growth of this field in recent years is indicated by the fact that the journal started as a quarterly, became a bi-monthly in September 1964 and a monthly in 1965. Covers theory and application, with alternate issues devoted to each, each series paginated separately. Theory includes the reporting of new methodological developments, position papers, and state-of-the-art surveys; the application series is primarily concerned with methodology and practice, regular features and book reviews that average about 500 words and are signed. A technical journal that emphasizes the mathematical approach to management, it is oriented primarily to graduate schools and specialists in the field; it is an important journal in the areas of operations research, information systems analysis, and other areas in management science and while it may be of interest to some undergraduates going into these fields, for most it is too advanced.

Indexed In: Bus.Per.I.   56-21107

MANPOWER. v. 1, 1969-

Monthly. Washington, D.C. $5.50

The official monthly journal of the Manpower Administration of the Department of Labor, it replaces the journals *Employment Service Review* and *Unemployment Insurance Review*. Intended "for officials in industry, labor and government who need authoritative information on what is being done about employment and why, where, how and for whom it is being done." Contributors include government and industry employees, and consultants who are involved in such programs, with brief, illustrated articles on policies and practices, case studies, features on individuals and groups affected by the programs, and news of new approaches and methods. Much of it reads like a publicity release, but since the Manpower Administration administers so many programs of interest to undergraduates—especially those relating to minority and other disadvantaged groups—it makes interesting and often useful reading. No book reviews; brief descriptions of recent government publications on manpower and of reports completed under research contracts or grants. A depository item.

Indexed in: P.A.I.S.

MONTHLY BULLETIN OF STATISTICS. v. 1, 1947-

Monthly.   N.Y. $25.00

Published by the Statistical Office of the United Nations, it contains monthly data on 70 subjects from over 180 countries and territories, updating the tables of the UN *Statistical Yearbook*. Most of these tables provide monthly figures for the last 18 months plus annual figures for the last 7 years. Subjects covered include population and employment, production, mining, construction, manufacturing, trade, transportation, power, wages and prices, national accounts, finance. Special tables in each issue present data for other economic developments and programs. The most comprehensive source of current statistics for the various countries, it is important as a reference tool and for students working in the various areas of international economics, but since most of the important information eventually appears in the *Yearbook,* binding or even permanent storage is not necessary for most college libraries.

50-3951

*MONTHLY LABOR REVIEW. v. 1, 1915-

Monthly.   Washington, D.C. $9.00

Published by the U.S. Bureau of Labor Statistics, it contains studies, articles and research summaries on trends and developments that affect working conditions, employment, wages or hours in general, or in particular industries and geographical areas. These are mostly by Bureau staff members, but also by experts in other government agencies and academic institutions. Frequently, a group of articles on various aspects of the same subject, and occasionally an entire issue is devoted to a single major topic, in particular to labor in a single state or region. Regular sections include: "Significant Decisions in Labor Cases"; "Major Agreements Expiring Next Month"; "The Labor Month in Review"; "Foreign Labor Briefs"; "Developments in Industrial Relations"; "Book Reviews and Notes," containing signed and critical reviews, usually 5 to 10 per issue, average about 500 words, plus a classified listing of other publications received, including books, pamphlets and documents. The final portion of each issue contains "Current Labor Statistics," 32 tables covering employment, labor turnover, earnings, hours, prices, work stoppages and productivity. An annual *Statistical Supplement,* containing more detailed information than the monthly numbers and including some series not in them, appeared between 1959 and 1965. Since many of the articles are important for sociology or political science as well as for economics and industrial relations, and since the journal is so widely cited in news stories and heavily used by economists for both its data and interpretative summaries of economic conditions, it is an essential item for every college library, and the back files are important. A depository item.

Indexed in: Bus.Per.I.   15-26485
           P.A.I.S.
           R.G.

NATIONAL TAX JOURNAL.   v. 1, 1948-

Quarterly.   Columbus, Ohio. $13.00

Official journal of the National Tax Association, an organization "promoting the scientific study of taxation and public finance." Contains scholarly, frequently technical articles and notes, by faculty members, governmental officials, and others working on or concerned with domestic or foreign public finance and tax policy at all levels of government. Issues sometimes focus on a particular topic—e.g., The Carter Commission Report, A Symposium on Problems of State and Local Government Finance—with a number of articles on the topic. No reviews since about 1957. A specialized journal, but useful for advanced students in public administration and public finance.

Indexed in: B.P.I.   A51-6579
           P.A.I.S.

NATION'S BUSINESS.   v. 1, 1912-

Monthly.   Washington, D.C. $9.00

In its first issue, the editor declared that the magazine would "set forth periodically affirmative information and thought regarding our progress as a nation. Its columns will not be controversial. It . . . will not muckrake, denounce, or defame." That is still very much its policy, and as the organ of the Chamber of Commerce of the United States, its view of the American business world and economic system is somewhat adulatory.

The articles, which are written in a lively style and are well illustrated, concern all aspects of business, and those of government and society that affect or are affected by, business. Many interviews with, and profiles of top executives and public officials; articles discussing trends and new developments; advice on personnel management, on personal improvement. Each month a different economist comments on an aspect of the current economic picture.

A readable journal, useful for presenting the viewpoint of the business establishment, but its lack of depth limits any serious value for academic libraries.

Indexed in: Bus.Per.I.   15-18456
           R.G.

OXFORD ECONOMIC PAPERS.   no. 1, 1938;   n.s.v. 1, 1949-

Monthly.   Oxford, Eng. $8.20

Originally established to permit publication of articles by Oxford authors, only 8 numbers appeared between 1938 and 1947; it became a regular and broader publication in 1949, and now includes articles by contributors from many British, American and Commonwealth universities. The number of articles varies from 4 to 10 per issue; they also vary greatly in length, from just a few to 30 and more pages, and cover all areas of both theoretical and applied economics. No book reviews. An important journal, but for advanced students and research.

Indexed in: Br.Hum.I.   40-1499
             P.A.I.S.

PERSONNEL.   v. 1, 1919-

Bi-monthly.   N.Y. $12.00

Published by the American Management Association, it contains usu-
ally 8 or 9 brief articles and discussions of programs and experiences in all phases of personnel management, with an emphasis on the practical approach. Authors are mostly personnel managers or other executives in business and industry, or occasionally academicians. Usually, one book review an issue, signed and critical, and between 500 and 1000 words. Annotated listing of other books. Publication was suspended between November, 1921 and April, 1927 during which time it was incorporated with *Personnel Administration,* which later became *Management Review.* An extensive backfile is not significant for college libraries.

Indexed in: Bus.Per.I.   28-10333 rev. 2

PERSONNEL JOURNAL.   v. 1, 1922-

Monthly (bi-monthly July/Aug.)   Swarthmore, Pa. $12.00

"The magazine of industrial relations and personnel management." Contains short, practical, non-technical articles written by personnel direc-
tors and executives in business and industry, government officials, and professors of sociology, industrial relations, and management on all as-
pects of personnel work: recruiting, training, testing, labor relations, job evaluation, counseling, incentives, morale, automation, record-keeping, etc. Regular features include: "Conference Calendar; "Personnel Research" (appearing occasionally), a lengthy summary with comments on a few important articles from other journals; "Across the Editor's Desk," notes and news from the field—conferences, courses, new publications, personnel appointments and promotions, association news, etc. The book review section contains usually 2 to 4 reviews, mostly 400-600 words in length, signed but not critical. Also a listing of other new books, with brief descriptive notes.

Indexed in: Bus.Per.I.   24-19564*

QUARTERLY JOURNAL OF ECONOMICS.   v. 1, 1886-

Quarterly.   Cambridge, Mass. $10.00

Edited for the Department of Economics, Harvard University, it is the oldest professional journal of economics in the English language. Scholarly articles, notes and comment, covering all aspects of economics, with some emphasis on theory, though in recent years, the proportion of articles in applied economics has increased. Many leading economists have been contributors, especially (but by no means limited to) those associated with Harvard, and Frank W. Taussig, one of America's most dis-

tinguished economists, was its editor from 1897 to 1937, so that its back files are important in the development of economic theory. Listing of recent publications but no book reviews except those that appear as articles. A basic journal in the field.

Indexed in: P.A.I.S.   7-41369 Revised
S.S.H.I.

QUARTERLY REVIEW OF ECONOMICS AND BUSINESS.   v. 1, 1961-

Quarterly.   Urbana, Ill. $8.00

Published by the Bureau of Economic and Business Research, College of Commerce and Business Administration, University of Illinois. Each issue contains usually 6 or 7 articles, brief to moderately long, that range over all fields of theoretical and applied economics with somewhat more attention to the latter category. Usually a few "Notes and Communications" that are reactions to previously published articles or briefer research items. Authors are faculty members from colleges and universities throughout the country, government economists, and research institute's staff. The number of reviews per issue has declined; there are now usually just 2 to 4, but they are almost always at least 1000 words. List of books received.

Indexed in: P.A.I.S.   A 61-4344
Bus.Per.I.
S.S.H.I.

REVIEW OF ECONOMIC STUDIES.   v. 1, 1933-

Quarterly.   Edinburgh. $12.50

Since 1958 the official journal of the Economic Study Society, whose object "is to encourage research in theoretical and applied economics and to publish results in the Review." Usually 8 to 10 articles per issue, varying greatly in length; most are highly sophisticated, with much mathematical or statistical presentation. No book reviews. Primarily for advanced students and research.

Indexed in: Br.Hum.I.   35-31091
P.A.I.S.
S.S.H.I.

REVIEW OF ECONOMICS AND STATISTICS.   v. 1, 1919-

Quarterly.   Cambridge, Mass. $12.00

Through 1947 titled the *Review of Economic Statistics,* it is published by the Department of Economics, Harvard University, but contributed to by outstanding government, academic and business economists from all over. Articles, usually 10 to 12 per issue, are mostly of moderate length and range over the entire field of theoretical and applied economics, with an emphasis on those using statistical or mathematical methodology. Supplements, devoted to a single subject or theme, or carrying the proceedings of a meeting, used to appear occasionally, but in recent years have decreased in frequency. However, papers delivered at symposia still appear fairly often as a group of articles in regular issues. Book reviews have not been published since 1962, but occasional review articles still appear. For advanced students and research.

Indexed in: Bus.Per.I.   20-22219*
P.A.I.S.

SAM ADVANCED MANAGEMENT JOURNAL.   v. 1, 1936-

Quarterly.   N.Y. $8.00

Official journal of the Society for Advancement of Management, the oldest professional management group, founded (as the Society to Promote the Science of Management) by Frederick W. Taylor and his colleagues. It has gone through several changes in title and format, most recently (in 1969) prefacing the previous title with "SAM". It is now devoted to fairly brief articles—averaging 2500 words—by corporation executives, management consultants and professors of management, on the theory and practice of management at various levels and in different types of application. The articles are rarely technical or based on research; more often they are expressions of personal philosophy or summaries of observations over the years. A few book reviews, signed, usually about 500 words.

Indexed in: Bus.Per.I.   NUC 69-25440

*SALES MANAGEMENT'   v. 1, 1918-

Semi-monthly (with 3 extra issues)   N.Y. $15.00

Now subtitled "The Marketing Magazine, " it concentrates "on both the strategies and the tactics of marketing, including the research and evaluation of markets for products and services; the planning, packing, advertising, promotion, distributing and servicing of them; and the developing, equipping and managing of the sales team." It has long been a force in the sales and marketing aspects of the business world, being one of the first publications to insist that advertising was a vital part of the selling process, and one of the first to promote radio as an advertising medium. Contains readable and well-illustrated articles in all these areas, and several regular departments on trends, on government actions and plans, on personnel shifts, and other news of interest to those in the field. There are a number of special issues. Seven times a year a *Sales Meetings* number is issued as Part Two; it carries articles and other information on exhibits, conventions and other business meetings. Since 1953, an extra issue on *Sales Incentives and Business Gifts* has appeared as the September 10th issue. The extra November 10th issue, *Marketing on the Move,* surveys the facts and factors that will affect marketing in the years ahead. The June 10th extra issue, *Survey of Buying Power,* providing comprehensive data on population, income, and expenditures, by various geographical areas, is an exceptionally important tool in market analysis. Though essentially a trade journal, *Sales Management* has many serious studies, and is essential in any library where there are courses in marketing or advertising.

Indexed in: Bus.Per.I.   20-15771

*SOCIAL SECURITY BULLETIN.   v. 1, 1938-

Monthly.   Washington, D.C. $2.75

Official publication of the Social Security Administration, though statements in articles "do not necessarily reflect official policies." Issues consist of 1) the section "Social Security in Review," news of program operations, special reports and developments; 2) two or three fairly short articles, mostly by SSA officials, on the concepts of social security, the administration, progress and impact of the federal program, the situation on the state and local level, and occasionally programs in other countries, usually with much statistical data (there are a number of regularly scheduled articles on employee-benefit plans, federal grants to state and local governments, income loss protection against short term sickness, private health insurance, and others); 3) "Notes and Brief Reports"—same basic subject matter as the articles, but even shorter; 4) "Recent Publications" (in most issues), a classified listing of books, articles, and documents, from many sources, most with brief annotations; 5) "Current Operating Statistics"—31 tables on federal benefits and beneficiaries, recipients and payments under state programs, gross national product and personal income, population and labor force, and consumer price indexes, mostly with some retrospective data; in the "Quarterly Statistics," there are 18 additional tables on the Old Age, Survivors and Disability Insurance system. The *Annual Statistical Supplement* was included in the September issue from 1950-55, but since then has been published as an unnumbered separate number, but issued very late. A depository item.

Indexed in: Bus.Per.I.   40-29327 rev. 4*
           P.A.I.S.

SOUTHERN ECONOMIC JOURNAL.   v. 1, 1933-

Quarterly.   Chapel Hill, N.C. $10.00

Published jointly by the Southern Economic Association and the University of North Carolina. Starting as primarily a regional journal, it has become a national one—in both coverage and authorship—treating all aspects of economics, with some emphasis on applied studies. Each issue contains from 6 to 10 articles, a few communications mostly responding to previous articles, and 5 to 10 signed, critical book reviews, usually 700-800 words in length; also notes of activities and personnel of the Association, and a list of books received.

Indexed in: P.A.I.S.   36-5384 Revised
           S.S.H.I.

STANFORD UNIVERSITY.   FOOD RESEARCH INSTITUTE STUDIES IN AGRICULTURAL ECONOMICS, TRADE AND DEVELOPMENT.
v. 1, 1960-

3 nos./yr.   Stanford, Calif. $10.00

Published by the Food Research Institute at Stanford University, and concerned with reporting the results of research in the production, distribution and consumption of food throughout the world. Generally 3 or 4 articles per issue, but sometimes just one, mostly by Institute staff, but also by professors and government officials elsewhere. Supplements, either the proceedings of a symposium on a problem or area, or a monographic study, are issued frequently. In its early volumes, most attention was given to the economics of food production and distribution, but later volumes have been increasingly concerned with broader problems of the developing nations, e.g., "On Measuring Technical Efficiency" —so, though fairly specialized, the journal has a real usefulness for the study of development economics, an area of increasing interest to students. Recently, numbers have been about a year behind schedule.

Indexed in: P.A.I.S.   63-43235

*SURVEY OF CURRENT BUSINESS.   v. 1, 1921-

Monthly.   Washington, D.C. $9.00

Published by the Office of Business Economics, U.S. Department of Commerce, it gives a monthly review of the level and trend of business. Issues contain just an article or two by OBE staff members, on the outlook for or a retrospective view of specific aspects of the economy, with much statistical and graphic data. The remainder is devoted to regular features, starting with "The Business Situation," a summary in text and charts of recent activity and developments with an examination of some specific aspect in detail. "National Income and Product Tables" provide data for the last two years through the present quarter. The January issue reviews the economic developments of the past year.

The major portion of each issue is devoted to "Monthly Business Statistics"—detailed indexes of over 2500 economic criteria, specific industries and products. These update the biennial supplement, *Business Statistics, 19--,* which is available separately. It gives monthly figures for the last 4 years and yearly figures, 1929 to date, for the same series covered in the monthly numbers. It also includes explanatory notes on sources and methods of the data. Included in the subscription price is a brief weekly supplement, providing "selected weekly and monthly data subsequent to those published in the latest monthly *Survey.*" Providing essential material for economic research and for reference, all these should be in every college library. A depository item.

Indexed in: Bus.Per.I.   21-26819*
              P.A.I.S.

WESTERN ECONOMIC JOURNAL.   v. 1, 1962-

Quarterly.   Long Beach, Calif. $10.00

Published by the Western Economic Association, though with only a few exceptions, the articles are not regional nor, as a matter of fact, are most of the contributors from the West. It does, however, carry abstracts of the W.E.A.'s annual conference. The articles are mostly brief to moderate length and on all areas of economics—theory, history, applied economics, etc. No book reviews.

                                                              68-5518

YALE ECONOMIC ESSAYS.   v. 1, 1961-

Semi-annual.   New Haven, Conn.

Serves both as an outlet for all doctoral dissertations in economics at Yale University, which appear either in full or in extended summary, and as a medium for comment by faculty and students of the Economics Department. The 5 or 6 articles per issue range over the field of economics, both theoretical and applied, and all, naturally, are quite long, averaging about 50-60 pages.

Indexed in: P.A.I.S.   64-55233

NOTE: Discontinued with Vol. 11, 1971

*AV COMMUNICATION REVIEW.   v. 1, 1953-

Quarterly.   Washington, D.C. $13.00

Published by the Department of Audiovisual Instruction of the National Education Association. Devoted to articles on educational media, learning systems, educational TV, computerized instruction—all aspects of the teaching-learning process related to technology and communication. The articles, usually 5 or 6 per issue, of moderate length, are of high quality; most report the results of research, but some are reflective or theoretical. The department, "Teaching Machines and Programmed Instruction," which carried shorter research articles and longer memoranda, was dropped after 1968. "Research Abstracts," now reported from ERIC, give in some detail significant findings as reported in theses, government or university sponsored projects, and other publications. The book reviews, generally about 10 per issue, are signed, thoughtful, and average 750-1000 words. From 1960 through 1963 two supplements a year were issued; some of these were quite significant. An important journal for students and scholars of audio-visual methods and educational communication; it is also a model of good typography and layout.

Indexed in: Ed.I.   56-4703

ADULT EDUCATION.   v. 1, 1950-

Quarterly.   Washington, D.C. $10.00

An official publication of the Adult Education Association, it "is devoted to research and theory in the field of adult education. The emphasis . . . is on research, the philosophy and history of adult education, development of theory, and interpretive reviews of the literature." Through 1967, the articles were less scholarly and more varied, and it carried news of the profession and reports on developments, plus several bibliographical features, including summaries of studies and research projects in the field; some of these have been transferred to *Adult Leadership.* Now, the 3 to 6 articles per issue, though still varying in length, are all quite scholarly, and each is preceded by an abstract. The book reviews, averaging about 10 per issue, are all signed and critical, and vary in length, with most about 500 words. Also list of books received.

The Association also publishes *Adult Leadership* (v. 1, 1952- $10.00), which carries news of personnel and programs, news and reports of the A.E.A., plus a number of short articles that are "primarily concerned with the implementation of the arts and techniques of practice" in adult education. An annual directory of summer training institutes and workshops appears in the last number of each volume. Several signed, critical book reviews in each issue, mostly 300-500 words in length.

Indexed in: Ed.I.   55-20548

*AMERICAN ASSOCIATION OF UNIVERSITY PROFESSORS.   BULLETIN. **v. 1, 1915-**

Quarterly.   Washington, D.C. $4.50

Official journal of the A.A.U.P., it is distributed to all members. Originally, it was to be devoted to general problems of higher education and to serve as a medium of interchange of information on the policies and activities of various institutions. However, it mostly reported Association business and activities, served to display placement notices, to report much incidental information of interest or service to members, and only occasionally did it present or discuss policies or problems of higher education. In 1955 it was recommended that the *Bulletin* "carry a larger percentage of articles on professional welfare, with special attention to those dealing with controversies on higher educational trends," but in 1965 a rough analysis of 8 issues showed only 7 per cent of the pagination dealing with problems of higher education generally, 16 per cent to articles of immediate concern to faculties, and 77 per cent to reports of Association business. There is more attention now to teaching, students and education generally, but the *Bulletin* is still perhaps most important for its factual information and reports. There are the reports of the various standing and *ad hoc* committees of the AAUP, the reports of investigations of censured administrations, and the very important "Annual Report on the Economic Status of the Profession," with appropriate statistical data and ratings of individual institutions. The statements and articles on academic freedom are also of prime significance. Usually 4 or 5 book reviews, signed and critical, mostly over 1000 words, plus a few shorter notices.

Though rarely used by students, the *Bulletin* is heavily used by faculty and administration, and the library should have a permanent bound file even though many faculty members will have personal files.

Indexed in: Ed.I.   16-21188 rev.*
             P.A.I.S.

AMERICAN BIOLOGY TEACHER. *see* BIOLOGY

*AMERICAN EDUCATION.   v. 1, 1964/65-

10 nos./yr.   Washington, D.C. $4.50

A publication of the Office of Education, it was begun after the demise of *School Life* and *Higher Education*, with the purpose of covering all of education and not, as those were, just for professional educators. So far it has succeeded admirably. The articles are not only by members of the Office of Education, but also by other government officials, professional educators, scientists, writers, and others interested in education; also, they are well written and profusely illustrated. Any subject related to education may be covered: desegregation in one city, the new look in college architecture, a profile of an experimental school, the Head Start program, developments in agricultural education, drugs and students, education in China, etc. There are several regular features: "Federal Funds" describes and tabulates the purposes, amounts, and beneficiaries of various federal aid-to-education programs; "Recent Publications" lists government publications of various agencies of interest to educators; "Statistic of the Month" graphically discusses one educational trend or development; "Research Report" describes the results of a recent research project of special significance funded by the Office of Education. Because of its wide coverage and excellent presentation, *American Education* should be in every library. A depository item.

Indexed in: Ed.I.   65-9862
             R.G.

AMERICAN EDUCATIONAL RESEARCH JOURNAL. v. 1, 1964

Quarterly. Washington, D.C. $8.00

Published by the American Educational Research Association, a department of NEA, it "publishes original reports of experimental and theoretical studies in education." Each issue contains 6 to 10 articles of short to moderate length (with an occasional long contribution) on all areas and levels of education, treating from the most limited subjects ("An Analysis of Errors in the Formation of Manuscript Letters by First-Grade Children") to those of general interest ("Social Class, Race and Genetics: Implications for Education"), with the overwhelming number "practical" or "applied" research articles, with learning and instruction the main focus. Beginning in late 1966, a summary of each article is contained in the table of contents. Early issues had just one or two book reviews per issue, usually from 1000 to 2000 words in length; now there are a larger number (usually 8 to 10), all signed and critical, varying widely in length, from 600 to 3000 words. An important journal, especially where there is an interest in educational research.

Indexed in: Ed.I.   64-9394
            Ment.Hlth.B.R.I.

AMERICAN SCHOOL BOARD JOURNAL. v. 1, 1891-

Monthly. Evanston, Ill. $8.00

Beginning in October, 1967, its publication was taken over from a private publisher (by whom it had been published since its inception) by the National School Boards Association, a federation of the state school boards associations. Contains discussions of ideas and issues and information on specific problems such as administration, maintenance, purchasing, transportation, personnel, etc., of concern to school boards and their professional staffs. While the journal has many fewer pages since the change in publisher, it is due mostly to reduced advertising and miscellaneous features, and there is much less attention paid to maintenance and purchasing aspects of administration. Brief, uncritical notices of new books, and some news of new products. A useful journal for courses in school administration.

Another journal useful for the study of educational administration is *American School and University* (v. 1, 1928- $8.00), also published monthly. It focuses even more on the practical aspects of school administration, and with its *Plant and Purchasing Guide* issue each May, is especially useful for college business and maintenance offices.

Indexed in: Ed.I.   E23-11
            P.A.I.S.

ARITHMETIC TEACHER. v. 1, 1954-

Monthly (Oct.-May) Washington, D.C. $10.00

An official journal of the National Council of Teachers of Mathematics, it serves as "a forum for the exchange of ideas, where responsible contributors may evaluate developments, share classroom techniques, or otherwise deal with any part of the broad spectrum of mathematics education in the elementary school." Each issue contains usually about 10 brief (often just a page or two) articles on the above areas and also on aspects of the education of mathematics teachers, from the elementary through the junior high school level. Three regular departments include: "Focus on Research" has reports summarizing the results of research projects in teaching, learning or methodology;"Forum on Teacher Preparation"; "In the Classroom," brief reports from teachers on their classroom demonstrations and lessons. Lists of officers; news and reports of the NCTM; calendar of other professional meetings. Usually two or three book reviews per issue, signed and critical, mostly around 300 words, but occasionally much longer; list of other books received. A good practical journal for prospective teachers.

Indexed in: Ed.I.   56-37587

ART EDUCATION.   v. 1, 1948-

Monthly (except July-Sept.)   Washington, D.C. $7.50

Journal of the National Art Education Association, a department of NEA. Contains articles, usually brief, on the teaching of art and its appreciation— both in theory and practice—on specific artists and techniques, and on other topics of interest to artists and art teachers. News of the NEA and its meetings. Each issue contains some reviews—of books in all areas of the arts as well as art education. They are signed, and vary in length from 100 to 1000 words. An attractive, interesting journal, important where there are courses in art education, but for the practicing artist or art scholar, other journals are more useful.

Indexed in: Ed.I.   57-45232

ARTS and Activities. see ART

*AUDIOVISUAL INSTRUCTION.   v. 1, 1956-

Monthly (except Aug.)   Washington, D.C. $12.00

Published by the Department of Audiovisual Instruction of the National Education Association "to help improve instruction through the more effective use of materials." Deals with the entire range of audiovisual materials and methods with an emphasis on products and equipment. The articles are of varying length, usually well illustrated, and are mostly descriptive of projects, programs, and systems. Each issue has a theme: Audiovisual Instruction and the Language Arts, Adult Basic Education, Media to Teach International Development, Professional Education, etc., with the June/July issue devoted to reports, news and summaries of sessions at the annual convention, and the March issue to plans for it. Regular features include: "News Notes" about the DAVI and of personnel and of developments in the field; a "Professional Placement" section; "AV Technical Notes" describes some process or equipment that can be built or set up; "Notes from ERIC" gives news about it and reports on specific items; "AV Innovation" tells about new methods or ways to use materials; "Index of Audiovisual Reviews" cites reviews of films, filmstrips, tapes and miscellaneous materials that have appeared in other journals (discontinued in 1969). The book reviews are mostly a few hundred words but occasionally much longer for important works; all are signed and criticize the books from the point of view of their usefulness to the A-V specialist. Beginning with 1967, an annual "AVI Guide to New Products" has appeared as a supplement to a fall issue. It is an extensive description of products recently released or to be released during the following school year.

Valuable for its advertising as well as its contents, this is an essential journal for courses in audiovisual education and for those working with A-V facilities, but because the field is changing so rapidly, a lengthy back file is not necessary for most libraries.

Indexed in: Ed.I.   59-30807 rev.

BULLETIN of the Center for Children's Books. *see* BOOK REVIEWS AND BOOK SELECTION

BUSINESS EDUCATION FORUM.   v. 1, 1947-

Monthly (except June-Sept.)   Washington, D.C. $15.00

Official publication of the National Business Educational Association. In 1970, with volume 25, it expanded greatly, combining the contents of the *National Business Education Quarterly* (which had existed since 1932) and the *Proceedings* of the NABTE, the Association's Teacher Education division, making it more useful for academic libraries. Contains 5 sections: "The Open Forum," with brief articles of general interest to business educators; "Focus," on a specific subject—e.g., The Secretarial Program, Marketing and Distribution, Typewriting, etc.—each month; "Of Special Interest," containing material—association rosters, summaries of studies, directories of members, proceedings of meetings, etc.—that relate to the Association or its division; "Selected Occupational Topics" containing articles on teaching techniques and developments; "NBEA in Action," carries news of personnel and association activities. The annual listing of *Research Studies in Business Education Completed or Under Way,* formerly in the Spring issue of the *Quarterly,* now appears in the March issue. Articles are brief and, for the most part, very practical, though with the incorporation of the *Quarterly,* more on theory is included. No book reviews.

An essential journal where there are courses in business education, it should also be useful where there are courses in business administration.

Indexed in: Ed.I.   31-2184 (rev. '40)

*CHANGE MAGAZINE.   v. 1, 1969-

Monthly (except bi-monthly, July/Aug. and Dec./Jan.)   N.Y. $8.50

Originally titled *Change in Higher Education,* it began under the auspices of the Union for Research and Experimentation in Higher Education, with funds from the Esso Foundation. Devoted to change in higher education, its causes and effects, methods and devices, in relation to student life, administration, faculty, curriculum, government policy, even physical facilities. Its contributors include some of the most highly respected names in higher education—in its first year, for example, Kenneth Keniston, Benjamin DeMott, Robert Paul Wolff, Paul Dressel, Edgar Friedenberg, Fred Hechinger and others. The articles are exceptionally well written, and provide valuable insights into the current and suggested changes in colleges and universities. Typical subjects are experimental colleges and curricula, radical students' demands, critiques of accepted philosophies of higher education, the revolt in the disciplines, dangers to academic freedom. The book reviews are done by one person; he has a lengthy column in which he covers one or a few titles in a very throghtful review-essay.

Perhaps the best journal to keep up with ideas behind the changing scene of higher education, it should be in every academic library, and faculty members should be encouraged to read it.

75-8434

*CHANGING EDUCATION.   v. 1, 1966-

Quarterly.   Chicago, Ill. $5.00 (with *American Teacher*)

Published by the American Federation of Teachers, AFL-CIO, its contributors are almost all presently teachers, or are AFT staff members who formerly taught. The articles, which vary greatly in length and number per issue, are not mostly, as one might expect, on teachers' rights, organizations and associated matters—although these do receive much attention—but on educational reform in the classroom, in the curriculum, in evaluation, in education of minority groups, in admissions and in student-teacher-administrative relationships. These are all presented with a strong bias, but since it is a bias that is having an increasing impact on educators, and is of special interest to undergraduates, it will be read and used in college libraries. "The World of Changing Education," in each issue, contains miscellaneous news items. At least one book review in each issue, many of them quite long. An important journal for a particular viewpoint.

The subscription price includes the monthly *American Teacher* (v. 1, 1912-) (actually *Changing Education* is published as a supplement to it) which appears in tabloid format, and is devoted mostly to news of the AFT's campaigns, to news of its programs and officers, and to items about specific school systems. There are, however, frequent feature articles on aspects of educational reform such as the use of paraprofessionals, schools of the 70's, in-service training of teachers, etc. A regular section on colleges and universities helps keep up with organizing campaigns at this level.

Together, these publications provide for the education major a view of the teaching profession that he might not readily get in classes or in other standard publications; yet it is an important view, and one which libraries should permit students to see for themselves.

Indexed in: E d.I

NOTE: In 1971, *Changing Education* began to appear only as a bimonthly insert in *American Teacher*.

*CHILDHOOD EDUCATION.   v. 1, 1924-

Monthly (except June-Aug.)   Washington, D.C. $12.00

Published by the Association for Childhood Education International, it
is concerned with children 2 to 12 years old—nursery school, kindergarten
and elementary school—with emphasis on problems of child development
and personality as well as classroom methods and procedures. With very
few exceptions, each issue is devoted to a single theme—e.g., Valuing the
Dignity of Black Children, Intelligence and Creativeness, Helping Children Identify—which is then discussed from a variety of vantages in short,
succinct, and sensible articles, in accord with the journal's purpose: "to
stimulate thinking rather than advocate fixed practices." Regular features
include: "Books for Children" and "Books for Adults," each of which
contains about ten short (100-250 words), signed, but not critical reviews;
an annotated listing of useful "Bulletins and Pamphlets"; "Among the
Magazines" (not in every issue) contains summaries of articles in other
periodicals; "Research," a report in some detail of a recent research project; news and notes of the state, and local branches in "ACEI Branch
Exchange." An essential journal where elementary school teachers are
trained, it is also useful for courses in child psychology and sociology.

Indexed in: Ed.I.   26-4861 rev.

*CHRONICLE OF HIGHER EDUCATION.   v. 1, 1966-

38 iss./yr. (bi-weekly Oct.-May; tri-weekly, June-Sept.)   Washington, D.C.
$20.00

Published in tabloid newspaper format, it covers all news of higher education: federal and state activities, new programs and developments, newsworthy student activities (excellent coverage of this) foundation news,
etc. Interviews with leading figures in the field, articles based on major
speeches by educators or public officials, and on reports of private and
governmental commissions, often with lengthy excerpts from these, appear
frequently. Regular features include a column containing notices of new
books and pamphlets on higher education, a section listing promotions
and new appointments, mostly of administrators, and a calendar of coming events. It is perhaps the best single source for current news and developments in higher education. Many institutions are probably already
receiving it somewhere on campus—most likely in the President's office.
It should, however, be more generally available to faculty and administration, and whether this is the library's responsibility will depend on institutional practices. In any case, binding is probably not necessary.

CLEARING HOUSE.   v. 1, 1920-

Monthly (except June-Aug.)   Sweet Springs, Mo. $5.00

"A journal for modern junior and senior high schools," it contains articles that report "interesting practices, experiments, research findings, or
new slants on persistent problems" relating to the programs, services and
personnel, with some emphasis on teachers and teaching methods. Articles
are brief (the maximum suggested is 2500 words), written by practicing
teachers and administrators, and by professors of teacher education, and
make useful introductory reading material for prospective teachers. Regular features: "The Humanities Today" (now appearing only occasionally),
provides space for opinion, usually on the study or teaching of the humanities, but often on a general topic in education; "Instructional Media"
mostly lists and evaluates new films, filmstrips and tapes, but also con-

tains brief articles on general A-V matters. The signed book reviews are
few in number (usually 1 to 3 an issue) and seldom more than 500 words
long. Also a brief listing of other books received.

Indexed in: Ed.I.   E 35-166 rev.
         R.G.

*COLLEGE STUDENT PERSONNEL ABSTRACTS.   v. 1, 1965-

Quarterly.   Claremont, Calif. $14.00

Published by the College Student Personnel Institute, "a private, nonprofit center for information exchange, research, and training in areas related
to college students and student services," it provides abstracts from a
wide variety of journals, from conference papers and proceedings, and
from research reports. Materials include almost every aspect of undergraduate education and administration (except teaching of specific subjects)—admissions, counseling, financial aid, foreign study, housing, placement, testing, student activities, attitudes and values, student rights and
behavior, etc. The Abstracts, mostly 100-200 words, but often more, are
not critical, and, with few exceptions, are done by the staff of the Institute. About 1000 items a year are now abstracted. Because it covers subjects of growing importance and interest to faculty and administrators (as
well as to students), and provides a starting point for investigation into
these subjects, it should be in the college library (and probably in the
reference collection), rather than in administrative offices.

COLLEGE AND UNIVERSITY.   v. 1, 1925-

Quarterly. · Menasha, Wis. $8.00

The journal of the American Association of Collegiate Registrars and Admissions Officers and titled first the *Bulletin* (through July, 1937) and
then the *Journal* (through July, 1947) of the AACRAO. Most of the articles are on admissions policies and procedures, including testing, scholarships and evaluation, on registration procedures and educational prediction, but there are also a large number on the general aspects and problems of higher education. Also carries news of the Association and proceedings of the annual meetings. Issues other than those carrying the proceedings contain "In the Journals," fairly long summaries of relevant
articles from academic and popular periodicals, and a section "Book Reviews." These signed reviews, usually about 8 an issue, are of books ranging
over all of higher education—theory, history, comparative education, reminiscences—as well as the entrance guides and manuals that one would
expect to find here; in addition, many of the reviews are fairly long—often
over 1000 words—and are among the better ones in journals of higher
education.

Indexed in: Ed.I.   39-12444 rev. 2

COLLEGE AND UNIVERSITY BUSINESS.   v. 1, 1946-

Monthly.   Chicago, Ill. $15 (see below)

Intended primarily for administrators responsible for the material needs
of higher education—business managers, buildings and grounds personnel,
architects, librarians, planning and development officers, audio-visual supervisors, etc.—it contains articles on all these aspects, many of them case
studies or comparative surveys with specific information compiled in tabular form. In recent years, the content has widened to include articles on
the purposes and problems of higher education—curricula, inter-institutional
cooperation, student life, teaching methods, administrative organization,
etc.—articles, in other words, also of interest to academic deans and teaching faculty. More or less regular sections on college law, governing boards,
plant operation, educational media, feeding and housing, carry brief
articles on these topics; "News from Washington" reports on new and
pending legislation and other developments affecting higher education;
"Product News" describes and illustrates new furniture, teaching equipment, business machines, etc.

Since many of the articles, features and advertisements relate to the
library, the librarian should see it regularly; because it is of interest to so
many individuals on the campus, it should be generally available. Subscriptions may be obtained without charge by qualified administrators
upon application. Similar in nature and also useful (especially since it
treats colleges rather than universities), is *College Management* (v. 1,
1966- $6.00).

Indexed in: Ed.I.   49-3413*
          P.A.I.S.

COLLEGE BOARD REVIEW.   no. 1, 1947-

Quarterly.   Princeton, N.J. $2.00

Published by the College Entrance Examination Board, it "offers a forum
for the exchange of information and opinion on all matters related to
students' school-to-college transition." Covers news of the CEEB, plus well-
written articles, generally 5 or 6 per issue, but varying greatly in length,
by staff members of the Board (though not necessarily expressing its policy), and faculty and administration of various colleges and universities.
These are on many topics of current interest to those in higher education—
guidance, curriculum, financial aid, minority group students, etc.—as well
as on subjects more specifically associated with the Board's interest, such
as admissions, advanced placement, and other subjects related to standardized testing. No book reviews. Of interest to faculty and various
administrators, it should be generally available to the campus.

COMPARATIVE EDUCATION REVIEW.   v. 1, 1957-

3 nos./yr.   N.Y. $10.00

Official organ of the Comparative Education Society. Carries scholarly
articles in all areas of comparative education—aspects of the educational
history of a country, comparisons of national systems, studies of specific
programs in individual countries, essays on the study of comparative education itself, etc.—with much attention to education in the developing

nations. About 7 articles or communications per issue, by scholars from
here and abroad, averaging about 5000 words, but varying greatly in
length. Most issues carry news of the Society, and a "Current Bibliography of Periodical Articles," grouped by geographical area. The June
issue has the annual listing of doctoral dissertations in progress and completed. Usually 7 or 8 book reviews, signed and critical, averaging about
700 words. Though a number of the books are foreign, all reviews are
in English. List of books received. Mostly for advanced students and faculty in education departments, but useful for comparative politics and
sociology as well, since so much attention is given to the role and changing
nature of education in developing nations.

Indexed in: Ed.I.   61-19503
           Ment.Hlth.B.R.I.
           P.A.I.S.

CURRENT Index to Journals in Education. *see* INDEXES

EDUCATION.   v. 1, 1880-

Quarterly.   Milwaukee, Wis. $7.50

The oldest educational journal published continuously, it began in Boston
as *Education and International Magazine*, changing to its present title in
1885. In 1902, it was taken over by the Palmer Company in Boston and
published as a monthly. A leading journal in the field in its early days,
its nature changed very little so that as education itself changed, the journal gradually declined in reputation. It was taken over by the Bobbs-
Merrill Company in 1959, but its existence was very much in doubt until
its present editors, located at the University of Wisconsin–Milwaukee,
took it over in 1967 and made it a quarterly.

Its stated purpose is to publish "original investigations and theoretical
papers dealing with worthwhile innovations in learning, teaching and education. Preference is given to innovations in the school, proposed or actual,
and theoretical or evaluative. Papers concern all levels and every area of
education. The journal is designed for use in teacher education programs,
and for the in-service education of teachers and educators." About 20
short articles per issue, almost never more than 5000 words in length,
and usually 1000 to 2000, by faculty members from all levels of
education, but mostly college and university. Each issue features a "Gold
Medal Educator of the 1960's"–an outstanding personality in the field
(e.g., B.F. Skinner, John A. Hannah) including a profile and usually an
article by him. The book reviews, which are scattered through issues,
are brief, signed, and not critical. Many of the articles are fairly trivial,
and the journal is not yet of prime importance.

Indexed in: Ed.I.   6-10193 rev.

*EDUCATION DIGEST.   v. 1, 1935-

Monthly (except June-Aug.)   Ann Arbor, Mich. $7.00

Each issue contains articles on all levels and in all areas of education, digested from educational, other professional and lay journals, and from speeches, pamphlets and documents. About 15 selections an issue, mostly 1000-1500 words. Also contains a few useful features: "With Education in Washington" reports news and comments about federal legislation and activities; "Educational Briefs" does the same for educational news generally; in "New Educational Materials" a few books are briefly noted, and there is a listing of other recent books and pamphlets. Especially useful for libraries with a limited number of education journals—the articles are well chosen and provide a useful survey of current educational discussion and developments.

Indexed in: Ed.I.   39-13631
          R.G.

EDUCATION Index. *see* INDEXES

EDUCATIONAL and Psychological Measurement. *see* PSYCHOLOGY

EDUCATIONAL FORUM.   v. 1, 1936-

Quarterly.   West Lafayette, Ind. $7.00

Published by Kappa Delta Pi, an honorary society in education, it was preceded by the *Kappa Delta Pi Record* and the *Kadelpian Review*. Sent to all members of the society, it publishes brief articles and essays on all aspects and levels of education, contributed by teachers, administrators and professors of education, including a few distinguished names. The articles almost never present the results of research, but are rather statements of attitude, philosophy or approach to education, or historical or autobiographical essays, or comments on recent issues or developments. In addition to these 7-10 contributions, there are some poems and miscellaneous comments. News of the society. Usually 15-20 signed and critical book reviews, mostly 300-500 words. List of books received.

An interesting journal for relaxed reading, with occasional significant articles, but not of first importance for teacher education.

Indexed in: Ed.I.   37-35898

*EDUCATIONAL LEADERSHIP.   v. 1, 1943-

Monthly (except June-Sept.)   Washington, D.C. $6.50

Published by the Association for Supervision and Curriculum Development, NEA. Most articles in each issue are devoted to a general theme on some aspect of education—e.g., Guidance: Education or Therapy? Updating the Humanities, Student Participation: Toward Maturity? Racial

Integration: Roads to Understanding—treating them from a variety of viewpoints, practical and theoretical. Almost all articles are brief, clearly presented and to the point. "Innovations in Education," in most issues, reports on an experimental program or project, either an organized one or one carried out by an individual teacher in her classroom. The regular feature, "Research in Review," describes recent research projects on one topic, or reports on needed research or on research methods. Beginning in 1967, each issue contains a "Research Supplement," a separate section containing mostly fairly brief articles, but ones that report data that are concerned "with the behavior of teachers (or their surrogates) and that of students as dependent variables," and that make the meaning of the research clear to readers. Some 10 to 15 books are reviewed in each issue, with several titles on the same topic frequently reviewed together. The reviews are signed and critical, usually about 500 words in length. Because of the ASCD's importance in the profession, this is a basic journal in the field.

Indexed in: Ed.I.   46-41369

*EDUCATIONAL RECORD.   v. 1, 1920-

Quarterly.   Washington, D.C. $10.00

Official organ of the American Council on Education, a most prestigious group comprised of national and regional associations, state education departments, school systems, and colleges and universities. While the Council is concerned with education on all levels, its primary interest is in higher education, and the *Record* is concerned solely with this level. Articles, by faculty members, administrators, foundation and government officials, are on all aspects of higher education, and particularly on the larger, more basic questions and problems. Often they are the texts of significant speeches or reports. Occasionally, an entire issue or part of one, will be devoted to a single topic; mostly, though, each issue consists of a dozen or so articles on a variety of topics. There were no book reviews until 1967 (although single articles in 1965 and 1966 surveyed "The Literature of Higher Education" for the past year); there are now about 3 an issue, signed and critical, mostly 500-700 words in length. Because so many of the contributors are important names in the field of higher education, and because their articles are mostly thoughtful and timely, the journal should be in every college library. College librarians should at least look through the journal; it sometimes carries articles relating to libraries, but even more important, perhaps, is its usefulness in keeping *au courant* with the concerns of higher education.

Indexed in: Ed.I.   E 21-40 rev.

EDUCATIONAL SCREEN AND AUDIOVISUAL GUIDE.   v. 1, 1922-

Monthly.   Chicago, Ill. $6.00

Originally *Educational Screen,* it assumed its present title in 1956 when it merged with *Audio-Visual Guide.* (Earlier journals it had taken over were *Moving Picture Age, Visual Education,* and *Visual Instruction News.*) Contains about 7 articles per issue—generally of a "practical" nature, on the problems, practices and developments in the uses of a-v materials in education. Regular reviewers cover "A-V in Religion," "Audio," "Film Evaluation," and "Filmstrips." All contain some discussion in addition to reviews of specific items. Other regular features include: a "Calendar" of meetings, conferences, and exhibits; "New Equipment," with brief descriptions and prices; "New Materials," a listing, with brief descriptions, of new films, recordings, tapes, etc.; "New Publications"—pamphlets, catalogs and books, but no reviews; "ERIC" presents a few abstracts from documents recently published. The August issue carries the *Annual Blue Book of Audiovisual Materials*, a classified listing of items produced during the year. Beginning in 1968, the November issue consists mostly of the *Annual Red Book of Audiovisual Equipment* doing for equipment what the *Blue Book* does for materials.

Indexed in: Ed. I. 54-32672

EDUCATIONAL TECHNOLOGY. v. 1, 1961-

Monthly. Englewood Cliffs, N.J. $18.00

Not just an a-v journal or one concerned with educational hardware, its object has been defined as "the development of a set of systematic techniques, and accompanying practical knowledge, for designing, testing and evaluating schools as educational systems." Thus, it draws upon many disciplines—architecture, the physical sciences, sociometrics, administration, psychology, etc.—all of which, in one way or another, contribute to systems for improved learning. A major portion of each issue is devoted to a single topic—e.g., The Computer and Education, Precision Teaching, Media and the Handicapped—with a number of short, succinct articles on it. Authors are mostly from the fields of education, psychology, and media development, associated with colleges and universities, research institutes, corporations and the government. Departments of news notes from the field and on new products, "ERIC Reports" from the ERIC Clearinghouse on Educational Media and Technology. Two supplements are issued with the journal (bound in, but paginated separately): *Training Technology* (beginning in 1969) devoted to short, practical pieces on techniques, equipment and materials in vocational education and in training for business, government, the military, etc.; *Teacher & Technology* (beginning in 1970) devoted to the same type of articles in academic education. No book reviews. While its publisher's claims for it are somewhat extravagant, it is a useful journal, certainly where a-v has a major role on campus, but also for teachers who are interested in new approaches to teaching and learning.

Indexed in: Ed.I. 68-1804

EDUCATIONAL THEORY. v. 1, 1951-

Quarterly. Urbana, Ill. $8.00

"A medium of expression for the John Dewey Society and the Philosophy of Education Society," its general purposes "are to foster the continuing development of educational theory and to encourage wide and effective discussion of theoretical problems within the educational profession." Usually 7 or 8 scholarly articles per issue, averaging 3500-4000 words, by professors of education or philosophy at various American and Canadian universities, on "the foundations of education, and in related disciplines outside the field of education, which contribute to the advancement of educational theory." No book reviews as such anymore, but usually a couple of review articles, at least 1500 words in length, on important books. Useful for philosophy students as well as those in education.

Indexed in: Ed.I.   67-119290
          Ment.Hlth.B.R.I.

ELEMENTARY ENGLISH.   v. 1, 1924-

Monthly (except June-Sept.)   Urbana, Ill. $10.00

An official publication of the National Council of Teachers of English, it contains short articles (about 12-15 per issue) on all phases of the language arts at the elementary level—curriculum, handwriting, dramatics, poetry, reading, spelling—and of course, on research methods and materials for teaching them. Children's literature, publications, authors, trends, contests, etc., receive much attention. Authors are elementary school teachers and administrators, and professors of education; the articles are fairly well divided between the "how-we-do-it" type and reports of research or on theoretical speculations. "The Educational Scene" contains suggestions from readers, buying information, and other miscellaneous notes and news. Official notices and news of the NCTE. Frequent bibliographies on professional topics or subjects useful for classroom use. The review section, "Books for Children," contains usually an essay on reading, the library or children's literature, and then 15 to 20 signed reviews of recent books, from 50 to 250 words. Professional books are usually reviewed in brief articles. Most issues carry an NCTE/ERIC report, citing recent articles and research reports held by ERIC in a specific area of interest—such as Linguistics Instruction, English Teaching, Listening and Learning Skills—all, of course, in the elementary school. An essential journal for the practicing teacher, it is also important wherever elementary education or children's literature is taught.

Indexed in: Ed.I.   26-17799*

*ELEMENTARY SCHOOL JOURNAL.   v. 1, 1900-

Monthly (except June-Sept.)   Chicago, Ill. $8.00

Begun as *Course of Study,* published by the Chicago Institute, it became the *Elementary School Teacher* in 1901, and assumed its present title in 1914. Now published for the Department of Education of the University of Chicago, it reports investigations pertaining to classroom procedures, the evaluation of teaching, supervision, school administration, the role of the school, child development, preparation of teachers, descriptions of school practices, and essays and articles on educational theory, with some emphasis on the language arts and reading. Generally about 8 articles per issue, almost without exception under 2000 words in length, written by professors of education and practicing teachers and administrators. From 1933 to 1965 a list of selected references on an area of elementary school education appeared in each issue. "From the Publishers," an unselected listing of books, pamphlets and miscellaneous materials, still appears regularly. Book reviews appear very infrequently. One of the basic journals in the field of elementary education.

Indexed in: Ed. I.   8-8939 rev. 2*

EXCEPTIONAL CHILDREN.   v. 1, 1934-

Monthly (except June-Aug.)   Washington, D.C. $10.00

Titled the *Journal of Exceptional Children* to 1951, it is the official journal of the Council for Exceptional Children, NEA, a group concerned with
children who require special services, including the gifted, mentally retarded, visually impaired, deaf, hard of hearing, physically handicapped,
emotionally disturbed and speech and language impaired. Contains articles, brief to medium length, on the theory and practice of teaching such
children; each article is preceded by an abstract. Shorter items appear in
the section "Clearinghouse," and news of interest to professionals in the
section "Bulletin." Calendar of meetings, conferences, and other events.
Usually 2 or 3 reviews per issue; these are signed and critical and range
from just a few hundred to over 1000 words. List of publications received.

Indexed in: Ed.I.   38-25527 rev*

FOREIGN Language Annals. *see* MODERN LANGUAGES/GENERAL

*HARVARD EDUCATIONAL REVIEW.   v. 1, 1931-

Quarterly.   Cambridge, Mass. $10.00

Published for the Graduate School of Education, Harvard University, it began as the *Harvard Teachers Record* and was intended primarily for alumni
of the Graduate School of Education, but in 1937, when it assumed its
present title, it became a national publication, though its Editorial Board
is made up of students in the Graduate School. Some articles on schools
and teaching, but emphasis is on the history and theory of education,
and the interrelationships of education with other aspects of society. All
levels of education, including teacher education, are treated. Articles and
discussions are frequently by those outside the educational profession,
including many eminent figures in American scholarship. Most contributions are fairly lengthy and scholarly; they are thoughtful, usually provocative, and sometimes of great significance in the field. For example, Arthur
Jensen's finding on the failure of compensatory education, which has had
national repercussions, appeared as a 120-page article in 1969. Issues sometimes are devoted to a single topic, and often carry reports from symposia.
There are generally about 15 signed book reviews per issue; these are
long (from 750-2000 words) and thoughtful. There is also a list of books
received. A journal of prime importance to anyone interested in educational
theory and its implications for society.

Indexed in: B.R.D.   34-7870
            Ed.I.
            P.A.I.S.

IMPROVING COLLEGE AND UNIVERSITY TEACHING.   v. 1, 1953-

Quarterly.   Corvallis, Ore. $6.00

Its purpose is "to print articles on college and university teaching written
by college and university teachers." The articles, usually 15 to 20 per

issue, are brief, often just one or two pages, many written in a personal style and theorizing about higher education from personal experiences, but sometimes reporting the results of research. They cover all aspects of the subject—curricula, student attitudes, independent study, teaching methods, testing, educational goals, etc. Contributors to this potpourri include teaching faculty and administrators from all sizes and types of institutions, and from all areas. In the journal's earlier years, the articles were mostly trivial; probably because of the increasing interest in the method and content of higher education, the contributions have improved, though consequential ones are still the exception rather than the rule. No book reviewing, but an annual book section lists 100 new books of interest to college and university teachers. These are mostly on higher education, but also on educational psychology and education in general. Perhaps 15 of them receive reviews of a few hundred words and these are good; the others are merely annotated.

Indexed in: Ed.I.   64-783

INDUSTRIAL ARTS AND VOCATIONAL EDUCATION.   v. 1, 1914-

Monthly (except July-Aug.)   Riverside, N.J. $5.50

Originally devoted to instruction in elementary and high school shops, its coverage gradually took in other types of vocational education. Now it has widened its interest to industrial arts (and graphic arts) as a part of general education. Includes articles on the theory and practice of teaching industrial arts, on new equipment, etc., mostly by high school teachers and those engaged in training such teachers. Frequently carries Special Reports, with several articles around such topics as "Using A-V Teaching Tools," "Teaching Materials Technology," etc. A bi-monthly supplement, "Technical Education," which began in 1969, reflects the growth of interest in this area at the community college level, and this section is concerned much more than the rest of the journal with educational theory and curriculum, as well as the relationship of other junior college courses to technical education. This recent aspect of the journal makes it that much more useful for college libraries. News of the American Industrial Arts Association and its activities. 10-15 brief (under 100 words), unsigned, uncritical reviews of books, plus descriptions of new products and other recent literature. An essential journal where there are courses in industrial arts or technical education.

Indexed in: Ed.I.   16-513 Revised

INSTRUCTOR.   v. 1, 1891-

Monthly (bi-monthly, June-Sept.)   Dansville, N.Y. $8.00

Begun as the *Normal Instructor,* a periodical accompanying a correspondence school course for teachers. Then, as now, it was devoted to "what happens in the classroom," and all its articles and features are aimed at the elementary classroom teacher. Many of the authors are practicing teachers and their articles are short, practical and to the point. While there are also many regular features of general interest to educators—new products, news of federal and state activities, travel tips, letters, etc.— most of the items are on graded teaching, activities, materials, bulletin boards, teaching units, music, poetry, stories, games and other ideas and items to be used in teaching. In addition, each issue features a topic of major importance—e.g., Communication Skills for the '70's, Finding the Right Book, Environmental Education, World Awareness and Understanding—with a number of articles by experts in the area. Most articles are thoroughly illustrated. A number of professional books, children's books, science, art and other instructional material, including records, tapes and films, are briefly reviewed, but only with enthusiastic approval.

Similar in nature, but somewhat more limited in its contents, is *Grade Teacher* (v. 1, 1882- $8.00). Both are much used by experienced teachers and are very helpful to the practice teacher or beginner; they are especially important for curriculum libraries but for other libraries only where there are programs in elementary education. Extensive backfiles are not necessary.

Indexed in: Ed.I.   A40-2787

*INTEGRATED EDUCATION: RACE AND SCHOOLS.   v. 1, 1963-

Bi-monthly.   Chicago, Ill. $8.00

Provides probably the best coverage of the subject of any periodical. In brief, pithy, well-written articles, by teachers, school administrators, governmental officials, and professors, and with documentary materials such as speeches, court decisions, and official releases, it treats segregation in education at all levels, in all geographical areas, and for all affected minority groups. While there is a good bit on the rationale of integrated education, most of the contributions consist of case studies and first-hand reports that make interesting reading and valuable source material. There are three regular features: "Chronicle of School Integration" contains brief items on the progress and problems of integration from around the nation; "School Integration and Related Topics: Bibliography" provides a monthly listing of books, articles, pamphlets, reports and documents, and is one of the most comprehensive continuing bibliographies on the subject available; beginning in 1970, a "Book Section" lists and briefly (50-200 words) but critically describes recent books in the field of education, or related to the history, literature and sociology of minority groups, including novels and children's books. Because of the raw material it provides for studying many aspects of the problem, and the useful bibliographical features—for courses in education, political science and sociology—it should be in every college library.

Indexed in: Ed.I.   76-1531
            In.Per.Negroes   .

INTERNATIONAL REVIEW OF EDUCATION.   v. 1, 1955-

Quarterly.   The Hague, Netherlands. $9.30

Edited on behalf of the UNESCO Institute for Education by an international board of editors. Scholarly articles, many of fairly general interest, on educational problems and practices in various countries and on educational problems and theories that concern all countries. Single issues are occasionally devoted to a single topic—e.g., Preschool Education: Aspects and Problems, Uses and Values of the Computer in Education, The Effects of Urbanization on Education—or contain the proceedings of a conference. Of the 5 or 6 articles per issue, about two-thirds are in English, the rest in either German or French; summaries are provided for each article in the other two languages. Other sections include one of communications and reports on specific developments and one containing notices of, and reports on international conferences. The book reviews, averaging about 750 words each, are signed and critical; there are generally about 15 an issue, many of them in either French or German. An important journal for the study of comparative education and for keeping up with developments and viewpoints of education in other countries.

Indexed in: Ed.I.   A 56-5061

JOURNAL OF AESTHETIC EDUCATION.   v. 1, 1966-

Quarterly.   Urbana, Ill. $7.50

"The major purpose of the *Journal* is to clarify the issues of aesthetic education understood in its most extensive meaning, including not only the problems of formal instruction in the arts and the humanities at all levels of schooling, but also the aesthetic problems of the larger society created by twentieth-century existence. The *Journal* thus welcomes the following types of manuscripts: articles devoted to an understanding of the basic problem areas of education in the arts and the humanities . . .; articles dealing with the aesthetic aspects of the art and craft of teaching in general; articles devoted to the appreciation and understanding of the aesthetic character of other disciplines and subjects . . .; and articles treating the aesthetic import and significance of the new communications media and the environmental arts in their various forms." Usually 10-12 articles per issue, averaging 5000-6000 words, contributed mostly by faculty members in university departments of education, philosophy and the arts, including some eminent names in their fields. The articles are fairly well divided among the types enumerated above, but there are often special issues on single, though broad topics—e.g., Art, Morals and Aesthetic Education; Films, New Media and Aesthetic Education; The Curricula and Aesthetic Education. "Notes and News" includes governmental and foundation activities of interest, suggestions from readers, news of programs, courses and conferences, and a listing of articles in related journals. Usually 15-18 book reviews per issue, signed and critical, mostly 600-700 words, but often much longer. A unique journal, and a useful one, it will undoubtedly become more important as increasing attention is paid to the improvement of the quality and style of civilization.

Indexed in: Ed.I.   66-9897

JOURNAL OF CREATIVE BEHAVIOR.   v. 1, 1967-

Quarterly.   Buffalo, N.Y. $8.00

Published by the Creative Education Foundation at the State University of New York, Buffalo, it treats aspects of creativity, intelligence and problem solving, including concept formation, cognitive functions, perception, and the language and thought process. Consists mostly of articles reporting research, but also those expressing points of view or describing new approaches, written by behavioral scientists from many universities, industry and research institutions. The length of articles varies considerably, from just a few pages to some quite long, but most are fairly brief. The number of book reviews per issue also varies widely; they are signed and critical, and usually around 500 words in length. A useful journal where there is much work in educational psychology, or where the interest in educational innovation is pronounced.

Indexed in: Ed.I.   68-7097
            Ment.Hlth.B.R.I.

JOURNAL of Economic Education. *see* ECONOMICS

*JOURNAL OF EDUCATION.   v. 1, 1875-

Quarterly.   Boston, Mass. $3.00

Published since 1953 by the Boston University School of Education, it is the oldest educational journal in the country, but from its beginning until 1953 it was primarily aimed at the classroom teacher, and by the time B.U. took it over, it had declined greatly in professional esteem. In its new format it contains studies "prepared mainly by Boston University School of Education faculty and students. Occasionally, under the sponsorship of our faculty, studies by other scholars, and by graduate students, are also published. As a general rule each issue is dedicated to one main educational topic. A special effort is being made to achieve appropriate representation of various educational activities of the School of Education." Recent issues have been devoted to Aesthetics in Education, Educational Methodology in Social Sciences, Supervision of Counseling, Crisis and Change in the Administration of Higher Education, with each topic treated by 4 to 6 articles or papers.

An important journal for all departments of teacher education; the early volumes are useful for the history of education.

Indexed in: Ed.I.   7-33787 rev.

JOURNAL of Educational Psychology. *see* PSYCHOLOGY

JOURNAL OF EDUCATIONAL RESEARCH.   v. 1, 1920-

10 times/yr.   Madison, Wis. $10.00

"Dedicated to the scientific study of education," it contains an average of 8 or 9 relatively short articles (1500-3000 words) on all aspects and at all levels of education. All articles are on very specific problems, most are statistically based, and each one is preceded by an abstract. The February or March issue carries the extensive and very useful annual "Summary and Reviews of Investigations relating to Reading," covering somewhat selective reports published in journals. "Field News" reports on miscellaneous developments—grants, special research papers, important publications, conferences, etc. Only 2 or 3 book reviews, usually about 500 words long, per issue, but they are good. Brief listing of other new books. An important journal in the field.

Indexed in: Ed.I.   61-58068
          Ment.Hlth.B.R.I.

JOURNAL OF EXPERIMENTAL EDUCATION.   v. 1, 1932-

Quarterly.   Madison, Wis. $10.00

Contains "specialized or technical education studies, treatises about the mathematics or methodology of behavioral research, and monographs of major current research interest." Treats all levels and aspects of education. Articles, each of which is preceded by an abstract, are usually brief to moderate length, fairly technical, almost all containing statistical data and using methods somewhat advanced for most undergraduates. The breadth of studies, however, makes it useful for courses in methodology.

Indexed in: Ed.I.   35-15218 rev.

JOURNAL OF GENERAL EDUCATION.   v. 1, 1946-

Quarterly.   University Park, Pa. $7.50

Originally devoted to the concept of general education and to presenting the "philosophical and social implications of the movement and descriptions of the practical experiences of those who have devised new courses of study or attempted innovations in teaching." With the waning of the movement, which had a real impact on the content of higher education after World War II, the original publisher, the University of Chicago Press, suspended its publication in 1959; in 1961, the Pennsylvania State University Press resuscitated it, but it has more and more become concerned with a wider range of topics relating to higher education, mostly on the role and content of particular disciplines, or on the purposes of higher education generally. Now contains some poetry; contributors are faculty members and administrators from a variety of institutions and disciplines. Only 2 or 3 signed reviews per issue, though frequently one review will treat several related titles. They cover books not only on education but in all areas of the social sciences and humanities, including on occasion fiction, are almost always at least 700 words and often much longer, and are excellent. The early volumes are important for the history of American higher education.

Indexed in: Ed.I.   48-562 rev.*

JOURNAL of Geography. *see* GEOGRAPHY

*JOURNAL OF HIGHER EDUCATION.   v. 1, 1930-

Monthly (except July-Sept.)   Columbus, Ohio. $10.00

"Published to serve as the professional journal of the faculties and admin-istrative officers in the colleges, universities, and professional schools of the United States. The editorial advisers and corresponding editors are representative of many fields in higher education." Its early volumes con-tained articles by the most eminent figures in higher education—Robert Hutchins, A. Lawrence Lowell, Alexander Meiklejohn, Arthur Morgan, and others; after that, the number of significant contributions declined, though the journal was still an important one. Usually 5 or 6 brief to moderately long articles, frequently plus a few shorter contribu-tions, on all aspects of higher education: instruction and grading, recruiting, undergraduate and graduate curriculum, administrative-faculty relationships, and general and specialized education, education abroad, student attitudes, etc. The section "Trends and Tangents" reports de-velopments in special areas—e.g., Graduate Education, Honors Programs, The Library, The Two-Year College—of interest to educators in general. The number of reviews varies, but averages 5 or 6 per issue, and about 750 words each. Usually, but not always on higher education, they are signed and critical. List of books received.

Beginning in 1969 the American Association for Higher Education has been co-sponsor of the journal; this connection should increase greatly the importance of *JHE*.

Indexed in: B.R.D.   E 32-99
            Ed.I.

JOURNAL OF NEGRO EDUCATION.   v. 1, 1932-

Quarterly.   Washington, D.C. $5.00

"The purpose of the Journal is three-fold: first, to stimulate the collection and facilitate the dissemination of facts about the education of Negroes; second, to present discussions involving critical appraisals of the proposals and practices relating to the education of Negroes; and third, to stimulate and sponsor investigations of problems incident to the education of Ne-groes." Three issues contain articles of moderate length on all aspects of Negro education, both practical and theoretical; shorter articles and briefer surveys are contained in the section "Current Trends in Negro Education, and Shorter Papers." The fourth (or on rare occasion, the third) number of each volume is the *Yearbook*. Concerned with a subject of major im-portance and of current interest—e.g., "Education and Civil Rights in 1965," "African Education South of the Sahara," "The Negro Voter in the South"—it contains a number of articles treating the subject system-atically. "Current Literature on Negro Education" contains a few signed and critical, fairly long book reviews on education books in general as well as on Negro education; finally, there is an annual listing of books received.

Contributors in the past include some of the most eminent names in Negro scholarship—W.E.B. Du Bois, E. Franklin Frazier, Ira Reid and others. Because of their contributions, and because this was really the only journal concerned with Negro education for many years, a backfile is important. Its current importance is somewhat reduced by the same circumstances—there are now many journals carrying more significant articles on the same topic.

Indexed in: Ed.I.   33-19995
            In.Per.Negroes
            Ment.Hlth.B.R.I.
            P.A.I.S.

JOURNAL OF READING.   v. 1, 1957-

Monthly (except June-Sept.)   Newark, Del. $15.00

Published by the International Reading Association, it carries brief articles on all aspects of reading beyond the elementary school, from junior high school to college, plus special problem groups. Articles report research, classroom experiences, analyses of materials, etc. There are a number of special features: preview program of the annual IRA convention; a "Report from ERIC/CRIER" (Educational Resources Information Center/ Retrieval of Information and Evaluation of Reading), listing available publications plus news of its activities; professional and association news; since 1961, there has been an annual listing of doctoral dissertations in the field. It is now in two parts: *Doctoral Dissertations in College and Adult Reading Instruction,* and *Doctoral Dissertations in Secondary Reading.* Both parts contain abstracts and complete purchasing information for each listing. Reviews of professional publications and (in alternate issues) instructional materials. These reviews are signed and critical—those of professional publications are usually about 500-600 words long; those of the instructional materials, somewhat shorter.

Indexed in: Ed.I.   64-32293 rev.
           Ment.Hlth.B.R.I.

JOURNAL OF RESEARCH AND DEVELOPMENT IN EDUCATION.
v. 1, 1967-

Quarterly.   Athens, Ga. $7.00

Each issue is devoted to a single theme—e.g., Early Childhood Education, Beginning Teachers and Certification, Evaluation for Program Improvement—which is treated by a number of articles or, where the theme was the subject of a conference, by a selection of papers from that conference or, in a few cases, by the contents of a project report. Though published by the College of Education, University of Georgia, its contributors are from many institutions and the quality of their reports is almost uniformly high. A significant journal, primarily for advanced students and faculty.

Indexed in: Ed.I.   68-127122

JOURNAL OF RESEARCH IN SCIENCE TEACHING.   v. 1, 1963-

Quarterly.   N.Y. $10.00

Published under the auspices of the National Association for Research in Science Teaching and the Association for the Education of Teachers of Science. Scholarly articles, about 10-12 per issue, deal with all sorts of educational matters—course content, approaches, educational theory, training of science teachers, etc.—of importance to science educators at all levels, from elementary school to the university; the contributors are also from various levels, but mainly from universities. Articles are usually 3-4000 words, or sometimes less if they contain much statistical data; shorter studies, 2-3 pages long, are included as "Research Reports." Only a few book reviews, about 500 words each, and not in every issue; an annotated listing of a few other books, also in only some issues. The books covered are in the fields of education or science generally, not just science education. A useful journal where many teachers of science are trained, or where there is much interest in innovative science teaching.

Indexed in: Ed.I.   65-9103

JUNIOR COLLEGE JOURNAL.   v. 1, 1930-

Monthly (except June/July, Aug./Sept., Dec./Jan. issues combined)
Washington, D.C. $5.00

Official journal of the American Association of Junior Colleges, it was originally published by Stanford University. With the creation of a full-time Executive Secretary of the AAJC, it moved to Washington, then to the University of Chicago, and from 1949 through 1962, to the University of Texas. Through all those years its format was modest and staid, and it had a relatively small circulation. The rapid post-war development of community colleges meant that in 1963 a full-time editor, working out of the Association's headquarters, could be appointed, and the circulation and coverage of the journal greatly expanded.

Each issue carries from 8 to 15 brief articles on all aspects of junior college administration, teaching and learning, from "Social Action and the Community College" to "How to Apply for a Teaching Position," or from an article on Japanese junior colleges to one on how a particular institution turned an abandoned warehouse into a usable building. Articles are mostly matter-of-fact, briskly written, and illustrated. Issues frequently focus on single topics—curricular innovation, environmental education, the art collection, private junior colleges, etc. News of the AAJC, of personnel, institutions and developments in the field. "Literature in Passing" lists recent books, pamphlets and documents of interest.

An essential journal for two-year college libraries, it is appropriate for all college libraries, not as much for student use as for faculty and administration.

Indexed in: Ed.I.   A 33-196 rev.

LANGUAGE Learning. see MODERN LANGUAGES/GENERAL

*LIBERAL EDUCATION.   v. 1, 1915-

Quarterly.   Washington, D.C. $5.00

An official publication of the Association of American Colleges, it was titled until 1959 its *Bulletin*. Carries articles and essays, mostly brief, on various aspects of college teaching, curriculum and administration and reports on the results of special studies or surveys. The March issue carries the proceedings of the Association's annual meeting, including addresses, papers and official reports; it also contains the roster of the Association and its administrative structure. Regular features are: "Among the Colleges," news of developments, new programs, buildings, etc; a listing of "New College Presidents." Usually a few book reviews, all signed and critical, and most of them quite long. Although it still does not encourage criticism or controversy, it has in the past decade or so been more concerned with issues relating to the improvement of higher education. Consequently, though not generally useful to or used by undergraduates, since it has become more readable and more useful to faculty and administration, it should be available to them in the library.

Indexed in: Ed.I.   24-11710 rev.*

MEDIA & METHODS.   v. 1, 1964-

Monthly (except June-Aug.)   Philadelphia, Pa. $7.00

Originally *Educator's Guide to Media and Methods*, it assumed its present title in 1969. Devoted to articles, news and reviews of educational films, TV and other audio-visual materials and their uses. A useful regular feature is "Telelog," a descriptive listing of worthwhile TV programs for the coming months; also it contains excellent reviews and commentary on new commercial and educational films.

An independently published journal, it is written in an informal style, from a creative, even radical educational viewpoint. It is unique among a-v journals for example, for its frequent articles on teaching controversial and/or unusual topics, accompanied by lists of relevant printed and a-v materials. Also, its focus on all kinds of teaching and learning materials that are generally neglected—or perhaps forgotten—is of special interest. It is by far the liveliest a-v journal to read. Certainly, an a-v journal that carries an article declaring that "books have never been more beautiful, more vital and alive—and they are the most stable element in the chaos of modern education" is worth serious consideration by librarians.

Indexed in: Ed. I.

NATIONAL ASSOCIATION OF SECONDARY SCHOOL PRINCIPALS. BULLETIN.   v. 1, 1917-

Monthly (except June-Aug.)   Washington, D.C. $30(membership)

Each issue contains 10 to 15 articles, mostly of moderate length, on all areas of secondary education—from case reports of experimental courses to sociological analyses of education, from discipline to learning theory. The authors are school administrators, government officials, and professors of education. Entire issues are frequently devoted to a single topic— e.g., The Authority Crisis in Our Schools, Learning in the Summer, The Computer in Education. The section, "About Books," which appears in most issues, usually carries extended reviews of one or a few books, but occasionally treats a larger number, each one briefly. The reviews are all signed, and most of them are critical. Since 1946, the annual annotated listing of "Best Books on Vocational Guidance" has been carried in one of the Spring issues.

The articles vary greatly in quality. Considering its expense (it is only available with membership) the *Bulletin* is necessary only where there are large departments of education.

Indexed in: Ed.I.   19-17387 rev. 2

MATHEMATICS Teacher. *see* MATHEMATICS

*NEA RESEARCH BULLETIN.   v. 1, 1923-

Quarterly.   Washington, D.C. $2.00

An average issue contains about six very brief articles, reporting through text, charts, statistics and responses to questionnaires, the situation on some current aspect of education—e.g., "State Minimum-Salary Requirements," "Do Teacher Characteristics Affect Opinion?" "Women and College Degrees Conferred," "Programs for Evaluating Classroom Teachers," etc. Through 1957, each number of the *Bulletin* was devoted to a single topic on the same subjects as the present issues, but was more technical and gave more detail. The new format was instituted to make a wide variety of essential facts accessible to a larger group, and to leave the more technical details to monographic publications. While this format may not be as useful for research, it does provide recent information on a wide variety of subjects, and is especially useful for reference purposes.

Indexed in: Ed.I. 58-59577 rev.
P.A.I.S.

NATIONAL ELEMENTARY PRINCIPAL. v. 1, 1921-

6 nos./yr. Washington, D.C. $20(includes membership)

Published by the National Association of Elementary School Principals, a department of NEA. Each issue carries 6 to 10 articles on various aspects of elementary school administration—curriculum, in-service education, child development, community relations, teacher organizations, etc.—as well as on developments in educational theory and practices. Most issues focus on a theme such as Education for the Spanish-Speaking, Humanizing the Elementary School, Health Education. Articles are usually brief, and are written mostly by school administrators, professors of education, and staff members of NEA. Notes and news of the Association, of state and local associations, and of other items of interest. The September issue carries the Association's Annual Report. From 1 to 3 book reviews per issue; they are signed and critical, but vary greatly in length, from several hundred to several thousand words. An important journal where there are courses in school administration.

Indexed in: Ed.I. E 33-506 rev. 3*

NATION'S SCHOOLS. v. 1, 1928-

Monthly. Chicago, Ill. $15.00

Aimed at school administrators, it is primarily concerned with presentations of problems and case studies of school finance, furniture and equipment, student logistics, etc., but frequently treats other concerns of the administration—desegregation, teacher supply, trends and developments in teaching, etc.—that affect school planning and administration. A large portion of one issue is sometimes devoted to a single topic: e.g., Electronic Teaching Aids, Desegregation, USOE: Plans and Priorities for the 70's. Many regular features including a newsletter, "Report from Washington"; "School Law," a column discussing a recent event or court decision relating to school legal rights or obligations; "About People," listing changes in administrative posts; "A-V Management," discussing new developments and products; "What's New," descriptions of new products and supplies, illustrated; "Opinion Poll," reporting results of a monthly survey of administrators on a topic of current interest; columns on "Public Relations," "Plant Operation," and "Curriculum"; "School of the Month," showing pictures and plans of a new school whose features are worthy of note. There is also an annual tableau of the schools cited for design excellence by the American Association of School Administrators. The May issue contains an annual review and listing, "Guide to Pertinent Articles for School Business Officials." Thoroughly illustrated, it is an important journal for administrators and school planners, and especially useful where there are courses in school administration. It is, furthermore, of interest to anyone concerned about schools, and should be available to the general reader.

Indexed in: Ed.I. 30-8315 rev.

NORTH CENTRAL ASSOCIATION QUARTERLY.   v. 1, 1926-

Quarterly.   Menasha, Wis. $6.00

The official organ of the North Central Association of Colleges and Secondary Schools. The first number of each volume consists of official
Association matters: the roster of officers and committees, reports to the
Association and proceedings of the commissions, with listings of member
schools, of accreditation actions, and statements of policies and criteria
for evaluation. The 3 other numbers contain, in addition to Association
notes and comment, articles on secondary and higher education: many
of these articles are on aspects of evaluation and accreditation, but others
are on more general problems. There is almost nothing on classroom procedures or other "practical" presentations, and the journal is undoubtedly
of more interest and importance to the administrator than to the teacher;
however, because the North Central Association covers so many states,
and because the articles are of a high quality, the journal is more useful
in libraries than one at first might think. No book reviews.

Indexed in: Ed.I.   A 40-3398*

OCCUPATIONAL Outlook Quarterly. *see* GENERAL

PTA MAGAZINE.   v. 1, 1906-

Monthly (except July-Aug.)   Chicago, Ill. $2.50

Official magazine of the National Congress of Parents and Teachers. Issues
contain about 7 articles, interestingly written, illustrated, mostly 1500-
2000 words, on all aspects of education and other matters relating to
children in home, school and community. The coverage is fairly well
divided among pre-school, elementary school children and adolescents,
with at least one article in each issue by a nationally known educator,
physician, writer or other personality. Regular features include: "Happenings in Education," 2 or 3 long news items and other comment;
"PTA—Where the Action Is," reports from the national body and local
happenings; "Time Out for TV," brief reviews of forthcoming shows with
some general comments; study-discussion guides that provide questions,
program suggestions and recommended readings, all related to a few of
that issue's articles; "Motion Picture Previews," evaluating and grading
the suitability of about 20 films. No individual book reviews, but one
article in almost each issue surveys books for children, usually treating
a number of recommended titles for an age group or in an area—adventure,
biography, etc. A useful, readable journal, but not of prime importance.

Indexed in: R.G.   12-15373 rev. 2*

PEABODY JOURNAL OF EDUCATION.   v. 1, 1922/23-

Quarterly.   Nashville, Tenn. $8.00

Published by George Peabody College for Teachers, it began primarily
as a regional journal, concerned with the educational problems of the
New South and having many prominent Southern educators as contributors. But today it has no geographical emphasis. Issues contain 8 to
10 short articles, almost all between 1000 and 2000 words, on all aspects and levels of education and teaching, mostly written by professors
of education, with preference given to members of the College and its

alumni, but with others liberally represented. About 40 books a year are reviewed. They include books on a variety of subjects, from children's stories to rather specialized studies in literature and the social sciences, with, of course, an emphasis on books relating to education, and the reviews, which are signed, range from under 100 to 1000 words, with the mean about 300 or 400. Somewhat pedestrian in content and style, it is, however, useful where there is much work in teacher education.

Indexed in: Ed.I.   E 25-69

PERSONNEL AND GUIDANCE JOURNAL.   v. 1, 1921-

Monthly (except July-Aug.)   Washington, D.C. $15.00

Its earlier title was *Occupations, the Vocational Guidance Journal*; its present title was adopted in 1952. The official publication of the American Personnel and Guidance Association, it is "directed to the common interests of counselors and personnel workers at all educational levels from kindergarten to higher education, in community agencies, and in government, business, and industry." There have been several analyses of the journal's content, in 1958, 1964 and 1969, showing that most contributions were by college personnel, with very little about school guidance, that the subject matter has been fairly diverse, with the most popular topics the counseling process, vocational psychology, academic achievement, professional training and problems of counselors and personnel workers, and testing. Also pointed out was the relatively unsophisticated methodology used—most articles have been descriptive rather than hypothesis-testing. In 1969, the format and, to a lesser extent, the content changed. The column reporting news from Washington, which had run since 1943, was discontinued. The number of articles, which averaged about 12, was reduced to 6 or 7, though they still are mostly 5-6 pages long. "In the Field" includes brief reports of programs, practices or techniques. About 6 book reviews per issue, mostly 500-750 words.

Indexed in: Ed.I.   28-749*
        Ment.Hlth.B.R.I.

*PHI DELTA KAPPAN.   v. 1, 1928-

Monthly (except July-Aug.)   Bloomington, Ind. $6.50

The journal of the Phi Delta Kappa, the professional fraternity for men in education. Contains readable, brief (usually 1500-2000 words) articles by teachers, administrators and public figures, including many eminent names in the field of education, on all aspects of education—current problems and controversial issues, trends, etc.—and on all educational levels. Articles tend not to be "practical," but are more general, relating aspects of public education and educational theory to the individual, to the community, and to society at large. Issues often focus on special topics—e.g., The Job Corps, The Politics of Education, Big Business Discovers the Education Market. Regular sections contains news of developments and miscellaneous items from the field and from Washington and the states. Several book reviews per issue; though unsigned, they are well done, and, for significant books, run to several thousand words. Because it does not shy from controversial issues, and because the articles are timely and by contributors who write well and are worth listening to, the journal is essential where there are courses in education, and important for all college libraries.

Indexed in: Ed.I.   46-35485

READING TEACHER.   v. 1, 1948-

Monthly (except June-Sept.)   Newark, Del. $15.00

An official journal of the International Reading Association, it was known as the International Council for the Improvement of Reading Instruction Bulletin for its first four years. Anywhere from 6 to 15 articles (mostly 2000-2500 words) reporting results of research, describing classroom experiences or discussing other aspects of reading and the teaching of it—almost all on the elementary level—by teachers, professors of education, psychologists. Issues often focus on a theme such as Primary Reading, Learning Disabilities, the International Scene, etc. Regular features include: "Research," usually reviewing recent research on a specialized aspect of reading; "Literature for Children," discusses authors, recent books or the subject itself; "In Other Magazines," summarizes a few recent articles; "The Clip Sheet," news of people, publications and professional activities; "ERIC/CRIER" gives news of its activities, publications and services, but does not include abstracts. From 1 to 4 book reviews per issue, signed and critical, varying in length from 250 to 750 words.

Where there is much interest in reading instruction, especially in its developments and trends and in controversy over method, libraries should receive the monthly *Reading Newsreport* (v. 1, 1966- $5.00). Since it is not connected with the professional organization, it can speak much more frankly—though this does not mean it is radical—which it does in concise, lively articles. Each issue also features an interview with a leading authority in the field. In addition to the articles and the interviews, there are several regular columns: on new products and materials; news of, and brief reports on reading research projects; in "The Science of Supervision," suggestions for supervisors; and in "The Classroom Scene," observations on real situations. Occasional brief, signed book reviews.

Indexed in: Ed.I.   58-26936
          Ment. Hlth.B.R.I.

RESEARCH IN EDUCATION.   v. 1, 1966-

Monthly.   Washington, D.C. $21.00

Published by the U.S. Office of Education, it is prepared "by the Educational Resources Information Center (ERIC) to make possible the early identification and acquisition of reports of interest to the educational community." Most of each issue consists of the Documents Section which gives resumés plus complete bibliographical and order information (on microfiche or hard copy) for the documents gathered by 19 ERIC clearinghouses across the country. There are subject, author and institution indexes for this section; the subject index uses the ERIC descriptors, which are listed with each item. A Project Section performs the same service for current Office of Education research projects, but since these are in

progress, no order information is given. An annual index cumulates all
the monthly indexes. Libraries taking *RIE* should have along with it ERIC's
Thesaurus of ERIC Descriptors, a guide to the subject headings used in
ERIC publications and necessary for making best use of ERIC. Since
RIE provides a thorough coverage of a field that is otherwise difficult
to keep track of, it should be in libraries where there is real interest
in recent educational research. A depository item.

72-216727

*REVIEW OF EDUCATIONAL RESEARCH.   v. 1, 1931-

5 times/yr.   Washington, D.C. $10.00

Official publication of the American Educational Research Association,
its purpose is "to report educational research findings and conclusions
by areas of interest. In five issues per year, it identifies, summarizes, and
critically analyzes research studies and seeks to synthesize significant findings and conclusions in such a manner as to stimulate further research."
Each issue is devoted to a major topic–e.g., Teacher Personnel, Adult
Education, Education for Socially Disadvantaged Children, Natural Sciences
and Mathematics, etc.–with articles treating different aspects of that topic,
each reviewing the literature that appeared on that aspect since the topic
was last treated (topics are generally, but not necessarily, repeated in
three-year cycles). Each contains a thorough and comprehensive bibliography. The *Review* helps to keep the *Encyclopedia of Educational
Research* (a project of the A.E.R.A.) up to date. It is, then, useful for
reference purposes as well as for those doing educational research, and
should be in any library where there are courses in education.

Indexed in: Ed.I.   33-19994 rev. 2

*SCHOOL & SOCIETY.   v. 1, 1915-

Monthly (except June-Sept.)   N.Y. $11.15

Founded by James McKeen Cattell, the eminent psychologist, teacher and
editor (he began *American Men of Science* and *Leaders in Education,*
among other things) to "emphasize the relations of education to the social order, scientific research in education and its application, freedom of
discussion, and reports and views of events of educational interest." During its history, some of the most distinguished names in education and
allied interests have contributed to it. In 1939 the Society for the Advancement of Education was founded to take over the publication; it is
still the publisher. A semi-monthly for years, it assumed its present frequency in 1969.

Issues consist of a number of articles and factual reports on all levels
of education, though in the last decade higher education has received
the most attention. The articles are frequently the texts of addresses,
and sometimes reprints from other sources, and tend to discuss educational philosophy or significant problems and programs rather than report the results of research. There is usually a section of "Reports" on
specific events, programs or institutions, and one of "Documents" that
includes significant federal, state, commission, institutional, or translated
foreign documents. "Conference Reports" summarize the proceedings of

recent institutes, meetings and conferences. The January issue includes the annual report, *Statistics of Attendance in American Colleges and Universities*, which has been published since 1919. While there are no book reviews as such, portions of important forthcoming books appear frequently, and the annotated roundup, "Books for Education," including about 300 foreign and domestic titles in education and related subjects comes out semi-annually. Also a listing of other recent publications. Though the contents are of very uneven quality, it includes so much that a good portion of it is bound to be useful—even significant—and it deserves to be looked at regularly by anyone interested in current trends and developments in education. Excellent coverage of the entire field; belongs in every academic library.

Indexed in: S.S.H.I.   17-1407 (rev. '31)

SCHOOL Arts. *see* ART

*SCHOOL REVIEW.   v. 1, 1893-

Quarterly.   Chicago, Ill. $12.00

Published for the School of Education of the University of Chicago, its purpose "is to encourage reflection and discussion by all persons who are interested in or concerned about education." Before 1957 it was a monthly, devoted almost completely to secondary education, and especially to descriptions and analyses of classroom problems and procedures, but after it became a quarterly it more and more centered its attention "on specific questions of educational policy and practice and on fundamental philosophical and theoretical issues," though still emphasizing the secondary school. In March, 1969, it changed policy again when, having added students to the editorial board, it began "to develop and support new sources of information, opinion and debate on educational problems and practice." This aspect is especially evident in the section "Comment" but it also appears in the nature of the articles which, though still scholarly, are much more closely related to the social implications and problems of education. The number of reviews has changed: whereas there used to be just one long essay review, there are now 6 to 8 reviews, but they are still long—at least 1000 words, and often several times that. Always one of the leading journals in the field (so that a backfile is important), it is now even better, and should be in every library.

Indexed in: Ed.I.   6-14090 rev.

SCHOOL SCIENCE AND MATHEMATICS.   v. 1, 1909-

Monthly (except July-Sept.)   Menasha, Wis. $10.00

Official journal of the Central Association of Science and Mathematics Teachers. Contains articles by school and college and university science teachers on scientific concepts and developments, but mostly on the theory, problems, techniques, and approaches in the teaching of science and mathematics, from the elementary to the college level, with by far the most attention given to secondary schools, and to mathematics and physics. Frequent bibliographical articles. "Problem Department," to "provide problems of varying degrees of difficulty which will interest anyone engaged in the study of mathematics," includes problems submitted by and for students. News of the CASMT, its meetings, reports and sections; annual listing of National Science Foundation Summer Institutes, Research Programs, and In-Service Institutes. A listing of *Doctoral Dissertation Research in Science and Mathematics*—that is, the teaching of them—has appeared the last few years. Each issue has only 2 or 3 reviews of texts and books on teaching; these are signed and 200-300 words long. "Book Vignettes" contains a larger number of titles, and of more general interest, with critical annotations of 75 to 150 words. Also an extensive listing of "Books and Teaching Aids Received."

Indexed in: Ed.I.   CA 7-2122 (unrev'd)

SCIENCE AND CHILDREN.   v. 1, 1963-

Monthly (except June-Aug.)   Washington, D.C. $8.00

Published by the National Science Teachers Association, "a professional organization for all teachers of science at all levels, elementary through college." Contains articles, brief and well-illustrated, on methods, projects, equipment, etc., for teaching biology, chemistry, earth science and physics, mostly at the elementary and junior high level. Also articles on science education itself, and reports on NSTA activities and from its offices and committees. Regular features include a listing of new materials, publications and events, and "Resource Reviews," briefly annotated reviews of new books and a-v materials. In 1971, a monthly "Sky Calendar" began. An important journal for prospective teachers of elementary school science.

The same organization publishes the *Science Teacher* (v. 1, 1934- $10) which is similar in purpose except that it focuses on high school science. It began as the *Illinois University Teacher*, then was published by several groups of midwestern science teachers, and in 1950 was taken over by the NSTA. Each issue contains about 6 articles, by college and university science faculty or professors of science education, on the theory and methods of teaching science, or on specific scientific questions and developments—e.g., "The Genetic Determination of Behavior," "Total Solar Eclipse." The section "With the Schools" discusses new projects and curricula; "Classroom Ideas" describes experiments, games, equipment and techniques of teaching. "Resources/Reviews" carries 10 to 20 short reviews of books and of other a-v aids. Much of the material is appropriate for beginning college students.

Indexed in: Ed.I.   71-790

SCIENCE EDUCATION.   v. 1, 1916-

Quarterly.   N.Y. $12.00

Founded as the *General Science Quarterly*, it assumed its present title in 1929 when it was taken over by the National Association for Research in Science Teaching. In 1946, the NARST turned ownership over to Clarence Pruitt, who had been associated with the journal since 1929, and he remained editor until his death in 1968, when John Wiley and Sons purchased it. Each issue contains 15-20 short articles (usually 1000-2000 words) on various aspects of science teaching and science education, from elementary grades through junior college. Authors are mostly professors of education, and the content seems to be changing from a stress on classroom suggestions to more basic discussions of the purposes, content and disciplinary relationships of science education, and on the nature of science itself. For institutions doing much in training teachers of science at the secondary and college levels, this will become an increasingly important journal.

Indexed in: Ed.I.   20-5630

SENIOR SCHOLASTIC (TEACHER'S EDITION).   v. 29, 1936-

Weekly (except June-August)   Englewood Cliffs, N.J. $6.00

The weekly numbers appear as a few pages (usually 8) bound around the outside of *Senior Scholastic,* which of course, is the popular newsmagazine distributed in many high schools and used in classes in government, history and current affairs, with many features in addition to the news stories and background articles. The basic purpose of the Teacher's Edition is to provide some news of education, and discussion of educational issues, but mainly to supply items for class use relating to articles in the week's issue of *Senior Scholastic,* that is, discussion and examination questions, background material, and cartoons, graphs or charts suitable for making transparencies; it also lists appropriate film, pamphlets and books relating to topics in forthcoming   issues, and worthwhile television shows for the coming week. Once a month, a separately published *Junior/Senior High Teacher's Edition* is issued, which focuses on educational news and discussions of problems and trends related to teaching, and also includes many regular features: evaluations of books, pamphlets, and audiovisual materials, teaching tips, items on summer travel, etc. Because it contains so much news about education, and so much practical information for class use, and because many students are familiar with it and can approach it through the *Readers' Guide,* this edition of *Senior Scholastic* is useful for college libraries.

Indexed in: R.G.   46-41545

*SOCIAL EDUCATION.   v. 1, 1937-

\ Monthly (except June-Sept.)   Washington, D.C. $10.00

Published by the National Council for the Social Studies (a department of NEA) in collaboration with the American Historical Association. Usually about 10 articles per issue, mostly by professors of education at universities, or teachers of history, geography or social studies in secondary schools, but occasionally by well known scholars or public figures. Issues now focus on one or several topics, with the articles grouped around them, on various aspects of teaching the social studies in elementary or secondary schools, though in recent volumes there has been a greater emphasis on current social problems and their relationship to the field. Topics treated recently have included: "The Elementary School: Focus on the Culturally Different," "Religion and the Social Studies," "Black Americans and Social Studies," "Asia: the New, the Old, the Timeless." Regular departments include: "Sight and Sound," a listing with brief descriptions of new films, filmstrips and other a-v items; "Sources and Resources," containing subject bibliographies of books and pamphlets, descriptions of services, government programs, and other aids for teachers; news and notes of meetings, courses, symposia and of the NCSS. There is an annual review of curriculum materials, with descriptions of the materials by practicing teachers. Usually 4 or 5 signed book reviews, of both professional books and relevant trade publications, that vary in length from several hundred to over 1000 words.

Well edited, with thoughtful and useful contributions, it should be in every library where there are courses in education. Many of the articles will be useful to other social science majors as well.

Indexed in: Ed.I.   40-12480

*SOCIAL STUDIES.   v. 1, 1909-

Monthly (except May-Sept.)   Brooklawn, N.J. $6.50

For its first ten years, it was the *History Teacher's Magazine*; in 1918 it became the *Historical Outlook*, taking its present title in 1933. In most of its early years it was published under the supervision of the American Historical Association, and in 1923, the recently established National Council for the Social Studies also became sponsor. The relationship with these organizations lasted until 1937, when *Social Education* was founded as the official journal of the National Council. At that time, *Social Studies* announced that it would be "devoted to the interests of teachers of history, civics, political science, economics, problems of democracy, sociology, and the new geography *in the secondary schools.*" (It had earlier treated college-level teaching and material as well.) It still retains this emphasis, with articles mostly on the purposes, methods, and problems of teaching the social sciences, but also frequent articles of some scholarly interest. The section "Instructional Materials" carries brief reviews of a-v materials; the book reviews (usually about 10 an issue) are mostly 150-500 words and are signed and critical. They treat scholarly works in the social sciences as well as textbooks and books on teaching. Also some briefer "Book Notes" and a list of publications received. Important for prospective teachers and also useful for students doing papers in history and political science.

Indexed in: B.R.D.   12-25956
            Ed.I.
            P.A.I.S.

SOCIOLOGY OF EDUCATION.   v. 1, 1927-

Quarterly.   Washington, D.C. $7.00

A publication of the American Sociological Association, and successor to the *Journal of Educational Sociology*, which was the title to 1963. Despite its announced interdisciplinary purpose, a large majority of its contributors are sociologists who are interested in applying the purposes and methods of sociology to educational situations at all levels. The articles, usually 5 or 6 an issue, are scholarly, average about 15 pages, and each is preceded by an abstract. According to an editorial in 1969, the contributions are of several kinds: (1) papers that extend sociological theory with reference to education; (2) discussions of research methods that are of especial relevance to the sociology of education; (3) reports of sociological research on education, most particularly those weaving together theory and data; (4) systematic analyses or summaries of the sociological literature on education; (5) articles applying sociological principles to educational practice; and (6) critical or programmatic statements on educational policy from the standpoint of sociology.

"Reports and Opinions" (or "Notes and Reports," or "Research Notes," depending upon the content) contains miscellaneous news items, talks, shorter essays and technical or procedural reports. There have been no book reviews since the journal changed title. An important journal for advanced students and research.

Indexed in: Ed.I.   30-8323 rev. 2

*TEACHERS COLLEGE RECORD.   v. 1, 1900-

Monthly (except June-Sept.)   N.Y. $10.00

An organ of Teachers College, Columbia University, it was known as the *Record* from 1967 to 1970. It was originally devoted "to the practical problems of elementary and secondary education and the professional training of teachers," and for a number of years was very specific in its purpose. Its character has slowly changed. The articles became less practical and more attention was paid to educational philosophy and broader problems. The source of contributions changed: the early articles were all by Teachers College faculty; later, those by outsiders, even persons outside the field of education, appeared more frequently. For many years, activities and publications of students, faculty and alumni of Teachers College were reported faithfully: supplementary listings to TC's *Register of Doctoral Dissertations* and *Register of Doctor of Education Reports,* summaries of some Reports, alumni and staff publications and activities, and other departmental notes; these have gradually disappeared. In the 1950's the *Record's* emphasis was that "the teacher, the counselor, the school nurse—everyone in education—needs insights and facts from many areas of professional activity," and in the 1960's it became a "journal of contemporary thought in the humanities and behavioral sciences as they illuminate the process of education," a forum for teachers and others "concerned with education through the institutions of the culture at large." Thus, there are now as many articles by those outside the field of teacher education as within, and education, on all levels, is viewed broadly. There is even some poetry. Other features include: "The Educators Speak," providing lengthy, thoughtful, personal, controversial views on educational theory and practice; the book reviews, about 8 per issue, are especially good—they are signed and critical, and range up to several thousand words. An important journal for everyone interested in the basic purposes and wider implications of education, it should be in every college library.

Indexed in: B.R.D.   6-14087 rev.*
            Ed.I.

THEORY INTO PRACTICE.   v. 1, 1962-

5 nos./yr.   Columbus, Ohio. $5.00

A journal of the College of Education, The Ohio State University. Each issue is devoted to a single topic, generally a fairly broad one—e.g., Curriculum Theory Development, Pressures on Children, The Middle School, The New Mathematics, etc.—with usually 6 to 10 articles by experts from different school systems and schools of education. The articles, of brief to moderate length, are mostly well written and tend to essays rather than articles reporting the results of research. Book reviews appear only occasionally; they are signed, but mostly only 150-250 words. An attractive format; interesting, thoughtful contributions.

Indexed in: Ed.I.   66-97728
           Ment.Hlth.B.R.I.

*THIS MAGAZINE IS ABOUT SCHOOLS.   v. 1, 1967-

Quarterly.   Toronto, Ont. $6.00

A magazine dedicated to the reform of education at all levels and in almost all aspects, but especially to making it more responsive to the needs of the disadvantaged and freeing it from tradition-bound approaches and techniques. Thus it concentrates on creative teaching, innovative techniques and experimental schools. Though much of it is Canadian, there is almost as much attention to U.S. education; moreover, most of its material is pertinent for schools and teachers anywhere. The articles, by teachers, students, administrators, and others—from community organizers and student activists to well-known authors and professors—who are interested in educational reform, are mostly on education; but also on youth culture, the peace movement, films, politics, segregation, etc.,

This magazine, then, is not *just* about schools, but about all aspects of society that need or are affecting change, and schools are central to this thrust. The format is also hard to describe—it consists of liberal use of photographs and drawings, poems, reproductions of newspaper items, documents and letters, and unorthodox typography. No book reviews as such, but important books are often treated in articles. A magazine that should be looked at by educators and prospective teachers, though students and faculty in general will browse in it regularly and thoroughly.

TIMES EDUCATIONAL SUPPLEMENT.   no. 1, 1910-

Weekly.   London. $36.00

Concerned with all levels and aspects of education in Britain, it is nevertheless useful for Americans because of the variety of news and features. Certainly for any serious study of British education today it is essential. It also contains news of educational developments from other countries, in particular those of the Commonwealth and Western Europe. Many articles and features on politics, literature, the arts, especially those events and developments affecting teachers or students. Many special supplements, from 4 to 16 pages, covering a variety of topics—during a 2-month period in 1970, 7 of the 9 issues contained these sections: on technical books, education in industry, equipment for science teaching, books for secondary science, educational equipment, geography, 50 makers of British education since 1870. There are a number of regular features: columns on equipment, on sport, on foreign news; a "Photoreport"; the "Week's Diary," listing meetings, lectures, institutes, exhibits, etc.; and news of appointments and other personal items. Book reviews abound throughout the journal; they vary in length, range over many subjects in addition to education, and are signed and exceptionally well done. It is almost impossible to describe *TES*—it contains so much. Its preservation in a library presents a problem: issues are mostly 70-100 pages (though at least half of most issues consist of classified ads), tabloid size, and of newsprint; microfilm may be the answer. But libraries with strong departments of education, especially where comparative education receives some attention, should not let that problem deter them from subscribing to it.

Indexed in: Ed.I.   18-6784

*TODAY'S EDUCATION.   v. 1, 1913-

Monthly (except June-Aug.)   Washington, D.C.   Membership (includes *Research Bulletin* and *Proceedings*) $7.00

Official journal of the National Education Association, it was titled the *NEA Journal* until September, 1968. Each issue features a symposium of opinions on a topic of current or perennial concern: Crushes—What Should You Do About Them? Professional Negotiation; Black Leaders Speak Out on Black Education; Campus Unrest, etc., with prominent educators, statesmen, scholars and other national figures contributing. In addition, there are about 10 articles, written more or less popularly, concerning today's students, schools, school systems, and other developments and problems of the teaching profession, with an increasing tendency in recent years to treat "controversial" subjects that, a decade ago, would have been shunned. All levels of education are covered. There are also good general articles, usually on topics relevant to young people, such as Voting for 18-Year Olds, Children of Mexican American Migrants, but also on public affairs, science, etc. There are a number of regular features, a few of which are: "Classroom Incident" describes the handling of an actual troublesome incident and provides various consultants' comments on it; questions concerning local school associations are answered; "Research Clues" gives summaries of studies that appeared in other journals; listings of new N.E.A. publications and of free or inexpensive materials; "Unfinished Story," for students to complete, with a didactic purpose; "News and Trends," a two-page newsletter of mostly national news; and others. A book feature is in almost every issue: sometimes a listing of books on a specific subject, or a few reviews; a Spring issue carries a listing of the year's outstanding books on education, and a Winter issue, a listing of outstanding children's books. Though not a scholarly journal, because it speaks to (and frequently for) such a large membership on all aspects of education, and has become more aware of the social problems and responsibilities of education, the journal is an important publication and should be in all college libraries.

Indexed in: Ed.I.   24-4821 rev.
            R.G.

VOCATIONAL GUIDANCE QUARTERLY.   v. 1, 1952-

Quarterly.   Washington, D.C. $8.00

Official publication of the National Vocational Guidance Association, a division of the American Personnel and Guidance Association. Each issue contains 10 to 15 articles on all aspects of "vocational development, vocational planning, occupational choice, preparation for occupations, labor market dynamics, job finding, and job satisfaction." Articles, by guidance specialists and counselors in high school, college and government agencies, or those teaching the subject, are brief (under 4000 words), and generally report the results of particular research or experiences, or describe individual programs and techniques—in other words, stressing the implications for practice. "Current Career Literature" in each issue lists and rates articles, pamphlets and books. "Current Career Films," synopsizing and briefly evaluating recent films, appears in most issues. "New Books" appears irregularly, but consists mostly of annotations rather than reviews Essential where there are courses in vocational guidance.

Indexed in: Ed.I.   61-34898

ABSTRACTS OF ENGLISH STUDIES.   v. 1, 1958-

Monthly (except July-Aug.)   Urbana, Ill. $12.00

Begun by the University of Colorado Department of English, it was soon taken over by the National Council of Teachers of English, of which it is still an official publication. Each issue now contains between 300 and 400 summaries (very brief—at the most 100 words) of articles on American, English and British Commonwealth literature and the English language. About 1100 journals are now examined (in the first volume there were only some 200); they range from obscure Indian periodicals and highly specialized newsletters to the most prestigious reviews. The monthly index contains, for each entry: 1) names of people referred to significantly, 2) titles of anonymous works dealt with, and 3) subjects treated (articles on a specific work, or works, are listed under the author of the work). The annual index cumulates these but also adds authors of the articles and sub-categories for subjects that appear frequently.

A useful service, but considering the many other indexes and bibliographies in the field, not an essential one for most undergraduate libraries.

A 58-3924

AMERICAN FORENSIC ASSOCIATION.   JOURNAL.   v. 1, 1964-

3 nos./yr.   Mt. Pleasant, Mich. $6.00

"Designed to increase knowledge in those areas of communication theory, practice, and instruction relevant to forensics in schools and colleges. . . interested in argumentation, persuasion, discussion, debate, parliamentary speaking, other types of forensic activities, and appropriate aspects of speech education." In 1953, the Association published its *Register*, which was originally a newsletter but gradually took on other, more substantive matters. In 1964, as a result of the income gained from the Association's sponsorship of a series of nationally televised intercollegiate debates, the *Journal* was founded.

Each issue contains one or several articles on the practice or theory of forensics and its teaching, but much of the contents are regular features more appropriate to a newsletter. These include: annual directories of summer forensic institutes for high school students; the AFA list of officers; an annual calendar listing debate tournaments throughout the country; a valuable annual *Bibliography of Argumentation and Debate* (beginning in 1968) that includes articles, books, theses and dissertations; the "Editor's Corner," which includes items of general interest. Usually 2-4 signed and critical reviews, 500-1500 words in length.

Important only where debating receives much attention.

*AMERICAN LITERATURE.   v. 1, 1929-

Quarterly.   Durham, N.C. $7.00

Published in cooperation with the American Literature Group of the Modern Language Association. At the time of its inception, it was perhaps the only scholarly journal devoted to American literary history, criticism, and bibliography. Though the situation has improved, it is still the leading journal in this area, so that (as stated in the Foreword to the *Analytical Index* covering volumes 1 to 30) "the development of the field of American studies can very conveniently be traced" in its pages. That same index shows that over 170 American authors have been treated in its articles.

In addition to the 5 or 6 main articles, and the briefer items in "Notes and Queries," each issue contains: an extensive book review section, averaging 20-25 signed and critical reviews per issue, mostly 500-600 words long, plus an annotated listing of other new books; *Research in Progress,* listing dissertations completed and in progress, and other projects under way; *Articles on American Literature Appearing in Current Periodicals,* an annotated check list covering a long list of American and foreign periodicals—a very useful bibliographical tool.

Indexed in: B.R.D.   30-20216 rev. 2
          S.S.H.I.

AMERICAN SPEECH.   v. 1, 1925-

Quarterly.   N.Y. $6.00

"A quarterly of linguistic usage," it contains articles dealing with current usage, pronunciation, lore of place names, dialects, derivation and use of slang and other special expressions, special scientific and other nomenclature, and non-English languages in North America. The articles, usually 4 to 6 per issue, mostly of moderate length, are often interesting to the general reader. The "Miscellany" section carries short notes and other news. There are several regular listings of books and articles: on Present-Day English in each issue; since 1934 on "Phonetics" and, since 1933, on "General and Historical Studies," both in alternate issues; and of other "Books Received" once a year. "Among the New Words," carried irregularly but frequently, records and identifies the first use of words and phrases. Only a few book reviews; they are signed and critical and quite long.

Indexed in: S.S.H.I.   27-21844 rev.

CAMBRIDGE Quarterly. *see* GENERAL

CANADIAN LITERATURE.   v. 1, 1959-

Quarterly.   Vancouver, B.C. $5.50

A quality literary review, it includes essays on new and established Canadian writers, on trends in Canadian literature, autobiographical essays by Canadian authors, and some original poetry. There are also reports from Canadian literary centers. Edited by George Woodcock, its contributors have included the most eminent Canadian authors, critics and poets, as well as American and English scholars. The annual bibliography, *Canadian Literature, 19—* , lists books, articles and theses about Canadian literature and creative works by Canadian authors; it includes both English

Canadian and French Canadian works. Usually about 12 reviews per issue; these are classified as "Review Articles" (over 1000 words) and "Book Reviews" (under 1000, but mostly 500 to 1000 words). These are all signed and critical. An essential journal where there is any interest in Canadian writing, and an important journal elsewhere.

63-27291

CHAUCER REVIEW.   v. 1, 1966-

Quarterly.   University Park, Pa. $7.50

Subtitled "A journal of medieval studies and literary criticism," it is published with the cooperation of the Chaucer group of the Modern Language Association. The articles, mostly of substantial length, are on all aspects of Chaucer studies and other literature of the medieval period, and an abstract of each is on the contents page. Contains the annual report of the Committee on Chaucer Research and Bibliography, *Chaucer Research*, which lists current research and completed projects, published books and articles that appeared or were announced during the year. These are mostly by American scholars, though "information submitted by others is not excluded." Unfortunately, the listings are just alphabetically arranged by author, so that items on specific works or topics are hard to find.

CHICAGO REVIEW.   v. 1, 1946-

Quarterly.   Chicago, Ill. $5.00

"A quarterly of art work, book reviews, drama, essays, poetry, prose fiction." While its purpose has been more to discover new writers, poets and artists rather than publish the established or well-known, "name" contributors do appear with some frequency, though not as often as they did in the journal's first 15 years. The attention given to each genre varies considerably from issue to issue, but overall there is a fair representation of short fiction, essays of literary criticism, and poetry (with translations appearing frequently), plus some art work and a few book reviews. The book reviews—of poetry, novels and works on literature—are all signed and critical, and usually 1000-1500 words, occasionally much longer. A useful journal where there is a strong interest in creative writing or the study of contemporary literature.

Indexed in: In.Ltl.Mag.   55-35686
                S.S.H.I.

*COLLEGE ENGLISH.   v. 1, 1939-

Monthly (except June-Sept.)   Champaign, Ill. $10.00

An official organ of the National Council of Teachers of English, it had been from 1928 to 1938 the college edition of the *English Journal.* Under its own name, it retained its character as a general literary journal—though more and more stressing the study and teaching of English; in 1966, it ceased publishing critical articles and explications entirely. Its present editorial policy is to publish articles "in the following areas: (1) the working concepts of criticism: structure, genre, influence, period, myth, rhetoric, etc. (2) The nature of critical and scholarly reasoning; implicit standards of evidence and inference; the nature of critical explanation. (3) The structure of our field; implications of the way we segment it; consequences of specializing in the usual ways; the place of rhetoric and composition. (4) The relevance of current thinking and research in other fields (e.g., philosophy, history, art history, psychology, linguistics) to the study and teaching of English. (5) Curriculum, pedagogy, and educational theory. (6) Practical affairs in the profession. (7) Scholarly books, textbooks, and journals in the field." In recent years the format has been a number of articles around a topic, plus a few departments for exchange of views among members, and news and notes of interest to the profession. Some original poetry. Before 1966, each issue contained a number of fairly short reviews of textbooks and books for students; since then, the number of reviews has been greatly reduced—usually not more than 10 or 15 a year — but they are very long and treat works of literary criticism and history. A basic title for every college library.

Indexed in: Ed.I.   41-6180

COMPARATIVE LITERATURE.   v. 1, 1949-

Quarterly.   Eugene, Ore. $4.50

Its stated purpose is to provide "a forum for those scholars and critics who are engaged in the study of literature from an international point of view. Its editors define comparative literature in the broadest possible manner, and accept articles dealing with the manifold interrelations of literature, with the theory of literature, movements, genres, periods, and authors—from the earliest times to the present." In 1965 it became the official journal of the American Comparative Literature Association. Each issue contains 5 or 6 scholarly articles, mostly 5-10,000 words; the number of reviews varies widely, from just a few to 20, and they are mostly long, from 750 to several thousand words. Primarily for advanced students and research purposes.

Indexed in: S.S.H.I.   50-13965

COMPARATIVE LITERATURE STUDIES.   v. 1, 1964-

Quarterly.   Urbana, Ill. $7.50

Contains "articles on literary history and the history of ideas, with particular emphasis on European literary relations with both North and South America." Begun by the Comparative Literature department of the University of Maryland, it moved in 1968 to the auspices of the Program in Comparative Literature of the University of Illinois. Each issue now contains about 5 articles of varying length, each article preceded by an abstract. Contributors include many of the more eminent names in the field, from both American and foreign universities. Occasionally an issue is devoted to a single theme—e.g., The Symbolist Movement, The Art of the Narrative. Usually 8 to 12 signed, critical reviews per issue, from 750 to several thousand words in length. List of books received. Most articles and reviews are in English, with some in other languages. For advanced students.

76-778

*CONTEMPORARY LITERATURE.   v. 1, 1960-

Quarterly.   Madison, Wis. $8.00

Until January, 1968 this was called *Wisconsin Studies in Contemporary Literature*. According to a policy statement, it publishes "articles on Anglo-American and continental poetry, fiction, drama and criticism chiefly, but not exclusively, since the Second World War. It welcomes full, informative studies of little-known writers and rigorous, documented analyses of the more established ones. Since most of the articles received deal with American and English fiction, the journal is especially interested in essays on poetry, critical theory and practice, and continental literature. It strongly favors a conceptual over an impressionistic approach." Most issues contain 6 to 8 articles, of short to moderate length, one usually an interview with an author, and others perhaps on a special theme for the issue. Special numbers have been devoted to single authors, e.g., Salinger, Nabokov, H.D.,—with a number of critical articles, a bibliography of the author's work and a lengthy checklist of criticism. While a number of books are reviewed, they are reviewed in clusters. In 1968 and 1969, for example, there were 34 review articles covering about 160 titles. Many of these review articles run to several thousand words, and often they survey the work in a genre over a period—e.g., The American Novel, 1966; French Literature in the 1960's; Poetry, 1965, etc. An important journal where there is any interest in modern literature.

Indexed in: S.S.H.I.   64-6922

*CRITICAL QUARTERLY.   v. 1, 1959-

Quarterly.   London. $4.00

A general literary quarterly, comprised of articles and essays of literary criticism and literary history, original poetry, and some reviews. Most pieces are brief, but both the prose and poetry are contributed by some of the leading poets, writers and critics. Emphasis, but by no means exclusive interest, is on twentieth century literature with primary attention to British writers. Only a few reviews in each issue of both fiction and literary criticism; signed and critical, these are usually around 750 words, though occasionally running much longer. This is literary criticism and modern poetry at their best, and the journal and its backfile belongs in every academic library where there is an interest in recent and contemporary English literature.

Indexed in: Br.Hum.I.   62-1042

CRITICISM.   v. 1, 1959-

Quarterly.   Detroit, Mich. $8.00

Published by the Wayne State University Press, its stated design is "to advance the study of literature and the other arts; it is a medium for the scholarly explication and evaluation of artists and their works. Formal aesthetics and the more technical studies in philology and linguistics are not within its scope. It examines the arts and literatures of all periods and nations, either individually or in their interrelationships, and critical theory regarding them." That may be its design, but it has mostly been concerned

with literature and especially English and American writers, and the articles, though perhaps not technical, are quite scholarly. Usually 5 or 6
reviews, signed and critical, that are rather long—rarely less than 1000
words, and usually 2 or 3 times that.

Indexed in: S.S.H.I.   60-51245

*CRITIQUE.   v. 1, 1957-

3 nos./yr.   Minneapolis, Minn. $2.50

Subtitled "Studies in Modern Fiction," it is devoted to fairly brief essays
in this area, with predominant attention to American writers. A number
of issues have been on just one or two contemporary authors; almost all
of these numbers have included among the articles a comprehensive checklist or bibliography of the author. Since they include works by and about
him, and are annotated, they are quite useful, though, of course, since
the authors are for the most part still writing, the bibliographies are soon
out of date. Some of the other issues are devoted to fiction of a geographical
area or a thematic topic, but most contain an assortment of articles, usually
6 or 7 to an issue, averaging 5-6,000 words. Though there are only a few
reviews (occasionally, none) in each issue, these are frequently quite long.

Indexed in: S.S.H.I.   64-32236

ELH.   v. 1, 1934-

Quarterly.   Baltimore, Md. $10.00

Beginning as the private project of some Johns Hopkins graduate students
who were members of the Tudor and Stuart Club, it was intended as a
journal of literary history limited to English studies, and its subtitle was
"A Journal of English Literary History." Its editorial purpose, however,
changed to emphasize critical and interpretive studies of English literature,
and in 1956 the subtitle was dropped. Usually 7 or 8 very scholarly articles
per issue, averaging 6-7,000 words, on all periods of English literature
through the Victorian period (with a rare article on American or modern
literature). From 1937 to 1949 it carried an annual selective bibliography
of American and foreign scholarly publications in the field of the *Romantic Movement (on the Continent and in England),* but limited to the years
1800-1837 in England. Since 1950 the *Philological Quarterly* has carried
this bibliography. *ELH* has no book reviews. A prestigious journal, important for advanced undergraduates and research.

Indexed in: S.S.H.I.   35-12114

ELEMENTARY English. *see* EDUCATION

ENGLISH.   v. 1, 1936-

3 nos./yr.   London. $4.85

Published for the English Association, the British counterpart of our National Council of Teachers of English. Each issue contains usually 3 or
4 articles, short to moderate length, on writers and their works, on the
theory of literature, and on problems related to the teaching of literature. Contributors include faculty from university departments of literature or education as well as teachers in secondary schools. Issues occasionally are devoted to single topics, such as The Contemporary Scene, Irish
Writing, Scottish Number, etc. Several poems in each issue. Review features appearing in most issues or fairly often are: "Poetry and Drama
on Record"; "Poetry Review"; "Reprints, New Editions, Books of Reference, and Recent Periodicals"; "For the Classroom," a listing of recent
texts and books on teaching; "Recent Reading," a personal review of a
number of recent books on literature. About 5 book reviews per issue,
a number of them grouping several books together. These reviews are all
signed and critical, mostly 700-1000 words in length.

Useful where there are strong departments of literature, in particular those
turning out secondary school English teachers, but limited by its lack
of indexing.

41-1492

ENGLISH JOURNAL.   v. 1, 1912-

Monthly (except June-Aug.)   Champaign, Ill. $10.00

"The official Journal of the Secondary Section of National Council of
Teachers of English," but containing many articles of general interest to
college students and faculty. A large number of short articles in each
issue, mostly by junior and senior high school teachers but also English
faculty at colleges and universities, on literary criticism, the theory and
methods of teaching English, bibliography, the teaching profession, classroom experiences, etc. Also some original poetry on students, teachers,
and the teaching of English. Regular features include: "This World of
English"—news of projects, summaries of recent useful articles, and notes
of NCTE affiliates; "The Scene," a collection of short, interesting, personal comments and notes on almost any aspect of teaching that strikes the
editor's fancy; "Teaching Materials," containing brief (averaging 250 words)
reviews of textbooks and audiovisual materials; "Professional Publications"
—signed, critical reviews, sometimes quite long, of books on teaching,
literary history and criticism; "Book Marks," reviews of usually 8 to 10
books for recreational reading or non-fiction in various areas, reviewed in
terms of their appropriateness for high school libraries; "NCTE/ERIC Summaries and Sources," in each issue, cites and abstracts documents on a
subject of interest to secondary school English teachers such as Literary
Analysis, In-Service Training, Poetry in Secondary Schools, etc.

Particularly useful for colleges in which beginning English courses must
remedy inadequate high school preparation, and those in which students
are prepared for high school teaching of English, but also generally for
most college libraries.

Indexed in: Ed.I.   14-13041 rev. 2
             R.G.

ENGLISH 163

*ENGLISH LANGUAGE NOTES.   v. 1, 1963-

Quarterly.   Boulder, Colo. $9.00

Its articles are really scholarly notes, mostly interpretations or explications—rarely are they more than 5 or 6 pages; more often, just 1 or 2 pages—treating all periods and genres of English and, occasionally, American literature (except for living authors). The reviews, usually about 10 per issue, are mostly from 500 to 1000 words, but occasionally much longer; they are signed and critical. Among the reviewers are some of the most eminent literary critics. The annual bibliography, *The Romantic Movement*, has been carried as a supplement to the September ELN beginning with the 1964 bibliography. Including "all books and articles of substantial interest to scholars of English and Continental Romanticism," along with descriptive and, when necessary, critical notes, plus references to reviews, This very useful bibliography (previously carried in *Philological Quarterly* and *ELH*), plus the excellent reviews, make *ELN* an important addition to the library, whereas the brief articles are primarily useful for advanced students and research.

66-91847

ENGLISH LITERATURE IN TRANSITION (1880-1920)   v. 1, 1957-

Quarterly.   Tempe, Ariz. $2.50

Originally (until 1962) titled *English Fiction in Transition*. Started as a free newsletter mimeographed in the Purdue University English Department, gradually getting more support and recognition, it is devoted to English literature of that 40-year period, a period the journal's founders felt was in limbo between the study of the Victorian period and the modern. In addition to the writers who thrived during that period (e.g., Conrad, Ford Madox Ford, Gissing, Forster, H. Rider Haggard, Kipling, H.G. Welles, etc.) it occasionally treats the earlier or later works of authors who thrived before or after the period, such as Joyce. Contains scholarly articles, mostly quite brief, with a good bit of attention paid to bibliography. Annotated bibliographies of writers of the period appear in almost every issue, and these are continually up-dated. There is also news of bibliographical projects and of other matters of interest—conferences, scholarship, etc. A few reviews in each issue. Signed and critical, they are usually 500-1000 words, with occasional longer review-articles. List of books received. The journal's format leaves something to be desired but that will probably change as it becomes more popular (in 1967 it went from mimeographing to photo-offset).

64-39174

ENGLISH STUDIES.   v. 1, 1919-

Bi-monthly.   Amsterdam, Netherlands. $13.00

"A journal of English letters and philology." Contains scholarly articles and notes on all periods of English and American literature and language with contributions from many countries. There are only a few articles per issue plus a larger number of "Notes." A regular feature is "Points of Modern English Syntax," a detailed analysis of the use of words or expressions. The reviews, 15 to 25 per issue, are signed and critical, and generally quite long, almost all over 1000 words, and often much more. They deal mostly with books on literature before 1830 and on language, treating books published in all modern languages. For advanced students and research.

Indexed in: S.S.H.I.   A 33-280 rev.

*ESSAYS IN CRITICISM.   v. 1, 1951-

Quarterly.   Oxford, Eng. $6.00

A scholarly journal, but one demanding that contributions be well written and interesting—as they usually are. (Footnotes are not permitted, and an Editorial Note has stated that "The Editors reserve the right, which is only sparingly exercised, to re-write phrases and amend the punctuation in contributors' articles, if they seem to them to deviate into inelegant English.") Almost all the articles (5 or 6 in each issue, varying greatly in length) are on English literature, but range over all genres and periods. The book reviews are few in number (5 to 8 in each issue) but they are frequently critical essays—lengthy, detailed and thoughtful. The lively "Critical Forum" carries criticisms of articles, rejoinders to criticisms, and miscellaneous comments. A journal that shows English literary criticism at its best—viewing literature with affection as well as intelligence—it should be in every academic library.

Indexed in: Br.Hum.I.   67-681

ETC. see GENERAL

*HUDSON REVIEW.   v. 1, 1948-

Quarterly.   N.Y. $7.00

Contains short fiction and poetry, and articles by distinguished writers and scholars on criticism, aesthetics, the arts, and general literary topics. Original, perceptive and sensible, it has generally adhered to its intention to "be on guard against the vagaries attendant upon a constant quest for novelty and timeliness," yet it has avoided academicism. Though the youngest of the American "big four" (now three) literary reviews, it is regarded as at least an equal of the others. Its fiction and poetry are nicely balanced between some of the best known American and foreign writers and the younger, more experimental ones. The regular sections in "Chronicles" reviewing music and dance, new films, the theater, and art, are all in charge of leading critics, such as John Simon, B.H. Haggin and Lucy Lippard. Excellent lengthy book reviews, and review articles of fiction and critical works; also especially good poetry reviews. These review articles attempt to cover every *important* novel and book of poetry published during the period, and since about 100 books are covered each year, the articles provide a useful selection guide. Letters from correspondents abroad comment on literary and artistic developments in other countries. An essential publication for all academic libraries.

Indexed in: S.S.H.I.   50-2532

ENGLISH165

JOURNAL of American Folklore. *see* SOCIOLOGY AND ANTHROPOLOGY

JOURNAL of Commonwealth Literature. *see* AREA STUDIES/GENERAL

JOURNAL OF ENGLISH AND GERMANIC PHILOLOGY. v. 1, 1897-

Quarterly. Urbana, Ill. $7.50

"Published under the auspices of the Graduate College of the University of Illinois." Scholarly articles, of varying length on English, German and Scandinavian languages and literatures. Covers all periods, but only rarely recent or contemporary figures. Though its early title (for the first 5 years) was the *Journal of Germanic Philology* and it did not treat English, now more attention is given to English than to both German and Scandinavian. Moreover, it has had an increasing emphasis on standard literary periods and figures, with a corresponding reduction in attention given to the study of Old English, Old Norse, Anglo-Saxon, etc. Beginning with the number for 1933-34, it has carried the annual *Anglo-German Literary Bibliography* (except those for 1941 and 1942 which were included in the more general bibliography in the *American-German Review*), which covers books and articles on the literary relationships between Germany and England or America, and citing reviews of the books listed. The book review section is excellent. The number of reviews varies from 25 to 60 per issue; they are all signed, mostly about one –though sometimes two or three-thousand words in length, and occasionally in German.

Indexed in: S.S.H.I.   10-26331 rev.*

JOURNAL of Popular Culture. *see* GENERAL

JOURNAL of the Folklore Institute. *see* SOCIOLOGY AND ANTHROPOLOGY

LITERARY REVIEW. v. 1, 1957-

Quarterly. Rutherford, N.J. $7.00

"An international journal of contemporary writing," published by Fairleigh Dickinson University, it contains original poetry and short stories, and essays on contemporary writers and writing. Most issues are now devoted to a single theme, usually on the contemporary literary scene of a country or area, and stressing those that are not covered well by other journals. One volume, for example, contained numbers treating Denmark, the Baltic, and Canada, plus a fourth number comprised of poetry and stories. The contributors include both well-known and new writers. No book reviews. A useful journal because of its coverage of the international literary scene.

Indexed in: In.Ltl.Mag.   59-65170
            S.S.H.I.

LITERATURE AND PSYCHOLOGY. v. 1, 1951-

Quarterly. Teaneck, N.J. $8.00

Sponsored by the Modern Languages Association Discussion Group General Topics Ten, its editorial policy is: "The application of depth psychology to literature, in which psychology is subordinated to the interests of textual explication. We shall continue to welcome criticism informed by such diverse approaches as the Jungian, the Existentialist, the Behaviorist, or any other which does not use the text merely as a springboard into theory." Usually 4 to 6 articles, brief to moderate length, per issue, mostly by literary scholars but also by psychiatrists, on all periods of literature. A few signed, critical reviews, some of them quite long. In 1968, the first annual *Bibliography* (for the years 1964-65) appeared, covering 69 journals, primarily American; the second, for 1966-67, appeared in 1969 as a supplement, and covered about 150 journals. When appropriate, each item is annotated, often at length, and frequently critically, making the *Bibliography* that much more useful. Because of the increasing interest in the psychological interpretation of literature, the journal will be useful to libraries where there are strong departments of English.

Indexed in: Ment.Hlth.B.R.I.   67-9054

*LITERATURE EAST & WEST.   v. 1, 1954-

Quarterly.   Austin, Texas. $8.00

"Journal of the Oriental-Western Literary Relations Group of the Modern Language Association." Its purpose is "to encourage study of the literature of Asia and Africa and especially study in comparative literature and East-West literary relations. We plan to print material on both classical literature and contemporary authors and literary movements." The contributions—poems, stories, selections from novels, plays, essays, and articles on literary history and criticism—are fairly brief. Many, of course, have been translated; all contributions are in English. About half the issues cover a variety of national literatures; the rest are devoted to the literature of a single country or area—e.g., Africa, India, Malaysia, the Philippines, Japan, China. The reviews, which are of both creative works and literary history and criticism, are all signed and critical, vary widely in length and in number per issue; more important is the fact that in many cases they are of books not reviewed elsewhere, at least not in readily available sources. Colleges with courses on Asian or African literature, or having any interest in these areas should have the journal, since it fulfills a unique purpose and since the material is appropriate for undergraduate interests and abilities.

65-9986

LONDON Magazine. *see* GENERAL

MALAHAT REVIEW.   V. 1, 1967-

Quarterly.   Victoria, B.C., Canada $5.00

"An international quarterly of life and letters," it is published at the University of Victoria. Except for occasional contributions outside the area of modern literature, particularly in art and music, it is devoted to original poetry and short stories, plus critical articles on authors or poets currently writing. Most of the contributors are from Canada, the U.S. or Great Britain, and well known ones (e.g., Richard Aldington, James Dickey, Roy Fuller, Frank Kermode, Denise Levertov, Joyce Carol Oates, Herbert Read, John Wain) appear very often, attesting to the journal's reputation and the editor's (Robin Skelton, poet and critic) expertise. There are some contributions from other countries, all translated into English, much of it by internationally known writers.

Of uniformly high quality, it should appeal to serious students of contemporary writing.

MASSACHUSETTS Review. *see* GENERAL

MEANJIN QUARTERLY. v. 1, 1940-

Quarterly. Melbourne, Australia. $9.05

In its early years it concentrated on establishing a characteristically Australian literary tradition and outlook, but the picture presented of Australian intellectual life through its pages was a fairly gloomy one, except for some of the poetry. In 1945, the journal moved from Brisbane ("Meanjin" is the aboriginal name for Brisbane) to Melbourne University, where the financial and intellectual support began to make a difference, and gradually it improved to the point where it is generally recognized now as the major literary periodical of Australia, with an international reputation for its poetry, fiction and criticism.

Each issue contains about 10 or 12 articles and essays, mostly on literary figures or topics, with an emphasis, of course, on Australia, plus 2 or 3 short stories, a number of poems, and 5 to 10 book reviews, mostly of Australian novels, poetry or criticism.

Although it is not yet one of the world's leading literary journals, because it does represent an entire continent which has an increasingly recognized group of writers, *Meanjin* should be seriously considered where there is a strong interest in contemporary fiction and poetry.

49-40567 rev.*

*MODERN FICTION STUDIES. v. 1, 1955-

Quarterly. Lafayette, Ind. $5.00

Published by the Modern Fiction Club of the Purdue University Department of English, it is "devoted to criticism, scholarship and bibliography of American, English and European fiction since about 1880." The Spring and Autumn issues almost always deal with individual writers; they include miscellaneous critical and biographical articles, plus a very useful selected checklist of criticism relating to the writer and his works. To show the variety, authors so treated in recent years have been Iris Murdoch, James Joyce, Hemingway, Mark Twain and Lawrence Durrell. The Summer and Winter issues are general numbers concerned with various writers and problems of modern fiction. These numbers carried (through 1968) the "Modern Fiction Newsletter" which did two things: first, commented informally on recent critical works; second, listed recently published books and articles "in English about writers of recognized stature." In 1969, this was changed to the review section, "Recent Books on Modern Fiction." It covers about 50 titles, mostly on British and American fiction, in reviews varying greatly in length and in number of books treated. A few short reviews will cover one or two titles each; longer review-essays may treat as many as 15 titles. Also list of books received. A very useful journal for undergraduates.

Indexed in: S.S.H.I. 56-651

MODERN Language Associations. Publications. *see* MODERN LANGUAGES/ GENERAL

MODERN LANGUAGE QUARTERLY.   v. 1, 1940-

Quarterly.   Seattle, Wash. $6.00

Devoted to scholarly studies in English, American, Germanic and Romance languages and literatures, but with the largest number by far on
English literature. 6 to 10 articles per issue, of short to moderate length.
The *Bibliography of Critical Arthurian Literature* for the year appeared
in the journal through 1963. Generally 7 to 10 book reviews per issue;
signed and critical, they are mostly between 800 and 1200 words in
length. Also a list of books received.

Indexed in: S.S.H.I.   43-5690

*MODERN PHILOLOGY.   v. 1, 1903-

Quarterly.   Chicago, Ill. $8.00

"A journal devoted to research in medieval and modern literature." In
its early years it carried articles in all aspects of these areas, but under
the editorship of Ronald Crane in the 1930's linguistic studies were dropped;
critical reviews, articles on the history and theory of criticism were given
prominence. Today, issues contain 3 to 5 articles on literary history,
interpretation and theory and textual studies, plus a few "Notes and
Documents" that are shorter research pieces and texts of newly discovered source materials. From 1933 to 1957 it carried the annual *Victorian
Bibliography,* listing American and foreign publications on that period of
English literature; in 1957 the bibliography was taken over by *Victorian
Studies* and its coverage expanded. Each issue contains 10 to 15 signed
and critical book reviews, mostly well over 1000 words. The review article, frequently running to more than 5000 words, has become an increasingly regular feature. List of books received. An important scholarly
journal.

Indexed in: B.R.D.   10-32832 rev.
            S.S.H.I.

MUNDUS ARTIUM.   v. 1, 1967-

3 nos./yr.   Athens, Ohio. $6.00

"A Journal of International Literature and the Arts," it is published by
the Department of English, Ohio University. It publishes foreign poets
in both their original language and English translation, younger and well-
known American poets, and brief essays in comparative literature and
the arts. Some of the better known poets and writers appearing have
been Richard Eberhart, Gunter Grass, Guiseppi Ungaretti, John Berryman,
Denise Levertov, and Robert Creeley. One issue concentrated on Latin
American poetry, and another on the Spanish poet Vicente Aleixandre.
Each issue has from 2 to 7 reviews of books of poetry, literary criticism
and occasionally fiction; they are signed and critical, and mostly 400-700
words in length. A useful journal where there is much interest in contemporary poetry, here and abroad.

NEW England Quarterly. *see* GENERAL

---

*NINETEENTH CENTURY FICTION.   v. 1, 1945-

Quarterly.   Berkeley, Calif. $7.00

Each issue contains 6 or 7 scholarly articles, mostly about 5-6000 words, dealing with major and minor English and American authors of the period, and with analyses and interpretations of their works. (The journal's original title was *The Trollopian*—a title that lasted, fortunately, only until 1949.) The section "Notes" contains briefer comments and observations, and occasionally newly discovered letters or other primary sources. The reviews, of which there are almost never more than five, are signed and critical, are at least 750 words, and often several times that. "Recent Books: American Fiction," and "Recent Books: British Fiction" appear in alternate issues; each reviews a group of recent critical works. An important scholarly journal.

Indexed in: S.S.H.I.   49-53317*

NOTES AND QUERIES.   v. 1, 1849-

Monthly.   London. $13.00

Until 1923 it was numbered in series of 12 volumes; since then it has been numbered sequentially. Contains a great deal of miscellaneous information, primarily in areas of literature and bibliography, history, genealogy, folklore, etc. Much of this is in the form of responses to requests from readers, but it also has articles and book reviews in the same areas. The number of reviews varies widely, but most are 500-900 words, though occasionally much longer for books of special importance. The reviews are all signed, and quite critical. In addition to its importance for English literature (references to it appear frequently in standard bibliographies), it is a most useful title for reference work, since it makes a point of correcting and updating standard reference works, and because the indexes are so thorough. Many libraries, as a matter of fact, shelve it in the reference collection.

Indexed in: Br.Hum.I.   12-25307-8
                 S.S.H.I.

---

*NOVEL.   v. 1, 1967-

3 nos./yr.   Providence, R.I. $4.50

Subtitled "A Forum on Fiction," it is a scholarly journal devoted to the novel of all periods and countries. Issues usually contain 4 to 6 articles, plus a few review-essays and from 8 to 12 excellent reviews, usually 1000-2000 words, on recent important novels or works of criticism, both English language and others. Contributors include many well known critics and scholars from American, British and Commonwealth universities; their contributions, though mostly brief to moderate length, are significant, especially since the editors insist on broader and deeper contexts of appraisal, rather than—as so many philological journals do—focus on the minutiae. An attractive, well-edited journal, important to any English department in which students do serious work.

*PARIS REVIEW.   v. 1, 1953-

Quarterly.   Paris. $4.00

A literary journal of high quality, dedicated to publishing fiction and poetry by talented but often unknown writers as well as materials from more eminent authors. In addition to the literary contributions, which are for the most part excellent, the feature for which the journal has become most noted, and for which it is perhaps most consulted, is its series of sensitive and revealing interviews with authors, poets, and play-wrights that appear in every issue. Since the first one with E.M. Forster, almost every outstanding literary figure (it seems) has been interviewed, providing invaluable biographical, historical and critical material. (A number of the interviews—but by no means all—have been collected in the three volumes of *Writers at Work: The Paris Review Interviews,* published in 1958, 1963 and 1967). Art work—drawings and photographs—appear fairly regularly. The editor's intention was to get away from the pattern of literary criticism to which most little magazines had become addicted, so that scholarly articles do not appear at all. Nevertheless, because of the quality of contributions and the interviews, the journal belongs in every academic library where there is any interest in contemporary litera-ture.

Indexed in: In.Ltl.Mag.   63-54853
                S.S.H.I

PARTISAN Review. *see* GENERAL

*PHILOLOGICAL QUARTERLY.   v. 1, 1922-

Quarterly.   Iowa City, Ia. $7.50

"A journal devoted to scholarly investigation of the classical and mod-ern languages and literatures." 3 of the 4 numbers consist of short to medium-length articles, usually 10 to 15 per issue, with the preponder-ance on English literature before 1800. The July issue consists almost entirely of the important annual bibliography, *English Literature, 1660-1800,* a listing of books and articles, with frequent (and sometimes ex-tensive) critical annotations, plus citations of reviews. It even picks up books previously listed that were the subject of important reviews in the year covered. From 1949 to 1964 it also carried the annual bibliography, *The Romantic Movement (on the Continent and in England),* which since then has appeared in *English Language Notes.* Only a few book reviews, perhaps 8 or 10 a year; these, however, are all at least 1500 words, and usually much more—indeed, some of them are included with the articles. There is also a list of books received. Though the journal is primarily for advanced students and research, the annual bibliography in it makes it important for all college libraries.

Indexed in: S.S.H.I.   27-13435

NOTE: In 1971, the bibliography *English Literature, 1660-1800* was changed to *The Eighteenth Century: A Current Bibliography.* It incor-porated its predecessor and also includes items in the social   sciences, philosophy, science, religion and the fine arts, though literature comprises the major portion.

*POETRY.   v. 1, 1912-

Bi-monthly.   Chicago, Ill. $12.00

Since its founding by Harriet Monroe, who remained as editor for almost 25 years, it has become the leading English language journal devoted solely to poetry. Almost every well known poet, British and American, has been published in it, many making their first appearances in it. While many of these poets were considered experimental or radical in the past, *Poetry* has been criticized in recent years for catering to a coterie of established poets. Be that as it may, the poetry in it is still some of the most important currently appearing, and the journal is essential to every academic library. A backfile is indispensable for studying the evolution of American poetry.

In addition to the poetry, there are reviews of new books of poems, either of single works or of a group of works. These reviews, by leading poets and critics, are almost always at least 1000 words, frequently more, and usually excellent, though here again, the journal has been criticized for relaxing its critical acumen. Also "News Notes" of prizes, conferences, festivals, special lectures and readings, new journals, etc. An extensive listing of "Books Received," both poetry and prose, in most issues.

Indexed in: B.R.D.   14-13059 rev. 2*
            R.G.

QUARTERLY JOURNAL OF SPEECH.   v. 1, 1915-

Quarterly.   Bloomington, Ind. $10.00

A scholarly journal devoted to the interest of speech education, it is the official publication of the Speech Association of America. The original title was the *Quarterly Journal of Public Speaking;* in 1918 it became the *Quarterly Journal of Speech Education*, assuming its present title in 1928. Articles on language and phonetics, on the history and theory of rhetoric (many related to matters of current political interest), suggestions and practices for teaching speech, the diagnosis and treatment of speech defects, on argumentation and debate, on drama, radio, television and film history and criticism, etc. Usually 9 or 10 articles per issue, mostly around 3000 words, with a maximum of 5000 words (longer articles are published in *Speech Monographs*), by professors of speech at colleges and universities. The section "Shop Talk," which for many years carried professional notes, news and schedules of campus drama activities, news of conferences and workshops, personnel changes, etc., and the annual publication of papers read at the convention, were both discontinued in 1966, having been transferred to the Association's membership publication, *Spectra.* There are a large number of book reviews, about 30-40 per issue, averaging 300-500 words each. This review section is of general use, since many of the books have seemingly little to do with speech—they are in the areas of politics, drama, psychology, sociology, literature and drama and others. A listing of books and plays received was discontinued in 1967; brief annotations of other books than those reviewed was discontinued in 1968. An interesting, useful journal, suitable for many areas of undergraduate study.

Indexed in: Ed.I.   56-53730

QUARTERLY REVIEW OF LITERATURE.   v. 1, 1943-

Semi-annual.   Princeton, N.J. $5.00

"A creative magazine devoted to poetry, fiction, and drama, emphasizes entire plays, novelettes, and large groups of a poet's work." For years, one number each year was devoted to creative and critical studies of a single novelist, poet or playwright, but since 1964, after *QRL* was located at Bard College, it has not followed this policy. In the last few years, only two double numbers a year have been published, one devoted to poetry, the other to prose. The mix of newer and well established writers has been good, with some of the most eminent names appearing—in 1969, for example, Sartre, Ralph Ellison, Marianne Moore, Robert Coover, Hayden Carruth, Robert Duncan, Richard Howard, Ted Hughes, Louis Simpson, W.S. Merwin and many others. Associated since 1969 with the Creative Arts Program of Princeton University, it is an important journal of creative writing.

Indexed in: In.Ltl.Mag.   45-10088

RENAISSANCE QUARTERLY.   v. 1, 1954-

Quarterly.   N.Y. $16.00

First issued as a section of the *Journal of Renaissance and Baroque Music,* then a separate publication as *Renaissance News,* it assumed its present title in 1967. Published by the Renaissance Society of America, it is devoted to all phases of Renaissance life and culture. Each issue contains usually just 2 to 4 articles (and these not very long) but a large number— 25 or so—of book reviews, signed and critical, and averaging about 1000 words. Also a list of books recently published, compiled from those received and from national bibliographies. News of conferences, news and notes of programs, grants, personnel, etc. "Reports on Renaissance Scholarship "—on some area of Renaissance studies, discussing recent publications and trends in research in that area—appears frequently. Subscription is by membership; this includes receipt of the annual volume *Studies in the Renaissance.* Especially pertinent for English and history departments, it is also useful for philosophy, art history, musicology, and Romance and German literatures.

Indexed in: Art I.   51-29088

REVIEW OF ENGLISH STUDIES.   v. 1, 1925;   n.s.v. 1, 1950-

Quarterly.   Oxford, Eng. $9.50

Though subtitled "A quarterly journal of English literature and the English language," its coverage, in scholarly articles and notes, is limited almost entirely to literature, treating language when it relates to literary criticism or explication. Usually 3 articles per issue, averaging about 5000 words, plus a few somewhat shorter "Notes," which consist of research on minor points, reactions to recent articles in *RES* or other journals, or the publication of newly-discovered letters or other materials. Almost half of each issue is devoted to reviews—some 20 to 30 longer, signed and critical reviews, mostly about 1000 words, plus about 5 "Short Notices," 300-600 words long, but also signed and critical. "Summary of Periodical

Literature," in each issue, lists the contents of recent issues of the more significant English and foreign-language journals in the field of English literature and philology. An extensive "List of Publications Received" appears in alternate issues. An important scholarly journal, especially for advanced students and research.

Indexed in: Br.Hum.I.   30-31955 rev.*
S.S.H.I.

*SEWANEE REVIEW. v. 1, 1892-

Quarterly.   Sewanee, Tenn. $7.00

The oldest existing critical and literary quarterly in this country, it was originally patterned after the English reviews of the nineteenth century. Its early contributions consisted of history, geography and literary essays, with much attention to the Southern regional aspects. While literary scholarship was always a prominent feature, there was no original poetry until the 1920's, and not until 1944, when Allen Tate became editor, did it achieve real eminence. Since that time it has become known as one of the most important literary quarterlies, with literary essays and criticism by both well-known and talented younger writers, especially those from or in the South. There is no pattern to the contents. One issue may contain all fiction, another, none. The section "Arts and Letters" contains review-essays on groups of related books and on single books. Treating fiction, poetry and works of literary scholarship, they are almost all quite lengthy, and all worthwhile. Every college library should have a backfile to at least 1944 (and further if possible) and a current subscription.

Indexed in: S.S.H.I.   9-33131

*SHAKESPEARE QUARTERLY. v. 1, 1950-

Quarterly.   N.Y. $10.00

Published by the Shakespeare Association of America and successor to its *Bulletin,* which led a struggling existence from 1925 to 1948. With a new group of officers in 1949, the new editor, Robert M. Smith, decided to resuscitate a journal, but one larger than the *Bulletin,* one devoted to just Shakespeare rather than the Elizabethan period in general, and one that would appeal not just to scholars, but to theater people, teachers, libraries, schools, and reading groups. Under the editorship of James G. McManaway, it has continued this pattern.

It contains critical and research articles, with frequent illustrations, by Shakespearian research scholars here and abroad, on all phases of the Bard's life and works—on the works themselves, on the characters, the commentaries, and the productions and interpretations of the works. The Summer number contains the annual *Shakespeare: An Annotated World Bibliography,* which "attempts to record annually all books, articles, and reviews of books and theatrical productions directly related to Shakespeare. A brief description of content or statement of theme is given for articles and for some books." Over 1300 items were included in the *Bibliography* for 1968.

Until 1963, there was an annual listing of Shakespearian productions throughout the year; this has been dropped in favor of articles covering the more important productions and festivals. A brief "Notes and Comments" section carries news of publications, Shakespeare festivals, etc. and items about the Association. The book reviews, about 20 a year, vary in length according to the significance of the work reviewed, but average 600 to 700 words; they are signed and critical.

Indexed in: S.S.H.I.   55-30403

SMALL PRESS REVIEW.   v. 1, 1967-

Quarterly.   Paradise, Calif. $3.50

Founded for two objectives: first, "to serve the small press/little magazine business"; second, "to go out from the center of that business to a world NEEDING small presses, which may be, with their attendant psycho-politico-literary ramifications, our last edge against modern man's cold invasive impersonality." Whether or not it is accomplishing much toward the second is beyond our necessarily limited observation; it can be said, however, that it does serve the first objective well. Starting as a very slight, and somewhat frenetic-looking publication, it has gotten more substance, though its format (typewriter plus offset) would hardly win it a place in *Graphis,* and makes browsing in it a bit difficult. According to the editor's plans of 1969, alternate issues will cover different things: even-numbered issues will list books of small presses and little magazines; the odd-numbered, features, news, letters and reviews. (He adds, however, that he will "feel free to violate [the pattern] at will.")

The publisher of the *Small Press Review,* DUSTbooks, publishes the annuals, *Small Press Record* and *Directory of Little Magazines* which the *Review* updates. A useful journal, especially since so many undergraduates are interested in the little magazines and the underground press, and since *Trace,* which was a very good guide, ceased publication in 1970. Librarians can use it for the selection and acquisition of books and periodicals hard to find elsewhere; it will also be consulted by students and faculty where creative writing is given much attention.

*SOUTHERN REVIEW.   n.s.v. 1, 1965-

Quarterly.   Baton Rouge, La. $5.00

The original *Southern Review,* edited by Cleanth Brooks and Robert Penn Warren, ran from 1935 to 1942, and is generally regarded as one of the important literary periodicals of its time, especially for its regional contributions, but also for those by eminent writers and critics from other areas. The sole connection with the new series is the title and place of publication. But even without those tenuous connections, the present *Southern Review* can stand on its own. It contains literary criticism, poetry, fiction, and book reviews, contributed by writers and scholars from all over the country—in other words, despite the title, it cannot be considered a regional journal. Most contributors are relatively unknown, but there are enough pieces by well-known writers and critics to keep a happy balance. Usually 8 to 12 reviews, but some of them cover as many as 15 books of poetry, criticism or fiction, so that each issue generally treats at least 50 books in the review section. The quality of the contributions is generally high; even, more than just occasionally, superb. And since a volume consists of a thousand pages or more, the journal is not only a useful resource for the library, but a very good buy.

Indexed in: In.Ltl.Mag.   36-25494 rev. 2

SPEECH MONOGRAPHS.   v. 1, 1934-

Quarterly.   N.Y. $15.00

Published by the Speech Association of America, it "is a research journal publishing learned inquiries concerned with speech and related communicative behaviors. It was established to provide an outlet for major research reports. Articles especially appropriate for publication in *Speech Monographs* are: substantial scholarly articles which must be somewhat longer than can be accommodated by other journals of the Speech Association of America, reports of research which are of greater interest to specialists than to the majority of communication scholars, and brief research notes." There are a number of regular bibliographies. *Graduate Theses: An Index of Graduate Work in Speech* has appeared annually since volume 2; *Doctoral Dissertations in Speech: Work in Progress* and *A Bibliography of Rhetoric and Public Address for the Year* since 1951, the latter including articles and books, citing reviews of the latter and with occasional brief annotations. Two listings of theses also appear annually: *Graduate Theses: An Index of Graduate Work in Speech* (since 1945) lists the Masters theses; *Abstracts of Theses in the Field of Speech*, including only Ph.D. theses, started in 1946. There are no book reviews.

Indexed in: Ed.I.
                                                              36-11379

*STUDIES IN ENGLISH   LITERATURE, 1500-1900.   v. 1, 1961-

Quarterly.   Houston, Texas. $8.00

Published by Rice University, each issue is devoted to one of four fields: winter, English Renaissance; spring, Elizabethan and Jacobean Drama; summer, Restoration and Eighteenth Century; autumn, Nineteenth Century. Each issue carries 10-12 articles, by faculty members from mostly American and (on occasion) Canadian universities, of moderate length and ranging over all aspects of the literature of the period covered. Articles "may present the results of historical research; they may be concerned with matters of interpretation; or they may offer conclusions which involve scholarly criticism," but they should "make significant contributions to an understanding of literature in its full biographical and historical context." Each article is preceded by a thorough synopsis. There are no book reviews as such; however, the last article of each issue consists of a survey-review of a large number (anywhere from 20 to 100) of books published during the year in the area of the particular issue. In these, the space devoted to each title varies, but for the more important works is often a thousand words or more. This is a useful feature for book selection and the journal as a whole is appropriate for college libraries because of the significance and breadth of the contributions.

Indexed in: S.S.H.I.   65-8010

STUDIES IN PHILOLOGY.   v. 1, 1906-

5 nos./yr.   Chapel Hill, N.C. $10.00

Published under the direction of members of the graduate faculty of the departments of languages and literatures in the University of North Carolina. Each of 4 issues carries from 5 to 10 scholarly articles, averaging about 5000 words. Covers all periods of English and West European languages and literatures, though the early volumes paid more attention to linguistic studies, even Roman and Greek; for many years, however, literature has been stressed and most attention given to English literature. Since 1923 it has carried (as the May number, recently) the extensive bibliography *Literature of the Renaissance,* which covers articles and monographs, citing reviews of the books listed; it includes a proper name index. An announcement was made in 1969 that the bibliography for 1968 would be the last published, and that a Texts and Studies number would supplant the bibliography. There are no book reviews. An important journal for advanced study and research; for smaller libraries the elimination of the bibliography somewhat reduces its importance.

Indexed in: S.S.H.I.   7-11058 (rev. '43)

STUDIES IN ROMANTICISM.   v. 1, 1961-

Quarterly.   Boston, Mass. $6.50

Published by the Graduate School of Boston University, it contains scholarly articles on literature, the arts and history of society and the arts during the romantic period, covering all countries; a large proportion of the studies, however, are on the standard figures in English literature. Articles, about 4 per issue, are mostly of moderate length, averaging about 5000 words; occasional shorter notes and documents.

Beginning in 1970, the September issue is "devoted to special subjects and representing the judgements of acknowledged experts in each." The first subject to be so treated was The Concept of Romanticism; another will probably be Rousseau. The journal began carrying book reviews in 1971—2 or 3 an issue, usually several thousand words in length.

Indexed in: S.S.H.I.   63-5154

*STUDIES IN SHORT FICTION.   v. 1, 1963-

Quarterly.   Newbury, S.C. $8.00

Published by Newbury College, it is "devoted exclusively to serious commentary on short fiction." Issues usually contain from 6 to 10 articles, limited to 5000 words, on mostly American and British subjects, plus some shorter notes *(explication de texte,* textual criticism, unpublished letters, etc.) and an average of 10 reviews, mostly 700-1000 words long, of books of criticism or collections of short stories. Occasional issues have been devoted to a single area (e.g., Contemporary European Short Fiction, Indian Fiction) or to a monograph, and even to a *Cross-Reference Index of Short Fiction and Author Title Listing,* a very handy reference item. There is an *Annual Bibliography of Explications of Short Fiction,* covering recent books and a substantial list of periodicals. A most useful

periodical for undergraduate libraries because of student interest in and
capability of dealing with this genre.

64-9357

TEXAS STUDIES IN LITERATURE AND LANGUAGES.   v. 1, 1959-

Quarterly.   Austin, Texas. $10.00

Though it is subtitled "A journal of the humanities," and the editors
invite contributions "in all areas of literature, linguistics, philosophy, social studies and nontechnical science," it has consisted almost solely of
articles on literary criticism, history and explication, with preponderant
attention to first, English, then American literature and occasionally to
others. Usually 10 to 12 scholarly articles per issue, averaging about 5000
words. Contributors are from colleges and universities throughout the U.S.
There are no book reviews.

61-46112

*TRI-QUARTERLY.   no. 1, 1964-

3/yr.   Evanston, Ill. $7.00

"An international journal of arts, letters and opinion," published at North-
western University. Though some issues have been devoted to single
topics—e.g., Contemporary Latin American Literature, Under 30 Issue,
The Art of Sylvia Plath—most issues contain a well balanced assortmentof
fiction, poetry, criticism and essays on society and the arts, with usually
some photographs and drawings. Dramatic works are published occasionally and translations frequently. Contributors range from some of the best
known authors, poets and critics to those appearing for the first time anywhere, and the contributions also range from experimental to conservative.

The quality is almost uniformly high, the format and typography superb,
and the journal has quickly become recognized as one of the best literary
reviews. Indeed, some of the single-topic issues have become collector's
items. Certainly considering the quality, quantity and price, it belongs in
any college library where there is much interest in contemporary
literature.

Indexed in: In.Ltl.Mag.   65-3811

*TWENTIETH CENTURY LITERATURE.   v. 1, 1955-

Quarterly.   Los Angeles, Calif. $4.00

Founded by Alan Swallow, and published by him until his death in 1966,
it contains "articles on all aspects of modern and contemporary literature, including articles in English on writers in other langrages." Through
1969, however, only American and British novelists, poets and dramatists
have been treated, but with a new format in 1970, the editor spoke about
plans for special supplements on Canadian, Anglo-Indian and African writing. Articles have rarely been more than 5000 words, and there are usually

just 3 or 4 an issue. Despite the slightness in size, the journal has been an important one for libraries, primarily for its bibliographical features. First of all, bibliographies of individual authors appear frequently—in the last few years, for example, on James Dickey, Djuna Barnes, Liam O'Flaherty, W.H. Auden, and John Dos Passos. Secondly, it has always carried in each issue *Current Bibliography*, a carefully annotated listing of critical articles about twentieth-century literature that have appeared in both domestic and foreign journals. Unlike the journal itself, this bibliography's coverage extends to authors from other countries as well as to English and American, and though it is far from thorough, it is extensive enough for most purposes. (A compilation of *Current Bibliography*, 1955-1968, is projected.) It is a most useful reference tool.

Indexed in: S.S.H.I.   56-1944

*UNIVERSITY OF TORONTO QUARTERLY.   v. 1, 1931-

Quarterly.   Toronto, Canada. $8.00

"A Canadian journal of the Humanities," it contains usually about 5 scholarly articles, mostly in the field of English literature, but occasionally in other areas of the humanities. The journal began with broader coverage, but concentrated more and more on literature, especially as new Canadian journals removed the need for outlets in the social sciences. Contributors are well-known scholars, primarily from Canadian universities, but also from American and British. The last number of each volume is devoted mainly to "Letters in Canada," providing an annual two-part review of Canadian scholarship and creative writing. The first part, covering works in English, reviews literary studies, art, light prose, religion, and education. The second, "Livres en francais," contains sections on the social studies, poetry, fiction and drama. An index to all books mentioned in these sections is helpful. Only a few book reviews—rarely more than 3 an issue—but they are excellent: critical and authoritative, almost always at least 1000 words, and often much longer. An important journal for the study of English literature, and for keeping up with Canadian scholarship.

35-10499

VICTORIAN Studies. *see* GENERAL

VOYAGES.   v. 1, 1967-

Quarterly.   Washington, D.C. $6.00

Subtitled "A National Literary Magazine," it is the first major literary magazine to be published in Washington. Issues consist mostly of poetry and poetry criticism, with one or more poets being treated at length. Some of the poets so treated in the first six issues were Ben Belitt, Hiram Hayden, Reed Whittemore, H.R. Hays, Josephine Miles and Robert Lax (to whom an entire issue was devoted)—their poetry, mostly new, plus interviews, comments by friends and analyses by well-known critics. Even when a poet is not treated at length, selections of his poetry are almost always accompanied by a critical essay. There are, in addition, single poems, mostly by younger poets. Occasional essays on the arts, portfolios of photographs and drawings. Signed, critical reviews of some recent books of poetry, novels and stories, also brief reviews of poetry and drama recordings. A substantial journal, with contributions by some well-known writers and critics, it should be in libraries where there is much interest in contemporary poetry.

WESTERN HUMANITIES REVIEW. v. 1, 1947-

Quarterly. Salt Lake City, Utah. $4.00

Sponsored by the Department of English at the University of Utah, it was titled the *Utah Humanities Review* for its first two volumes. Originally emphasized regional interests, and consisted mainly of articles on Western topics, with some poetry and no fiction. Now, relatively conservative poetry and fiction make up a large portion of its content, but neither the authors (most of whom are relatively unknown) nor subjects are regional. The articles and essays are mostly on literary topics, especially contemporary literature, and only occasionally concern the West. A regional bibliography of books and articles ran regularly for the first 5 volumes. The book reviews are good: there are usually 7 to 10 an issue; they are signed and critical, mostly 600-1400 words, and on a variety of subjects. Commentary on recent films is another regular feature. A literary review of substance.

Indexed in: In.Ltl.Mag. 48-27220 rev*

WRITER. v. 1, 1887-

Monthly. Boston, Mass. $7.00

Since its beginning, its purpose has been the same—to help aspiring authors to improve their work and find a market for it. The articles are by well-known or at least, successful, authors or by book or magazine editors, and are very practical, giving advice and instruction on how to prepare, improve and sell stories, scripts, poems, plays, fillers, and other saleable items. Many of the articles are autobiographical, and provide good source material on authors. "Where to Sell Manuscripts" contains market notes and announcements of literary prize offers, plus listings of specialized magazines, with descriptions of kinds and length of material they buy and how much they pay. "Writer's Library" lists and briefly describes some recent books on the theater, film, literary figures, etc., as well as how-to-books on writing.

Similar in intent, and with very much the same kinds of material arranged slightly differently, is *Writer's Digest* (v. 1, 1929- $4.00). Its interviews with writers are especially valuable, and its columns on TV writing, photojournalism, and poetry (now conducted by Judson Jerome) are good, and the general tone is somewhat livelier than *Writer*.

Both publications are indexed in the *Readers' Guide,* and would be useful for courses in creative writing, as well as of interest to any undergraduate who considers writing for pay.

Indexed in: R.G. 17-19531

YALE LITERARY MAGAZINE.   v. 1, 1836-

Bi-monthly.   New Haven, Conn. $9.00

"Exists to publish outstanding writing and graphs for the Yale community."
The earliest of long-lived college literary journals, it was for most of its
life edited by students, and during its long history has published the early
works of many well-known writers and poets. Most of the poetry and
stories are by undergraduates or graduate students at Yale and while they
are mostly good, they are not any better than those in many other little
magazines. What does give the journal its special value is the fact that
Yale alumni or faculty members with established reputations frequently
contribute some very good things. Contains comments on recent films,
books and records. Of uneven quality, but its interesting graphics and
undergraduate contributions make it useful for college libraries. A backfile is not important.

Indexed in: S.S.H.I.   7-19863-4

AMERICA.   v. 1, 1909-

Weekly.   N.Y. $10.00

"The national Catholic weekly review," published by the Jesuits of the U.S. and Canada, it is much more than a religious periodical, commenting on and analyzing all aspects of contemporary society and culture, much of it related to Catholic religious and social concerns. In its earlier years, *America*—reflecting the Church's ideas—was a fairly conservative religious publication (though liberal on economic issues), but in the last few decades has become known as a spokesman for rather progressive Catholicism, with a wide-ranging interest in social and political issues, and a strong internationalist viewpoint, as well as a lively interest in cultural matters. The contributors, when not on the journal's staff, are usually Jesuits or faculty associated with Catholic institutions of higher education, or prominent Catholic laymen. Two issues a year generally focus on Catholic education, including higher education; other issues occasionally are devoted to special topics: Latin America, Ecumenism, Youth, Loyalty and Dissent, etc. Some poetry, regular reviews of films, music and drama. Usually 5 or 6 book reviews per issue, mostly 300-500 words, plus Spring and Fall book issues with a much larger number of short reviews. In 1970, a regular feature, Note/Book, lists books of special interest to be published the next week.

Because of the wide interests and expertise of the Jesuits, and because the magazine is read widely and carefully, with high public regard for its integrity, it should be in most academic libraries, but especially in those with a large number of Catholics. A backfile to 1953, when it began to be indexed by the *Readers' Guide,* would be desirable.

Indexed in: B.R.D.   10-2400
            R.G.

AMERICAN ASSOCIATION OF UNIVERSITY WOMEN.   JOURNAL. v. 1, 1884-

Quarterly.   Washington,D.C. $3.00

The AAUW was an outgrowth of the Association of Collegiate Alumnae; the organization's present status began in 1910. The journal generally was published as a series of the ACA's *Publications;* in January, 1911, the *Journal* began as Number 1 of Series 4, and has carried that title since, though in varying form through the next few years. The articles in earlier volumes were primarily on women's higher education, child study, the economic and legal status of women, careers, etc.—articles mostly by or about women, or on problems of particular interest to women. The *Journal* has reflected the expanding interests of the organization, so that there has been an increasing number of subjects of interest to all intelligent readers, especially on social problems and world affairs. These articles, which are frequently by eminent personalities, provide excellent, often provocative, introductions or overviews of their subjects. Other than these articles, the journal is given over to news and articles of interest only to members: reports of committees, convention programs and plans, news of fellowships, branches, local, regional and state groups, legislative program, etc. It is not as useful to libraries since it was dropped from the *Education Index* in 1961, but it still makes good reading and should be available in undergraduate libraries.

Indexed in: P.A.I.S.   16-10444 rev. 2*

AMERICAN IMAGO.   v. 1, 1939-

Quarterly.   Detroit, Mich. $10.00

"A psychoanalytic journal for culture, science and the arts," it is published under the auspices of the Association for Applied Analysis. The original *Imago,* edited by Freud and others, was published from 1912 to 1937, and was the first journal to focus on the non-medical applications of psychoanalysis, specifically on the humanities, including language, customs, religion and mythology as well as art and literature. *American Imago* was its successor—indeed, Freud's name appears in the first number as editor, but he died before it was published. Issues contain, on the average, 5 or 6 articles, of fairly brief to moderate length, mostly analyzing from the psychoanalytic point of view literary or artistic work and characters, or discussing themes in these areas. Issues are occasionally devoted to a single topic—e.g., Shakespeare, a Theodor Reik Festschrift. A few signed and critical reviews, usually less than 500 words, appear in most numbers. A list of books received also appears occasionally. Many undergraduates are interested in doing papers on psychological interpretations of literature and the arts, and this provides good source material.

Indexed in: Ment.Hlth.B.R.I.   A 41-2485
             R.G.

*AMERICAN PHILOSOPHICAL SOCIETY.   PROCEEDINGS.   v. 1, 1838-

Bi-monthly.   Philadelphia, Pa. $5.00

Contains papers read before the Society and a few others accepted for publication. The subject matter covers all fields, with perhaps a slight emphasis on history, the history of science, and the social sciences. The contributions are scholarly, but not highly technical, and many are by eminent authorities. They vary greatly in length, from brief to quite long, with an average of about 10,000 words. Issues are occasionally devoted to single topics, some recent ones being Law and Liberty, New Evidence for Continental Drift, Frontiers of Cultural Anthropology, The Planet Venus, but most issues are widely varied; for example, one in 1970 containing "Huxley in America," "Reuben Peale's Experiments with Mesmerism," "Benjamin Rush, David Hartley and the Revolutionary Uses of Psychology," "Ramus and Socrates," "Jean-Philippe Rameau: the Musician as *Philosophe,"* "The Bristol Artillery Company and the Tory Triumph in Bristol, 1679-1684." An inexpensive source of scholarly, reliable articles, it will probably not serve as browsing material, but should prove useful for a number of fields.

Indexed in: P.A.I.S.   12-30215

*AMERICAN QUARTERLY.   v. 1, 1949-

5 nos./yr.   Philadelphia, Pa. $8.00

Official journal of the American Studies Association. Its aim is "to aid in giving a sense of direction to studies in the culture of the United States, past and present. Editors and contributors therefore concern themselves not only with the areas of American life which they know best but with the relation of those areas to the entire American scene and to world society." Thus, the quarterly issues contain scholarly articles and briefer "Notes" on American politics, society, history, art, belles-lettres, etc. The "Reviews" section begins with one or two essay-reviews, either on a group of recent books, or discussing older books about a subject occasioned by a recent publication, or even on an art exhibit; the regular book reviews are signed and critical, usually less than a page in length. "American Calendar" reports news of the American Studies Association and its chapters, and other news of interest to members. Since 1955 there has been an annual bibliography, *Articles in American Studies,* an annotated listing that "is quite selective, the principal editorial criterion for listing an article being the extent to which it manifests a relationship between two or more aspects of American Civilization." The number of entries has grown from 164 items in 1955 to over 900 in 1969. In 1957 a fifth number was started as a Supplement to the summer issue. In addition to the bibliography, *Articles in American Studies,* this number contains articles on the theory, study and teaching of American studies; a listing of doctoral and master's dissertations in progress and completed; (beginning in 1963) a directory of American Studies programs; (beginning in 1960) a report on financial aid available to students of American civilization; an annotated bibliography of *Writings on the Theory and Teaching of American Studies*; and (beginning in 1968) an "Annual Review of Books" pertinent to American studies published during the previous year. It is a very selective listing of 100-125 titles, each review signed, and though only 150-250 words, expertly evaluated.

The articles plus the many bibliographical features make this, along with a complete backfile, an essential item for every college library.

Indexed in: In.Rel.Per.Lit.   50-4992
            S.S.H.I.

.

*AMERICAN SCHOLAR.   v. 1, 1932-

Quarterly.   Richmond, Va. $5.00

Official organ of Phi Beta Kappa, it was begun by William Shimer, Executive Secretary of the United Chapters, who acted as editor from 1932 to 1943. Marjorie Hope Nicolson then edited it for a year, and Hiram Hayden has been editor since 1944. Non-technical articles, essays and discussions on topics of cultural, intellectual and social interest ranging over all fields of learning. Recently, all or large portions of some issues have treated single topics relating to current problems: e.g., revolt on the campus, the electronics revolution, the challenge of youth, etc. The Editorial Board is comprised of some of the most prominent names in American letters and its members have—as "A Note on the History of the *American Scholar"* in *The American Scholar Reader* comments—"held the magazine to the middle line between lightness and learning, that has opposed pedantry as a stultifier of knowledge, and that has made of the hazardous inability of quarterlies to consider the contemporaneous a strength rather than a weakness." Many of its contributors are eminent figures in scholarship, letters or higher education.

There is some poetry, both by established and new poets. Joseph Wood Krutch had a regular column from 1955 until his death in 1970; there are frequent bibliographical features, though reflecting personal rather than scholarly preferences. Signed reviews of a variety of books, by a variety of reviewers, with frequent review-essays. An outlet for the scholar giving

perspective to current affairs, it is an essential journal for every academic
library.

Indexed in: B.R.D.   33-20171 (rev.'43)
            P.A.I.S.
            R.G.

AMÉRICAS. *see* AREA STUDIES/LATIN AMERICA

*ANTIOCH REVIEW.   v. 1, 1941-

Quarterly.   Yellow Springs, Ohio. $6.00

Founded by 7 members of the Antioch College faculty who believed "in
the application of scholarship to the solution of social problems," it was
perhaps the only academic journal of that period with a political purpose.
Throughout its career, it has emphasized the social sciences, but it has
also published literary criticism and history, short stories and poetry. Contributors have been faculty members from many institutions, government
officials and others, including many well known in academic and public
life. Issues were occasionally devoted to single topics; beginning in 1969
the policy is for at least half the issues to be devoted to examining specific
aspects of a contemporary problem, such as the academic professional organizations, the new world of Freudian psychology, trends in magazines.
Book reviews, which were really review-essays, have been replaced by a
section of annotations of recent books read and enjoyed by the editors,
and by articles occasioned by books of special significance.

With the Fall/Winter, 1970/71 issue, the *Review* "absorbed" *Monocle*, the
journal of political satire. Founded in 1957 by a group of Yale law and
graduate students, *Monocle* achieved a national reputation and no small
circulation in its first few years, but in the late 1960's staggered along before being absorbed. How much of the *Review* will now be devoted to
satire is undetermined, nor can anyone predict what the relationship between the two will be. But it does make the *Review* an even more enjoy-
able title.

Well rounded, with solid contributions, it is an outstanding quarterly,
and should be in every academic library, along with a substantial backfile.

Indexed in: P.A.I.S.   44-660
            S.S.H.I.

ARTS in Society. *see* ART

*ATLANTIC MONTHLY.   v. 1, 1857-

Monthly.   Boston, Mass. $8.50

Its long and distinguished history—among its early editors were William
Dean Howells, James Russell Lowell and Thomas Bailey Aldrich, and

contributors have included just about every major figure in American letters—has made it almost an institution for the literate reader. Though never a "popular" journal, its influence on literary and social affairs has been significant, and in the history of American magazines, the *Atlantic* stands out as one of the most important.

After World War II, however, its influence somewhat declined, and in the 1960's it began to change from an essentially staid literary journal to one carrying distinguished reporting on current issues as well as important literary works. In the last few years it carried, as previews of forthcoming books, Jessica Mitford's "The Trial of Dr. Spock," James Watson's "The Double Helix," the memoirs of Svetlana Alliluyeva, Charles Silberman's "Murder in the Schoolroom," and others. It has not neglected literature, and many of today's better writers, poets and critics, such as Joyce Carol Oates, Saul Bellow, James Dickey, Mary McCarthy, Dan Wakefield, appear regularly. The significant difference between its issues today and ten years ago, however, is the attention to topical matters, such as women's liberation, military life and justice, poverty, the shortcomings of education, etc., most of which are treated by distinguished authors.

Additional features include its reports, mostly political, from Washington and other cities in the U.S. and around the world, and the reviews of books, music, art, films and drama. There are usually about 10 long reviews, done by guests and by Edward Weeks, the regular reviewer, all of which are excellent, plus a larger number of very brief reviews.

An essential journal for every library; a complete backfile is most desirable.

Indexed in: B.R.D.   4-12666 rev. 2
R.G.

*ATLAS.   v. 1, 1961-

Monthly.   N.Y. $10.00

"Best from the world press," it selects and translates in each issue some twenty articles, editorials, stories, reviews and cartoons from periodicals and newspapers of all foreign countries, though contributions from Latin America are relatively infrequent. Each issue begins with "Talk of the World" (formerly "World Press Comment"), reviewing major developments of the past month with brief selections from foreign newspapers taking various positions on these developments. The material, which is translated as faithfully as possible, is on political affairs or on subjects reflecting political attitudes on business, literature and the arts, religious and social affairs, etc. Reviews in translation of significant fiction and non-fiction and of important new plays and movies; political and satirical cartoons are reproduced. Earlier volumes frequently carried poems, short stories, and novellas or portions of novels. Almost every item is preceded by a brief paragraph setting it in context. In 1964, two features were added—"Listening In On the World" and "Listening In On World Business"—both consisting of a series of one-paragraph items of "inside news," predictions, and miscellaneous bits provided by the magazine's own correspondents.

Its interesting articles, well-chosen and translated, and astute comments make this an excellent way for students to gain some understanding of the thinking of other nations. It is especially useful in libraries where there are few foreign newspapers and journals, but it is important for every academic library.

Indexed in: S.S.H.I.   63-24771

*BLACK WORLD.   v. 1, 1942-

Monthly.   Chicago, Ill. $5.00

Its title was originally *Negro Digest*, and it assumed its present title only in May, 1970. Started on a shoestring, it struggled during its first decade, but was discontinued from 1951 to 1961 because the publisher, the Johnson Publishing Company, was concentrating on its more successful magazine, *Ebony* (q.v.). Upon resuming publication, its nature changed: whereas in the decade 1942-1951 it was fairly moderate in tone, and was closely patterned after the *Reader's Digest*, it now began to carry original material—articles, fiction and poetry—almost all by black writers, which increasingly rejected the values and means of a white society. It is perhaps the most militant of the large-circulation black periodicals (though its 70,000 circulation is still small compared with *Ebony*) and its contributors include many of the best known black militant writers and many good younger ones.

Its new title signifies a broader interest that "will probe and report the condition of peoples and their struggles throughout the Black World." The emphasis, however, is still on this country, and the special annual issues on Black History, Theater, Fiction, Poetry, contain provocative and significant articles. A regular feature, "Perspectives," contains notes on current books, writers, artists and the arts. A journal aimed at the black intellectual, it is an important title for all college libraries. A backfile is very useful for early writings of some of today's leading black writers and for tracing the development of black consciousness.

Indexed in: B.R.D.   46-44888
              In.Per.Negroes

*BULLETIN OF THE ATOMIC SCIENTISTS.   v. 1, 1945-

Monthly (except July-Aug.)   Chicago, Ill. $8.50

Now subtitled "Science and Public Affairs," it was started by scientists who participated in the atomic bomb project during World War II, and is now published by The Educational Foundation for Nuclear Science. While its original concern was the relationship between the release of atomic energy and the course of mankind, its interests have expanded to include many aspects of the contemporary scientific revolution—the promises of the constructive uses of science as well as the dangers of its destructive uses. Thus there are articles on foreign policy and international relations, the problems of developing areas, air and water pollution, space exploration, education, scientific developments affecting the public, and a variety of other subjects. Among the contributors are some of the best known scientists, plus other scholars and men of public affairs. Frequently there is a symposium on a single topic, but most issues have a variety of articles, some of which are quite long. Other sections contain excerpts from speeches, books, etc., appropriate to the interest of the journal, brief essays, miscellaneous news, and responses to articles from readers. There are generally about 5 books reviewed in each issue; while they are generally on the same topics as the *Bulletin* is concerned with, they frequently are significant works in other areas of public affairs. All the reviews are excellent, almost all over 1000 words, and frequently several times that.

A responsible, thoughtful journal, ranging over a wide area of contemporary issues, it has steadily gained in reputation and, along with a back-file, should be in all academic libraries.

Indexed in: B.R.D.   48-34039*
            R.G.

CAMBRIDGE QUARTERLY.   v. 1, 1965/66-

Quarterly.   Cambridge, Eng. $5.00

A general review stressing contributions on literature, but also on the arts, history and politics. The essays are not necessarily scholarly, but are thoughtful, well-written and often provocative, and are contributed by scholars in the humanities and social sciences from a variety of British universities. The editors (who are also the publishers) are also faculty from various universities. If the contributions are primarily literary, they are not by choice but, as an editorial stated, "We have had little else offered to us." The same editorial (in vol. 2, no. 2) declared that "The one uniting and unifying principle governing our behaviour is our determination to print good criticism (in the widest, Arnoldian, sense) regardless of the shade of opinion." Since that editorial the contributions have gotten somewhat more diverse, though literature is still predominant.

Usually from 4 to 7 articles per issue, some of them written as review-essays on recent books. Also a few other reviews, all excellent, and frequently several thousand words long.

Most contributions are solid rather than exciting, and the journal might be considered where there is serious interest in literary criticism.

Indexed in: Brit.Hum.I.

*CENTER MAGAZINE.   v. 1, 1967-

Bi-monthly.   Santa Barbara, Calif. $15.00

Published by the Center for the Study of Democratic Institutions, an independent educational institution sponsored by the Fund for the Republic. Devoted to examining the basic issues confronting a democratic society, its primary method is the dialogue—between resident scholars and a continuing procession of eminent visitors to the Center from all over the world, in all fields. Each issue contains articles, essays, interviews, transcriptions of discussions, etc., by and with these eminent individuals, on the gamut of contemporary issues that affect democratic institutions: race, religion, the military, education, law, politics, population, etc. Most of the contributions are, by their very intent, not the results of research, but rather of experience, reflection and provocative discussions. An attractive publication, with some very worthwhile—indeed, significant—contributions. Subscription is on the basis of membership which includes receipt of the Center's papers and special reports as well as the periodical. Because of the eminence of the contributors, the substance of their remarks, and the timeliness of the topics, it should be available in every academic library.

Indexed in: Alt.Pr.I.
            P.A.I.S.

CHANGING Times. *see* HOME ECONOMICS

CHRISTIAN Century. *see* RELIGION

*CIVIL RIGHTS DIGEST.   v. 1, 1968-

Quarterly.   Washington, D.C.   Free.

Published "by the U.S. Commission on Civil Rights as part of its clearing-house responsibilities. The articles in the *Digest* do not necessarily represent Commission policy but are offered to stimulate ideas and interest on the various current issues concerning civil rights." Brief to moderate length, illustrated and well-written, they are mostly by staff members of the Commission, but also by others in government or private affairs interested in the various aspects of civil rights—economics, voting, housing, law enforcement, education, labor, the mass media, etc. Each issue contains a few signed reviews, mostly 750-1000 words, plus a list of other recent books, reports and films, all briefly annotated.

Though it will obviously not publicize criticism of the government's policies and/or actions in the civil rights area, there is much in it that *is* fairly outspoken, and it provides excellent material for undergraduate papers. It should be in every college library, especially since not only is it a depository item, but can be obtained for the asking from the Commission.

*COLUMBIA FORUM.   v. 1, 1957-

Quarterly.   N.Y. $6.50

Originally the *Columbia University Forum,* it began as an outlet for articles of general interest by contributors who had "a connection, as members or alumni, with the University." Since it is not much of an exaggeration to say that almost everyone in the academic world has had, at one time or another, in one capacity or another, some connection with Columbia University, the authors eligible to write for the journal have been numerous and, indeed, have included many of the most eminent scholars from all fields in this country. In 1969, for example, contributors included John Ashbery, Noam Chomsky, Donald Keene, Jean Piaget, Paul Lazarsfeld, Jean Mayer, Rene Dubos, Barbara Ward and Ned O'Gorman, and the contributions ranged from a discussion of an oriental classic to one on the sociology of marijuana users, from philosophical speculations to polemics on the war in the Middle East.

Usually 3 to 5 articles per issue, on a variety of subjects—from the classics to contemporary world problems, plus poetry by both young and established poets. Also a number of essays on books, recent or otherwise, or on topics occasioned by books. Letters from readers, and exchanges triggered by earlier articles are a frequent and valuable feature.

In all, it is one of the most interesting and informative journals published by an institution of higher education. Because of its quality, timeliness and eminence of contributors, it should be in every academic library. Back issues can frequently be obtained from Columbia alumni, to whom the *Forum* had been sent free of charge.

64-32237

*COLUMBIA JOURNALISM REVIEW.   v. 1, 1961-

Quarterly.   N.Y. $9.00

Published by the Graduate School of Journalism of Columbia University, it was founded "to assess the performance of journalism in all its forms, to call attention to its shortcomings and strengths, and to help define—or redefine—standards of honest, responsible service . . . [and] to help stimulate continuing improvement" in the profession of journalism. It covers all communications media—newspapers, magazines and television and radio—and the articles, which are fairly brief, but well illustrated, are frank in their analyses and evaluations. Most are on the problems and practices of the media during recent events, with only a few historically oriented. Contributors are working journalists as well as teachers. Regular features include editorials and comments; "Report on Reports" summarizes and reviews articles and other materials dealing with journalism; the book reviews, usually 3 or 4 per issue, are excellent—signed and critical, they average around 500 words. Essential where journalism is taught, it is also important (and good) reading for anyone interested in the role of communications media in society.

Indexed in: P.A.I.S.   68-5391

*COMMENTARY.   v. 1, 1945-

Monthly.   N.Y. $10.00

Published by the American Jewish Committee, it was begun "to meet the need for a journal of significant thought and opinion on Jewish affairs and contemporary issues." Its reputation as one of the best general periodicals has resulted from the latter of these purposes which it has fulfilled most successfully. Most issues contain about 6 major contributions, mostly articles, but frequently a story or two, plus a few shorter essays. The articles, generally 5-10,000 words, with occasional longer ones, range over all fields; many are by important figures and—those on social problems and on contemporary affairs, especially—are of real significance and lasting value though this is not to demean its contributions in literature and the arts. In keeping with the magazine's original purpose, there is always at least one article relating to an aspect of Judaism—its history, theology, social implications, reminiscences of well-known Jewish writers, etc. Occasional symposia. The book reviews are outstanding. 5 or 6 per issue, they are done by authorities in the field or by well-equipped critics; they are all thorough and lengthy, invariably over one, and sometimes several thousand words long.

In recent years it has been criticized for a conservatism on both domestic and international issues, and has lost the loyalty of many supporters. Yet, as a journal that is intellectual without being narrowly academic and that has maintained a consistently high quality of writing and scholarship, it should be in every college library along with a substantial backfile.

Indexed in: B.R.D.   47-24208
      R.G.

*COMMONWEAL.   v. 1, 1924-

Weekly (bi-weekly, July-Sept.)   N.Y. $14.00

Edited by Catholic laymen, it is primarily a journal of opinion on religious and public affairs, literature and the arts. Its approach has been
expressed editorially as "a magazine published by men who are themselves Catholic and who endeavor to express a point of view on temporal
matters in conformity with their religious principles." Not, in any sense,
an "official" Catholic publication, it has frequently expressed opinions
quite different from many diocesan and Catholic journals; it has been
one of the leaders in moving for reform in the Church, and generally
it expresses a liberal viewpoint on matters religious, political and social.
Articles, by Catholic and non-Catholic writers, range over all topics, but
more attention is given to social and public affairs and, of course, the
relationship of Catholicism to them, though at times, one must admit,
it is stretching a point to classify it as a "religious periodical." Frequent
poems, sometimes by noted poets. Excellent movie and stage criticism.
The book reviews (usually 4 or 5 an issue) are good: on all sorts of
books—poetry, fiction, politics, religion, etc.—they are signed and critical,
generally between 500 and 1000 words long, and often by well known
critics and scholars. Fall and Spring Book Issues.

Equal to any weekly journal of opinion in its influence, quality and the
eminence of its contributors, *Commonweal*—along with a substantial backfile—should be in every academic library.

Indexed in: B.R.D.   26-14152
            R.G.

CONTEMPORARY REVIEW.   v. 1, 1866-

Monthly.   London. $13.50

Thoughtful, mostly brief articles, primarily on current affairs, but occasionally on education, history, archaeology, religion or the arts. While it
has never been a party organ, it has generally concurred with the views
of the Liberals. In 1954 it incorporated the *Fortnightly Review*, which
had been founded in 1864 and was one of Britain's most respected literary
and political journals. A "Literary Supplement" in each issue contains
usually 5 to 7 signed, critical reviews of all types of books, ranging in
length from a few hundred to over 1000 words, plus several brief, unsigned
reviews. Independent and straightforward, it presents good general articles
by reliable writers.

Indexed in: Br.Hum.I.   CA 7-657 unrev'd
            S.S.H.I.

*CURRENT.   v. 1, 1960-

Monthly (except July) Plainfield, Vt. $10.00

A reprint magazine, it selects portions of books and articles from a variety
of journals and newspapers—primarily those read by the educated layman,
e.g., the *Atlantic, Commonweal, Encounter, Foreign Affairs, Psychology
Today, Trans-Action*, etc.—and digests them only slightly. It is especially

concerned with social and political problems, so there is almost nothing on literature or the arts. The 10-15 items are well selected, but *Current* has somewhat limited use for many college libraries since they probably already subscribe to the journals covered. It is, however, useful for browsing, as a backup for journals that may be temporarily unavailable, as well as for the material that supplements the library's collection. Edited by members of the faculty of Goddard College and published there, its appropriateness for the liberal arts college is obvious.

Indexed in: R.G.   63-24770

*CURRENT BIOGRAPHY.   v. 1, 1940-

Monthly (except Aug.)   N.Y. $6.00

Impartial, informal, well-written sketches of contemporaries in all fields—authors, statesmen, politicians, scientists, industrial and labor leaders, entertainers, religious leaders, athletes, etc.—and from all countries, the only criterion being that they are prominent in the news. Sources of information are newspapers, magazines and books; where possible and useful, the words of the biographees themselves are used. There are 17 or 18 biographies per issue, of 2500-3000 words each; whereas 10 years ago, there were about twice as many biographies, but of varied length. Each biography also contains individual photographs, pronunciation of difficult names, and a list of references to additional material. The index for each issue is cumulative for that year; there is also a necrology of persons who had appeared in *Current Biography.* The bound annual cumulation ($7.00) includes all the biographies in the monthly issues (updated and corrected by the biographees), plus "new and updated sketches that supersede earlier, outdated articles." There is an occupational classification of all biographees; a necrology for the year of persons previously listed; finally, a name index is cumulative for all volumes of that decade.

Both the monthly and a complete file of the annual volumes should be in every college library. They are essential reference tools, and the current issues may be read for enjoyment as well as information.

40-27432

*DAEDALUS.   v. 1, 1846-

Quarterly.   Cambridge, Mass. $8.00

The journal of the American Academy of Arts and Sciences, it was originally the Academy's *Proceedings,* assuming its present title in 1958. Its nature changed completely from one of fairly limited interest to one that has become a major vehicle for interdisciplinary communications. Each issue is devoted to a single topic and is book-size—indeed, most issues, in slightly expanded form, have also later appeared as books in hardback and (usually) paperback editions, and some of them, such as the ones on the American Negro, on youth, on American foreign policy, have become landmarks in their fields. The topic covered in each issue is under a separate editor, and treat subjects ranging over all fields of learning, with emphasis on the social sciences and humanities, and especially matters of current import, and all have contributions by some of the most eminent scholars and men of letters.

Providing superb source material on a variety of topics of current and perennial concern, *Daedalus*, along with a backfile to 1958, belongs in every academic library.

Indexed in: S.S.H.I.   12-30299*

DIOGENES. no. 1, 1953-

Quarterly.   Montreal, Canada. $6.00

A publication of the International Council for Philosophy and Humanistic Studies. Designed for the intelligent reader, it contains general interdisciplinary articles, of varied length, treating subjects which contribute directly to the knowledge of man. Generally from 6 to 8 articles per issue that are erudite but not esoteric, and well-written (or well-translated) by contributors who are outstanding scholars and literati from all nations. Issues are often devoted to a single topic—e.g., New Problems in Sociology, Problems of Latin America, Looks at Africa. Book reviews were carried up to a few years ago. Editions are also published in French and Spanish. Many significant contributions that provide provocative reading for the thoughtful undergraduate and faculty members.

Indexed in: P.A.I.S.   A 55-3452

*DISSENT.   v. 1, 1954-

Bi-monthly.   N.Y. $7.00

Founded by survivors of the radical movements of the 1930's and 1940's, it was at first known as "a quarterly of Socialist opinion." Always opposed to totalitarianism, in whatever form, it veered away from the Marxist tradition and now declares that "it is a journal devoted to radical ideas and the values of socialism and democracy. It seeks to serve as a forum for writers devoted to these ideas and values, while also welcoming a wide variety of other opinions." Edited by Irving Howe, it has on its editorial board or as contributing editors a notable group of leftist and liberal creative writers and social scientists, such as Michael Harrington, Jeremy Larner, Bayard Rustin, Dennis Wrong, Erich Fromm and Paul Goodman. Each issue consists of comments and opinions and articles (mostly brief) on all areas of contemporary political, economic and social affairs. The book reviews, usually about 4 an issue, are also in these areas; signed and critical, and usually provocative, they range greatly in length, but most are 750-1000 words. Devoted to fundamental, reasoned criticism of the status quo, and presenting the ideas of many prominent thinkers and scholars, it is perhaps the best spokesman for a particular viewpoint, and should be in every undergraduate library.

Indexed in: Alt.Pr.I.   57-2963

*EBONY.   v. 1, 1945-

Monthly.   Chicago, Ill. $8.00

Published by the Johnson Publishing Company, which specializes in publications for blacks. *Ebony* has always emphasized the "positive, everyday achievements" of blacks, something other periodicals had ignored. Its readership is overwhelmingly black, and predominantly middle-class. Because of this and its openness to readers' suggestions and approval, *Ebony* can be regarded as reflecting fairly accurately the opinions and aspirations of this sector of population. Success stories of individual blacks, especially those due to individual merit, have always been featured.

Its format is similar to *Life*; replete with illustrations, and many articles on food, dress, leisure, travel, personalities, etc. With regard to civil rights, its transition from a relatively placid stance to a militant one took place in the middle 1960's, again probably reflecting its readers' views. All the while, however, it has still stressed black progress through programs of individual and group self-help. Black history and culture have received increasing attention and there have been many contributions of real significance which alone would justify its purchase; in addition, its representative role makes it important source material, and for this reason an extensive backfile is useful—a current subscription is essential.

Indexed in: In.Per.Negroes   52-42074
            R.G.

ECONOMIST. *see* ECONOMICS

*ENCOUNTER.   v. 1, 1953-

Monthly.   London. $14.00

Founded with the aid of a grant from the Congress for Cultural Freedom to promote discourse between British and American intellectuals, it has become one of the more respected and influential English-language journals. Articles range over current affairs, sociology, biography, literature and the arts, many by leading American and English intellectuals, critics and scholars. To give some idea of the variety and eminence of the contributors, here are some of those who appeared several times between 1965 and 1969: Arthur Koestler, Maurice Cranston, Melvin Lasky, H.R. Trevor-Roper, Zbigniew Brzezinski, George Steiner, Ignazio Silone, James Morris, D.W. Brogan, Eugene Ionesco, Max Beloff and Anthony Burgess. It is politically independent, though its reputation was a bit tarnished by the exposure of the Congress for Cultural Freedom's relationship with the CIA. Though its literary criticism is first-rate, it has been criticized for not keeping up with the current literary scene. A good bit of poetry, mostly by well known British, American and European poets, and occasional fiction, also mostly by well known writers. Major portions of some issues are devoted to a single topic, e.g., Student Revolt, Jorge Luis Borges, Unreason and Revolution. Book reviews, covering all types of works, are really essays. Many of them, in fact, are featured on the covers since most reviewers are as notable as the regular contributors. The reviews are seldom less than 1500 words, and frequently run to several thousand.

A stimulating and important periodical that belongs in every academic library along with a substantial backfile.

Indexed in: B.R.D.   57-43677
            Br.Hum.I.
            S.S.H.I.

*ESQUIRE.   v. 1, 1933-

Monthly.   N.Y. $8.50

This general magazine for men carries sophisticated but not highbrow articles on many topics of more masculine interest—fiction, current politics, people in the news, sports, the arts, fashion, travel, humor, food and liquor, gifts. Its emphasis on men's fashions, on the feminine form divine and on the risqué cartoons—the features which made it an almost immediate success and gave it its reputation—has noticeably declined since World War II. In the 1930's and 40's, *Esquire* was also known for its fiction, with Hemingway, O'Hara, Wolfe and Fitzgerald among the contributors, and the early efforts of many authors who later became well known. In the last two decades *Esquire* has continued publishing articles, stories, and the texts of plays by many of the nation's leading writers, such as Arthur Schlesinger, Tennessee Williams, Saul Bellow, Norman Mailer, Truman Capote, and John Kenneth Galbraith. In recent years, the attempt to be "with it" has been a little too apparent, with articles on student radicals, the liberated woman, the new morality, somewhat sensational approaches to politics, and a rather pretentious attitude toward literature and the arts. Nevertheless, the quality of the worthwhile stories, essays and articles greatly outweighs the ephemeral material.

Also its columnists are well known and are discerning and provocative. Since 1964, Malcolm Muggeridge has written the book reviews, usually one or two long reviews and a couple of shorter ones. They range over all topics and are in his irreverent, incisive style. Films were reviewed for some years by Wilfrid Sheed and recordings are still done by Martin Mayer. Dwight MacDonald wrote on books, films and politics during the 1960's, and Richard Joseph contributes an excellent travel column.

Extremely popular for browsing, because of the eminence of its contributors and the quality of much of its material, *Esquire* should be in college libraries. An extensive backfile is not essential for most libraries since so much of the material has been published in various collections.

Indexed in: R.G.   35-10505

ETC.: A REVIEW OF GENERAL SEMANTICS.   v. 1, 1943-

Quarterly.   San Francisco, Calif. $6.00

Official organ of the Society for General Semantics, an organization founded to promulgate the ideas of Alfred Korzybski. A preliminary statement of the editors declared that *ETC.* would contain: "(1) Original articles on the theoretical foundations of General Semantics and Non-Aristotelian systems . . . (2) Articles not dealing specifically with General Semantics but which either (a) clarify special problems and offer illustrations of the theories of General Semantics, or (b) give expression to points of view or aims parallel to the Society. . . . (3) Reviews of books which, for one reason or another, may be of importance to students of General Semantics." This very large editorial umbrella has grown even larger: edited from its start until 1970 by S.I. Hayakawa, it reflects his widening interests, so that now, in addition to articles of obvious interest to semanticists, *ETC.* contains poetry and articles on prejudice, education, psychoanalysis, political attitudes, and other subjects more or less controversial. A substantial portion of the articles are reprinted from other sources, ranging from scholarly quarterlies to women's monthlies. The book reviews, usually 4 to 6 per issue, are at least 750 words, and frequently much longer; on just as wide a range of subjects as the articles, they are always frank and often stimulating. Notes and news of the Society and of general interest of semanticists and educators. Because it is almost always provocative, well written and contains many articles of real significance, it is recommended for college libraries.

Indexed in: Ment.Hlth.B.R.I.   49-16047*

EVERGREEN REVIEW.   v. 1, 1957-

Monthly.   N.Y. $10.00

At one time perhaps the leading widely-circulated journal of avant-garde writing, it is now more concerned with political and cultural radicalism, frequently expressed through erotica, or even pornography and scatology. This is unfortunate, because the very worthwhile contributions are overshadowed by the more sensational ones. For libraries, the magazine presents special problems—official displeasure or even censorship, and constantly disappearing issues.

Up until 1964, when it changed from pocket-size to its present quarto dimensions, it was almost solely concerned with literature, and was the first to make easily available the works of many American writers who later became standard (e.g., Ginsberg, Terry Southern, William Burroughs, John Logan, Robert Creeley, Michael McClure) and the first translations of many well-known foreign authors, including Beckett, Jakov Lind, Ionesco, Robbe-Grillet, as well as many lesser-known ones. About 1966 it began to give more attention to social and political issues, and writers such as Julius Lester, Jack Newfield, Eldridge Cleaver and Mark Rudd, or the publication of Che Guevara's diary, and Nat Hentoff's regular column, indicated its new interest. Yet it still published excellent fiction, poetry and criticism, and these contributions, even though some of them (and the cartoons) may be considered in poor taste by many, make *Evergreen* an important journal for students of the contemporary cultural and social scene.

57-6933 rev.

L'EXPRESS.   no. 1, 1953-

Weekly.   Paris. $34.00

Founded as a tabloid journal of leftist opinion and edited by Jean-Jacques Servan-Schreiber, it was highly regarded as a stimulating publication, "anti-government and, indeed," according to Janet Flanner, "anti-everything except criticism and vigorous information." But it was only a moderate financial success, and in 1964 it changed to a newsmagazine very much like *Newsweek* or *Time* (even similar typographically to the latter) except that all its articles are signed. Since that change, its circulation increased from 170,000 to 655,000 (in 1970).

Each issue is divided into departments: France, Monde, Vie Moderne, Affaires, Les Environment, Livres, Editoriaux, etc., in which the news is covered, but there is, of course, a special emphasis on political news and politically related items. The articles vary greatly in length, from just a paragraph or two to feature-length, and most are well illustrated. Usually about 6 books are reviewed, both fiction and non-fiction, popular and scholarly, in signed, critical reviews that average mostly 400-700 words, but are occasionally much longer. Books soon to be published are frequently excerpted or summarized, especially those in history or public affairs.

Political, but relatively impartial, *L'Express* provides an excellent way for keeping up with current events in France.

67-123931

FACTS ON FILE.   v. 1, 1940-

Weekly.   N.Y. $187.00

A weekly synopsis—in loose-leaf form—of world events digested from leading newspapers, magazines, foreign and U.S. government dispatches, etc., though sources are not always indicated. Comes in two parts. The first is the weekly news section. Arranged under various headings such as World Affairs, National Affairs, Foreign Affairs, Economy, Education, Religion, Sports, Obituaries, Motion Pictures, etc. Items include a large number of references to relevant previous items. The second part is the index, which is issued semi-monthly, cumulating monthly and quarterly, the final quarterly index being the annual index. Unbiased, matter-of-fact, and up-to-date (issues appear only about a week after the last day covered) it is a handy, easy-to-use source, useful for locating and identifying specific information quickly. An expensive item, not essential to libraries, but useful if one can afford it.

42-24704

FIELD AND STREAM.   v. 1, 1895-

Monthly.   N.Y. $5.00

Beginning as *Western Field and Stream,* it dropped the regional designation after just 2 years; since then, it has become almost a byword with hunters, fishermen and campers, and through the years has reflected and encouraged the growing interest in the outdoors. Many well known popular writers have contributed—e.g., Zane Grey, James Oliver Curwood, Robert Ruark, Irwin S. Cobb—and the magazine has always published many articles on conservation and problems of the environment. Now issues usually contain 5 or 6 articles on wildlife, types of equipment, geographical areas, game laws, plus how-to-do-it accounts and many regular columns and features on shooting, fishing, boating, camping, conservation, and new products and equipment. Frequent stories, humorous episodes and personal experiences. All are well illustrated with photographs, drawings and paintings. Most issues contain 2 or 3 signed book reviews, 200-300 words in length.

Another magazine, very similar in appearance and content, even in its circulation and longevity, is *Outdoor Life* (v. 1, 1898- $5.00). Either will be browsed through regularly and thoroughly, but most libraries will not need to keep permanent files of them.

Indexed in R.G.   CA 6-1657 unrev'd.

FLYING.   v. 1, 1927-

Monthly.   Chicago, Ill. $7.00

Intended for the general reader, the private pilot and the aviation enthusiast rather than for those in the airplane industry. Contains well illustrated articles: personal adventure accounts; thorough reports on the design and testing of new models (including foreign makes); education and training for a career in aviation; biographies of flyers, airplane designers and manufacturers; aviation history; shows and meets; itineraries for long and short trips; descriptions of mechanical and engineering features; trends and developments in the industry and the design of airplanes; the care and repair of planes and equipment; etc. Many regular features, including reports of new products, news from federal agencies, a calendar of meets, conferences and other events, as well as editorials and personal columns. Each issue contains from one to 4 or 5 book reviews; these are signed but fairly short—at the most, 300-400 words, and cover all types of aviation books—history, biography, how-to books, texts, etc. Notes on other literature—pamphlets, documents, etc.; brief reviews of films on flying—films for home use as well as of the commercial films. A good item for browsing, but for most libraries, a backfile is not essential.

Indexed in: R.G.   28-30218 (rev. '43)

FREEDOMWAYS.   v. 1, 1961-

Quarterly.   N.Y. $4.50

"A quarterly review of the Negro freedom movement," it contains articles, fiction, poetry, art and reviews on black culture and history, on contemporary or recent political or social issues affecting black America. The articles are mostly brief—usually less than 12 pages—but many are contributed by well known black writers and public figures. In the past few years, for example, Gwendolyn Brooks, Langston Hughes, Saunders Redding, and James Baldwin have appeared here. Issues are occasionally devoted to single topics—e.g., W.E.B. DuBois, Education, the Caribbean, Paul Robeson. About 8 or 10 good book reviews in most issues, usually 500-1000 words, plus an annotated listing of large number of titles.

Expertly and responsibly edited, it is an important journal for all academic libraries.

Indexed in: In.Per.Negroes   68-3518

GERMAN TRIBUNE.   no. 1, 1962-

Weekly.   Hamburg. $9.00

"A Weekly Review of the German Press," it translates into English and reprints articles from the leading newspapers of the Federal Republic of Germany. Covering all aspects of German life and culture, and newspapers of various political leanings, but mostly from the major ones—*Die Zeit, Frankfurter Allgemeine,* and *Die Welt*—it uses complete translations of the original text. Published in tabloid form on thin paper, issues are sent airmail to New York and then distributed from there, so they arrive fairly soon after the originals appear in Germany. A useful and handy way of keeping up with what's going on in Germany as well as seeing how Germans view foreign affairs.

67-37984

EL GRITO.   v. 1, 1967-

Quarterly.   Berkeley, Calif. $5.00

Founded "to provide a forum for Mexican-American self definition and expression," it is the only journal of Chicano culture and thought. Carries poetry and prose, journalistic and academic articles on current issues, and reproductions of Chicano art. Some material is in Spanish, but most in English; sometimes a story or poem will appear in both languages. The contributions are generally of high quality and they are of interest to the student of literature as much as to the social scientist. If there is any major theme, it is the cultural conflict between Anglo and Mexican values, a conflict that is brought out in the many facets of Mexican-American history that have created the Chicanos. Other topics treated are the relationships with other minority groups and social or political problems of general concern.

With superior articles, stories, poetry and art work, *El Grito* is essential for any library where there is an interest in Mexican-American culture, and because of its unique contributions to an issue of increasing importance, should be available in most academic libraries.

*HARPER'S MAGAZINE.   v. 1, 1850-

Monthly.   New York. $8.50

It enjoyed an almost immediate popularity after its founding—a popularity first resulting from the serialization of the best-selling British authors of the period, then from the stories, articles and illustrations by many of the great names in American literature. By the end of the 19th century, when it had become an institution for many homes, it began to devote more attention to non-fiction, especially biography, exploration, travel, science and literary history, though creative literature still remained its most important component. In the late 1920's, to counter a continuing decline in reputation and circulation that began after the First World War, it included more on contemporary political and social affairs, so much so that Frederick Lewis Allen, the editor from 1941 to 1953 noted in his first year that it had become "almost an organ of politics, economics and sociology." In the 1940's and 1950's, under Allen and his successor, John Fischer, more attention was given to international affairs, and since then it has kept a happy mix of content, with some excellent fiction and poetry

(James Dickey, Lawrence Durrell, John Ashbery and Louis Simpson in 1970, for example).

In 1967 Willie Morris became editor. Under him, there have been some newsworthy items: a long excerpt from *The Confessions of Nat Turner*, entire issues given to Norman Mailer's "The Steps of the Pentagon" and Bill Moyers' "Listening to America." Other significant contributions in 1965-70 included those by Oscar Lewis, Seymour Hersh, Nat Hentoff, Arthur Schlesinger, Jr., Bayard Rustin, Arthur Miller, Eric Goldman—many of the contributions being published later as parts of books—and the journal has helped develop the reportorial article, a literary form of increasing significance and prominence. John Fischer still writes the "Easy Chair"—a monthly essay, usually on a matter of political or social concern. Irving Howe contributes a long essay-review, and there are a number of shorter reviews, up to a few hundred words, of fiction and non-fiction by various reviewers. All are excellent.

An essential title for every library, and because of its continuity, eminent contributors, and historical importance as an institution in American intellectual life, college libraries should have a complete backfile.

Indexed in: B.R.D.   4-12670 rev. 2
                R.G.

HOLIDAY.   v. 1, 1946-

9 nos./yr.   Indianapolis, Ind. $7.00

Though its original purpose was "dedicated to the pursuit of happiness," for many years *Holiday* paid increasing attention to the real world—seriously treating politics, sociology, history and the arts, and personalities in these fields. In 1961, for example, it received an award from the American Association for the United Nations for a series on the U.N. and its affiliated agencies, and another series on the federal government's executive departments was outstanding. This trend, however, was not long-lived, and the sybaritic aspects of *Holiday* are now quite pronounced. It does contain superb travel articles. Most of these—on countries, cities, historic landmarks, and just interesting or unusual places (bars, opera houses, resorts, etc.)—are by authors who write engagingly, and who have a sense of involvement with the places about which they write, and many of whom are very well known—for example, E.B. White on New York, James Morris on Salamanca, John Marquand on Boston, Laurens van der Post on Russia, Aubrey Menen on India, Paul Bowles on the Sahara. Perhaps 4 or 5 issues a year are devoted to single subjects: New York City, Travel U.S.A., Travel in Europe, American Youth in Europe, Italy, etc. All articles are superbly illustrated. There are articles and shorter pieces on recreational activities, on clothing, food and drink, and the "Holiday Travel Handbook," a special section in recent issues, offers suggestions for various locales. *Holiday's* annual survey of outstanding restaurants throughout the United States is well known. Good movie reviews. In all, *Holiday* is a well-produced and well-edited periodical, with some substance as well as a handsome appearance. (Though with the reduction in size in 1971, its attractiveness is much less.) It is perhaps not as significant a periodical as it once was—not just because its emphasis has shifted—but because so many other periodicals have gotten in on coverage of international travel and foreign culture. Nevertheless, it should still be in every library, but now primarily for pleasure rather than source material.

Indexed in: R.G.   47-23455

NOTE: By mid-1971, the deterioration in *Holiday's* appearance and content became very obvious, and it can no longer be regarded as important for academic libraries.

*HORIZON.   v. 1, 1958-

Quarterly.   N.Y. $20.00

A sumptuous "Magazine of the Arts," (a sister publication of *American Heritage*) each issue is bound in a hard cover, printed on heavy coated paper, profusely and beautifully illustrated, with 10-15 articles by many of the world's leading scholar-writers. They cover all aspects of history and culture—from tipped-in reproductions of masterpieces from the Chinese imperial art treasures to an article by Arthur C. Clarke on "The Social Consequences of the Communications Satellites," from "The World's Worst Animals" to "Escoffier: God of the Gastronomes." John Canaday on Manet, Morris Bishop on Pascal, Toynbee on Religion and History, Tyrone Guthrie on drama, Andre Malraux, Hesketh Pearson, Ben Shahn, Malcolm Cowley, Phyllis McGinley—almost any contemporary English and American writer of eminence one could name has contributed.

Some may sneer at it as "instant culture," and perhaps the intellectual content of the articles is not always challenging, but the subjects are for the most part significant, and are always interestingly and frequently authoritatively treated. A prime item for browsing and for undergraduate papers, it should be in every college library.

Indexed in: R.G.   58-4110

HUMANIST.   v. 1, 1941-

Bi-monthly.   Buffalo, N.Y. $6.00

Published by the American Humanist Association and (since March, 1969) the American Ethical Union, it "is a journal of contemporary ethical concern that attempts to serve as a bridge between theoretical philosophical discussions and the practical application of humanism to ethical and social problems." It is a successor to the *New Humanist*, which was founded in 1927 by students from the Meadville Theological School, but because of financial problems, was discontinued in 1936. In 1941 the American Humanist Association was incorporated, and Edwin Wilson was made editor of the *Humanist*, a position he held until 1957. In 1965 it assumed its present format and its more academic content.

Contains articles, which vary greatly in number and length, on all aspects of contemporary affairs, especially those which are concerned with moral or ethical ideas—e.g., peace, race relations, education, family relations, religion, economics, etc.—and because so many eminent scholars and writers belong to one of the two organizations, it has some very worthwhile contributors. In 1970, for example, among the authors were Paul Goodman, David Bazelon, Howard K. Smith, Charles Frankel, H.J. Eysenck, Buckminster Fuller, Leslie Fiedler, Jacques Barzun, Noam Chomsky, Sidney Hook, A.H. Maslow, U Thant and Barry Commoner. Frequently presents differing positions on issues, so that the articles are especially useful for students.

Occasional film and drama reviews, always a book review or two (up to 4) on a variety of topic. These are mostly 500-1000 words in length and are rather good. Also news of the two associations, and news of interest to them.

Indexed in: Br.Hum.I.   44-49467
            P.A.I.S.

ILLUSTRATED LONDON NEWS.   v. 1, 1842-

Weekly.   London. $10.00

More significant for its past than its present, it still provides a well illustrated view of many aspects of the contemporary world, with a great emphasis, of course, on Britain. When illustrated periodicals were unusual, or at least not very good, the *News* was eagerly and widely read for its superb drawings and photographs—of news events, technological developments, scientific and archaeological expeditions and finds, and personalities. It does much of this same thing today, but it now has many competitors throughout the world, a number of which are more expert in photojournalism, and the *ILN* appears much less interesting than it used to be. Also, since Britain is no longer so pivotal in political, social, economic and cultural affairs, the *ILN's* significance as a reporting medium has diminished. For example, its drawings and photographs of British warships, airplanes and military exploits used to be fascinating; they are not of nearly as much interest now.

In addition to the few articles on local and international topics, all of which have a good balance of text and pictures, each issue now contains reviews, usually 750-1000 words, of one to 3 or 4 books, primarily of trade titles, but generally those of quality. Also reviews of theatre, films and records, and regular columns for gardeners and collectors, on food and wine, bridge and chess, travel and local events.

An attractive and well-edited periodical, even though not nearly so important as it once was, it is still useful, especially for those interested in contemporary Britain. An extensive backfile would be a superb resource for 19th and early 20th century history; current issues will still be used regularly for browsing.

INTERCOLLEGIATE REVIEW.   v. 1, 1965-

4 nos./yr.   Bryn Mawr, Pa. $5.00

Published by the Intercollegiate Studies Institute, an organization founded by a group "concerned about the preservation and extension of individual liberty" and the importance of a good liberal arts education in nurturing "the broad knowledge and understanding essential for good judgment."

Each issue (often 2 numbers combined) contains 4 or 5 articles, mostly 5-10,000 words long, by some of the country's leading conservative scholars—Russell Kirk, Will Herberg, Stefan Possony, Willmoore Kendall, Thomas Molnar and others. The articles cover a wide range of topics—education, world affairs, ethics, economics, religion, literature, etc.—and all express an intelligent, responsible conservative viewpoint. There are 2 to 5 book reviews per issue, covering a wide variety of topics, but with some emphasis on world affairs. Almost all the reviews are over 2000 words long, and many are several times that. All, of course, are signed and critical.

A reliable, literate journal with a bias that should be represented in the college library. Individual students, faculty members or librarians can, upon application, receive it without charge.

65-9854

INTERNATIONAL SOCIAL SCIENCE JOURNAL.   v. 1, 1949-

Quarterly.   Paris. $7.00

Through 1958 titled the *International Social Science Bulletin,* it is published by UNESCO. The first part of each issue is devoted to discussions of a particular topic of interest to social scientists, often a topic related to methodology, or one interrelating various interests. Topics treated recently have included: Towards a Policy for Social Research, Documentation in the Social Sciences, Futurology, Social Science in the Third World, etc. Each of these is treated from several vantage points, usually by authors from different parts of the world, who are almost always eminent in this field. Articles unrelated to the topic, usually on basic questions of theory and methodology, appear occasionally.

The latter portion of each number contains several regular features: a calendar of approaching international conferences; brief meeting reports; international appointments vacant; a listing of recent documents and publications of the U.N. and the specialized agencies, and a list of books received.

An important journal for the study of all social science, but particularly useful where there is much interest in its theory, methodology, or relationship with other areas.

Indexed in: P.A.I.S.   51-4294 rev.
          S.S.H.I.

JOURNAL OF COMMUNICATION.   v. 1, 1951-

Quarterly.   Lawrence, Kans.

Published by the International Communication Association (before September, 1969, the National Society for the Study of Communication), it is "devoted to an interdisciplinary approach to the study of communication in human relations." Contributors are faculty members from a variety of fields—sociology, psychology, speech, journalism, communications research etc.—and their articles, which average 5 or 6 per issue and are short to medium length (2-6000 words), report the results of research in this area. Each article is preceded by an abstract. Topics treated include communication theory, listening, reading, writing and speaking skills, propaganda and mass media, cross-cultural communication, and many others relating communications with human behavior. Usually about 8 or 10 book reviews, signed and critical, mostly under 500 words. Also a few other titles briefly noted, and a list of books received. An important title where there are majors in journalism, speech or communication, but also useful for courses in sociology and social or educational psychology.

Indexed in: Ed.I.   56-46080
          Ment.Hlth.B.R.I.

JOURNAL OF POPULAR CULTURE.   v. 1, 1967-

Quarterly.   Bowling Green, Ohio. $8.00

Official publication of the Popular Literature Section (Comparative Literature II) of the Modern Language Association and the Folklore Section of the Midwest Modern Language Association. Contains usually 5 or 6 scholarly and semi-scholarly articles on popular culture which, defined in the broadest sense of the term, includes such diverse topics as the appeal of Garbo, *McGuffey's Reader*, detective fiction, the impact of television, folk music, pop art, Nigerian chapbooks, etc., in addition, of course, to those articles on the uses, interpretation and methodology of popular culture itself. Some signed and critical reviews, mostly 500 words and more. The articles make interesting reading and are useful for undergraduate papers.

Indexed in: Music I.

*JOURNALISM QUARTERLY.   v. 1, 1924-

Quarterly.   Minneapolis, Minn. $10.00

Published by the Association for Education in Journalism, cooperating with the American Association of Schools and Departments of Journalism and the Kappa Tau Alpha Society. Articles, most fairly brief to moderate length, are concerned primarily with the practice of and education for journalism, but they also treat the total field of mass communications: radio, television and motion pictures, advertising, content analyses, public opinion, etc. There are a number of regular features: "Journalism Education," a forum for members of AEJ, treats educational trends, fields of study, laboratory techniques and student problems, in journalism and mass communications; "Research in Brief" is "devoted to shorter reports on research in the communications field"; "Book Reviews" usually contains 25-30 signed, critical reviews, varying in length from 100-200 words for works of lesser importance to 700-800 words for significant books and includes many works of general interest; there is also an annotated listing of "Other Books and Pamphlets on Journalistic Subjects"; a useful bibliography, *Articles on Mass Communications in U.S. and Foreign Journals,* covers the previous three months, and includes brief annotations for most items; "News Notes" contains news of personnel, scholarships, new courses, activities of the Association, etc. The Summer issue contains the annual *Report on Graduate Research in Journalism and Communication,* which includes abstracts of doctoral dissertations accepted, a list of dissertation titles approved and a list of Master's degree theses completed during the year. In 1971, a much abbreviated listing was substituted—just doctoral dissertations accepted and titles approved, without annotations—because *Journalism Abstracts* took over the previous function.

Because of the interest of students in mass media, the breadth of *Journalism Quarterly's* coverage, and the many useful features, it should be in every academic library, even where journalism is not part of the curriculum.

Indexed in: P.A.I.S.   28-13599 (rev. '39)

*LIBERATION.   v. 1, 1956-

Monthly (bi-monthly Sept.-Oct.)   N.Y. $15.00

An articulate journal of news and opinion from the radical, non-violent, non-Marxist, academically (now) respectable left. Its editorial board consists of the well known radicals, Dave Dellinger, Barbara Deming, Paul Goodman, Sidney Lens and Staughton Lynd, and its contributors have numbered such writers as Carl Oglesby, Kenneth Boulding, Noam Chomsky, Nat Hentoff and Jack Newfield, among many others. It is concerned with radical reform of all aspects of American society, politics, education, and economic affairs, with special emphasis on the elimination of racism and the establishment of peace, and on "revolutionary humanism," a phrase that aptly describes its stance. It of course is also concerned with international affairs; usually carries some poetry, which is chosen for its "feeling" more than for its literary quality, though the latter is often evident. No book reviews as such, but occasional articles discuss single works at length. Since it is representative of the responsible radical left, *Liberation* is especially important for college libraries, both for research and for browsing.

Indexed in: Alt.Pr.I.
　　　　　　In.Per.Negroes
　　　　　　P.A.I.S.

*LIFE. v. 1, 1936-

Weekly.   Chicago, Ill. $10.00

An instant and resounding success (with almost a quarter-million subscribers before the first number was issued, it achieved a circulation of over a million 4 months later, and by 1946, over 4 million) it has had a tremendous impact on magazine publication over the world—the use of candid and expert photography to present the news created many imitators, though none (in this country, certainly) as successful. But it was because of more than just its photo-journalism—which often emphasized the sensational, or at least the dramatic aspect of news, rather than its significance—that *Life* became important for libraries. It has been especially useful for its pictorial features, and picture-and-text essays: superb reproductions of art, traditional, exotic and contemporary (which have been indexed in separately published books); explanations of scientific and medical phenomena through technically excellent drawings and diagrams; presentations of particular historical periods and events, persons and places, often done by eminent authorities; selections from forthcoming political and historical (and, on occasion) literary works. Many of these served as the basis for books.

The amount of textual matter has gradually increased (partly because of the inevitable success of television as a medium for the presentation of current events) and departments have been added. In 1964, book and movie reviews became more or less regular features, and by 1970 they *had* become regular, along with reviews of television programs. the theatre and recordings. Editorials and essays, on politics and social issues, are now common, and the column The Presidency, commentary on national politics by Hugh Sidey, appears regularly.

The reviews are good. Albert Goldman writes on the pop scene, Richard Schickel on movies, John Leonard and others on television. The book reviews, usually between 500 and 1000 words and on popular fiction and non-fiction, are by guest reviewers who are not only eminent, but highly competent. Within a few months in 1971, for example, there were reviews by Budd Schulberg, Wilfrid Sheed, Fred Cook, Eric Goldman and John Kenneth Galbraith. For a mass magazine, the reviews are among the best.

An essential purchase for all libraries, with a complete backfile desirable for its wealth of pictorial material.

Indexed in: R.G.   37-8367*

LONDON MAGAZINE.   n.s. v. 1, 1961-

Monthly.   London. $10.00

While the new series began as a purely literary journal, it treats the visual and dramatic arts as well, though still devoting most of its space to litera- ture. Each issue contains about a dozen contributions, with an excellent balance of short stories, poetry, literary criticism, essays and commentary on the arts. Contributors include some of the best known critics, writers and poets (in the 1970/71 volume, for example, were Robert Lowell, William Sansom, Richard Brautigan, Nadime Gordimer, Daniel Hoffman, Lawrence Durrell, Dan Jacobson, T ed Hughes) plus many well known in Britain but not in the U.S. Lesser known writers and poets are also well represented, and all contributions are of a consistently high quality. There are frequent translations of short stories and poetry. Reproductions of art work in almost all issues.

Regular sections on art, drama and cinema criticism. Most issues contain several longer book reviews plus a few shorter ones; these are of fiction, literary criticism or on the arts. They are all signed and critical, and range from several hundred to 2000 words in length.

Exceptionally well balanced, with eminent contributors, it is one of the better literary journals, and belongs in any library where there is much interest in contemporary literature or the current Anglo-American cultural scene.

Indexed in: Br.Hum. I.   55-42405

*LOOK.   v. 1, 1937-1971.

Bi-weekly.   Des Moines, Iowa. $5.00

Generally considered an imitator of *Life,* though actually planned before the latter had begun, *Look* differed in containing much more general material, such as interviews, photo quizzes, articles on fashions and health, humorous cartoons, as well as lengthy articles on personalities and public issues. Somewhat sensational in its early years, with not much that was useful for academic purposes, it was not even included in the *Readers' Guide* until 1953, by which time it had improved greatly and was be- coming known for its "photojournalism." Later in the decade, it gained even more respectability by running articles on matters of social signifi- cance, which were treated with intelligence and in some depth.

Most issues contain a well balanced mix of articles—the national scene, world affairs, health, science, entertainment, sports, the arts—with issues frequently focusing on a major topic, e.g., The Seventies, The Negro in America, California, The Cities, or devoting a large portion of issues to similar topics. Book condensations have appeared occasionally—usually of more sensational works such as *Education and Ecstasy, Death of a President,* or *Notes From the Future.* Book reviews began in 1968; now they appear regularly, written mostly by the regular reviewers, but occas- ionally by guest experts. They are long, usually over 1000 words, and treat a wide variety of works, though only one or two titles per issue.

Because it is read so widely (over 7 million circulation) and treats many worthwhile topics with intelligence and imagination, it should be in all college libraries. A backfile before 1953 is not essential, but after that, is desirable.

Indexed in: R.G.   39-5737

(NOTE: *Look* ceased publication with the issue for Oct. 19, 1971.)

*MANCHESTER GUARDIAN WEEKLY. v. 1, 1919-

Weekly.   London. $19.50

Based on articles and "services of the British morning newspaper, the 'Guardian,' published daily in London and Manchester," it provides superb reporting by what is generally considered one of the world's outstanding newspapers.

Each issue of 24 pages on thin paper reports the week's news, emphasizing, of course, Great Britain and the Commonwealth nations, but with much attention also to the United States. The reporting is objective, clear and often incisive, though the articles are not usually very long. Background articles are just as important as the news items, and the *Guardian's* reporters are recognized for their knowledgeability. (Alistair Cooke, for example, has been the American reporter, as well as having a regular column for years.) Regular features include sections on chess, bridge, a crossword puzzle, financial comment, sports and reviews of music, drama, art, dance, movies and books. All reviews are good; usually 10 or 12 books, ranging over all areas, are reviewed, most by regular reviewers, but often by outside experts, in reviews usually between 700 and 1000 words.

Because of the *Guardian's* reliability and readability, it should be in all libraries. It is especially important for smaller libraries that cannot supply an assortment of current foreign newspapers; the *Guardian* will help greatly toward balancing an ethnocentric selection. A substantial backfile is perhaps not necessary, especially since it is not handily indexed.

Beginning with the August 4, 1971 issue, the *Manchester Guardian Weekly* has added a 4-page section devoted to a shortened version of the English edition of *Le Monde, Selection Hebdomadaire*, which had been published from April, 1969 until then. *Le Monde* is one of the world's great newspapers, known for its balanced but incisive reporting of the French political scene and the arts, as well as its superb coverage of African and Asian affairs, and gaining access to its columns, even in this highly truncated form, makes the *Guardian Weekly* even more important for college libraries.

MAIN CURRENTS IN MODERN THOUGHT. v. 1, 1940-

5 nos./yr.   New Rochelle, N.Y. $14.50

Published by the Foundation for Integrative Education, its purpose is "to call attention to significant contributions currently being made in a variety of fields, relating these to each other and to American, European and Eastern thinking, both classical and contemporary. Its editors assume that the laws of nature and of man as formulated by science, the universals of philosophy and the principles of art, as well as the truths of comparative religion, can be orchestrated into a harmonious, meaningful, ethically compelling body of teachings which can and should be made the central core of study in the educative process at all levels."

Usually about 5 articles, brief to moderate length, per issue and, as one might expect from the journal's purposes, they are rather general in nature. "Reason in Science and Conduct," "The Problem of Past and Future," "Humankind as a Cosmic Phenomenon" are perhaps not typical, but do convey the thrust. Yet mostly they are not superficial, and among the contributors are some very distinguished names, from all over the world. Many of them relate to education, and it is, of course, in "integrative education" that the journal is primarily interested. Usually 2 or 3 book reviews, on works in the same areas as the articles. They are signed and critical, mostly 750-1000 words, but often much longer.

An eclectic, often provocative journal, it will appeal to more thoughtful readers and is most appropriate for the liberal arts college library.

51-17477

*MASSACHUSETTS REVIEW.   v. 1, 1959-

Quarterly.   Amherst, Mass. $7.00

Begun by a group of faculty members—mostly from the English Department at the University of Massachusetts, it is "a quarterly of literature, the arts and public affairs," now "published independently with the support and cooperation of Amherst College, Mount Holyoke College, Smith College, and the University of Massachusetts." Contains much original poetry and fiction, mostly by young, little-known writers, and essays on literature, art and (only occasionally) social or political affairs, many by well-known critics and scholars. A few issues have been devoted to book-length "Gatherings," collections of survey and critical materials on authors such as Thoreau, William Carlos Williams, and others. Occasional articles on artists, with reproductions of sculpture or drawings. It was, as a matter of fact, perhaps the first such quarterly to pay much attention to the graphic arts. Usually about 5 book reviews per issue, of fiction, literary criticism, poetry and the social sciences; these are signed and critical, and quite long, mostly 1000-2000 words, but frequently even longer. A review of almost uniformly high quality.

Indexed in: In.Ltl.Mag.   61-19086
          S.S.H.I.

MINERVA.   v. 1, 1962-

Quarterly.   London. $10.00

Subtitled "A review of science, learning and policy," it is published by the Committee on Science and Freedom, an affiliate of the Congress for Cultural Freedom. Contains thoughtful articles by outstanding educators, scientists, and public figures from here and abroad on science, education (at all levels, though with an emphasis on the college and university level) and public policy, and on their interrelationships. The articles—usually 3 or 4 per issue—are not research articles, but rather are surveys of a situation or development, or an essay on an idea or concept (e.g., "Organizing for Science in Britain: Some Relevant Questions," "Universities in Turkey," "Legal Frameworks for the Assessment and Control of Technology," "The International Evaluation of Human Capital"). The "Reports and Documents" section carries addresses, reprints of articles, and texts of documents relating to the above subjects. "Chronicle" reports important recent developments (mostly in higher education), country by country. An important journal for keeping up with the international scene in science, education and public policy.

Indexed in: P.A.I.S.   67-5277

MODERN AGE.   v. 1, 1957-

Quarterly.   Chicago, Ill. $4.00

A general review, published under the auspices of the Foundation for Foreign Affairs, dedicated to the conservative viewpoint in politics, sociology, economics, philosophy, literature, art, and education. Edited by Russell Kirk through its first 3 volumes, it has carried contributions by the most eminent conservatives—Peter Viereck, Ernest van den Haag, Frank S. Meyer, Wilhelm Ropke, Will Herberg, Stefan Possony, William Henry Chamberlin, and many others. Each issue consists of about 7 articles and essays, some quite scholarly, on a wide variety of subjects. In 1959 and 1960 it carried the *Burke Newsletter,* including brief articles on Burke and reviews of works about him as well as news in the field of Burke scholarship. Frequently contains poetry and short stories. Generally 5 to 10 reviews per issue (the number has been increasing) treating all types of books, though rarely fiction or poetry. The signed reviews, frank and critical, vary greatly in length, but are often several thousand words. An important journal for college libraries, responsibly and intelligently representing a significant section of intellectual thought, and balancing, in a sense, the left-of-center editorial policies of the many other journals of opinion.

Indexed in: P.A.I.S.   59-36894

*NATION.   v. 1, 1865-

Weekly (bi-weekly in July, part of Aug. and Dec.)   N.Y. $12.50

Since its founding, it has numbered among its editorial staff some of the most distinguished names in American journalism and letters, particularly those identified with liberal movements and progressive policies: E.L. Godkin, Oswald Garrison Villard, Freda Kirchwey, Joseph Wood Krutch, Max Lerner, Charles Angoff. This is even more true of its contributors, a list of which reads like a Who's Who of American belles-lettres, scholarship and political comment: Henry and William James, William Dean Howells, Francis Parkinson, John Fiske, Charles Peirce, Joel Chandler Harris, Irving Babbitt, Carl Van Doren, and many, many others.

Frequently advocating unpopular causes—supporting strikers when it was unfashionable, pleading for Sacco and Vanzetti, advocating the election of Debs and LaFollette, for example—its impact has been much greater than its circulation (rarely over 40,000) might indicate, and a complete backfile is most important for the history of American social and political thought, and should be in every academic library. In 1955 its new owner stated that it "has been and will continue to be frankly partisan. Our hearts and our columns are on the side of the worker, the minority group, of the underprivileged generally. We side with the intellectual and political nonconformist. . . ."

Most issues consist of several editorials and 3 to 5 articles on all aspects of contemporary politics, economic, social and cultural concerns foreign affairs, and education, with occasional issues devoted to single topics in one of these areas. Contributors include journalists, academicians, and public figures. There is some poetry in almost every issue, practically all of it by relatively unknown poets. Its reviews are notable. One of the *Nation's* original purposes was good criticism and it still adheres to this. These are usually 4-6 long book reviews, mostly 1000 -2000 words, done by guest reviewers, plus regular columns on the Dance, Films, the Theatre and Art. All are excellent.

Though not nearly as influential as it once was, and without the eminent contributors it used to display, the *Nation* is still an important journal of opinion (though that opinion is sometimes expressed a bit shrilly) and it should be available in every library.

Indexed in: B.R.D.   4-12681 rev.
            R.G.

*NATIONAL REVIEW.   v. 1, 1955-

Bi-weekly.   Bristol, Conn. $12.00

An outspoken outlet for the New Conservatism, voiced most articulately through its editor, William F. Buckley, it is a journal of news, views and opinion. Each issue contains commentary, articles and editorials on domestic and foreign politics, social and economic problems, literature and the arts, education, religion, etc. The writing, especially by the editorial staff, is superb—usually irreverent and witty, often acerbic and occasionally bordering on the libelous. Well known conservatives in all fields, such as James Burnham, Ralph de Toledano, Will Herberg, Frank Meyer, Willmoore Kendall, Russell Kirk, Ernest van den Haag, M. Stanton Evans, Henry Hazlitt, are always represented either as regular or occasional contributors.

The section "Books, Art, Manners" contains reviews of from 2 to 10 books (usually 4 or 5) in all areas, but with an emphasis on political and social affairs and recent history. Signed and critical, often outspokenly so, they are mostly 500-1000 words, but often longer; several briefer reviews, and "Random Notes" about many other new and forthcoming books. The section also contains reviews of movies, art, television and music, though none regularly.

The *National Review Bulletin* appears in alternate weeks. It is a newsletter of fact and opinion, but because it does not provide extended treatment or depth, and because it is not indexed, libraries don't need it. However, the *National Review* itself belongs in every college library. Not only does it represent a significant part of the political spectrum, but it is often intellectually solid—it is certainly almost always interesting, articulate and forthright. For studying the development of modern American conservatism, a backfile is important.

Indexed in: B.R.D.   57-3062
            R.G.

*NEW AMERICAN REVIEW.   no. 1, 1967-

Irregular.   N.Y. $6.50

Some may dispute this title's claim to being a magazine; certainly it does not fulfill some of the usual qualifications—it appears irregularly (about 3 times a year), is published in paperback format (the first few numbers were also available in hardback) and it can be ordered by standing order rather than by annual subscription. Nevertheless it calls itself a magazine; so be it. A revival, in a sense, of the New American Library's *New World Writing,* which appeared from 1952 through 1959, it carries on that tradition of quality and diversity in its essays, articles, stories, and poetry. Contributors range from those appearing nationally for the first time (the *NAR* is one of the few periodicals of any major publisher that still seeks unsolicited manuscripts) to some of the best known names in American poetry, fiction, essays, and criticism—e.g., Philip Roth, Kate Millett, Donald Barthelme, Ted Hughes, Gary Snyder, Benjamin DeMott, Eric Bentley— with a happy balance among the genres. All of it is worthwhile reading; some of it is memorable and significant.

Because of *NAR's* singular format and nature, unlike other periodicals it should be available for circulation. There are various ways of permitting this, such as having duplicate copies, or classifying and binding issues to circulate as books—in any case, several numbers should not be bound together. Despite the problems this may present, *NAR* should be available in every library.

67-27377

NEW ENGLAND QUARTERLY.   v. 1, 1928-

Quarterly.   Brunswick, Maine. $8.00

Subtitled "A Historical Review of New England Life and Letters," it is published in conjunction with the Colonial Society of Massachusetts. As one would expect of a journal with a board of editors that includes some of the most distinguished names in American letters, the articles— 4 to 6 an issue—are scholarly and thoughtful, but most readable; they are divided almost equally between the history and literature of New England, though ranging over all aspects and periods of these two fields, and excluded are articles that are purely local, antiquarian, or genealogical. A "Memoranda and Documents" section on miscellaneous events, personalities or incidents. The annual *Bibliography of New England*, comprising articles dealing with New England in periodicals, "including bound volumes of historical societies that publish no serials," was discontinued in 1967. There are now usually 20-30 book reviews per issue, 750-1000 words in length. They are all signed and are excellent. Occasional review-essays.

Though regional in interest, the significance of New England in the history of American life and letters makes the journal an important one for every academic library, and the many key articles in the past means an extensive backfile is most useful.

Indexed in: B.R.D.   29-23850
           S.S.H.I.

NEW Hungarian Review. *see* AREA STUDIES/SOVIET UNION AND
  EAST EUROPE

NEW LEADER.   v. 1, 1927-

Bi-weekly (except semi-monthly, July; monthly, Aug.)   N.Y. $10.00

Founded by the American Socialist Party, it served as its organ until
1936, when there was a split in the party. Sol Levitas, who had es-
caped from Russia in 1918, served as its editor for almost 30 years, and
under him, it became known as a leftist, but severely anti-Communist
publication, with contributions from some of the most eminent liberal
writers and commentators of the period—John Dewey, Granville Hicks,
Max Eastman, James Farrell, and Sidney Hook, as well as public officials
of various political outlooks. In 1954, in an editorial tribute, the *New
York Times* wrote that the New Leader served as a "forum for all sorts
of liberals, a term which automatically excludes both Communists and
the strange gentry of the Nazi or Fascist right."

Since Levitas' death in 1961, it has continued to represent a steadfastly
liberal, but anti-Communist, viewpoint, one that can be defined most
easily by listing its "regular contributors": Daniel Bell, Theodore Draper,
Walter Goodman, Milton R. Konvitz, Irving Kristol, Robert Lekachman,
Richard J. Margolis, Reinhold Niebuhr, John P. Roche. It contains, then,
articles on all phases of national and international affairs, and eminent
foreign personalities frequently contribute.

Regular reviewing columns on films, art, television, music and poetry,
all of which are good. Several lengthy, signed book reviews in each issue,
plus seasonal Christmas and Spring book issues. The book reviews are
outstanding.

An independent, thoughtful journal of opinion, with some notable contributors. A backfile is important for the history of American leftist
thought; college libraries should receive it currently.

Indexed in: P.A.I.S.

                                                    36-11311 rev*

NEW LEFT REVIEW.   v. 1, 1960-

Bi-monthly.   London. $7.50

"Its aim is to provide a forum for left-wing thought of as wide a variety
as possible, bringing together strands from Europe, America and the Third
World." While many of the contributions relate to leftist or specifically
Marxist political theory, just as many relate to other aspects of society
and culture as seen from a leftist viewpoint. Thus, Isaac Deutscher writes
on the Arab-Israeli War, Jan Myrdal on a Chinese village, Conor Cruise
O'Brien on the Congo, Herbert Marcuse on Max Weber, Ronald Laing on
schizophrenia, Noam Chomsky on linguistics and politics, and a number
of other lesser known figures on art, music, the cinema, literature, etc.
Most issues contain 1 or 2 reviews. These are frequently article length.

Excellently edited, with uncompromising intellectual standards and many
eminent contributors, it is probably the most highly regarded journal of
present-day socialist thought, and should be in those libraries where

there is much interest in contemporary political theory or the history of socialism.

Indexed in: Br.Hum.I.   63-28333
          P.A.I.S.

*NEW REPUBLIC.   v. 1, 1914-

Weekly (except end of July, Aug., and end of Dec.)   Washington,
D.C. $14.00

A respected journal of commentary on politics, economics and social problems, with domestic issues emphasized strongly. Although its original purpose was not partisan or ideological, but educational, it has always been identified with the "liberal" point of view (somewhat to left of center, but not as far as the *Nation*) and its editorials and articles represent that segment of public opinion fairly accurately. Founded by a group that included Herbert Croly, Walter Lippmann, Willard Straight and Francis Hackett, it achieved almost immediate acceptance among the nation's intellectuals, and contributors in the 1920's numbered some of the best known writers and commentators of England and the U.S.: John Dewey, J.M. Keynes, Lewis Mumford, H.L. Mencken, Virginia Woolf, Van Wyck Brooks, and many others. Its articles of opinion today tend to be more from staff members and regular contributors, frequently journalists.

There is some poetry in almost every issue. Most of it is short and by the better known poets. Except for the Spring Book Review, issues contain just a few reviews, sometimes only one. They are mostly by expert reviewers, are usually on political and social affairs—seldom fiction—and quite long (amounting in many cases to review-essays). For years, its reviews of the theater, music and art were one of its strong points, but there are very few of these now. Films are still reviewed regularly and they are excellent.

An essential journal for every library, along with a complete backfile.

Indexed in: B.R.D.   15-11657
          R.G.

*NEW STATESMAN.   v. 1, 1913-

Weekly.   London. $16.20 by air express $23.20

Founded by a group of Fabian Socialists, including the Webbs and George Bernard Shaw, it was for many years a small, left-wing paper, without a great deal of influence, except among the already committed. In 1930 Kingsley Martin, a journalist with a strong scholarly background, became editor; the following year it absorbed the *Nation* and was titled until 1957 the *New Statesman and Nation*. Under Martin's editorship, which lasted to 1960, the journal became one of the most influential left-wing journals in Britain, with J.M. Keynes and G.D.H. Cole two of its directors. Though its circulation rarely exceeded 100,000, it has had a real impact on British domestic and international policy because it influenced people with influence, and top figures in the Labour Party as well as other writers and critics have been frequent contributors. Today it still represents an independent radical viewpoint, and within that context, offers some of the most perceptive opinion and comment on world affairs, politics, and economics and social matters from its own correspondents and other name writers. Its reviews—of books, theatre, music and the arts—are highly regarded. There are generally 10-15 (fiction and non-fiction) books reviewed per issue (except for the special seasonal book numbers, which carry many more); these vary greatly in length, with reviews of important books almost always over 1000 words. A significant journal for all academic libraries, it is especially useful for courses in current affairs, with the backfile important for modern British history and politics.

Indexed in: B.R.D. 14-11950 (rev.)
            Br.Hum.I.
            S.S.H.I.

NEW York Review of Books. *see* BOOK REVIEWS & BOOK SELECTION

*NEW YORK TIMES MAGAZINE. 1896-

Weekly. N.Y. Available with Sunday *New York Times* only.

With occasional variations, each issue contains 5 or 6 articles within these subject areas: politics (national usually, but sometimes of local or regional interest to New Yorkers); international affairs, especially concerning a current issue; social problems, also related to a current issue; art or drama; modern history ("20 Years Ago Today Was . . ."); a humorous look at some current fad or social practice. Contributions, by *Times* staffers, by other well-known authorities, and by free-lancers, are always interestingly written and well illustrated, and many are of serious intellectual depth and significance. Regular features include several pages on fashions, on parents and children, on home furnishings, and on food preparation. These are shorter than the articles, but are also illustrated and well written. Advertisements—especially for clothing—fill a major portion of the pages. The crossword puzzle page is an institution in itself.

Libraries having the *Times* on microfilm may also want to keep and bind the *Magazine* section, since it is asked for so frequently by students working on papers. Binding is expensive since, as Christmas approaches, so many pages are devoted to advertising. Whatever the decision, it should be available in all college libraries.

Indexed in: R.G.

*NEW YORKER. v. 1, 1925-

Weekly. N.Y. $12.00

Its success formula had been for many years sophisticated cartoons and humor, plus excellent stories and reminiscences. In the past few decades, there have been several significant changes. First, the average length of contributions has increased markedly; on a few occasions, whole issues have even been given over to single items, most notably, John Hersey's *Hiroshima* and James Baldwin's *The Fire Next Time*. Other lengthy pieces (some in several parts) have been Truman Capote's *In Cold Blood,* Rachel Carson's *Silent Spring* and Hannah Arendt's *Eichmann on Trial.* The second significant change, accompanying the other but becoming more pronounced even more recently, has been its increased social concern and frank political stance, and it is now regarded among intellectuals as much for its politics—which is quite liberal—as for its literature.

Its regular features—"Talk of the Town," profiles of individuals, the cartoons, reviews of movies, plays, art, music and books—are still excellent, with some of the country's leading critics doing them: Pauline Kael, Winthrop Sargeant, Anthony West, Edmund Wilson, and others. The fiction and poetry are also outstanding, most of it by well-known authors, but occasional contributions by younger, experimental writers. The political reporting, the accounts of social history, and other non-fiction, are always interesting and often incisive.

For browsing, an essential journal for every library; a substantial backfile is very useful, though because of the large amount of advertising, binding is expensive.

Indexed in: B.R.D.   28-5329
           Music I.
           R.G.

*NEWSWEEK.   v. 1, 1933-

Weekly.   N.Y. $14.00

Founded as *News-Week* by a former *Time* editor, it struggled for its first few years until 1937, when it merged with *Today*, a magazine that attempted to popularize the New Deal, and, instead of merely digesting the news, decided on a three-dimensional approach: reporting the news, providing its background, and interpreting it. The last dimension became its most notable characteristic, for instead of anonymously writing its opinions along with the news reporting, it featured signed columns. Among its columnists have been eminent commentators with a variety of political and economic stances: Walter Lippmann, Raymond Moley, Henry Hazlitt, Stuart Alsop, Paul Samuelson, Milton Friedman, Emmett John Hughes.

News is covered by subject: National Affairs, International, Religion, Sports, The Media, The Cities, Life and Leisure, Science and Space, etc., all of which are unsigned (except for the special reports frequently accompanying some articles) but the reviews, movies, theater and book, are signed. There are usually 3 to 6 book reviews, mostly about 500 words, but often much longer. Regular features include "Periscope," containing "inside" briefs and predictions and "Where Are They Now?" updating the life of individuals who were newsworthy years ago but have since dropped from the public eye. *Newsweek's* special issues, treating a current topic in depth, such as those on racial attitudes in the U.S. or the Negro in the U.S, have often been significant.

A basic title for every library, with a substantial backfile (most of which could be on microfilm) very useful.

Indexed in: B.R.D.   35-9615
           R.G.

NORTH AMERICAN REVIEW.   v. 1, 1815;   n.s. v. 1, 1964-

Quarterly.   Cedar Falls, Iowa. $6.00

The history of the original *North American Review* from 1815 to 1940 has been told thoroughly by Frank Luther Mott. Suffice it to say here that after its first relatively undistinguished 60 years, it became one of of the most important journals in American history and letters, a position it retained for another half century before it declined in the 1920's and then died ignominiously in 1940.

In 1964, Cornell College in Iowa revived it as a bi-monthly. The revival had no connection with the original in any way other than its title and numbering. The first volume was auspicious enough, with some eminent contributors, but after that the magazine became very lacklustre, a quality that prevailed until 1969, when it was taken over by the University of Northern Iowa, and became a quarterly. Most of the contributors are relatively unknown, but the writing style is excellent (if somewhat conservative) and there is a good mix of articles, fiction and poetry. Several book reviews in each issue, usually between 750-1000 words in length.

Indexed in: In.Ltl.Mag.   4-12673 rev. 2*
            S.S.H.I.

NOUVEL OBSERVATEUR.   v. 1, 1950-

Weekly.   Paris. $19.85

Begun as *Observateur Politique, Economique et Littéraire*, it was known for about 6 months in 1953/54 as *L'Observateur d'Aujourd'hui*, then, from 1954 to November, 1964, as *France Observateur*. One of the most respected general periodicals in France, it is not a newsmagazine in the usual sense, but consists of articles, reports and interviews that provide background for or commentary on the current scene. Except for its preliminary section of letters (which are lengthy and thoughtful) and the listing of outstanding weekly attractions and brief reviews of current movies, the contents fall into four sections. "L'Evenement" mostly contains fairly brief items on political and economic affiars, covering all geographic areas, but with some emphasis on France and French-speaking ones. Interviews with authors who have written on current affairs, with government officials, and with other experts also appear frequently and provide excellent source material. "Notre Epoque" provides a variety of contributions on matters of social concern, contemporary culture, travel, etc. "Lettres, Spectacles, Arts" carries reviews of television, theatre, movies and books. All are signed and critical; the book reviews, usually 4 or 5 an issue, vary from a few hundred to several thousand words, and cover all areas of non-fiction and fiction. Frequent articles on authors, publishing news, etc. Finally, "Le Dossier [or Documents] de la Semaine" provides a special report on a topic that may be in almost any area, from group sexuality to 19th-century history to the Palestine refugees. All contributions are signed and profusely illustrated.

With a circulation of over ¼ million, *Nouvel Observateur* is widely read by intellectuals and well informed laymen. Written from a somewhat left-of-center viewpoint, its reporting of national and foreign affairs is especially highly regarded. (For example, K.S. Karol and Jean Lacouture write on Asian affairs.) Because of its reliability, breadth of coverage and perceptive reporting, it is an outstanding periodical, and is perhaps the best single journal for presentation of a French viewpoint. It should certainly be in any library where there is much interest in contemporary France or where students may want a French viewpoint on world affairs.

54-22821 rev

OCCUPATIONAL OUTLOOK QUARTERLY.   v. 1, 1957-

Quarterly. Washington, D.C. $1.50

Published by the Bureau of Labor Statistics, it serves to supplement the *Occupational Outlook Handbook,* with articles on new careers, opportunities in established fields, discussions of manpower supply and demand problems for particular segments of society, educational and training programs, etc. Usually about 6 articles per issue, well illustrated and almost all written by staff members of the BLS's Division of Manpower and Occupational Outlook. Regular features include: "Counseling Aids," a listing, briefly annotated, of government and professional leaflets and catalogs useful for guidance or career planning; "Recent Publications" describes more substantial studies.

Useful for students investigating career possibilities, it also provides information for those studying guidance or manpower economics. For college libraries used much by high school students, it is especially important. A depository item.

67-5477

*PARIS MATCH.   v. 1, 1949-

Weekly. Paris. College Ed. $13.00   Reg. Ed. $25.00

Founded at a time when France was starting on the road to recovery after World War II, it has become something of a national—perhaps international—phenomenon, and is by far the most popular French magazine. Big stories are covered thoroughly, but it is the photographs (for which it is renowned) that appeal to its readers; the text is limited in quantity and often in quality. Treating all aspects of French life, politics and culture (and often the international scene), it emphasizes personalities rather than issues. Carries many features: crossword puzzles, cartoons, reviews of books, records, movies and the theatre, and often runs the text of a somewhat recent book in installments. Though it leans to the sensational and its reporting is rarely incisive, it is useful for students of contemporary French culture as a reflection of a significant portion of that culture. It is, of course, very popular for browsing, and a painless way to keep up with one's French.

Important for libraries where there is any interest in contemporary France, its moderate cost and popular appeal should encourage all libraries to take it, though not necessarily keep it.

56-19110

*PARTISAN REVIEW.   v. 1, 1934-

Quarterly.   New Brunswick, N.J. $5.50

Founded by the John Reed Club, an organization of Communist intellectuals, it provided an outlet for the views of their group. But with the
Spanish Civil War and the Moscow trials causing a split in the American
Left, the magazine suspended publication for a year, and in 1937 a new
board of editors took control, a board representing an anti-Communist,
Trotzkyist sector. This association waned, and the journal became more
and more concerned with aesthetics and current literary affairs. In the
1940's and 50's it was best known as an outlet for the *avant-garde,* though
today its contributions could hardly be regarded as experimental. In fact,
PR is now one of the most prestigious and influential reviews and is
generally regarded at the center of the "Literary Establishment." In addition to the poetry and fiction, which is of very high quality, it carries
many articles of literary criticism, many of them concerned with the social
and psychological implications of literature. There are frequent translations of poetry, fiction and prose, from some of the best known foreign
writers. Articles on current social and political issues also appear frequently, and if the journal can be said to have a political viewpoint, it is
one of liberal radicalism. Symposia on contemporary matters affecting
intellectuals also appear frequently, sometimes over several issues. Usually
between 5 and 10 books are reviewed in each issue; they are mostly
of poetry, fiction, literary criticism and works of social significance.
Usually these are critical essays, not just reviews, and are an important
part of the journal.

Because of the many outstanding writers and personalities who have been
associated with and represented in it, and because its opinions are usually
original and stimulating, and its critical acumen high, *PR* —past and present
—should be in every library.

Indexed in: S.S.H.I.   42-20197

POPULAR SCIENCE MONTHLY.   v. 1, 1872-

Monthly.   N.Y. $5.00

Founded to help popularize the theory of evolution, and, at the same
time to take advantage of the great interest in science of the period, it
published in its early years some very sophisticated works by some of
the leading academic scientists, and kept a happy balance between natural and social science. In 1915, however, the name was sold to a magazine that emphasized mechanical devices and other "things" (as opposed
to ideas), while the original idea was taken over by *Scientific Monthly.*
Since then, "practical" science and mechanics has been its specialty.

Today, while it does occasionally feature "scientific" articles, these are
rare, and it is primarily devoted to information for the automobile owner,
the amateur mechanic or craftsman, and the handyman-about-the-house.
Articles and features on new cars and equipment, television, cameras,
machine tools, camping and boating equipment, all well illustrated with
photographs and drawings, are its mainstay. Some freshmen may use it
for papers, but in most academic libraries it will be used primarily for
browsing and personal projects and need not be bound.

Very similar in appearance and nature is *Popular Mechanics* (v. 1, 1902-$5.00). Both are indexed in the *Reader's Guide,* so that neither has a decided advantage over the other.

Indexed in: R.G.   1-8317 rev.

PROGRESSIVE.   v. 1, 1929;   n.s.v. 1, 1936-

Monthly.   Madison, Wis. $8.00

The successor to *LaFollette's Magazine,* which was begun in 1909 to permit Senator Robert M. LaFollette express his progressive viewpoint. The aim of the *Progressive,* which had LaFollette's family as publishers and editors, was the same—to speak "for the progressive forces of the country"—and it has remained consistent. Even when it opposed F.D.R.'s policy on "foreign entanglements" in 1939 and 1940, it supported him for election in 1940 because of his liberal domestic policy. In the 1940's, a group of regulars began contributing: Milton Mayer (whose articles still appear) first wrote in 1942; others were James Wechsler (who also still contributes), Fred Rodell, Stuart Chase, Quincy Howe and Louis Fischer.

Financial difficulties led to an announcement of its demise in October 1947, but its readers contributed enough for it to start again by January, 1948—an example of reader loyalty that is probably unique. This loyalty and the magazine's steadfast liberal position has permitted it to get some eminent contributors—in 1970, for example, Barry Commoner, Ralph Nader, Mayor Lindsay, Senators Fulbright, McGovern and Church—and the list of occasional contributors reads like a Who's Who of American liberalism.

Treats all aspects of political, social and economic affairs, with great emphasis on national problems—other nations are treated usually only in relation to American foreign policy. Entire or a major part of issues are occasionally devoted to a single topic, e.g., The Power of the Pentagon, Latin America: Dynamite on Our Doorstep, A Century of Struggle (on the American Negro). Regular features include: "Notes in the News" and "The Word From Washington," both containing brief, interpretive news items. Usually about 6 book reviews per issue. Averaging about 1000 words, they are excellent, critical, and cover a wide variety of books.

An impressive journal of news analysis, very useful for courses in current affairs.

Indexed in: Alt.Pr.I.   33-15217
            P.A.I.S.

*PUBLIC INTEREST.   v. 1, 1965-

Quarterly.   N.Y. $7.50

"The aim . . . is to help all of us, when we discuss issues of public policy, to know a little better what we are talking about—and preferably in time to make such knowledge effective."

Edited by Daniel Bell and Irving Kristol, and contributed to by some of the best known names in the social sciences (in 1969, for example, contributors included Daniel Moynihan, Charles Frankel, James Q. Wilson and Nathan Glazer), it has been termed "the voice of the eastern intellectual establishment" and there's no question that it does have an urban, liberal outlook. With this in mind, however, its articles, which range over all social, political and economic problems of contemporary American society, are outstanding. Occasional issues are devoted to single topics—e.g., Focus on New York, Capitalism Today, The Universities—but most issues contain articles grouped around several topics, often examining their pros and cons. There are no book reviews, but a section "Current Reading" summarizes and comments on a few recent titles.

Informative, non-partisan and almost always provocative, it should be in every college library, and because so many of the articles are of real significance, a backfile is most desirable.

Indexed in: P.A.I.S.   72-16984

PUNCH.   v. 1, 1841-

Weekly.   London. $19.50

Although it is best known as a humor magazine, it began as a satirical commentary on current political and social affairs, and much of this same tone is evident today. Throughout its history, it has had notable writers and artists as contributors, but it was really Tenniel's cartoons in the 1850's and later that made *Punch* a national institution. It has always emphasized London life and one of its regular features, "Punch Choice," which briefly annotates "things worth doing, things worth seeing" in the London theatre, cinema, museums and galleries, provides an excellent guide.

Its cartoons, especially the political commentaries, are internationally reproduced, and in retrospect provide a delightful way of examining the social customs and foibles of particular periods. Each issue contains political comments, humorous articles and stories and other miscellaneous items. Its reviews of movies, drama, television and books are excellent. There is usually just one or a few book reviews per issue, but they are often quite long.

Because it is not covered by the standard indexes, it has little reference value, but it will be much used by browsers, and for those interested in the contemporary British scene, it provides a lively and often controversial viewpoint.

10-3698

QUARTERLY JOURNAL OF THE LIBRARY OF CONGRESS.   v. 1, 1943-

Quarterly.   Washington, D.C. $3.50

Until 1964 it was titled the *Library of Congress Quarterly Journal of Current Acquisitions,* and its content was focused on descriptions of recent acquisitions by LC—important single items as well as collections—and on materials of special interest already in the library. It also contained the annual reports of various divisions and sections. With the change in title, the scope of the journal changed to include not only articles on materials in LC and reports of the divisions, but articles on a variety of subjects of general scholarly interest, usually based on materials in the library. Recent issues, for example, contained articles on the international protection of human rights, legal developments in Communist China, West German education, Albanian customary law, the history of American papermaking, and others. In 1970, the administrative reports were dropped and some issues are devoted to single topics—poetry in one instance and Africa in another—but both are still focused around the Library's collections and personnel in these areas.

An attractive, informative periodical, of particular interest to scholars and librarians, it is a depository item.

Indexed in: Lib.Lit.   44-40782
           P.A.I.S.

*RAMPARTS.   v. 1, 1962-

Monthly.   Berkeley, Calif. $8.50

It began as a liberal Catholic quarterly, but the lack of response (when it became a monthly in 1964, it had a circulation of only 2500) caused it to turn to major social, political and moral issues. Its primary concerns have been the war in Vietnam (along with its ramifications, such as the draft, the military-industrial complex, etc.), the race issue, and civil rights in general, but it treats every issue that questions traditional assumptions or ways of life. Often it does this with what has been described as "shock-for-shock's sake," but there's no question that through its skillful writing, effective use of pictures and recognition of ripe issues, it does have an impact on its readers. Nor is there much doubt that there have been some important stories and, indeed, complete issues: "The Diary of Che Guevara," the relationship of the CIA to Michigan State University and to the National Student Association, Tom Hayden's "The Trial," articles by Eldridge Cleaver. Book reviews appear in most issues; there may be just 1 or 2, but they are long—really review-essays—and they are on the same topics as the articles. Many of the articles, incidentally, are parts of forthcoming books.

Because it is one of the most widely read radical publications, and because it contains so many articles by significant writers, treating issues that are unsettling in a frank, though sometimes sensational, manner, *Ramparts* is read and used avidly by undergraduates—indeed, it is difficult to keep issues in shape for binding, or even keep them at all—and should be in every college library, particularly since it has been indexed since 1968.

Indexed in: Alt.Pr.I.   64-50228
           R.G.

*READER'S DIGEST.   v. 1, 1922-

Monthly.   Pleasantville, N.Y. $4.97

Its history has been told so many times that it is by now Americana. Even if it were not so well known, the mere fact that each month it sells 17 million copies (plus another 13 million in 12 other language-editions) would make it important for the impact it must have on American thought.

Most people assume that it still is largely a reprint magazine—as it was originally and throughout its early years. Today, however, probably two-thirds to three-quarters of the 25-30 articles in each issue are either staff-written or planned by the editors, then planted in other magazines and reprinted from there. This practice, which began in the early 1930's, became more prevalent as the editors found fewer and fewer items that reflected their policies.

Its outlook is a conservative one—it emphasizes, for example, traditional morality, basic religious beliefs, and has consistently opposed big government and the welfare state, and expressed hostility to Communist China and Cuba. Its attitude toward Democratic administrations in the last 30 years has been generally unfriendly; toward Republicanism, much friendlier. Unfriendliness is one thing, but there's not much doubt that much of the criticism has been unfair and its reporting even shoddy, added to which is the fact that it prints no letters or permits no debate on controversial issues. To be sure, the editors have supported many liberal causes: conservation, anti-trust action, consumer protection, civilian control of the military, and various UN activities. The assortment of articles, from wherever they come, is very wide, but make no demands on the intellect, and they reflect—perhaps unfortunately—the reading level and interests of the average American home.

There are a number of short features—anecdotes, quotes, character sketches, humor, etc., plus the regular book condensation.

Because it does not reprint many articles from other journals, it is not as important for academic libraries as it used to be, except as it reflects consumer tastes and is a popular browsing item. The earlier volumes are perhaps more useful for college libraries than the recent ones.

Indexed in: R.G.   36-36138 (rev. '44)

RÉALITÉS.   v. 1, 1946-

Monthly.   Paris. $18.00

A beautifully produced periodical, with exquisite color photographs and art reproductions, it contains well written articles on a variety of aspects of life and culture. A few issues, for example, may contain articles on pre-school education, new automobile safety devices, the C.I.A., new building materials, some recommended Paris restaurants, problems of alienated youth, French bureaucracy, fashions in suede, and Leningrad architecture. The regular section, "Le Mois," comments on events of the month, and includes some reviews of books, theater and recordings.

The articles are good, but lack depth, and the periodical is really one to be browsed through rather than retained for its resource material. Where there is much interest in contemporary French culture, it will be a popular and useful journal, but an extensive backfile is not necessary.

Réalités appears in an English edition, with somewhat different articles, but justifying the English edition for academic libraries would be difficult since the contents are not that important.

Indexed in: P.A.I.S. (English ed. only)   49-16452*

REVUE des Deux Mondes. *see* MODERN LANGUAGES/FRENCH

*SATURDAY REVIEW.   v. 1, 1924-

Weekly.   N.Y. $12.00

Begun as a literary supplement to the *New York Evening Post*, its original title (retained until 1952) was the *Saturday Review of Literature*. Time,

Inc. was its original publisher, with Henry Luce as its president; other officers and editors included Henry Seidel Canby, Amy Loveman, William Rose Benet, and Christopher Morley. For the next 20 years, despite financial hardships, it was one of this country's best and most influential literary periodicals, with leading writers and critics contributing reviews, criticism and poetry. Only occasionally did it venture to comment on the world outside literature, but after Norman Cousins became editor in 1942, the nature of the magazine changed. Cousins, who had been book critic of *Current History*, and executive editor of *SRL* since 1940, was very much concerned with the issues of war and peace. He included many more contributions on world affairs and the arts of communication. Circulation increased rapidly, and the magazine devoted less and less space to books and literature, at least until the last few years.

Today it must be considered a general magazine—certainly its large readership is not due to its reviews, but rather to its regular features and sections. The contents fall into about 6 categories. First, the columns—among which are humor by Goodman Ace, social commentary by Cleveland Amory, the literary world by John Ciardi, Robert Lewis Shayon on TV and radio. Second, the lead articles and editorials, generally on social or political affairs, or other matters with social implications. These are often contributed by outstanding writers, social critics and persons in public affairs. Third, reviews of the arts—Irving Kolodin on music, Hollis Alpert on the movies, Walter Terry on dance, Katherine Kuh on art. Fourth, the book sections—one or a few lengthy review-essays, plus some shorter reviews, but almost always over 1000 words, usually done by highly competent reviewers. Fifth, the monthly special section, alternating science or environment, education, travel, communications and recordings. Each of these sections is under its own editor, and they often contain significant articles. The education section, for example, edited by James Cass (and earlier by Paul Woodring), is highly regarded by educational reformers. Finally, the games—"Your Literary I.Q." and the very popular double-crostic, among others.

The features of the many special issues are also of great interest: these include educational travel, annual advertising awards, National Library Week, writers' summer conferences, Spring children's books, annual university presses issue, Fall travel, semi-annual reference book roundups, Christmas books. The regular record ratings are helpful in their selection and are generally regarded as reliable as well as informative.

A well edited, interesting and informative journal, it will be used heavily and should be in every library along with a complete backfile.

Indexed in: B.R.D.   27-5407 rev.
            Ed.I.
            Music I.
            R.G.

SCANDINAVIAN STUDIES.   v. 1, 1911-

Quarterly.   Lawrence, Kansas. $15.00

A publication of the Society for the Advancement of Scandinavian Study, it was originally titled *Publications of the Society for the Advancement of Scandinavian Study,* then *Scandinavian Studies and Notes,* dropping the last two words in 1941. Issues contain from 2 to 5 scholarly articles in some area of Scandinavian studies—literature, history, linguistics, folklore, etc. Includes the annual *American Scandinavian Bibliography,* a list of books, articles, reviews, reprints and dissertations which appeared in

the U.S. and Canada, also works on Scandinavia by Americans but published abroad, and American translations from the Scandinavian. News
of the Society, of other meetings and conferences, of courses and programs around the country. Generally 7 to 10 signed and critical book
reviews per issue; they are almost all at least 500 words long and often as
much as several thousand words. Of limited use to most libraries, but important where there is much interest in the area.

Indexed in: S.S.H.I.   28-8246 (rev. '28)

SCIENCE & SOCIETY.   v. 1, 1936-

Quarterly.   N.Y. $6.00

"An independent journal of Marxism," it contains articles on all the social
sciences, on religion and the arts, and on the practice and theory of socialism, past and present. The articles, averaging 4 or 5 per issue—mostly of
medium length, though often some quite lengthy—are by professors, graduate students and unaffiliated scholars, with well known names appearing
frequently. A "Communications" section, containing lengthy responses to
earlier articles, and rebuttals to responses, is a regular feature. The book reviews, signed and critical, are mostly 1000-1500 words; there are generally
8-10 per issue, plus some shorter book notes. The journal was founded at
a time when there was a strong scholarly interest in the implications of
Marxism for natural and social sciences; it has also emphasized history,
sociology, political science, philosophy and literary criticism. Especially
useful for courses on the history of socialism, also for its particular interpretation of developments and trends in the other social sciences.

Indexed in: S.S.H.I.   40-10163

*SIERRA CLUB BULLETIN.   v. 1, 1893-

Monthly.   San Francisco, Calif. $5.00

The Sierra Club was founded in 1892 "to explore, enjoy, and preserve
the Sierra Nevada and other scenic resources of the United States and
its forests, waters, wildlife, and wilderness; to undertake and to publish
scientific, literary, and educational studies concerning them; to educate
the people with regard to the national and state forests, parks, monuments, and other natural resources of scenic beauty and to enlist public
cooperation in protecting them." Its magazine contains articles on national
parks and forests, on other scenic and recreational areas and facilities, and on
the activities, programs, and policies of governmental and private organizations affecting these resources. The articles have always been illustrated,
but in the last few years, the journal (as well as the Sierra Club's other
publications) has become renowned for its beautiful photography of national scenes, much of it by noted photographers such as Eliot Porter
and Ansel Adams. One issue features a listing of the Club's outings; these
outings—foreign trips, family outings, high trips, knapsack trips, burro
trips and others—have become so popular that, beginning in 1970, the
entire January issue is devoted to them. News of scheduled outings and
places for camping, trips, etc. News of conservation activities and developments and of the Club; "Washington Report" contains comments and
notes on federal legislation and actions. Book reviews appear occasionally.

Because of the increased interest in conservation, and the growing influence of the Sierra Club in the movement, the journal has become much more important than it used to be; because it is now so attractive, it will also be much in demand for browsing.

Many libraries will also want to subscribe to the quarterly *Living Wilderness* (v. 1, 1935- $4.00) and/or the bi-monthly *National Wildlife* (v. 1, 1962- $5.00). The former is published by The Wilderness Society; the latter, by the National Wildlife Federation. Both have the advantage of being indexed in the *Readers' Guide*, and while their purposes are very much the same as the *Sierra Club Bulletin*, they are not as attractive or as interesting, and perhaps not as influential.

9-892 rev

*SOUNDINGS.   v. 1, 1917-

Quarterly.   Nashville, Tenn. $7.00

A "Journal of Interdisciplinary Studies," it is successor to the *Christian Scholar*, which was discontinued at the end of 1967 and earlier (through 1952) was titled *Christian Education*. That journal, published by the Department of Higher Education of the National Council of Churches of Christ in the U.S.A., was originally concerned with the problems of a campus ministry, but with its change of title in 1952, and reflecting the current theological renaissance, proposed that Christianity "may serve as the intellectual foundation for all areas of scholarly inquiry as well as for Christian, and ultimately human, reunion in our century." This hope grew dim, and *Soundings*, which is published by the Society for Religion in Higher Education, is much more secular: its opening editorial stated that "few now see Christianity or any other religious tradition as the necessary foundation of the various academic disciplines," and it substituted "common human concerns" for religion. Its purpose now, then, is "to publish articles that combine boldness with professional competence and that highlight those insights, findings, and issues in'diverse fields of study which disclose serious humane concerns."

Each issue contains 5 to 8 articles, mostly 5-10,000 words, by contributors, some well known, from various colleges and universities and from many disciplines. There is some emphasis on religion—or, rather, on the relationship of religion with other subjects—though a recent editorial has asked for a correction to this emphasis. Few are research articles; rather, they are thoughtful essays .on or explorations of ideas, concepts, literary works or figures, etc. A few issues have been devoted to single topics— e.g., Toward A New University, Philosophy of Law. No book reviews, but occasional review-essays.

Thoughtful, provocative essays make this an important journal for all college libraries.

Indexed in: In.Rel.Per.Lit.   75-12364

*SOUTH ATLANTIC QUARTERLY.   v. 1, 1902-

Quarterly.   Durham, N.C. $6.00

Founded by a scholarship society at Trinity College (now Duke University) to develop Southern writers and literature, and to encourage conditions in which literature could thrive. Early numbers were iconoclastic enough to endanger the journal's existence, but the college supported the editors and they continued their campaign of liberal Southern thought. Many notable scholars of the region were contributors. While there were many articles on literary history and criticism, there were surprisingly few attempts to record or encourage regional creative writing, and the *Quarterly* has always been known for its articles rather than fiction or poetry. Its interest in Southern society and politics broadened, and by the 1930's articles on the international scene became standard. It is no longer a regional journal, though it probably does pay more attention to Southern culture and politics than, say, the *Yale Review*. Now contains about 10 articles of moderate length per issue, pretty well divided among international affairs, history, literature, and miscellaneous subjects. Most authors are college or university faculty; the articles are scholarly, but well written and interesting. From 10 to 20 book reviews, signed and critical, mostly 500-700 words.

A well-rounded, reliable and interesting review, for all academic libraries.

Indexed in: P.A.I.S.   8-84
              S.S.H.I.

SOUTHWEST REVIEW.   v. 1, 1915-

Quarterly.   Dallas, Texas. $4.00

Founded by Stark Young as the *Texas Quarterly*, it assumed its present title in 1924 when it moved from the University of Texas to Southern Methodist University. Although the early volumes had national and even international contributors, it was a distinctly regional publication. Now the review contains mostly short stories and poetry which, as often as not, are on subjects or by writers not related to the region. These contributors are mostly younger and not widely-known, but the quality is high. The few articles are mostly concerned with regional matters, especially its history, folklore and biography. There are generally 7 or 8 reviews per issue, signed and critical, mostly 500-1000 words in length, but often longer for works of special importance. Most of them have some regional relevance: either the books are on the area, the authors from the area, or the books published by southwestern presses.

Indexed in: In.Ltl.Mag.   17-4968

SPECTATOR.   v. 1, 1828-

Weekly.   London. $18.00

Conspicuous for the independence of its views, it has long been an important spokesman in British life. In its early years it was known for its opposition to the government's colonial policies; in recent years it has become identified as representing the independent conservative viewpoint, and many of its editors and major contributors have been associated with the Tories. Politics, in particular domestic politics, is its main focus, with both political and non-partisan contributors, many of them eminent in academic as well as political circles. Other aspects of British life—religion, society, the arts, the economy, etc., are also covered, as of course are events around the world. The editorials and Letters to the Editor are read carefully by many. Reviews and notes of television, the theatre, films, art, etc., travel notes.

The book reviews have always been noteworthy—there were for years usually 1 or 2 very long ones and 6 to 10 shorter ones. In 1971 the reviewing format changed to perhaps 10 long reviews, 1500 words or more, many done by eminent scholars and writers. The first few numbers under the new policy, for example, included reviews by Auberon Waugh, Brian Crozier, Dennis Donoghue, and H.R. Trevor-Roper. The seasonal book numbers, Fall and Spring, and the issue focusing on children's books, are also useful.

An important journal of opinion where there is any interest in contemporary Britain. A backfile is very useful for British history.

Indexed in: Br.Hum.I.   4-12682

DER SPIEGEL.   v. 1, 1947-

Weekly.   Hamburg, Germany. $34.00

A post-war success story, it reflects the prosperity of contemporary Germany, yet has had a significant impact on its thinking and actions, even being the cause in 1962 of a governmental crisis and the resignation of a defense minister. It began on a shoestring, achieving a reputation and remarkable growth in circulation by being outspoken in editorials, cover stories or news items—yet at the same time fastidious about the facts. facts.

It resembles *Time* in format, with even many of the same categories of news, though with many more, and wider coverage. However, there are several significant differences: *Der Spiegel* contains frequent verbatim interviews with a variety of public (and sometimes private) figures, weekly editorials, and frequent campaigns against social and political practices and movements.

Combining a lively style, excellent coverage, and sufficient attention to temporary culture, it appeals to both the well educated reader and the politically interested mass public, and its circulation is now over one million. Its impact is not confined to politics. In the Spring of 1966, for example, it ran a series of articles that focused on the differences between fundamentalism and modern theology, a series that caused a nationwide discussion of the issue.

Irreverent and independent, but responsible, supporting the present form of government yet quick to point out its shortcomings, it is perhaps unique in its accurate measurement of national opinion. To keep up with German politics, especially, and with German opinion on international affairs, as well as other aspects of German life and culture, *Der Spiegel* is unexcelled. Book reviews are a regular feature, and feature stories on important works appear frequently.

Any library where there is real interest in contemporary Germany should take it, and a backfile is most useful for the study of postwar West Germany.

                                                                48-27909*

*TEXAS QUARTERLY.   v. 1, 1958-

Quarterly.   Austin, Texas. $4.00

A beautifully produced general review, Texas-sized in number of pages, but maintaining high quality along with quantity. While there is usually at least one piece about Texas in an issue, the journal is by no means a regional one. While issues sometimes are devoted to single subjects (e.g., Newton, Spain, Mexican Graphic Art) or contain a number of contributions on a theme (e.g., The Role of the Intellectual in Politics), most issues are general, with a generous number of essays, short stories, and

poems, many by distinguished names in scholarship, belles-lettres and
poetry, and there is usually a substantial section of photographs, drawings or paintings. In its first few years each issue also contained a separately paged supplement—collections of poems, proceedings of conferences, novellas, monographs, etc.—some of which were also published
separately in hard covers.

Without doubt, a "best buy" in periodicals. This is certainly true if one
considers just the price per page (there are well over 1000 pages in most
volumes), but the quality of the contributions is so high, the design so
attractive, no good college library should be without it.

Indexed in: In.Ltl.Mag.   58-8635
            S.S.H.I.

*TIME.   v. 1, 1923-

Weekly.   Chicago, Ill. $14.00

Its beginning and quick success is almost legendary in the history of American journalism, and for many years it was the undisputed leader of
national newsmagazines. Perhaps it still is—its reputation and influence are
considerable, though there's not much doubt that its competitors and the
impact of news reporting on television have greatly reduced its preeminence. Surely it has been the most written-about newsmagazine, and
more often than not with indictment rather than praise. Critics claimed a
lack of objectivity, and to them *Time* style, one of the most parodied of
journalistic trademarks, meant the insertion of opinion into news stories
through choice of descriptors rather than a straightforward statement of
position.

Time has also been criticized for its chauvinism. Henry Luce had made The
American Century his credo, and *Time* seemed oblivious to contrary evidence: unlike other magazines, it appeared unconscious of the revolutionary
changes of the 1960's, and its reporting from Southeast Asia was myopic,
to say the least. After Luce's death in 1967, *Time* began to change. Some
things had already changed (the *Time* Essay, which began in 1965, perhaps
the most significant) but the special section, To Heal a Nation, appearing
in January 1969, marked a real shift. In 1970, one of its hallmarks—
anonymity of authorship—was modified when the authors of the *Time*
Essays, cultural criticism and occasional other stories were given credit.

Its reviewing sections have long been one of *Time*'s strongest points. From
1941 to 1955 James Agee edited the movie reviews and Louis Kronen-
berger did the drama reviews from 1938 to 1961. The reviews are still good,
and the Art section, with excellent color reproductions (which are indexed
in a separately published book) has done much over the years to call
attention to the work of younger artists and interpret that of more famous
ones. Usually about 5 book reviews per issue, mostly 500-800 words, but
occasionally quite long, and sometimes, when a large number of books are
reviewed, much shorter.

An essential periodical for all libraries, with an extensive backfile
desirable.

Indexed in: B.R.D.   25-11669
            R.G.

*TRANS-ACTION.   v. 1, 1963-

Monthly (bi-monthly, Jan./Feb., July/Aug.)   New Brunswick, N.J.
$9.75   v. 1, 1963

Originally published by Washington University, St. Louis, then becoming
an independent publication in 1968, its purpose is "to further the understanding and use of the social sciences" by presenting the results of significant research in a readable and useful manner. It does not cater, however,
to popular taste; indeed, as one editorial stated, "it is written by academics
for their peers"—and especially for social scientists and community leaders.
The articles, by social scientists in all fields, including many who are nationally prominent, treat topics that are of current interest in politics,
economics, race relations, education, urban problems, social psychology,
criminology, foreign affairs, etc. Most are provocative and many controversial; if there is a single thrust to the journal, it is a dedication to social
change, and a major portion of the articles point up the inadequacies and
inconsistencies of our society. All articles are exceptionally well written
and well illustrated, and each has a list of suggested further readings. Excellent book reviews (about 5 per issue) of both scholarly and trade books
in the social sciences, mostly 1000-2000 words. It has an impressive group
of editorial advisors from many areas and disciplines, a large number of
whom are dedicated to the "new sociology"—that is, they are sociological activists. Certainly one of the most important social science journals begun in the last decade, it should be in every library.

Indexed in: Ment.Hlth.B.R.I.   70-3678
            R.G.

NOTE: *Trans-Action* now called *Society*.

TWENTIETH CENTURY.   v. 1, 1877-

Quarterly.   London. $10.00

Titled originally *Nineteenth Century*, it became *Nineteenth Century and
After* in 1900, assuming its present title somewhat belatedly in 1951.
Each issue has as a theme a topic of current interest—in politics, society,
foreign relations, culture, religion, etc., with some emphasis, perhaps, on
socio-political themes—e.g., From Protest to Revolution, Contemporary
Morals, The Consuming Urge. These are treated by a number of mostly
brief articles and essays that are more or less closely related to the theme.
Issues usually also contain other articles and essays, plus a number of
poems and occasional short stories. While contributors include some well-
known names, most are not familiar to American readers; their contributions, however, are well written and usually with some substance; much
of the time they are provocative, occasionally bordering on overstatement
or even sensationalism—but this is rare. The book reviews, which were
once an important feature, have gradually been reduced. Now there are
5 to 15 an issue, varying in length from 100 to 1500 words, and covering
all sorts of topics, but with some emphasis on literature and belles-lettres.
The character of the journal has changed radically since it went from a
monthly to a quarterly in 1961. It had been since its founding "a general
monthly review, which publishes articles of all kinds," including only
occasionally fiction or verse, and "keenly interested in documentary writing, in the form of biography, autobiography, diaries and descriptive
accounts." It was contributed to and read by eminent literary, political
and scholarly figures of the Victorian period and early twentieth century.
Later, it lost some of its eminence, but remained a solid journal representing an independent, conservative viewpoint, with good general arti-

cles and a very respectable review section. Though its nature has changed, it is still a worthwhile periodical, especially for insight into contemporary English trends of society and patterns of thought.

Indexed in: Br.Hum.I.   9-17518*
            S.S.H.I.

*U.S. NEWS & WORLD REPORT.   v. 1, 1933-

Weekly.   Washington, D.C. $12.00

Founded and still edited by David Lawrence (he was also owner until 1962), a respected political journalist in the 1920's who had originally published a newspaper (first a daily, then a weekly) which reported national news along with the full text of important speeches and documents. *U.S. News* grew out of this, but never gave much competition to *Time* or *Newsweek,* and in 1948 Lawrence combined it with his other weekly, *World Report,* which was devoted to international news. It grew rapidly, and today has a circulation of over 1½ million.

Its appeal is based on a conservative viewpoint, and a no-nonsense approach to the news, often in the form of interviews and documents. Economics and business are also given much attention, reflecting the interests of readers, and many articles and features analyze their personal impact e.g., "How Tax Reform Will Affect You," "What Savings Bonds Owners Need to Know Now." Analysis, forecasting and interpretation of the news, then, are major aspects of its approach. There is almost no attention to culture, entertainment or intellectual pursuits.

The most useful single feature is the interview. During the first half of 1970, there were interviews with (among others): the President's science advisor on "How to Control Pollution"; the Secretary of State on "Changing Role of the U.S."; Nixon's Advisor on Youth, on "Closing the Generation Gap"; the Postmaster General on "Overhauling the Mails"; President Nasser of Egypt; the Director of the Narcotics Bureau on drugs; Samuel B. Gould, SUNY Chancellor, on "Changes Coming in American Colleges." These interviews are conducted by members of the magazine's staff, and most provide good source material.

Its reporting is often incisive, and always readable. It is a popular journal for browsing as well as for undergraduate research, and should be in every library, along with a substantial backfile.

Indexed in: P.A.I.S.   40-23787*
            R.G.

*UNESCO COURIER.   v. 1, 1948-

Monthly (bi-monthly, Aug.-Sept.)   Paris. $5.00

While its primary purpose is to describe the work of UNESCO and the problems and situations with which that organization is concerned, it is by no means simply a public relations medium or an apologist for UNESCO. As a matter of fact, except for the title and the page or two giving some news of UNESCO's activities and publications, a reader would be hard put to make the connection with the association. Rather, it is a magazine of general interest and appeal, deriving its breadth from the diversity of UNESCO's interests. Most issues consist of 8 articles, frequently by world famous authorities, written in a popular but literate style and profusely illustrated. These articles are usually all on a single topic; Life in an African Village; Cymatics; Gandhi—the Heritage of Non-Violence; the International Geophysical Year; Great Literature of East and West; Fair Play and the Amateur in Sport, etc. (Some idea of its breadth can be gotten from the August-September, 1969 issue which is an anthology from the first 21 years.)

It began publication with 3 language editions—French, English and Spanish; now there are 12, including Hindi, Tamil, Hebrew and Persian. Since it is intended for a wide readership, the level of the articles—though they are reliable and often authoritative—makes it less appropriate for advanced research than for general reading and as an excellent introduction to other peoples and cultures. In this capacity, it admirably fulfills its aim to serve as "a window open on the world." For all libraries.

Indexed in: R.G.   51-2322

UNIVERSITY of Toronto Quarterly. *see* ENGLISH

*VICTORIAN STUDIES.   v. 1, 1957-

Quarterly.   Bloomington, Ind. $12.00

In its first number, *Victorian Studies* claimed "two distinguishing features: concentration on the English culture of a particular age; and openness to critical and scholarly studies from all the relevant disciplines." While requesting contributions from the subject specialist, the journal is interested in these only if he makes clear the relation between his topic and the "important ideas, movements, and personalities" in the Victorian age. The articles, then, cover every aspect of Victorian life and thought, with literature perhaps receiving a bit more attention than other facets in the earlier volumes, and social history more in later ones. The articles are sometimes illustrated, and the format of *Victorian Studies* in general is unusually pleasing. At least one special supplement has appeared.

The annual *Victorian Bibliography*, prepared by the Victorian Literature Group of the Modern Language Association, was taken over from *Modern Philology* (where it had been published since 1933). It lists books (along with reviews of them) and articles from a wide variety of periodicals, arranged by broad subject and by individual authors; in *Modern Philology,* it emphasized literature—in *Victorian Studies* its coverage has become more general. The signed book reviews, of which there are generally around 15, average 750-1000 words, but not infrequently run to twice that.

Because of the breadth of its coverage, the quality of the contributions, and the growth of interest in the Victorian era, the journal and its back-file should be in all academic libraries.

Indexed in: S.S.H.I.   A 58-5527

*VIRGINIA QUARTERLY REVIEW.   v. 1, 1925-

Quarterly.   Charlottesville, Va. $5.00

Though it does emphasize matters relating to the South, it is not a regional journal; rather, as its subtitle declares, it is "a national journal of literature and discussion." Contains 3 or 4 articles or essays in each issue, covering economics, art, the sciences and, in particular, politics and literature. Fiction and poetry are by established and newer authors; these are of high quality, but there is little experimental writing. The main book review section covers less than a dozen books, but the reviews are lengthy. The section "Notes on Current Books" contains brief (150-250 words usually), unsigned but critical reviews of 75 to 100 books per issue, covering fiction, poetry, literary criticism, biography and political affairs. These are tightly written and though brief, contain a good bit of evaluation. There is also a section listing "Reprints and New Editions."

Indexed in: B.R.D.   30-14637 rev.
            S.S.H.I.

*VITAL SPEECHES OF THE DAY. v. 1, 1934-

Semi-monthly. Pelham, N.Y. $10.00

"The best thought of the best minds on current national questions," through the texts of important addresses. The publisher's policy is "to cover both sides of public questions and to print all speeches in full. Where it is necessary to condense a speech for reasons of unusual length or the use of extraneous matter, it will be so stated when printing." Issues contain mostly 7 to 10 speeches, of varying lengths, on a variety of subjects (though occasionally, for an extraordinary situation, most of the issue will be devoted to speeches on it—e.g., The Middle East crisis of June, 1967)—politics, economics, civil rights, education, social mores, technology, health, law, labor, etc. Many of the speeches are by public figures, but also many are by fairly obscure individuals, and their texts would be difficult to find elsewhere.

An important source of primary materials, it is also useful for students of public speaking. Its modest cost makes it essential for even the smallest library, and most should purchase a backfile (the cost of a microfilm copy is nominal).

                                              38-12994

Indexed in: R.G.

WESTERN Humanities Review. *see* ENGLISH

*YALE REVIEW. v. 1, 1892; n.s.v. 1, 1911-

Quarterly. New Haven, Conn. $6.00

"A national quarterly" published by Yale University, it contains articles that are outstanding for their substance and literary merit. They range over a wide variety of subjects with two emphases: one on current affairs, both domestic and foreign; the other on literary criticism and history. Contributors of articles include eminent scholars, writers, and public officials. Mostly they have no, or only a tenuous connection with Yale University, though in its earlier years the *Review* was primarily contributed to by Yale faculty and alumni. There is excellent poetry in almost every issue, much of it by well known poets; short stories, mostly by new writers, appear less often.

The reviewing function of the journal has long been an important one. "New Books in Review" contains 7 to 10 reviews, all of them long, and many article-length. Each reviews a single work or a group of related titles; they are excellent reviews, often by noted scholars and critics, covering poetry, novels and non-fiction. "Reader's Guide" contains usually 6 to 8 unsigned but critical reviews, each 750-1500 words. "New Records in Review," by the eminent critic, B.H. Haggin, reviews a number of outstanding recent recordings. The "Letters and Comment" section, in most issues, contains miscellaneous contributions—often really articles—on a variety of topics, but most frequently on a recent visit to a foreign country.

Erudite, eclectic and interesting, with outstanding contributors, the *Review* should be in every library, along with an extensive backfile.

Indexed in: B.R.D.   8-8158 (rev. '22)
            P.A.I.S.
            R.G.

AMERICAN METEOROLOGICAL SOCIETY.   BULLETIN.   v. 1, 1920-

Monthly.   Boston, Mass. $15.00

"Official organ of the Society, devoted to editorials, survey articles, professional and membership news, announcements, and Society activities." Usually a few articles in each issue, ranging from a general (though authoritative) survey on "Tornadoes" to highly technical and specialized reports of research. Correspondence from members also contains useful reports of research activities. Usually 3 to 6 reviews per issue, of books ranging from general works (though not popularizations) to highly specialized foreign publications; these vary widely in length, but many are between 1000 and 1500 words. A listing of New Publications in each month's "Announcements" section is extensive and annotated, and includes books, documents, private and governmental reports, and pamphlets.

Useful only where there's strong interest in the subject.

33-13377

*ASSOCIATION OF AMERICAN GEOGRAPHERS.   ANNALS.   v. 1, 1911-

Quarterly.   Washington, D.C. $16.00

Contains both technical and non-technical articles, with the emphasis on those that are original in treatment or methodology. The articles vary in length, but are limited to 20,000 words. Both physical and non-physical geography are covered, with more attention paid to the latter, especially demography, urban and regional planning, and economic and political geography. Each article is preceded by an abstract. Published as an annual until 1927, it has always carried the Association's presidential addresses, abstracts of papers delivered at the meetings, and committee reports of general interest or significance. Illustrations—maps, photographs and diagrams—are numerous. Map supplements, inserted loose, appear occasionally (number 12 came out in 1970). Until 1970, there were no individual reviews, but only occasional review articles; now reviews "will occupy a major segment of each issue."

Indexed in: S.S.H.I.   GS 12-296 rev.

CURRENT GEOGRAPHICAL PUBLICATIONS.   v. 1, 1938-

Monthly (except July-Aug.)   N.Y. $10.00

Published by the American Geographical Society, it lists all items of geographic interest, both those published separately and those appearing in periodicals (geographic and non-geographic) or other collective works, that are added to the Society's Research Catalogue. Each issue is comprised of 3 sections: General, Regional, Maps. (Prior to 1964, maps were included in the first two sections.) Items in the General section are arranged by subject; the other two are arranged by region. Both subject and regional classification schemes are given in each issue for easy reference. As a list of acquisitions of the largest geographical library in the Western Hemisphere, its value should be obvious, especially since so much geographical material is fugitive.

41-27154

ECONOMIC GEOGRAPHY.   v. 1, 1925-

Quarterly.   Worcester, Mass. $11.50

"Published by Clark University for the benefit of geographers, economists, teachers, professional and business men, and all others who are interested in the intelligent utilization of the world's resources." Carries research articles which pay special attention to agricultural, industrial and urban geography—although fields adjacent to economic geography, especially economic history, are covered as well—with numerous photographs, diagrams, and maps. There are usually 6-8 book reviews in each issue, mostly 750-1000 words. With a new editor taking over in 1970 (there were only 2 editors during the previous 45 years) a few changes are being made. A "Books Received" section, which describes each title very briefly, now appears and space will be given to special reviews, bibliographic essays and critical essays. "A fifth issue will be published each year; this larger issue will focus on a special theme and occasionally reflect the work of symposia sponsored by *Economic Geography.*" The first supplement is the *Proceedings of the IGU Commission on Quantitative Methods;* the topic for the second is Urban Spatial Structure.

An important interdisciplinary journal, especially useful where the social sciences are strong.

Indexed in: P.A.I.S.   GS 25-119
             S.S.H.I.

*FOCUS.   v. 1, 1950-

Monthly (except July-Aug.)   N.Y. $3.50

A publication of the American Geographical Society. Each issue is devoted to a country or region (and occasionally to a resource or geographical factor), "stressing historical influences and the interaction of physical, social and economic factors." In recent years, almost all issues covered one of the developing nations of the world. The attractive maps are specially prepared to illustrate the particular topic, and a selective bibliography of recent publications is also included. One page is now devoted to "Trends and Techniques," a regular section discussing such topics related to geography as pipeline transport of liquid and solid materials, artificial photosynthesis, pollution and affluence. *Focus* is small (each number, for years just 6 pages, is now 12) but it does provide authoritative and up-to-date background geographical information on areas of current interest. Though its permanent reference value is limited, so that libraries may want to keep *Focus* with pamphlet material, every library should take it.

Indexed in: R.G.   61-3604

GEOGRAPHICAL ABSTRACTS.   1966-

6 nos./yr.   Norwich, Eng. $45.00 (for all 6 series; or $7.50 for each)

The successor to *Geomorphological Abstracts* (1960-66), it is published in 6 series, each of which is available separately. A—Geomorphology; B—Biogeography and Climatology; C—Economic Geography; D—Social Geography and Cartography. Series A is the lineal successor to *Geomorphological Abstracts;* the other 3 are really expansions of the service.

Almost 8000 abstracts were published in 1970, most of them 100-200 words, but often several times that. Annual author and regional indexes for each series; comprehensive subject and author indexes may be purchased separately. Many libraries may not want all sections: those with strong geology departments should take A and B, whereas those emphasizing the social sciences may want just C and D. Yet, considering its relatively low cost, and because of its breadth of coverage in subject and materials, the entire service should be seriously considered.

NOTE: Sections E and F also available, beginning in 1972. Section E is Sedimentology; F, Regional & Community Planning.

GEOGRAPHICAL JOURNAL.   v. 1, 1893-

Quarterly.   London. $15.50

Published by the Royal Geographical Society, perhaps the world's leading geographical organization. Each issue contains usually 6 to 8 articles in various areas of geography: reports on the results of research—in physical, political, historical or cultural geography; on geographical theory or methodology; on geology; reports of explorations and expeditions to lesser-known parts of the world have long been a specialty of the *Journal* since the Society sponsored many of them. Many articles are well illustrated with photographs and drawings. Contains news and reports of the Society's meetings and discussions; news of geography departments and related fields in British universities. A large portion of the journal—over one third—is devoted to reviews. Most issues have at least one, but usually several, review essays of a single book or of several on a like subject. Then there are many other reviews—sometimes over 100—of books on all geographical subjects, from simple travel guides to technical works, on all areas, and in many languages. These reviews, which vary greatly in length, are all signed and critical. Also list of books received, briefly annotated. The section "Cartographical Survey" contains extensive reviews of the more important maps and atlases, and books on cartography, and notes on significant articles. An important journal for all departments of geography.

Indexed in: Br.Hum.I.   28-17564 rev.
            S.S.H.I.

*GEOGRAPHICAL REVIEW.   v. 1, 1916-

Quarterly.   N.Y. $17.50

The American Geographical Society of New York was founded in 1852 by a group of business and professional men to advance the science of geography in the United States and to provide a central clearinghouse for geographical information. The Society began publication of its *Bulletin* in 1852; it was published until 1915, when it was superceded by the *Geographical Review* which appeared monthly from 1916 to 1920, and quarterly since 1921. It has long been one of the basic American journals in the field, and its backfile is important.

The Society is one of the world's leading geographical organizations, and the *Review* reflects this stature. Its articles (usually 6 or 7 an issue), are authoritative and cover all areas and a variety of fields of geography—economic, historical, social, physical, etc.—and are accompanied by many illustrations and maps, some of the latter as separate fold-outs. Abstracts of the articles appear at the end of each issue. There are frequent bibliographical or review articles. The section "Geographical Record" contains notes on activities and developments relating to research on particular areas, other geographical studies, notices of important surveys, reports and other publications, and news and reports of the Society and its members. About 15 books are usually reviewed; the reviews are signed and critical, and average about 750 words. The reviews of maps and atlases are especially valuable for librarians. Essential for every academic library.

Indexed in: P.A.I.S.   17-15422
              S.S.H.I.

JOURNAL OF GEOGRAPHY.   v. 1, 1902-

Monthly (except July-Aug.)   Chicago, Ill. $12.00

Successor to the *Journal of School Geography,* it has been the official journal of the National Council for Geographic Education since 1915. It is primarily concerned with the teaching of geography on elementary, high school, and college levels, and most articles are on the programs, methods, and materials of instruction. While there is only an occasional article of interest to the advanced student or professional geographer, there are a number of articles useful to the beginning student, especially on newer geographical methods and techniques, and introductory articles on particular areas and concepts. In addition to the 6 articles per issue (up to 4000 words each) it also contains news of the Council, brief reviews of films, and a listing of geographical materials received. The number of books reviewed varies widely; all of the reviews are signed but most of them are only about 300 words long. A useful journal for the beginning student, it is especially important where geographical education is taught and will also be of help in the selection of materials.

Indexed in: Ed.I   E 16-885*
              P.A.I.S.

MONTHLY WEATHER REVIEW.   v. 1, 1873-

Monthly.   Washington, D.C. $10.50

Published by the U.S. Weather Bureau, it is a depository item. Up to the early 1960's, its primary purpose was to give the monthly meteorological and climatological data for the United States and adjacent regions, plus a few mostly brief contributions in the field of meteorology, principally in the branches of synoptic and applied meteorology. Since then, though not reducing the number of articles in these areas, ones that are more theoretical, that contain more mathematics, or that treat extra-terrestrial weather, have become more common. It is, then, a more technical journal than it was, though the articles on recent weather phenomena and general climatology and meteorology still make it useful for undergraduate courses, though not introductory ones.

Institutions where there is much interest in climatology should also receive other government publications in this area. First, the *Weather Outlook* (Washington, D.C., v. 1, 1946- $5.00), which appears semi-monthly, summarizes average rainfall and temperature data for the preceding month and the outlook for the following month. It also is a depository item. Second, *Climatological Data,* both (a) the Monthly National Summary (v. 1, 1950- $2.50) which gives a general summary of weather conditions, condensed climatological summary for the states, climatological data by station and includes an Annual Summary, and (b) the appropriate State Section (v. 1, 1914- $2.50 per section), also published monthly with an Annual Summary for 47 sections (either a single state, a possession, or a group of states), containing all climatological observational data for all reporting stations. Finally, *Local Climatological Data* (Monthly, 1897- $1.00 per set) for nearby stations. It is issued for approximately 287 cities and airports where Weather Bureau offices are located, and most include an Annual Summary.

Agr. 9-990

*NATIONAL GEOGRAPHIC MAGAZINE.   v. 1, 1888-

Monthly.   Washington, D.C. $9.00

The official journal of the National Geographic Society, a "scientific and educational organization for increasing and diffusing geographic knowledge and promoting research and exploration." Articles mostly of moderate length on particular countries or regions, familiar and non-so-familiar tourist attractions, little-known and remote places and peoples, points of historical interest, flora and fauna, and exotic and primitive ways of life. Articles are popularly written but reliable, although they have been criticized for glossing over social problems and scenes that might be distasteful to most readers. For example, in a regional survey of the South appearing in 1949, Negroes were not even mentioned or shown. An article on Germany in 1937 omitted the reprehensible aspects of Nazism, and readers of an article on China in 1948 would not have known a civil war was going on. This, however, is changing. The articles are exceptionally well—often beautifully—illustrated in color and black-and-white. Now about three-quarters of the pages contain illustrative material, and all are in color.

The Society has supported more than 200 major expeditions and research projects on land, on and under the sea, and in the sky; many of these, such as that of Byrd in the Antarctic, Leakey in Olduvai Gorge, or Cousteau's oceanographic studies, to name only a few popular ones, have been of crucial scientific importance, and have been fully covered in these pages. Also valuable are the separate maps frequently accompanying issues; some libraries keep these in their map files rather than with the magazine.

A backfile of the *National Geographic* is important for several reasons: the wealth of information from its scientific expeditions; the view of peoples and places as seen years ago; the many illustrations valuable for reference. A basic item for all libraries.

Indexed in: R.G.   14-7038 (rev. '38)

*POPULATION BULLETIN.   v. 1, 1945-

5 nos./yr.   Washington, D.C. $5.00

Published by the Population Reference Bureau, Inc., "to provide and interpret facts of population change and relate them to world affairs."

Each issue of 20 to 40 pages contains a demographic analysis of a region or a country, or discusses some specific aspect of the population problem—e.g., "The World Bank Tackles Population," "Soviet Population Theory from Marx to Kosygin," "China: A Demographic Crisis," "The Brain Drain: Fact or Fiction?" These usually contain a list of references. Issues sometimes consist of selections from other publications or proceedings of conferences. Every few years one issue is devoted to "A Sourcebook on Population," a useful item, (November, 1969 is the latest) which consists of an annotated population bibliography of some 400 items arranged by topic and area, a listing of population programs and organizations, and a brief glossary of demographic terms. Because the population problem has become such an important one for so many disciplines, and because the information on it is presented simply and objectively here, this title should be in all academic libraries.

Indexed in: P.A.I.S.   52-19281

POPULATION INDEX. v. 1, 1935-

Quarterly.   Princeton, N.J. $15.00

Published for the Population Association of America by the Office of Population Research at Princeton University, it consists of two types of contents. The first, called "Current Items," contains news of the Office and the Association, new programs at universities and institutes and other professional news, plus an occasional article on some aspect of population studies. The second, and major portion, is devoted to the "Bibliography" of books, articles and other publications on demography arranged under 19 main headings, some of which are: general and regional population studies, spatial distribution, trends in population size, mortality, fertility, migration, demographic and economic interrelationships, bibliographies, new periodicals, and official statistical publications. Each of the 5000 or so entries a year is briefly (10 to 200 words) summarized, and there are geographical and other indexes in each issue, cumulated annually. A final but brief feature of each issue is the group of statistical tables and charts; they are of general demographic interest, and the area of interest changes for each issue. Though of primary interest to research scholars, the *Index* is important for college libraries because of the scarcity of materials on areas it covers, and because demography is a subject of increasing concern and study, and is related to so many other social science interests.

Indexed in: P.A.I.S.   39-10247

PROFESSIONAL GEOGRAPHER.   n.s.v. 1, 1949-

Quarterly.   Lawrence, Kans. $8.00

Published by the Association of American Geographers, it "serves as an outlet for short scholarly articles, as a forum for the expression of professional opinions, as a journal for reports on activities of the Association and other items of interest to the geographic profession." Articles cover all areas and aspects of geography, including professional training for geographers and the teaching of geography. The November issue contains the annual listing of *Recent Geography Dissertations and Theses*

238   GEOGRAPHY (including Population and Meteorology)

Completed and in Preparation. News from geographic centers of new programs, new periodicals, conferences, institutes, notices of meetings. Usually now about 20 book reviews per issue; though signed and critical, they are mostly only 200-300 words long. Very important works are sometimes discussed in an entire article. A listing of new maps appears twice a year, but there are no critical comments. Useful for faculty and libraries rather than for students.

52-48680

WEATHERWISE.   v. 1, 1948-

Bi-monthly.   Boston, Mass. $7.00

Started by the Amateur Weathermen of America, it has been published since 1952 for the American Meteorological Society, with which the original organization merged. Contains many news items of interest to meteorologists, professional and amateur, and also instructive or popular articles, mostly brief, on synoptic or even more technical meteorology by authorities. "Weathermatch," in each issue, includes a summary of weather happenings for the previous two months, with reproductions of all daily weather maps. Features are well illustrated with photographs, diagrams and charts. An Education Issue, appearing every four years, is devoted to the problems and progress of education in meteorology. The first issue of each year, the Almanac Issue, reviews the weather of the previous year and summarizes advances in the atmospheric sciences. Though there are no book reviews, a Bibliography Issue appearing every two years contains *A Selective Bibliography in Meteorology,* a very useful guide for libraries since it includes older as well as new titles; those added since the previous listing are briefly annotated. Essential where there are courses in meteorology, it also is useful for the interested layman.

Libraries desiring a similar publication, but one that covers more than the U.S., might consider *Weather* (v. 1, 1946- $4.35), published by the Royal Meteorological Society. Not only is its geographical interest wider (although it is primarily, but not exclusively interested in the British Isles and Western Europe) but also it has a larger number of articles and does include a few lengthy signed book reviews. It is indexed in the *British Humanities Index.*

Indexed in: R.G.   60-40716

*ABSTRACTS OF NORTH AMERICAN GEOLOGY. v. 1, 1966

Monthly. Washington, D.C. $9.00

Published by the United States Geological Survey, it contains "abstracts of technical papers and books and also citations of maps on the geology of North America including Greenland, the West Indies, as well as the states of Hawaii, Guam, and the other island possessions of the United States." ". . . Abstracts are prepared only of material that is believed to be generally available." Abstracts are arranged alphabetically by author, followed by a complete index of subject, geographical areas, taxonomic indexes. Since the USGS *Bibliography of North American Geology* indexes the same literature, after its annual volume appears the *Abstracts* become less important. However, since the *Bibliography* appears 3 or 4 years late, the individual issues of the *Abstracts* are useful for several years at least. Larger libraries may want the *Bibliography and Index of Geology* in addition to this.

GS 66-78

AMERICAN ASSOCIATION OF PETROLEUM GEOLOGISTS. BULLETIN. v. 1, 1917-

Monthly. Tulsa, Okla. $45.00

Publishes the results of original geology research, done in the field, laboratory, or office, and pertaining to petroleum discovery and production. However, many articles are relevant to and important for wider geological interests. This wider appeal is due to its policy, expressed by the editor in 1962, of placing emphasis "on articles presenting *basic* geologic data, principles, philosophies, and techniques *applicable* to: (1) the interpretation of earth history and therefore (2) usable in the search for natural resources, especially hydrocarbons."

It does, then, include articles on paleontology, stratigraphy, structure, geophysics, photogeology, etc. The number and length of articles varies considerably, but all are thoroughly illustrated with maps, photographs and charts. "Geological Notes" contain briefer research items, critiques and other comments. The June issue (since 1946) carries oil and gas developments for the preceding year by states or regions of the U.S., Canada and Mexico. The July or August issue does the same for foreign countries. The March issue contains the membership directory of the Association, along with other official rosters. In each issue the section "Association Round Table" carries news of the Association and its sections and, in the July issue, minutes and reports of the annual meeting. Part 2 of the October or November issue is devoted to the Association: a membership list, committees, reports, constitution, etc. Reviews of texts, monographic works, guidebooks, maps, etc. Many of the reviews used to be fairly lengthy; recently, reviews have been limited to 300 words. An extensive listing of publications—books, pamphlets, guidebooks, documents, etc.— from petroleum producing areas throughout the world.

An important journal for all geology departments.

Indexed in: A.S.T.I.

GS 18-129

AMERICAN GEOPHYSICAL UNION.   TRANSACTIONS.   v. 1, 1920-

Monthly.   Washington, D.C. $5.00

The oldest publication of the Union. For most of its existence it carried
the proceedings of the AGU's annual meetings, but gradually added a
number of regular sections—general articles, book reviews, bibliographies,
business meeting reports, and news of members. However, in 1969 it
changed completely. It moved from quarterly to monthly publication and
the format was redesigned. It is now "devoted to the publication of contributions dealing with the interface of all aspects of geophysics with
society, and of semi-technical reviews of currently exciting areas of geophysics." Usually just one or two articles an issue, non-technical in nature,
on topics such as education, the environment, trends in the field, methodology. Regular sections include: "News" of people, programs, explorations, findings, grants, obituaries, etc.; "AGU" containing news of the
Union and its sections; "IHD Bulletin," a quarterly survey of programs
and finding of the International Hydrological Decade; "The Geophysical
Year," a calendar of coming meetings, conferences and symposia, all over
the world. "New Publications" contains one long critical, signed review,
a listing of books and translations, and AGU publications in press, which
includes the contents of its journals. The April issue contains abstracts
of papers delivered (over 1000) at the annual meeting; the November
issue those of the Fall meeting.

28-1813

*AMERICAN JOURNAL OF SCIENCE.   v. 1, 1818-

Monthly (except July and Sept.)   New Haven, Conn. $15.00

The first scientific journal in the United States, it was founded by Benjamin Silliman of Yale, perhaps the most prominent and influential American scientist of the early nineteenth century, who remained sole editor
until 1838 (it was also known as *Silliman's Journal*). Many famous American scientists appeared in the journal; its first three associate editors, for
example, were Wolcott Gibbs, Asa Gray and Louis Agassiz. Though titled
the *American Journal of Science and Arts* until 1879, it never did much
with the arts, but did range over the sciences, with much on the technology of industry and transportation. A large portion of it was always
devoted to geology, Silliman's main interest, and it gradually became
solely devoted to geology and related fields.

Now covers all aspects of geology, with more attention, perhaps, to theory
and methodology than most other geologic journals. Entire issues are
occasionally devoted to a single subject, often the papers given at a symposium; every article is preceded by an abstract. Discussions of previous
articles, with replies, appear frequently. The number and length of book
reviews vary considerably: some issues contain none, others as many as
ten; in length they range from a few hundred words up to 1000, with
occasional lengthy essay-reviews. All are signed and critical. Reviews of
important works in the other sciences used to be carried but recently
only geological and closely related titles have been reviewed. The listing
of recently received publications was dropped in 1963.

A basic journal in the field, its backfile is especially useful for the history of American science.

Indexed in: A.S.T.I.   17-24348 (rev. '43)

AMERICAN MINERALOGIST, v. 1, 1916-

Bi-monthly. Washington, D.C. $24.00

Official journal of the Mineralogical Society of America. Its main purpose "is to publish the results of original scientific research in the general fields of mineralogy, crystallography and petrology, including such areas as: descriptive mineralogy and properties of minerals, experimental mineralogy and petrology, geochemistry, isotope mineralogy, mineralogical apparatus and techniques, mineral occurrences and deposits, paragenesis, petrography and paragenesis, and topographical mineralogy." Issues contain 15 to 25 articles of varying length, all well illustrated and each preceded by an abstract. A large number of "Mineralogical Notes" report on the results of briefer studies. "New Mineral Names" is a feature of each issue. (The extra issue for August, 1966 was an "Index of New Mineral Names, Discredited Minerals, and Changes of Mineralogical Nomenclatures in Volumes 1-50 of *The American Mineralogist.*") Carries Proceedings and Abstracts of Papers delivered at the annual meetings. The number of book reviews varies considerably: often none, rarely more than 6. They are signed and critical, but vary in length from 100-200 words to 600-700, with most around 300 words.

Indexed in: A.S.T.I. 19-12811 rev.*

BIBLIOGRAPHY AND INDEX OF GEOLOGY. v. 1, 1934-

Monthly. Boulder, Colo. $250.00

The history of the indexing of English-language geological serials is a confusion of titles started and then soon discontinued. There were a number of earlier titles, and more recently *Geoscience Abstracts,* a most important source published by the American Geological Institute, ceased in 1966 after only seven years, leaving geologists without any current index to the serial literature on North American geology. The world outside North American was being covered by the *Bibliography and Index of Geology Exclusive of North America,* which appeared as an annual for the years 1933 through 1965, was then published as a monthly for 1967 and 1968 (when it was an abstracting service with an annual index); in 1969 it expanded its coverage and assumed its present title.

Published by the Geological Society of America, the monthly issues of the *Bibliography and Index of Geology* are divided into 21 intradisciplinary categories. Within the categories, each entry contains bibliographical information, a UDC number, and a group of descriptors. There is an author and subject index for each issue; also annual cumulative indexes. Entries are compiled by the staff and from other national and foreign geological organizations as well as from other abstract journals; in 1970 about 30,000 entries—books, articles, pamphlets, maps and documents—were listed.

Important where there is serious interest in geological research, but its expense may force smaller libraries to confine their current geology bibliography to *Geophysical Abstracts* and *Abstracts of North American Geology* (q.v.).

34-32191

*EARTH SCIENCE.   v. 1, 1946-

Bi-monthly.   Downers Grove, Ill. $3.00

Known as *Earth Science Digest* through 1955, it is the official publication of the Midwest Federation of Mineralogical Societies. Most articles are by amateurs, but there are some by experts, all written in non-technical language and with many illustrations. Short to medium-length articles on geomorphology, mineralogy, paleontology and gem collection are intended primarily for those interested in the earth sciences as a hobby, but are also useful for the beginning student. Plays a role in geology similar to that played by *Sky and Telescope* in astronomy. In addition to the 3 to 5 articles there is news of collectors' clubs and societies and signed, brief book reviews.

55-17213 rev.

EARTH SCIENCE REVIEWS.   v. 1, 1966-

Quarterly.   Amsterdam, Netherlands. $23.00

Each issue contains usually two lengthy (40-50 page) articles that review developments in an area under one of these four main headings: 1) mineralogy, igneous and metamorphic petrology, geochemistry; 2) geophysics, volcanology, geotectonics; 3) sedimentology, paleontology, historical geology; 4) economic and applied geology. In addition, there have been some articles on techniques and methodology. Each article, of course, has an extensive bibliography. The journal's function, then, reflects the modern trend in geology of treating processes and subjects rather than geographical areas. A newsletter, *Atlas,* appearing as a supplement in each issue, contains a calendar of forthcoming events, news of international organizations, news of recent developments, some historical notes, a listing of the contents of selected other geological journals, and usually 8 or 10 book reviews, signed and critical, mostly 500-1000 words. Contributors are from many countries, but all material is in English. An essential journal for departments with an active interest in research and current developments.

66-9960

ECONOMIC GEOLOGY AND THE BULLETIN OF THE SOCIETY OF ECON–OMIC GEOLOGISTS.   v. 1, 1905-

8 nos./yr.   Houghton, Mich. $15.00

Includes 9 or 10 articles of varied lengths dealing with geology as applied to mining and allied industries. Besides the long articles, there are shorter "Scientific Communications," which are usually briefer research reports, and "Discussions," which are comments on previously published articles. All contributions are well illustrated. Also news of the Society and abstracts of papers presented at the meetings. Issues conclude with "Scientific Notes and News," covering news of personnel and activities. 2 to 5 signed book reviews, a substantial portion of which are the detailed summaries of each issue of the Russian journal that is *Economic Geology's* counterpart. Also a listing, with very brief annotations, of other books received. A specialized but important journal.

Indexed in: A.S.T.I.   7-22687

*GEOLOGICAL SOCIETY OF AMERICA.   BULLETIN.   v. 1, 1888-

Monthly.   N.Y. $50.00

Official organ of the Society. The articles are primarily reports of field investigations, accompanied with many photographs, maps and drawings. "Notes and Discussions" contains several shorter papers (up to 12 manuscript pages), also reporting research results, and also discussions relating to previously published reports. Before 1933 and from 1960 to 1967 the Society's Proceedings, Memorials, etc., were carried as part of the *Bulletin,* which also used to carry abstracts of the papers presented at the Society's meetings. Now, despite the fact that all material other than articles and reports has been removed to other publications, the *Bulletin* is still much larger than it was only a few years ago. In 1970 the total number of pages was over 3000; in 1960, even with the other kinds of material included, it was only about 2000. Most articles are fairly brief (5-15,000 words) and are on all areas (geographic and subject) of geology and their authors are from many countries, though a large majority of the reports relate to North American geology.

Because of the many folded maps, binding is expensive, but libraries should make the effort to bind it, since it is the most important general research journal for geologists, and should be available wherever geology is studied seriously. A backfile is important, both because of the outstanding geologists who have been contributors, but also because so many of the articles are still important sources for research.

Indexed in: A.S.T.I.   1-23380 rev 3

*GEOPHYSICAL ABSTRACTS.   no. 1, 1929-

Monthly.   Washington, D.C. $7.00

Issued first by the Bureau of Mines through June, 1936 then again from 1943 through 1946, it was issued July 1936 through 1942 and since January, 1947 by the U.S. Geological Survey. Includes "abstracts of technical papers and books on the physics of the solid earth, the application of physical methods and techniques to geologic problems, and geophysical exploration." In 1970 sections on "Meteorites and Tektites" and "Moon and Planets" were added. Abstracts are not usually prepared for material with limited circulation (such as dissertations) or oral reports. Coverage is world wide, but all abstracts are in English. Now 6-7000 abstracts per year, arranged by topic, with author and subject indexes in each issue, and an annual cumulative index (which appears fairly late—the 1968 index appeared in May, 1970).

With the discontinuance of *Geoscience Abstracts,* this title has become even more important. Given its low price and breadth of coverage, it should be available in every geology department. A depository item.

GS 37-206

*GEOTIMES.   v. 1, 1956-

Monthly (except bi-monthly May-Aug.)   Washington, D.C. $4.00

Published by the American Geological Institute (and distributed free to members of its supporting societies) it is the professional news magazine of the scientific and technical societies with interests in the area of geology. The articles do not report research, but are of much more general interest—on major trends and developments in areas of geology; biographical or historical treatments; matters relating to education or employment generally. Contains reports and news of scientific and professional matters, and developments in education and professional services—courses and programs, awards, fellowships and scholarships, legislative and governmental issues, personnel news, news of new products, etc. A calendar of symposia, regional, national and international meetings appears regularly. Usually about 3 book reviews per issue; these tend to be on books of general interest to geologists, or even on semi-popular works, rather than specialized studies; often, important new maps are reviewed. The reviews are all signed and critical, and are lengthy, mostly over 1000 words. Also listing of other books received. A useful journal for all geologists, beginning and advanced.

58-44252

INTERNATIONAL GEOLOGY REVIEW.   1959-

Monthly.   Washington, D.C. $150.00

Published by the American Geological Institute, it contains from 10 to 20 articles translated "from a large number of Russian geological journals in all disciplines. Non-serial works are reviewed and on occasion significant portions translated and published." Abstracts in English for all articles. Most issues also contain a "Review Section" containing reviews (as many as 15, but usually only a few) of recent Russian geological monographs. "New Books" lists prepublication announcements of forthcoming Russian geologic works with brief descriptive notes.

For colleges with strong geology departments actively involved in research.

61-39930

*JOURNAL OF GEOLOGICAL EDUCATION.   v. 1, 1951-

5 nos./yr.   Washington, D.C. $8.00

Published by the National Association of Geology Teachers. Each issue contains about 4 articles of moderate length. While most are on aspects of the teaching of geology—instructional methods and devices, the role of geology in higher education, course content, etc.—there are many articles on the history of geology, on developing areas, and other issues of general interest. Also contains professional news and notes, and over 10 lengthy, signed book reviews. "Brief Reports" are 1 to 3-page articles on geology teaching. The "Bulletin Board" provides information on grants, summer programs, and other news. Official reports and other news of the NAGT. The number of book reviews varies widely—from just 1 or 2 up to 15. They are all signed and critical, and vary in length from just a few hundred to several thousand words, but most are 500-750 words. Beginning in 1970, reviews of films in the geological sciences. Because of the journal's purpose, the reviews are keyed to the college level, and are especially useful for book selection purposes.

64-35765

*JOURNAL OF GEOLOGY.   v. 1, 1893-

Bi-monthly.   Chicago, Ill. $18.00

Technical articles on all phases of geology, with emphasis on papers that present new concepts, and perhaps more attention to geologic formations and methodology than to other areas. Usually from 4 to 6 articles per issue, mostly around 20 pages long, each preceded by an abstract, with many illustrations, charts, tables, etc. The regular section, "Geological Notes," contains shorter contributions; "Discussion" contains comments on earlier articles or on other matters and replies to these comments. From time to time entire issues have been devoted to single subject or divisions of geology. The number of book reviews has varied in recent years: in 1955 over 30 titles were reviewed, but by 1966 this had dropped to just 2; by 1969, however, the number of reviews had increased again to almost 30. They are all signed and critical, but range in length from a few paragraphs to several thousand words. A basic journal for all geology departments.

Indexed in: A.S.T.I. 25-13118

JOURNAL OF GEOPHYSICAL RESEARCH. v. 1, 1896-

3 nos./yr. Washington, D.C. $75.00

Published by the American Geophysical Union, it contains reports of original research in fields of geophysics. Although the geophysical aspects of planetary science have been included for a number of years, beginning in 1967, every other issue was devoted exclusively to space physics. In 1969, the frequency increased to 3 times a month: the first section, published on the first of the month, containing papers on solar physics, planetary atmospheres and exterior planetary magnetism; the second section, issued on the 15th, carries papers on the physics and chemistry of the solid earth, planetology, geodesy and materials science related to geophysical problems; the third section, published on the 20th, carries papers on the physics and chemistry of the atmosphere, the air-sea interface, the oceans and the ocean basins. The papers vary greatly in length, but all are quite technical. For advanced students and research only.

12-7247*

*JOURNAL OF PALEONTOLOGY. v. 1, 1927-

Bi-monthly. Tulsa, Okla. $40.00

Published by the Society of Economic Paleontologists and Mineralogists along with the Paleontological Society, as alternate sponsors of issues. Issues consist of articles reporting research in various branches of paleontology, with some emphasis on systematic classification of North American species, but with both authors and subject matter from many areas. All articles are thoroughly illustrated. In addition to the research reports, there are a number of other types of articles, reports and features: professional and Society news and announcements, lists of members (for the SEMP, carried before 1969 in the *Journal of Sedimentary Petrology*), "Nomenclatural Notes" and, because of the nature of the field, frequent bibliographies and review articles. The number of reviews varies from none to 8 or so; they are all signed, but their length also varies from just a paragraph or two to over 1000 words.

Beginning in 1968, the Paleontological Society began to issue a Memoirs series, "occasional publications consisting of monographs and symposia that are too long for publication in the *Journal*." As Supplements to the *Journal,* they are included with a subscription, but should probably be kept as a separate series.

A basic publication for every library where geology is a major.

GS 28-114 rev.

JOURNAL OF SEDIMENTARY PETROLOGY.   v. 1, 1931-

Quarterly.   Tulsa, Okla. $26.00

A publication of the Society of Economic Paleontologists and Mineralogists (a division of the American Association of Petroleum Geologists)
it began when its sister publication, the *Journal of Paleontology* (q.v.)
had too large a backlog of manuscripts. Its first volume was just 101
pages, and though it continued to be issued 3 times a year through 1949,
in 1950 it became a quarterly. Even so, it has grown substantially: in
1950, 260 pages were published; in 1960, 654; in 1969, 1670 pages.

It covers all aspects of sedimentary formations, with special attention
to the problems of oilfield discovery and development. There are now
usually 20-30 articles, reporting the results of research in this field—
describing new approaches to fundamental problems, or dealing with a
geological phenomenon that is of wider than local interest. Shorter items,
describing new techniques or very limited studies, appear as "Notes."
All articles and notes are thoroughly illustrated. Contributors include
government, academic and industrial geologists, about two-thirds from
this country, the remainder from around the world. Also contains "Discussions" of previously published papers, announcements of professional
interest and news, reports and announcements of the Society. Through
1968 it carried a list of the Society's members (moved to the *Journal
of Paleontology* in 1969). Book reviews appear irregularly, perhaps 6 to
10 at the most during the year; they are, however, mostly over 1000
words. List of publications received in each issue, including new serial
titles.

An important journal where there is any emphasis on research.

67-6582 rev.

MINERALOGICAL MAGAZINE.   v. 1, 1876-

Quarterly.   London. $19.50

Until 1969, titled *Mineralogical Magazine and Journal of the Mineralogical
Society*. Contains reports of both experimental work and field studies on
all aspects of minerals. The articles, mostly of moderate length and well
illustrated, are primarily by British scientists, with many others by Commonwealth residents, and only occasional ones by Americans. A number
of short (1-page) Communications, plus proceedings and news of the
Society. Important only in institutions with strong geology departments
engaged in mineralogical research.

14-6066-7

HISTORY

AGRICULTURAL HISTORY. v. 1, 1927-

Quarterly. Berkeley, Calif. $5.00

The journal of the Agricultural History Society, it "is designed as a medium for the publication of research and documents pertaining to the history of agriculture in all its phases and as a clearinghouse for information of interest and value to workers in the field. Materials on the history of agriculture in all countries are included, and also materials on institutions, organizations, and sciences which have been factors in agricultural development." A majority of the articles relate to American agricultural history, but this is interpreted broadly, and includes economics, politics, education, technology, sociology, even literature. Articles on the agricultural history of other countries frequently appear. Issues are occasionally devoted to single topics —e.g., Eighteenth-Century Agriculture: A Symposium, The Structure of the Cotton Economy of the Antebellum South. In addition to the 5 to 7 articles in most issues, there are frequent review articles, plus "News Notes" of the Society and its members and of other activities; beginning in 1953, an annual listing, "Books on Agricultural History," has appeared, and in 1954, a book review section was started. The reviews vary in length from a paragraph to a few pages, but they are all signed and critical; there are also some brief, unsigned book notes. In the past 5 years, the journal has become much more substantial, and it is now an important title for the study of agricultural development and history and their ramifications.

Indexed in: Bio.Ag.I.   33-20319

*AMERICA: HISTORY AND LIFE. v. 1, 1964-

Quarterly. Santa Barbara, Calif. Service basis (from $35 to $115, depending on book fund, with special consideration to public libraries, junior colleges, and foreign subscribers)

Published by the American Bibliographical Center—Clio Press, this "Guide to Periodical Literature" of U.S. and Canadian history and contemporary life covers about 500 periodicals of these countries, plus *Festschriften,* serial publications, and more than 1000 foreign journals. (The list of periodicals covered is available from the publisher.) Through 1969, the 3000-odd abstracts were contained in 3 numbers, the fourth being the annual index. Beginning with mid-1969, the abstracts are in all 4 numbers, with a separate index for each number. The abstracts are arranged by geographical area, subdivided by period, with separate sections for general historiography, bibliography and methodology. For each abstract, full bibliographical information is given along with the name of the abstracter. The indexing employs a unique notation system ("The Cue System") which takes some getting used to, but is explained carefully in each issue and, considering its thoroughness and versatility, is worth the trouble. A new format in mid-1969 improved the appearance greatly. An important reference tool for research in U.S. and Canadian history, even on the undergraduate level.

64-25630

*AMERICAN HERITAGE.   n.s.v. 1, 1949-

Bi-monthly.   N.Y. $20.00

Taking the name of a magazine that had been aimed at educators, the American Association for State and Local History began this new series as a quarterly in 1949 with new color, more illustrations and features of wider and more popular interest. It was successful enough so that five years later, in 1954, a separate publishing company bought it out in what was then an unusual and daring format—a bi-monthly, beautifully printed on fine paper, in hard covers, selling for the price of a book, but available only on subscription. It was even more successful. The articles—on major and minor aspects of American history, institutions, personalities, manners and mores, battles, inventions, etc., have been written mostly by scholars who are also polished writers. The illustrations are not only perceptively chosen and exquisitely reproduced in both color and black-and-white, but comprise an extremely valuable source for research. There are no book reviews, but excerpts from new books frequently are published; documentary materials and photographs sometimes appear here for the first time. With the December, 1969 issue (the 20th anniversary issue), there began a new section, "The American Land," devoted to "the preservation of our visibly endangered natural heritage." It contains illustrated articles and features, similar to the rest of the journal, and a regular column, "The Environment: Notes on the Continuing Battle." The 10-year index thoroughly indexes all contents—articles, reviews and illustrations—thus making a back file even more valuable.

Still sponsored by the American Association for State and Local History, plus the Society of American Historians, *American Heritage* is reliable and readable, and a pleasure to look at; it provides an excellent means of stimulating interest in American history, and should be in every library.

Indexed in: R.G.   54-14502

*AMERICAN HISTORICAL REVIEW.   v. 1, 1895-

Quarterly.   Washington, D.C. $15.00

Official journal of the American Historical Association, it has carried over the years articles and addresses of great scholarly significance, and the major American historians have served on its editorial board. Scholarly articles—generally 4 or 5 fairly long ones per issue, including the Association's annual Presidential Address—on historiography and on all areas and periods, though a majority of the articles treat either American or modern European history. Review articles have become a fairly regular feature. The section "Historical News" carried—until October, 1966—news of the Association, of important new publications and library acquisitions, of awards, various professional activities and news, and notices of members' deaths, and communications. With the October, 1966 issue, this section became known as "Association Notes." It still contains news of the Association, notices of deaths, and communications, but other news—professional, individual and institutional—is carried in the *AHA Newsletter,* which goes to all members. The *Review* serves as a valuable bibliographical and book selection aid: well over half the journal now is devoted to reviews and bibliography; a recent issue (December, 1969), for example, had some 180 signed, critical reviews extending over 175 pages, plus a 65-page listing of articles and other books received. These cover all areas and periods, and include both foreign and domestic publications.

The most important and prestigious American journal of history, *AHR* and its backfile is indispensable for every college library.

Indexed in: B.R.D.   5-18244
          In.Rel.Per.Lit.
          R.G.

*AMERICAN WEST.   v. 1, 1964-

Bi-monthly.   Palo Alto, Calif. $9.00

Though published privately, it is sponsored by the Western History Association which, though open to the public, has close academic ties. Each issue contains about 7 or 8 articles on some aspect of Western history in its widest sense—that is, political and military history, biography, folklore, social history and literary history, etc. The articles and short features, contributed by scholars, journalists, authors, and laymen interested in the area, are of brief to moderate length, exceptionally well illustrated in color and black-and-white with reproductions of photographs, drawings and maps. The material, on interesting topics and well written, has been reliably researched. An issue will occasionally be devoted to a single topic—e.g., The Pacific Railroad, 1869-1969; The Republic of Texas—but the format is still very much the same. A substantial book section, "The American West Review" appears in each issue. It contains a few reviews of 750-1000 words, but a much larger number (perhaps 15 or 20) of short reviews. All are signed and critical. Through 1968 each issue contained a fairly comprehensive listing of recently published western books; this became an annual feature beginning with the January, 1970 issue which listed 1969 publications. An exceptionally attractive publication, its readability and reliability make it essential for every academic library where there is some interest in Western history—and where is there not?

Indexed in: R.G.   64-9374

AMERICAS.   v. 1, 1944-

Quarterly   Washington, D.C. $6.00

"A quarterly review of inter-American cultural history," it is published by the Academy of American Franciscan History, Washington, D.C. The purpose of the Academy was "to stimulate, coordinate and perpetuate interest in American Franciscan studies," and though the early volumes stressed Franciscan history, the journal now is a much broader one, covering all of Latin American history. Usually about 5 articles per issue, contributed by scholars from U.S. colleges and universities, on aspects of political, social, and cultural history, with little (though increasing) attention to recent events. Bibliographical articles and texts of documents frequently appear. "Inter-American Notes" contains news of conferences, programs, publishing and research projects, new periodicals, biographical material. Usually 10-13 book reviews per issue, signed and critical, mostly 500-1000 words.

Indexed in: S.S.H.I.   46-7807

CANADIAN HISTORICAL REVIEW.   v. 1, 1920-

Quarterly.   Toronto. $8.00

Official journal of the Canadian Historical Association, it was founded to be as "broadly national" as possible, but interpreting Canadian "history" liberally to include "geography, economics, archaeology, ethnology, law, education, and imperial relations, insofar as they relate to Canada." Since its beginning, the format has remained much the same: one-half articles or edited documents; the remainder, reviews and bibliography. There are now 3 or 4 scholarly articles in each issue, only occasionally in French, plus 20-30 book reviews, usually 600-1000 words in length. All are signed and critical, and they cover books on areas outside Canada, though most of them have some relationship. Also a list of books received. Each issue carries the bibliography, *Recent Publications Relating to Canada,* an extensive listing that covers all types of publications.

The basic journal in the field of Canadian history, it should be in all libraries where there are especially strong departments of American history.

Indexed in: S.S.H.I.   23-16213

CIVIL WAR HISTORY.   v. 1, 1955-

Quarterly.   Kent, Ohio. $7.50

Now subtitled "A journal of the Middle Period," its original purpose was to present "on a non-partisan, scholarly basis, that period of national turmoil. Not only the battles, but the men and women who made the battles, the literature, the music, the art, the journalism," and it excluded political history. Due, perhaps, to some decline of interest after the end of the Civil War Centennial, and to the competition of other journals that emphasized social history, in 1966 it began to change. While on the one hand it expanded its chronological coverage, on the other its subject coverage has become mostly limited to political and military history. An average of 4 scholarly articles per issue, mostly of medium length. *The Bibliography of Civil War Articles* (covering, however, from the antebellum period through Reconstruction) has appeared annually since 1962, and irregularly before then. Earlier regular features—"Notes and Queries," reports of research on "The Continuing War," and "For Collectors Only," have been dropped. Frequent review articles, and a large number (between 15 and 30 usually) of signed and critical reviews, averaging 600-700 words. A section of "Book Notes," listing and annotating briefly a number of other titles, appears in most issues. A useful journal where there are strong departments in history.

57-2353 rev.

COMPARATIVE STUDIES IN SOCIETY AND HISTORY.   v. 1, 1958-

Quarterly.   London. $14.00

Publishes original research on "problems of change and stability that recur in human societies," today and in the past. Contributions, by eminent scholars in universities all over the world, are from many disciplines besides history—sociology and anthropology, political science, psychology, religion, etc.—and the articles, usually 6 per issue, averaging about 6000 words each, range over all these areas and treat a great diversity of societies. Some of the topics treated in several articles have been the comparative study of modernizing elites, the role of intellectuals, the causes and functions of different kinds of knowledge, revolution, and social mobility. A few issues have been devoted to single topics, and three supplements (available separately) have been published. For advanced students and research.

Indexed in: S.S.H.I.   60-23653

ENGLISH HISTORICAL REVIEW.   v. 1, 1886-

Quarterly.   London. $15.25

Each issue contains just a few articles—usually 3 or 4, and never more than 6—but they are rather long, and of course, scholarly, treating the history of Great Britain (with great emphasis on England proper) from medieval times to modern (but almost never after 1914). "Notes and Documents" contains generally shorter pieces devoted to the examination of a limited point, descriptions of new sources, publication of new material with commentary, corrections of mistaken chronology, and other minor historiographical matters. About half of each issue (100 to 125 pages) is devoted to book reviews. Usually 10 to 20 are long reviews (from one to several thousand words); the remainder, more than 100 in recent issues, are from 200 to 750 words long. The reviews cover books in all historical periods and areas; all reviews are signed and critical— the longer ones are outstanding. Also a list of other publications received. There is an extensive annual listing of "Notices of Periodical and Occasional Publications," covering many areas, though emphasizing General and European history, and excluding "articles of a bibliographical or archeological character or which deal exclusively with North American history." Some of the articles are briefly described. An important journal where there is serious work in English or European history.

Indexed in: B.R.D.   5-40370 rev. 2
           Br.Hum.I.
           S.S.H.I.

HISPANIC AMERICAN HISTORICAL REVIEW.   v. 1, 1918-

Quarterly.   Durham, N.C. $8.00

Published in cooperation with the Conference on Latin American History of the American Historical Association. The scholarly articles cover all areas and periods of the history of Latin America, though emphasizing the 17th-19th centuries, and with more attention to Mexico than any other single country. Bibliographical contributions have always been an important part of the *Review*: descriptions of archives and libraries,

texts of documents, and frequent bibliographical or review articles. Moreover, from one-third to one-half of each issue is devoted to book reviews:
usually 50 or more reviews, averaging 500-600 words and another, somewhat smaller group of "Book Notices." Both groups are signed and critical.
The two cumulative indexes, covering 1918-45 and 1946-55, which
are guides rather than just indexes, are especially useful since the
listing of each article is accompanied by an annotation. A basic title
where there is any interest in Latin America.

Indexed in: S.S.H.I.   19-14875 (rev '28)

HISTORIAN.   v. 1, 1938-

Quarterly.   Allentown, Pa. $6.00

Published by Phi Alpha Theta, the international honor society in history. Contains scholarly articles in all areas and periods of history, though
with an emphasis on U.S. history. Issues usually contain 4 articles, by
professors of history, plus one essay or article by a student. All contributions are limited to 6000 words. News of the society and its chapters
and listing of new members. The journal has always emphasized reviews;
there are now usually more than 50 per issue, signed and critical, mostly
500-600 words. A useful journal for all college libraries, it is certainly
important where there are strong history departments.

Indexed in: S.S.H.I.   45-52201

*HISTORICAL ABSTRACTS.   v. 1, 1955-

Quarterly.   Santa Barbara, Calif.   Service basis (varies   from $40   to
$150, depending on book fund, though "Special consideration is given
public libraries, 2-year colleges, and foreign subscribers.")

A "Bibliography of the World's Periodical Literature." Published by the
American Bibliographic Center—Clio Press, it covers over 1300 foreign
and domestic periodicals, listing over the year some 4000 abstracts of
articles (including those in many other serials and *Festschriften*) that are
on world history from 1775 to 1945. (The list of periodicals covered is
available from the publishers.) Before 1964 it included Canada and the
U.S., but with the beginning of *America: History and Life* (q.v.) references to these countries were limited to their foreign relations; in 1970
they were removed altogether. It also excludes articles of limited local
interest and those on the history of other subjects (such as the history
of music) unless they bear on the development of a more central topic.
For each abstract, full bibliographical information is given, along with
the name of the abstracter. Abstracts are arranged by topic and country,
with many cross references. Up to 1970, not all topics and areas appeared
in every issue; also, there was an annual index (which usually appeared
quite late). Beginning in 1970, all parts and sections appear in each issue
and a separate index is issued for three issues, and a cumulative annual
index with the fourth issue. The indexing employs a unique notation
system ("The Cue System") which is a bit difficult at first, but since it is

explained carefully and provides thorough access to the abstracts, is worth learning to use.

The final brief section of each number, "Bibliographical News," is especially helpful to librarians in keeping up with new reference works in the field. It also lists new historical sets, other significant works and notices of new history periodicals, or news about older ones. Also list of books received.

An essential item for any library where there is research in history, and also important for undergraduate use. It may appear expensive, but the reference value is very high.

56-56304 rev.

Addendum:

In 1971, the time span of *Historical Abstracts* was extended from 1945 to 1970, and the publication divided into two parts. *Part A: Modern History Abstracts,* covers 1775-1914; *Part B: Twentieth Century Abstracts,* covers 1914-1970. As with the earlier format, each will appear quarterly— 3 numbers of abstracts, plus an annual index. It is anticipated that the number of abstracts "will virtually double."

HISTORICAL JOURNAL.   v. 1, 1958-

Quarterly.   London. $15.50

Successor to the *Cambridge Historical Journal* and, like it, supported by the Cambridge Historical Society, it publishes scholarly articles (usually 6 or 7, of varying length, per issue) on all aspects of history but with great emphasis on modern history, and especially British history. Briefer articles and comments appear as "Communications," and occasionally documents of historical importance are published. Its reviewing policy has two aspects: at least one, but more often two review articles per issue, each covering usually just a single work and very long, offer their own interpretations; 8 to 10 book reviews, though not as long, but still substantial (usually 1000-2000 words) cover only other important works. Here again, the emphasis is on modern Britain. An important journal for this field of history.

Indexed in: Br.Hum.I.   62-52664

HISTORY.   n.s.v. 1, 1916-

3 nos./yr.   London. $6.05

Published by the Historical Association, the British Counterpart of the American Historical Association. Until 1957, although it contained some good material, its drab appearance discouraged readership. In that year, Alfred Cobban assumed the editorship and gave it new life. The quality of articles, admittedly good before, became even better—they are solid and well written—the appearance improved greatly, and the reviewing function expanded considerably. Usually 5 or 6 articles per issue, on all areas and periods, but with some emphasis on British history. There is a continuing interest in historiography, and in descriptions of primary sources, but while the teaching of history is still emphasized, there is less attention than before to teaching on the secondary level, although the annual surveys of "History Books for Schools" are still carried. At least half of most issues is devoted to reviewing; review articles appear in almost every issue, and an average of 100 other titles are covered in signed, critical reviews that range from a few hundred to 1000 words, averaging about 500. An important journal where English history receives much attention.

Indexed in: Br.Hum.I.   14-14748
           S.S.H.I.

HISTORY AND THEORY. v. 1, 1960-

3 nos./year.   Middletown, Conn. $7.50

Subtitled "Studies in the philosophy of history," it publishes scholarly articles, essays, comments, bibliographies and monographic supplements in four areas: the theory of history; historiography in terms of individuals, schools, and events; the historical method—interpretations, evidence, and the political and cultural implications of the historian's method; related disciplines—the relationship of historical theory and method to the other social sciences. Each issue contains usually four fairly long articles (often 20-25,000 words) and 4 or so - review essays of usually about 3000 words, but frequently much longer. The contributors include some of the world's most eminent historians and social scientists. The *Beihefte,* included in the subscription cost, appear about once a year, and are frequently bibliographical. Only for advanced students and faculty.

Indexed in: S.S.H.I.   63-47837

*HISTORY TODAY. v. 1, 1951-

Monthly.   London. $10.50

Intended for the general reader rather than the historian, it is not confined geographically or chronologically (though some emphasis, as might be expected, is given to British history, and there is perhaps more attention to recent periods) and covers social and intellectual history as well as political and military. There are generally 7 or 8 articles, 3000-5000 words long and illustrated, written mostly by professional historians, with some by eminent authorities in their respective fields. Each article contains a brief listing of titles for further reading. The book review section, which has expanded, usually contains about 8 reviews. Though varying greatly in length (from several hundred to over 2000 words) they are all good. Particularly useful for reading assignments and papers in introductory courses, and good, reliable recreational reading for the young historian.

Indexed in: Br.Hum.I.   53-39027
           S.S.H.I.

INTERNATIONAL REVIEW OF SOCIAL HISTORY.   v. 1, 1956-

3 nos./yr.   Amsterdam, Netherlands. $9.00

Edited by the International Instituut voor Sociale Geschiedenis, each issue contains 2 to 5 scholarly articles, varying greatly in length, on aspects of social history by contributors from many countries. The areas of social history range widely, though the histories of radical and revolutionary movements and labor history receive much attention. The articles tend to be of somewhat specific interest; a 1970 issue, for example, contained articles on union representation in the British merchant marine, the relationship of the French Communist party and the Comintern, early

Victorian household structure, and an analysis of Prussian schoolbooks. Most articles are in English, with a few in German.

There are no book reviews, but a "Bibliography" in each issue lists, with brief but evaluative annotations, a large number of recent monographs in social history from all over the world. All the annotations are in English, making the bibliography, which describes works overlooked in many reviewing media, even more useful.

Indexed in: S.S.H.I.   57-27360

ISIS. *see* SCIENCE

JOURNAL OF AFRICAN HISTORY.   v. 1, 1960-

Quarterly.   London. $17.00

Edited by outstanding Africanists of the University of London's School of African and Oriental Studies, it contains scholarly articles—usually 7 to 10 per issue, limited to 6000 words each—on all of Africa from the earliest times to the present. Covers all aspects of African history—archaeological, anthropological, economic, political, etc.—but treats early African history more than other journals. Contributors are international in their affiliations. Generally about 10-12 signed, critical book reviews, averaging 600-750 words, plus a few shorter notices, and a list of books received. Review articles, on a single work or a group of related works, are carried frequently.

An important journal not just because there is a growing interest in this area, but also because the reappraisal of earlier work on African history is proceeding rapidly, and the findings are reported in this journal (and a few others) long before they appear in book form.

Indexed in: Br.Hum.I.   63-5723
            S.S.H.I.

*JOURNAL OF AMERICAN HISTORY.   v. 1, 1914-

Quarterly.   Bloomington, Ind. $15.00

For the first 50 volumes, it was the official journal of the Mississippi Valley Historical Association, titled the *Mississippi Valley Historical Review.* With the June, 1964 issue it assumed its present title in "recognition of a decided shift in contributor emphasis from regional to nationally-oriented history"—i.e., in the journal's early years, over 80 per cent of the articles had dealt with the Mississippi Valley, whereas in recent volumes less than 10 per cent have. Each issue contains 5 or 6 scholarly articles of moderate length, all on American history. Includes an extensive section of signed book reviews, now 70-100 an issue, averaging about 500-600 words; "Book Notes" now lists a number of other books received, but in past years annotated many of them. "Historical News and Comments" contains news of the Organization of American Historians (which the Mississippi Valley Historical Association had been renamed in 1965), plus announcements of grants and awards, and of miscellaneous historical activities. Finally, the useful section "Recent Articles," contains a listing, arranged by geographical regions of the U.S., of historical articles appearing in a variety of periodicals. Along with the *American Historical Review,* it is the leading scholarly periodical in the field of U.S. history, and, with its backfile, should be in every academic library.

Indexed in: B.R.D.   41-15235 rev. 2*
            S.S.H.I.

JOURNAL OF CONTEMPORARY HISTORY.   v. 1, 1966-

Quarterly.   London. $10.00

Published for the Institute for Advanced Studies in Contemporary History, London, which was founded in 1964 "to promote research, mainly
in twentieth-century European history. . ." Most issues focus on a single
topic—e.g., International Fascism, 1920-1945; Urbanism; Colonialism and
Decolonisation—with 10 or so articles; a few issues have had a miscellaneous group of articles. The chief editor is Walter Laqueur, and the contributors are historians and social scientists from Europe and the United
States, with some very distinguished names included. The Editorial Board
includes some of the most eminent historians here and abroad. There are
no book reviews.

Indexed in: Br.Hum.I.   66-9877
            P.A.I.S.

*JOURNAL OF MODERN HISTORY.   v. 1, 1929-

Quarterly.   Chicago, Ill. $8.00

Published in cooperation with the Modern History Section of the American Historical Association, it contain scholarly articles, usually 4 or 5 an
issue, by contributors from American and foreign universities, on political,
diplomatic, intellectual, social and economic history from 1500 to the
present, excluding the domestic history of the Americas and with emphasis on European political and diplomatic history. Many issues contain
one or several review-articles or a bibliographical survey of recent literature
on a particular subject—e.g., "Recent Writings on William III," "Nazi
Germany and the United States: A Review Essay." Up to 1958, it frequently published the texts of recently discovered or released documents.
A listing of recent monographic works, arranged by country treated, was
carried until 1960, but was dropped to permit a larger number of reviews.
Now, the book review section carries anywhere from 25 to 70 signed,
critical reviews in each issue, averaging about 1000 words. A basic journal,
essential for every academic library.

Indexed in: S.S.H.I.   31-5078

*JOURNAL OF NEGRO HISTORY.   v. 1, 1916-

Quarterly.   Washington, D.C. $7.00

Published by the Association for the Study of Negro Life and History,
it was founded by Carter G. Woodson, a pioneer scholar in Negro history. He had organized the Association in 1915 and was editor of the
Journal from its founding through 1950. Contains scholarly articles on
the history of the Negro in the U.S., Latin America, the West Indies
and Africa, and on events and personalities related to that history. Until
recent years, when the subject matter became academically respectable, it was the major repository for new material and new interpretations of Negro history. These were treated both *per se* and as
a part of the larger American history, and the journal's articles and essays
have led to new points of view on slavery, on the Civil War and on the
Negro in Reconstruction.

With the increase of interest in this subject, and the consequent proliferation of publications, the number of reviews has more than doubled. Whereas, as late as 1960, there were just 5 or 6 reviews per issue, there are now usually 10 to 15, signed and critical, averaging 600-700 words. Documents are still frequently carried, and there is, finally, news of interest to members of the Association, including its Annual Report, as well as other historical news of interest to a wider audience. Through April, 1959 each issue carried a bibliography of books, articles and documents on Negro history. A backfile is especially useful because of the journal's preeminence in the field for so many years; a current subscription is important for all academic libraries.

Indexed in: In.Per.Negroes   17-5861 rev.*
            S.S.H.I.

JOURNAL OF SOCIAL HISTORY. v. 1, 1967-

Quarterly. Babson Park, Mass. $12.50

Reflecting the gradual *rapprochement* between historians and sociologists, this journal's editorial board contains some of the most eminent names from both fields. The scholarly articles, 3 or 4 per issue, are moderately long to lengthy, and contributed by sociologists, historians, demographers, and other social scientists. Subjects include all areas and periods of social history with some emphasis, as might be expected, on the United States. Issues contain a few book reviews; these are signed and critical and, in the main, quite long, never less than 1000, and often more than 2000 words. Also occasional short reviews, 100-200 words. Because of the growing interest in this field, it is an important journal where there are strong departments of history or the social sciences.

                                                    76-9450

JOURNAL OF SOUTHERN HISTORY. v. 1, 1935-

Quarterly. New Orleans, La. $7.00

Published by the Southern Historical Association. Each issue generally contains 3 or 4 scholarly articles on U.S. history with particular reference to the South; contributors, though, are by no means limited to the region. A "Notes and Documents" section frequently contains shorter articles, the text of and comments on letters, diaries and other documents. There are a number of other regular features: the report of the Association's annual meeting, "Historical News and Notes" in each issue, noting changes in personnel, awards, professional meetings and activities, and news of important library and archival acquisitions. Some 40 or 50 signed, critical reviews, averaging about 500 words, are carried in each issue; there is also a "Book Notes" section, describing other new publications. Beginning in 1964, the annual *Southern History in Periodicals, 19–: A Selected Bibliography* lists, by general subject, articles in a variety of periodicals; however, descriptive and genealogical articles of restricted interest are not included, and full coverage of articles relating to the Civil War has not been attempted since *Civil War History* began its annual bibliography. An important journal for most libraries, but essential where Southern history receives much attention.

Indexed in: S.S.H.I.   36-35310

*JOURNAL OF THE HISTORY OF IDEAS.   v. 1, 1940-

Quarterly.   N.Y. $10.00

"A quarterly devoted to cultural and intellectual history," its purpose is "to foster studies which will emphasize the interrelations of several fields of historical study—the history of philosophy, of literature and the arts, of the natural and social sciences, of religion, and of political and social movements." Usually 5 or 6 scholarly articles, mostly 6-8,000 words, plus some shorter "Notes"; written by scholars here and abroad, contributions discuss the influence of thought of one age or individual on the thought or culture of later ages or individuals, of philosophical ideas in the arts or sciences, of scientific discoveries; it covers all fields of the social sciences and humanities. Usually only a single book is reviewed, but this review is lengthy, almost always 4 or 5 pages, but occasionally up to 15 or 20 pages. There is also a listing of books received.

A journal of sound scholarship, important for many disciplines, it belongs in every academic library.

Indexed in: S.S.H.I.   42-51802

JOURNAL OF THE WEST.   v. 1, 1962-

Quarterly.   Los Angeles, Calif. $9.00

"Devoted to Western history and geography," it also covers "Western archaeology, anthropology, geology, and related sciences, as well as works on exploration, settlement, commerce and industry, culture and literature, politics and government." Each issue contains usually from 6 to 10 articles, mostly fairly scholarly, of short to moderate length. Issues often have a single theme, e.g., Irrigation, Conservation and Reclamation; National Parks and Monuments; Paleontology in the West. The book review section, "Books for the Western Library," has steadily expanded so that between 30 and 60 titles are reviewed in each number. These are signed and critical and usually 400-700 words long. An essential journal for institutions where there is an interest in the region.

Indexed in: S.S.H.I.   66-84755

JOURNAL OF WORLD HISTORY.   v. 1, 1953-

Quarterly.   Neuchâtel, Switzerland.   Bill Later.

Also titled *Cahiers d'Histoire Mondiale* and *Cuadernos de Historia Mundial*, it is sponsored by Unesco. Publishes "materials dealing with culture in its most diverse aspects" with emphasis on: "1. Culture, its history and evolution (cultural life and development) in the major regions of the world. Cross-cultural influences on regional, national and local life. 2. Contacts between cultures, with emphasis on the channels, means and organization and exchanges.... 3. The history of ideas, and of the development and evolution of artistic expression and scientific pursuit. The growth and role of institutions in cultural life. 4. Cultural creativity. 5. The cultural approach to history and civilization; the various concepts and definitions of culture; theories and problems involved in the study of culture and of intercultural, inter-regional, and inter-national relations."

Most issues consist of 5 to 10 articles, usually of moderate length, grouped around one or several topics. The articles, as indicated in the editorial excerpt above, are much broader in scope than the typical historical journal and, as one might expect from a Unesco-supported publication, deal frequently with the history of non-western areas. Contributors include eminent historians and other social scientists from all over the world. Most articles are in English with the others in French.

Its wide range of articles and eminence of contributors make it an important journal for academic libraries.

Indexed in: S.S.H.I.   58-21447

LABOR HISTORY.   v. 1, 1960-

Quarterly.   N.Y. $7.50

Published by the Tamiment Institute, an adult educational organization devoted to the study of contemporary American society especially through the development of the labor movement and associated groups. Contains scholarly articles (about 3 an issue, mostly fairly long), notes and documents relating to "original research in American labor history, studies of specific unions and of the impact of labor problems upon ethnic and minority groups, theory of labor history, biographical portraits of important trade union figures, analyses of foreign labor movements or cooperative studies which shed light on American labor developments, studies of radical groups or of radical history related to American labor history." Issues are occasionally devoted to a single topic—e.g., Labor Radicalism, 1880-1919, The Negro and the American Labor Movement. The section "Problems and Sources," appearing in most issues, carries articles on libraries, special collections, archives and news relating to research materials in labor history; beginning with the one for 1965, the journal published an *Annual Bibliography of Periodical Articles on Labor History;* other special bibliographies are carried frequently. Each issue, beginning in 1968, also contains the "Labor Historians Newsletter," containing appointments, new courses, news of manuscripts and archival acquisitions, fellowships available, etc. The number and length of book reviews varies widely from issue to issue, but there are 40-50 a year, mostly 700-1000 words. An important journal for strong departments of recent American history or economic history.

Indexed in: S.S.H.I.   61-37555

*NEGRO HISTORY BULLETIN.   v. 1, 1937-

Monthly (except July-Sept.)   Washington, D.C. $3.50

Published by the Association for the Study of Negro life and History "to promote an appreciation of the life and history of the Negro, to encourage an understanding of his present status, and to enrich the promise of the future." Contains fairly popular but reliable articles, usually illustrated, on all aspects of Negro history and biography and frequently on other aspects of Negro life and culture, including recent events. Issues are sometimes devoted to a single topic, e.g., Haiti—A Black Government, Negroes in the Armed Forces. Each issue begins with an editorial, and most issues contain some original poetry, a section devoted to news of individual achievements, special events, exhibitions, and miscellaneous news, and a section containing news of the Association's branches. A few signed and critical book reviews per issue, varying in length from just a paragraph or two to 500 words. The increased interest in the subject, and the relative difficulty of finding materials, makes the journal and its back files important for college libraries.

Indexed in: In.Per.Negroes   40-4269
          R.G.

NEW England Quarterly. *see* GENERAL

PACIFIC HISTORICAL REVIEW.   v. 1, 1932-

Quarterly.   Berkeley, Calif. $5.00

Published for the Pacific Coast Branch of the American Historical Association, it treats mostly the history (after 1500) of the western United States, but also Mexico, China, Australia, Japan, Hawaii, and other Pacific areas, and is especially useful for the study of American political, military and social relationships with the governments and peoples of those areas as well as, of course, the history of western U.S. Reports news in the area that is of interest to the profession, and carries the Association's reports. The books received are mostly in the same areas as the articles, though important works on other areas are also treated. The number of book reviews varies widely from less than 10 to more than 40; they are all signed and critical, and average 600-700 words. Usually "Other Recent Publications" are briefly noted. An essential journal for institutions concerned with the history of western U.S., it is important for all academic libraries.

Indexed in: S.S.H.I.   34-33508

SOCIAL Studies. *see* EDUCATION

SPECULUM.   v. 1, 1926-

Quarterly.   Cambridge, Mass. $18.00

"A journal of mediaeval studies," it is published by the Mediaeval Academy of America, whose purpose is "the promotion of research, publication, and instruction in mediaeval records, art, archaeology, history, law, literature, music, philosophy, science, social and economic institutions, and all other aspects of mediaeval civilization." The usual 5 to 7 articles are fairly well divided over these subjects; the articles are, of course, scholarly, but vary greatly in length. There are a number of signed, critical reviews, 35 to 45 per issue, generally 1000-1500 words. Proceedings of the Academy's meeting are reported, as are Memoirs of its Fellows. There are announcements of activities, awards, scholarships, etc., of interest to mediaevalists. Each issue also contains a "Bibliography of American Periodical Literature" on mediaeval studies, arranged (since 1957) by general subject, and a list of books received. A very scholarly journal, it is especially useful for history, but it will be used in all areas of the humanities, such as philosophy and religion, for which the mediaeval period is important.

Indexed in: S.S.H.I.   27-15446

TECHNOLOGY AND CULTURE.   v. 1, 1959-

Quarterly.   Chicago, Ill. $12.00

Official publication of the Society for the History of Technology, an interdisciplinary organization "concerned not only with the history of technological devices and processes but also with the relation of technology to science, politics, social change, the arts and humanities, and economics." Only a few articles per issue, ranging from the very specialized to general, from "The Ski: Its History and Historiography," to "The Meaning and Measure of Economic Progress." A number of other sections cover research notes, reports on professional programs, reviews of special exhibits in museums and other sites, descriptions of new developments and academic programs, news of the society. The April number carries the important annual *Current Bibliography in the History of Technology* (it began with the one for 1962), a classified and briefly annotated listing of books, articles, pamphlets, and other publications. The number of book reviews has been increasing steadily; now, there are usually 20-30 per issue, covering books in all languages. The reviews, all signed and critical, vary in length, but average about 700 words. An important journal for courses in the history of science, economic history and social history.

62-25340

VICTORIAN Studies. *see* GENERAL

WILLIAM AND MARY QUARTERLY.   v. 1, 1892;   3rd. ser., v. 1, 1944-

Quarterly.   Williamsburg, Va. $8.00

"A Magazine of early American history," it is published by the Institute of Early American History and Culture in Williamsburg, the purpose of which is to further "study, research, and publications bearing upon American History approximately to the year 1815." The articles, 3 or 4 an issue, are scholarly and mostly quite long, and, unlike the first two series, which focused on Virginia history, cover all aspects. of early America, with particular emphasis on political history. "Notes and Documents" contain shorter articles and texts of documents that have either been newly discovered or have acquired some new significance. A section that makes pleasant browsing is "Trivia," containing short whimsical, humorous, or just plain odd selections from early American newspapers, diaries, and other sources, all contributed by readers. The review section generally covers 15 to 20 titles; the reviews are signed and critical, averaging about 750 words. An important journal for the study of U.S. colonial history.

Indexed in: S.S.H.I.   5-32195 rev. 2

AMERICAN DIETETIC ASSOCIATION.   JOURNAL.   v. 1, 1925-

Monthly.   Chicago, Ill. $18.00

"Publishes reports of original research and other papers covering the broad aspects of dietetics, including nutrition and diet therapy, community nutrition, education and training, and administration." Usually 6 to 8 articles per issue, almost all under 3500 words, contributed by M.D.'s, public health officers, professors of dietetics, nutrition, or home economics, etc. Topics range widely from the very technical to those of general interest; a few issues from 1970 included such diverse articles as "Programmed Instruction for Nursing Students," "Food of College Students," "Vitamin A in Adult Diets," "Plasma Amino Acids." It will be used then, by those in a variety of fields, including educators, sociologists, psychologists, chemists, biologists, as well as those in the specific fields of diet and nutrition. "Association Section" carries news of the personnel, programs and activities of the ADA; "News Notes," of other organizations, state associations, and developments in the field, as well as full descriptions of recent pamphlets, booklets and government publications. The extensive monthly section, "Current Literature," contains full abstracts of relevant articles from about 80 periodicals in the medical, hospital, personnel, home economics, food chemistry and other fields, as well as nutrition. Book reviews appear irregularly, but in just about every other issue. Some 30 or 40 books a year are covered in signed and critical reviews, mostly 500-1000 words. An important journal in a field that has been of growing interest.

Indexed in: Bio.Ag.I.   27-10036

AMERICAN FABRICS.   no. 1, 1946-

Quarterly.   N.Y. $24.00

Primarily a trade journal for the textile and clothing industry, and unquestionably one of the most luxurious trade journals produced. Folio-size, colorful, typographically imaginative, it has the unique feature of many articles, features and advertisements containing swatches of the materials being discussed or displayed. Brief, well-illustrated articles on developments in fibers and textiles, their dyeing, weaving or spinning and the machines involved, the chemical processes used for man-made fibers, profiles of designers, weavers and artists in the field, on the business and marketing of textiles, and clothing. Of most academic interest are the studies in some depth of particular fabrics—their history, techniques, etc. "Directions in Fabric and Fashion" in each issue contains brief descriptions of new fabrics, blends and weaves, trends in clothing design, and other short features on the coming seasons. "The World of Textiles" contains news and commentary related to the textile industry throughout the world: personnel, meetings, exhibits, major construction, special projects, technical developments, etc. "Marketing Presentations" are really multi-page advertisements for particular companies, but prepared by the publishers.

Primarily for the student of textiles and fashions, the journal is also useful for those interested in graphic arts and weaving.

48-11592*

BETTER HOMES AND GARDENS.   v. 1, 1922-

Monthly.   Des Moines, Iowa. $4.00

Titled *Fruit, Garden and Home* until 1924, it was founded by E.T. Mere-
dith, a former Secretary of Agriculture and publisher of *Successful Farm-
ing. BH&G* became a success very quickly, reaching the million-circulation
mark by 1928, and since then, with only slight changes in emphasis, it has
remained this country's most popular home magazine, with a circulation
now of over 7 million. After World War II the space devoted to gardening
(and the size of "and Garden" in the title) decreased, while that given to
home building and improvement increased. Home and money management
have received more attention, and food preparation has received about the
same amount through the years. The emphasis throughout its history has
been practicality—hints for the handyman, home plans within the means
of its readers, attractive but sensible decorating ideas, edible and simple
recipes.

Some libraries may also want *American Home* (v. 1, 1938- $4.00)
which has much the same approach, though is probably not as substantial.
It is published monthly, except for bi-monthly issues in January/February
and July/August. Libraries in the West should certainly consider—perhaps
in preference to either—*Sunset*, "the magazine of western living," (v. 1,
1898- $3.95) which began as a promotional publication of the Southern
Pacific Railroad; it was only after 1928, when it was sold to L.W. Lane,
that it became really popular, and today, by catering to regional interests
in foods, housing, travel and recreation, and gardening, it has achieved
a circulation of about a million. All three are indexed in the *Readers'
Guide.*

Indexed in: R.G.   27-6944

CHANGING TIMES.   v. 1, 1947-

Monthly.   Washington, D.C. $7.00

Published by the Kiplinger organization (best known for its Washington
Letter) and originally titled (through April, 1949) the *Kiplinger Magazine,*
it contains articles, written by its staff, on matters of interest to the
consumer, the homeowner, the taxpayer, and the parent, the emphasis
on ways of economizing and managing finances. Representative articles
might include: "Jobs Where the Action Is"—on the possibilities of careers
in municipal public service; "Which Encyclopedia Should You Buy?";
"Last Call to Check the Furnace"; "Investments That Protect You Against
Inflation"; "Colleges That Still Have Room"—an annual survey, run since
1959, on colleges that have openings; "Moving—It's Tough on the Kids";
"The Ins and Outs of a Lease." These are readable and brief and not very
thorough, but they almost always mention sources of additional information. Regular features include: "Things to Write For"—recent pamphlets,
reports and circulars from government and business; "Paperback Bookshelf"—a listing with brief descriptions, of recent works, mostly non-
fiction; others, answering questions from readers, describing new developments in products and services, etc. Because of its lack of depth, it has
a limited use for courses in home economics; it is mostly of general
interest.

Indexed in: R.G.   49-53787

CHILD Development. *see* PSYCHOLOGY

CHILD DEVELOPMENT ABSTRACTS AND BIBLIOGRAPHY.   v. 1, 1927-

3 nos./yr.   Chicago, Ill. $10.00

Issued by the Society for Research in Child Development. Consists of two major parts: the first, and by far the larger, is a section of rather full abstracts (often 400 words or more) of articles from about 140 American and foreign journals covering all aspects—medical, physiological, psychological, sociological, educational, etc.—of child development; the second, Book Notices, contains non-critical summaries (generally between 150 to 300 words) of important books published during the period covered. These are mostly technical and professional works; selected non-technical materials are also indexed. List of other books received. Each volume now contains about 800 abstracts and 100-150 book notices. There is an author index in each issue and a subject index for the year. Essential where any advanced work is done in this area.

Indexed in: Ment.Hlth.B.R.I.   46-31872

*CHILDREN.   v. 1, 1954-

Bi-monthly.   Washington, D.C. $2.00

"An interdisciplinary journal for the professions serving children," it is published by the federal Children's Bureau and is successor to *The Child*. Contains usually 5 or 6 fairly basic but reliable articles by case workers, professors, physicians, psychologists, and federal and local agency officials on all aspects of the health, welfare and development of children, with emphasis on children handicapped by their environment or by their physical or mental condition. "Here and There" reports news and developments in the field; a short listing of "Guides and Reports" with brief annotations; "In the Journals" summarizes a few recent articles of especial interest; "Book Notes" supplies uncritical annotations of a small number of publications; "Films on Child Life" describes new films but offers no evaluations. Listing, with brief descriptions, of recent federal publications. Useful for students in social work and child psychology. A depository item.

Indexed in: Ed.I.   56-43779
           P.A.I.S.

*CONSUMER REPORTS.   v. 1, 1936-

Monthly.   Mt. Vernon, N.Y. $8.00

Published by Consumers Union, a nonprofit organization founded "to provide consumers with information and counsel on consumer goods and services, to give information on all matters relating to the expenditure of the family income, and to initiate and to cooperate with individual and group efforts seeking to create and maintain decent living standards." Each issue contains usually 5 to 7 thoroughly illustrated articles, each

of which describes and rates a consumer product—clothing, food, automobiles and equipment, home appliances, cosmetics and drugs, etc. (even
metronomes)—based on laboratory tests, controlled use tests, panels of
consumers, experts, or a combination of these. Brand names are given,
items rated "Best Buy," "Acceptable" or "Not Acceptable" on the basis
of price and quality, and advantages or deficiencies in specific products—
quality, safety features, durability, etc.—carefully noted. An issue in the
Spring is devoted to an in-depth report of the new model automobiles.
In addition to these product tests, there are frequent articles useful for
other family expenditures: how to choose a doctor, shopping for insurance, government aids for consumers, borrowing money, etc. Also articles on health and medicine; legislation affecting consumers; economics
for consumers; gardening and household hints, etc. Brief but good record
reviews; movies are not reviewed but rated by polling readers and summarizing results. The December issue is the *Annual Buying Guide,* a
compendium of previous ratings. Important for home economics study,
but will also be used frequently by faculty families and married students
in guiding their purchases.

Similar in purpose, but not as thorough or broad in scope, is *Consumer Bulletin* (v. 1, 1931- $8.00). Published by Consumers' Research,
Inc., and earlier titled *Consumers' Research Bulletin*, it was actually
the progenitor of *Consumer Reports.* In 1936, however, because of a
labor dispute, the organization split, Consumers Union was founded, and
in a short while outdistanced the original. Both publications will probably be used, though the *Reports* is to be preferred.

Indexed in: P.A.I.S.   43-33888 rev.*
          R.G.

FORECAST FOR HOME ECONOMICS.   v. 1, 1956-

9 nos. (Sept. to May/June)   N.Y. $6.00

Published by Scholastic Magazines, Inc., it is actually the Teacher Edition
of *Co-ed,* a magazine for high school students in home economics. Each
issue of *Forecast* includes the entire issue of *Co-ed,* which contains articles
on fashion, foods, health, personal finances, and home furnishings, in
addition to some fiction and other miscellaneous features; *Forecast* contains articles on these subjects, written for the teacher, and frequently
keyed to an article in that issue of *Co-ed.* A regular feature, as a matter
of fact, is one titled "Suggestions for Using This Issue of *Co-ed* in the
Classroom." Other articles and features for the teacher of home economics.
Especially useful for the practicing home economics teacher and the student of home economics, it may also be of interest to other coeds.
Another journal that is important where there are courses in home economics is *What's New in Home Economics* (v. 1, 1936- $7.00). It also
contains brief, well-illustrated articles on all aspects of home economics,
including the teaching of it. Some very brief, uncritical reviews.

Indexed in: Ed.I.   57-34510

HOUSE AND GARDEN.   v. 1, 1901-

Monthly.   N.Y. $7.00

Originally a modest publication devoted to home styles and horticulture,
it was purchased in 1909 by Conde Nast, who gave the editorship to

Richardson Wright, a newspaper journalist, gourmet and *bon vivant*. Under Wright, who remained editor from 1914 to 1949, *House and Garden* assumed its present tone, that is, articles and features emphasizing the most fashionable (if not the latest) styles, developments and trends in home architecture, furniture and decorating, gardening, leisure activities, travel, foods and wine, etc., all aimed at readers who are, or yearn to be in the upper income brackets. Its success really came after World War II, with the growing affluence of American society and the move to the suburbs.

The articles are all well written, beautifully and profusely illustrated, usually in color. A backfile is useful to show the changing style of life, but the magazine's bulk, due to the heavy proportion of advertising pages, makes the cost of binding and storage fairly expensive for most college libraries.

Very similar in content and format—in fact, almost interchangeable with it—is *House Beautiful* (v. 1, 1896- $6.00). Both titles will be browsed through fairly regularly, and both are indexed in the *Readers' Guide,* but the cost of binding and storage, weighed against the few articles of real academic usefulness make their permanent acquisition questionable.

Indexed in: R.G.   12-16045 rev.

INTERIORS.   v. 1, 1888-

Monthly.   N.Y. $9.00

Beginning as *The Upholsterer,* it added *and Interior Decorator* in November, 1934, then left it just as *Interior Decorator* the following month; it changed to its present title in 1940. It is published for "interior designers, architects and industrial designers, who offer interior designing services, and the interior decorating departments of retail stores." Each issue features the interior design for a clientele group—i.e., restaurants and hotels, offices and banks, private homes, retail stores, etc.—or some special event or project, or the work of an outstanding designer or a survey of the year's work in residential design; also articles on design theory and trends, clientele relationships, etc. Regular features include: news of exhibits, awards, personnel; "Market" includes photographs and descriptions of new products and lines; the December issue includes a classified listing of all the manufacturers and suppliers who advertised during the year. A section on books contains a review or two, usually about 300-500 words; a few other books are briefly noted. Profusely illustrated, sometimes in color. The most important journal in the field of interior design, it will be useful to art students and for home economics courses on decoration.

Indexed in: Art I.   45-44542

*JOURNAL OF HOME ECONOMICS.   v. 1, 1909-

Monthly (except July-Aug.)   Washington, D.C. $12.00

Official organ of the American Home Economics Association. Articles on all aspects of home economics: food and nutrition, careers in the field, home economics education, government activities, family economics, child development, family relations, housing and household equipment, institutional administration, textiles and clothing, etc. Most of these are fairly short, even those reporting the results of research. Full coverage of the Association's activities, programs, and meetings, with one number devoted entirely to the annual meeting. A large number of departments and regular features. "Washington News," from various agencies, appears in each issue. There has been an annual listing, arranged by subject, of *Titles of Theses* (masters' and doctors') since 1964; from 1949 through 1963 it carried abstracts of selected doctoral dissertations. Each issue also carries a section of periodical abstracts, arranged by subject. Several reviews of books per issue; they are signed, but usually around 200-300 words. "From the Editor's Mail" contains brief descriptions of new free or inexpensive materials—commercial brochures, government documents, university studies.

Indexed in: B.R.D.   10-34271 (rev. '20)
     Ed.I.
     P.A.I.S.

*JOURNAL OF MARRIAGE AND THE FAMILY. v. 1, 1939-

Quarterly. Minneapolis, Minn. $12.00

Published by the National Council on Family Relations, an organization formed "to advance the cultural values now principally served through family relations for personality development and the strength of the nation" by bringing together those in research, teaching and professional service. The first two volumes appeared under the title *Living*; in 1941 the title became *Marriage and Family Living*, and in 1964 the present title was adopted. In 1952 came a shift in emphasis: whereas it had previously published speeches and reported professional news and developments, it began to emphasize research, education for marriage and family living, and articles on marriage and family counseling.

In 1967, with the NCFR's acquisition of the journal *Family Life Coordinator* which it retitled *Family Coordinator* (see below), it again changed its character. Articles relating to family life education, counseling and other applied areas of marriage and the family were dropped, as was the department, "Teacher Exchange for High Schools and Colleges," which described new teaching materials and provided space for teachers to share approaches, methods, problems and questions. That same year a new "International Department" was added. It contains usually 4 or 5 articles, similar to those in the rest of the journal, but about the family in other countries. The main part of the journal consists of 10-12 research articles, rarely more than 10 pages in length, and often just 3 or 4, on all aspects of family life and marriage, child rearing, marital and family adjustment, sex attitudes and behavior, etc., and on research methodology for those topics. Each article is preceded by an abstract. Occasionally, issues are devoted to single topics—Government Programs and the Family, American Adolescents in the Mid-Sixties—and articles in these tend to be longer. Except for the special issues, there is a book review section with usually 6 to 10 signed reviews, averaging about 700 words.

The basic journal in the field, it is just as important for sociology as it is for home economics.

Libraries where there are strong departments in home economics or social work, especially in institutions training teachers for those fields, should also probably take the other NCFR quarterly, *Family Coordinator* (v. 1,

1952- $5.00) which, when it became an NCFR publication in 1967, took over the articles and features relating to family life education, counseling and other applied areas of the field.

Indexed in: Ment.Hlth.B.R.I.   42-51034 rev.*
            S.S.H.I.

JOURNAL OF NUTRITION.   v. 1, 1928-

Monthly.   Bethesda, Maryland. $30.00

Official organ of the American Institute of Nutrition, it contains "concise reports of original research bearing on the nutrition of any organism." Usually about 15 to 20 articles per issue, contributed by clinicians, faculty members and research workers in government, industry and institute laboratories from this country and abroad. Studies range over all areas of animal and human nutrition, and all are very technical. Carries annual proceedings of the AIN. Supplements, consisting of those articles too long for inclusion in regular numbers, appear occasionally. No book reviews. An important journal for all those interested in nutrition, its high technical level makes it appropriate only for advanced students and faculty.

Indexed in: Bio.Ag.I.   33-14482 rev. 2

McCALL'S.   v. 1, 1870-

Monthly.   N.Y. $3.95

This, along with *Ladies' Home Journal* (v. 1, 1883- $4.00) and *Good Housekeeping* (v. 1, 1885- $5.00), comprise the "big three" of women's magazines. None of them is essential for the college library, but all will be used by browsers (in coeducational institutions). A backfile of the *Ladies' Home Journal* is especially useful for American social history: when Edward Bok was editor, from 1889 to 1919, it became one of the country's most popular and influential periodicals, and under the editorship of Beatrice and Bruce Gould, from 1935 to 1962, its circulation was double the combined total of *McCall's* and *Good Housekeeping.* In recent years, however, *McCall's* has improved greatly, containing much more sophisticated material than it used to, and its circulation has surpassed *LHJ.* Well-known authors, public officials and experts in many fields write for all three journals, and the attention to controversial issues has significantly increased, but still their major appeal is the story or article with which the homemaker—better educated than previous generations of readers, to be sure—can identify. The household hints, articles on decorating, fashions and beauty, on entertaining and home management, as well as the recipes, make the journals useful for home economists, but their mass appeal is based on the other articles and fiction, much of which is good. Because they are indexed, there may be some call for them, but most academic libraries will not need to bind them, or even keep them for any length of time.

Indexed in: R.G.   CA 6-1199 unrev'd

*MADEMOISELLE.   v. 1, 1935-

Monthly.   N.Y. $6.00

Contains articles, stories and features intended for an audience of college-educated women, aged from 18 to 25. The articles are on topics and personalities of current interest, especially in the areas of literature and the arts, careers, travel, fashions, personal care, colleges and universities, and social concerns, with an emphasis of course on those relating to women. Frequently by eminent personalities and authorities, these are always well written and often incisive, but generally lack real significance. The fiction is good, much by well known writers, but sometimes by new ones, and the interviews with writers are very useful. Regular features include a number of departments, but of special interest is the August College Issue, which contains the annual prize-winning stories, poetry and photographs, plus articles and fashions relating to colleges. All contributions are thoroughly illustrated.

The current issues of *Mademoiselle* will be used heavily (except, of course, in all-male schools). The back issues will be used to some extent, especially where trends in home economics and fashion are studied, but for most college libraries, binding is probably not essential.

The major difference between *Mademoiselle* and both *Vogue* (v. 1, 1892-$10.00) and *Harper's Bazaar* (v. 1, 1867- $6.50) is that the latter two are aimed at an older and wealthier audience. There is still much attention to topics that are "in," but a special emphasis is given to gracious dining, entertaining and travel, and the general tone, including the famous fashion photos, is more sophisticated. The fiction and articles are often by important writers, and there is some poetry, almost all by established poets.

Both *Vogue* and *Harper's Bazaar* are, for academic libraries, at least, probably more important for their backfiles than currently, especially where there is much interest in the changing role of women and in their fashions. A current subscription will be useful since both are indexed in the *Readers' Guide,* but the space and binding costs they entail make them of marginal value for most college libraries.

Indexed in: R.G.   41-20669

*PARENTS' MAGAZINE & BETTER FAMILY LIVING.   v. 1, 1926-

Monthly.   N.Y. $5.00

Contains brief, illustrated, practical articles on all aspects of family life with an emphasis on children—their emotional and physical health, education, feeding, etc., from newly-born through adolescence. Family relationships that are crucial to the child's personality—marital problems, sibling rivalry, etc.—also receive much attention. Contributors are frequently national figures—physicians, psychiatrists, educators, even politicians writing about matters of social concern. The September issue generally focuses on education; the November issue, on health. Sections of each issue are: Child Rearing and Family Health (the largest section); Family Food, including recipes and menus, with special attention to nutrition and ease of preparation; Family Home—items on furnishing and decorating; Family Fashion; Family Fun, including the "Family Film Guide," a "complete guide to current films rated for adults, teenagers, and children." Most issues contain 4 or 5 brief reviews of children's books plus a longer review or two (up to 500 words or so) of books of interest to parents.

Because of its wide readership, the down-to-earth quality of its articles, and the eminence of many contributors, it is one of the best journals for studying contemporary thinking about family life and child development.

Indexed in R.G.   30-5589 rev. 2*

APPLIED SCIENCE & TECHNOLOGY INDEX. v. 1, 1958-

Monthly (except Aug.)   N.Y.   Service basis

One of the two indexes which replaced the *Industrial Arts Index* in 1958, it is a subject index to (currently) 227 periodicals "in the fields of aeronautics, automation, chemistry, construction, earth science, electricity and electronics, environmental science, food technology, industrial and mechanical arts, machinery, petroleum, physics, telecommunications, thermodynamics, transportation, and related subjects." An annual bound cumulation. For many liberal arts college libraries, it is not essential: many of the periodicals covered are trade journals, and, to satisfy general readers, enough of the other titles are duplicated in the *Readers' Guide,* and for institutions with strong science or engineering departments it cannot supply the depth or breadth of the professional abstracting and indexing services. It is primarily useful for public or special libraries and for institutions that cannot afford the specialized indexes and abstracts.

14-5408 rev 2

*ART INDEX.   v. 1, 1929-

Quarterly.   N.Y.   Service basis

Indexes about 125 foreign and domestic periodicals "in the fields of archaeology, architecture, art history, arts and crafts, fine arts, graphic arts, industrial design, interior decoration, photography and films, planning and landscape design, and related subjects." It also includes museum bulletins and periodicals on museology. Indexing form is similar to the other Wilson indexes, except that both book reviews and illustrations are separately covered: book reviews are indexed both under the author reviewed and the subject; illustrations and reproductions that are parts of articles are indexed only under entries for that article; illustrations not a part of an article are indexed under the artist's name. Bound annual cumulative volumes (biennial before November, 1967; triennial before November, 1955). An important index, even where art is not especially strong because of its coverage of film and photography journals, craft magazines, and architectural periodicals.

1-7513 rev.

B.A.S.I.C. *see* BIOLOGY

*BIBLIOGRAPHIC INDEX.   v. 1, 1938-

3 nos./yr.   N.Y.   Service basis

Under subjects, it indexes recently published bibliographies of 40 or more items, including those published separately as books or pamphlets, and those appearing as parts of books, pamphlets, and articles, both in English and foreign languages. About 1700 periodicals of all types—from the most general to the most technical—are regularly examined. All types of books are also examined, so that the coverage is quite extensive. Cumulated annually into bound volumes; from 1960-68, the permanent bound cumulations each covered 3 years; earlier permanent volumes covered even more. A basic reference title for every academic library, it should be better known by students.

46-41034 rev.*

*BIOGRAPHY INDEX.   v. 1, 1946-

Quarterly.   N.Y.   Service basis

Covers biographical material appearing in the approximately 1700 periodicals indexed in all other Wilson indexes, in current books of individual or collective biography in the English language, obituaries (of national interest) from the *New York Times,* and incidental biographical material. It covers all kinds of material—autobiography, diaries, fiction, poetry, juvenile literature, etc.—and all countries and periods. Portraits are indicated. Arranged by names of subjects, giving for each the full name, dates, nationality and occupation or profession. The latter part of each number also contains an index by profession or occupation. Bound annual and permanent 3-year cumulations. In many instances perhaps the best place to start a search for biographical information, it is a basic reference item for all libraries.

47-6532 rev.*

BIOLOGICAL & AGRICULTURAL INDEX.   v. 1, 1916-

Monthly (except Sept.)   N.Y.   Service basis

A Wilson publication, it is the successor to the *Agricultural Index* (whose volume numbering it continued, beginning with volume 50), though the list of periodicals covered is quite different. A subject index to about 150 periodicals in the fields of agricultural economics, agricultural engineering, agriculture and agricultural research, animal husbandry, antibiotics, bacteriology, biochemistry, biology, botany, dairying and dairy products, ecology, entomology, feeds, forestry and conservation, genetics, horticulture, microbiology, mycology, nutrition, poultry, soil science, veterinary medicine, and zoology—pretty evenly divided, in other words, between agriculture and biology. More useful for biology than its predecessor, it is less useful for agriculture, since the publications most important to that field—the reports, bulletins and circulars from the various government and university research bureaus and experimental stations—are no longer covered. However, since almost all of the articles important in biology covered here are also in *Biological Abstracts,* college libraries taking the latter may not feel this index is essential. For libraries that cannot afford *Biological Abstracts,* however, this may suffice. Cumulates in annual bound volumes.

17-8906 rev. 3

BRITISH HUMANITIES INDEX. v. 1, 1962-

Quarterly. London. $36.00

Published by the Library Association, it superceded the *Subject Index to Periodicals,* which had existed since 1915 (except for 1923-25). Covers about 375 British periodicals in the social sciences and humanities, including such major general titles as the *Spectator,* the *Listener, Contemporary Review, TLS,* etc., plus many of the important scholarly journals, as well as a number of historical and archaeological magazines of strictly local interest. Lead articles from the *Times,* the *Guardian* and the *Observer* also are listed, adding to its usefulness. However, the indexing does not cover poetry or fiction, film, book, theater or art reviews (except for some review-essays), nor briefer items. It is, in other words, much less thorough than the Wilson indexes.

The quarterly numbers contain subject listings only; annual bound cumulated volumes (included in the cost) contain two sets of listings—one by subjects and the other by author.

A very useful index for most academic libraries since it covers so many important British journals not in the standard American indexes.

63-24940

BUSINESS PERIODICALS INDEX. v. 1, 1958-

Monthly (except July). N.Y. Service basis

A subject index to about 170 periodicals "in the fields of accounting, advertising and public relations, automation, banking, communications, economics, finance and investments, insurance, labor, management, marketing, taxation, and specific businesses, industries and trades." Together with the *Applied Science and Technology* (q.v.) it succeeded in 1958 the *Industrial Arts Index,* the coverage of which was then divided between them. Not only trade periodicals are covered, but publications of professional associations and some government publications. There are quarterly unbound, and annual bound cumulations. Of basic importance for students of business administration, it is also useful for economists, but for institutions without a major in business administration the field is sufficiently covered by other indexes.

58-12645

CHRISTIAN SCIENCE MONITOR INDEX. 1960-

Monthly. Ann Arbor, Mich. $15.00 (with annual cumulation)

A subject index to all 4 editions of the *Monitor*—the Eastern, Western, Midwestern, and London & Overseas (this last indexed since 1967). "Some sports and feature articles, also metaphysical articles have not been indexed. Non-fiction and some fiction book reviews are indexed by subject or by author under literature." The annual or monthly numbers alone are $10.00 each. Libraries should try to have the files of the *Monitor* along with the index; it should be pointed out that the edition microfilmed is the Eastern edition. Privately compiled, the format is a bit difficult to read (especially in the annual) and the indexing is not always as helpful as it might be, but because the *Monitor* is such a superb resource for undergraduate research, with excellent background articles and almost unimpeachable objectivity, the *Index* is an important reference tool.

64-1455 (for annual cumulation)

*CUMULATIVE BOOK INDEX.   v. 1, 1928-

Monthly (except Aug.)   N.Y.   Service basis

A current "world list of books in the English language" wherever they are. Government documents, pamphlets, maps, sheet music and ephemera are excluded. The index combines author, title and subject entries; also numerous translator and illustrator entries. Information for each title includes: price, publisher, binding (other than cloth), paging, edition, date of publication and LC card and SBN numbers where available. Beginning in 1969, when one title is issued by two or more publishers, each is treated as a separate entry. Also in that year, books without price information began being listed. This meant a substantial increase in the number of items listed. An appendix contains a directory of publishers and distributors, very useful because it is inclusive and up-to-date. Bound semi-annual and, since 1957, permanent two-year cumulations. (Earlier permanent volumes covered four to six years). Even though other bibliographical tools have become much more useful and have, to some extent, reduced the reliance on *C.B.I.*, it still provides enough unique services for both acquisitions and reference to be regarded as indispensable for every library.

28-26655

CURRENT INDEX TO JOURNALS IN EDUCATION.   v. 1, 1969-

Monthly.   N.Y. $41.50

A companion to ERIC's *Research in Education* (q.v.), it covers the journal literature in the field. Over 500 periodicals are covered, a number of them unrelated to education, but on occasion carrying articles important to some area of education—for example, *Architectural Record, Journal of Clinical Psychology, Journal of Urban Law, New York Review of Books.* Each issue consists of 3 major sections: 1) Subject Index, using the ERIC Descriptors as subject headings; 2) Author Index; 3) Main Entry Section, listing the articles, arranged by descriptor groups, with complete bibliographical information and including the appropriate descriptors and a brief descriptive annotation. It is this feature which gives *CIJE* special usefulness, doubling as an abstract journal as well as an index. This, plus its comprehensive coverage of journals in the field and selective coverage outside the field, make *CIJE* an important reference tool where there is any work done in education. A semiannual cumulation of the author and subject index is issued, and an annual cumulation of all three sections. Many libraries will want it instead of *Education Index*; libraries that can afford both should keep them side-by-side.

75-7532

DISSERTATION ABSTRACTS INTERNATIONAL.   v. 12, 1952-

Monthly.   Ann Arbor, Mich. $75.00

"A monthly compilation of abstracts of doctoral dissertations submitted to University Microfilms by more than 250 cooperating institutions in the United States and Canada." The "International" was added to its title in 1969 "to reflect the projected . . . addition of dissertations from European universities." Since July, 1966, it has been divided into two sections, A (Humanities and Social Sciences) and B (Science and Engineering) which may be subscribed to separately. In each section, the arrangement is by subject field, then by author. Each listing includes author, title, university, degree approved, the abstract (generally 450 to 700 words), order number, prices for microfilm and Xerox copies, number of pages. Keyword title and author indexes for each issue, and cumulative indexes for each volume; the keyword title index began in July, 1969, and replaced the subject index which used LC subject headings. Volumes 1 to 11, 1935-51, were known as *Microfilm Abstracts,* and had a much more limited scope, but now it is an important reference tool, especially where students or faculty are doing research.

Indexed in: Music I.   39-21214 rev. 2*

*EDUCATION INDEX.   v. 1, 1929-

Monthly (except July-Aug.)   N.Y. $18.00

"An author subject index to educational material printed in the English language. Although primarily a periodical index, proceedings, yearbooks, bulletins, monographs and material printed by the United States Government are included. Subject areas indexed include administration; pre-school, elementary, secondary, higher and adult education; teacher education; counseling and guidance; curriculum and curriculum materials. Subject fields indexed include the arts, applied science and technology, audio-visual education, business education, comparative and international education, exceptional children and special education, health and physical education, languages and linguistics, library and information science, mathematics, psychology and mental health, religious education, social studies, and educational research relative to areas and fields indexed." Some 240 publications are regularly covered. Book reviews are indexed, but all under the heading "Book Reviews."

From July, 1961 through June, 1969, items were indexed by subject only and there were almost no entries for anything but periodical articles nor were book reviews covered. The resumption of the pre-1961 indexing policy was a most welcome one, and the index is more useful than ever, essential in every academic library. Quarterly unbound cumulations, and bound annual cumulations.

30-23807

*ESSAY AND GENERAL LITERATURE INDEX.   v. 1, 1934-

Semi-annual.   N.Y. $20.00

An index to essays and articles contained in collections of essays and miscellaneous works. In 1969, 203 volumes, containing 3,410 essays and articles in all disciplines, were indexed. Lists authors, subjects and some titles in a dictionary arrangement, with copious cross references. The books indexed, which are chosen by a large group of consultants, are listed in each issue; this list, which is also issued separately month-by-month, is useful as a buying guide. Because the *Essay and General Literature Index* makes available so many important shorter essays and articles—biographical, critical, historical, literary, etc., items that would really otherwise be almost impossible to find—it should be in every library and should be better known by students and faculty. Annual bound cumulations with five-year final volumes.

34-14581

INDEX TO LATIN AMERICAN PERIODICALS; HUMANITIES AND SOCIAL SCIENCES.   v. 1, 1961-

Quarterly.   Metuchen, N.J. $25.00

Prepared by the Columbus Memorial Library of the Organization of American States, it indexes some 110 periodicals in the social sciences and humanities published throughout Latin America in Spanish, Portuguese or English. Beginning with volume 3, the structure has been "an alphabetical list of subject entries as the main body of information, coordinated by cross references, under which pertinent articles are grouped and numbered progressively." Also an author index. About 6-7000 items are listed per year.

Because it covers the leading Latin American periodicals, many of which are not covered elsewhere (at least for several years) it is a very useful item for all larger libraries, and essential for those where all or parts of Latin America receive special attention.

63-24514

LIBRARY LITERATURE.   v. 1, 1933-

Bi-monthly.   N.Y.   Service basis

An author and subject "index to materials in the field of library and information science as reflected in the curricula of library schools." Covers both foreign and domestic materials—about 175 periodicals, plus books, pamphlets, audio-visual materials and theses, as well as pertinent articles that have appeared in non-library periodicals which are indexed in other Wilson indexes. Through 1958, abstracts or digests of many theses and books, and some articles were carried. Book reviews are indexed only under the main entry. Beginning with 1969, each issue carries a list of "Selected Recent Accessions of the Clearinghouse for Library and Information Sciences of the Education Resources Information Center (ERIC/CLIS)" at the University of Minnesota. In 1970, issues began carrying a "Checklist of Monographs Cited for the First Time in Library Literature," a feature especially useful for library schools; the Checklists, however, are not cumulated in the permanent volume.

36-27468

*MONTHLY CATALOG OF UNITED STATES GOVERNMENT PUBLICA-TIONS. v. 1, 1895-

Monthly. Washington, D.C. $7.00

A current, practically complete bibliography of publications issued by all agencies of the federal government—about 18,000 items annually—including Congress, the Supreme Court, the Office of the President, as well as the administrative and regulatory agencies, bureaus, etc.; does not, however, include some mimeographed documents and titles printed outside the Government Printing Office. Items are arranged by issuing agency, and numbered consecutively through the year. Since 1951, periodicals and subscription publications have been listed separately—twice a year (in February and August) until 1960; in the February number only, since 1961.

Each listing includes complete bibliographical information, price, and ordering information when necessary, LC card number and Super-intendent of Documents classification number, and indicates whether or not a depository item. The December number contains a detailed index (to subjects, key words of titles, issuing agencies—but not authors) for the year; monthly indexes also since 1945. Each issue contains a "Pre-views" section, listing important titles before issuance, so pre-publication orders can be placed; also gives complete instructions for ordering.

A depository item, it is an essential item for every college library, whether or not it is a depository, and is invaluable for bibliographic, ordering, and reference purposes. Some libraries may also wish to receive the bi-weekly, free list, *Selected United States Government Publications* (1928-). This lists and annotates publications of more general interest; it is useful for calling attention to these items, both for the staff and for the public, and the lists themselves are not worth keeping very long.

4-18088

MONTHLY CHECKLIST OF STATE PUBLICATIONS. v. 1, 1910-

Monthly. Washington, D.C. $8.00

Prepared by the Exchange and Gift Division of the Library of Congress, it is "a record of State documents issued during the last five years which have been received by the Library of Congress." Arranged by State and by issuing agency, it includes two separate lists: one for mongraphs, monographs in series, and annual publications; the second, for periodicals, appears in the June and December issues, cumulating in the latter. Also it includes publications of associations of State official and of regional organizations, and, since 1960, a section listing library surveys, studies, manual and statistical reports. (A few categories of materials are not included: college and university catalogs, slip laws, loose-leaf additions, and certain ephemeral materials.) Information for each publication in-cludes price, issuing agency, LC card number, etc. There is an annual index to publications listed. Though not complete, its coverage has stead-ily improved (from about 3500 entries in 1910 to about 20,000 in 1969) and it is an important item for any library where there is any research in state government or activities. A depository item.

10-8924

MUSIC INDEX.   v. 1, 1949-

Monthly.   Detroit, Mich.   Bill Later.

"A subject-author guide to current music periodical literature," it indexes now about 250 periodicals, from all over the world. These are primarily in music—all areas and periods, including popular, folk and country music—but also in closely related fields, such as folklore and aesthetics, as well as a few general periodicals, such as the *Saturday Review* and the *New Yorker*; even *Dissertation Abstracts* is covered. In addition to the monthly issues there is an annual Subject Heading List which replaces the cross-references in the monthly issues; cross-references, however, are included in the annual cumulation. Book reviews are listed under "Book Reviews."

Publication is very late. The monthly issues appear about a year late, and the 1966 annual cumulation appeared only in early 1971. Nevertheless, even considering this along with its expense, it is an essential item for any library with a strong music collection, and a very desirable one for all other libraries where there is any work done in music, especially since the *Social Sciences & Humanities Index* no longer covers the major music journals, and only a few of the most popular ones are covered in the *Readers' Guide*.

50-13627 rev./MN

*NEW YORK TIMES INDEX.   v. 1, 1913-

Semi-monthly.   N.Y. $150.00 (with annual cumulation)

"Presents a condensed, classified history of the world as it is recorded day-by-day in the *New York Times*." Based on the Late City Edition (the one that is microfilmed), the news and editorial matter is summarized and entered under appropriate headings arranged alphabetically. Under these, detailed entries are arranged chronologically, and each entry is followed by a reference to the news story (giving date, page, and column of the paper) where it can be found. Frequently, the references contain enough information in them to obviate the need for looking up the original item. In 1965, the inclusion of some illustrations, especially charts, maps and diagrams, was begun.

Because of the *New York Times'* extensive coverage, its index is valuable as an index to current events generally, even to other newspapers. The semi-monthly issues alone are $87.50 per year; the annual alone is also $87.50. Having both is useful, but if only one can be afforded, the annual should be preferred. Most desirable, of course, is to have both services along with a file of the *New York Times* on microfilm. Its many advantages—the extensive news coverage, the provision of texts of many important speeches and documents, the reviews, the signed articles, the features and reporting of the cultural scene—make it as much a national newspaper as the country is likely to have, and though the cost is great ($475 per year altogether), the expenditure can easily be justified.

13-13458 rev. 2*

PHILOSOPHER'S Index. *see* PHILOSOPHY

*PUBLIC AFFAIRS INFORMATION SERVICE. BULLETIN. v. 1, 1915-

Weekly (bi-weekly, Aug.)   N.Y. $100.00 (includes weekly numbers, cumulated numbers, and bound cumulated annual)

"A selective subject list of the latest books, pamphlets, government publications, reports of public and private agencies and periodical articles, relating to economic and social conditions, public administration and international relations, published in English throughout the world." Covers an enormous number and assortment of titles; many entries have brief annotations or lists of contents. References to separate publications give buying and bibliographical information. Subject headings (the only entry form) unfortunately are not standardized with LC or Wilson indexes. Because of the extensive coverage, the preliminary sections are useful for other purposes: the "Key to Periodical References" for acquisitions information on periodicals that have started recently or may be difficult to find elsewhere; the "Directory of Publishers and Organizations" for hard-to-find addresses. Cumulated 5 times a year, the fifth cumulation being the annual bound volume.

For many libraries the 5 cumulated numbers (at $50) will be adequate, and for a few the annual volume alone (at $25) will suffice. But because *PAIS* covers such a variety of materials, serving as an index to books and government publications as well as periodical articles, every academic library should receive it on *some* basis, and should encourage students to become familiar with it.

NOTE: Now available only by membership.   16-920 (rev. '32)

*READERS' GUIDE TO PERIODICAL LITERATURE.   v. 1, 1900-

Semi-monthly (except monthly, July-Aug.)   N.Y.   Service basis

A dictionary index covering about 160 current American general and non-technical periodicals. Its value to academic libraries is now perhaps not as much, relatively, as it was before March, 1953, when many of the scholarly titles it had indexed were transferred to the *International Index*, now the *Social Sciences & Humanities Index*. Some of this value, however, was restored in February, 1968, when it added a number of titles especially useful for students—e.g., *American Imago, American Scholar, Chemistry, Film Quarterly, Physics Today, Trans-Action,* among others, and it should always be kept in mind that the *Readers' Guide* has always indexed many periodicals basic to any academic library and beyond scholarly reproach, such as the *Annals, Department of State Bulletin, Foreign Affairs, Yale Review, Science* and *Scientific American,* to say nothing of the solid, standard periodicals of news and comment and the arts. Because these, as well as the more popular periodicals, are so thoroughly indexed—and because so many students already know how to use it—the *Readers' Guide* should be in every library, and the titles covered in it carefully evaluated for subscription. Cumulated frequently with final, annual bound volumes.

6-8232

SCIENCE CITATION INDEX.   1961-

Quarterly.   Philadelphia, Pa. $2,550.00

A computer-produced index that is unique in many ways but especially in that it indexes footnotes and bibliographic references of articles (plus reviews, letters and corrections) in over 2000 scientific journals (all the natural and physical sciences, technology, and medicine, plus some social sciences) and U.S. and foreign patents. The assumption on which the index is based is that scientific research builds on previous research, so that related information can be found by tracing the research forward in time to subsequent papers related to the earliest paper, and this, of course, can be done fairly simply by using the footnotes. There are 5 sections: Citation Index, arranged by author; Patent Citation Index; Corporate Index; Source Index, which gives the complete bibliographic information for each item; Permuterm Subject Index, a subject index based on the titles of source articles. There is also a list of the journals covered, with geographical and subject breakdowns, and an index of anonymous articles.

Needless to say, it is not the easiest scientific reference tool to use. It is, however, not as difficult as it first appears, and the publisher offers a variety of printed, audio-visual and personal aids to help explain it. Unfortunately it is expensive, and because it offers a unique approach to searching the literature, does not mean that other expensive services (*Chemical Abstracts* or *Biological Abstracts,* for example) can be dispensed with. Once students do become accustomed to it—and it does not take long—they do make good use of it, and considering its thoroughness (it listed over 4 million articles in 1969) it should be considered by libraries where there is much emphasis on research and use of primary sources in the sciences.

63-23334

*SOCIAL SCIENCES & HUMANITIES INDEX.   v. 1, 1907-

Quarterly.   N.Y.   Service basis

An author and subject index to over 200 American, Canadian and British periodicals "in the fields of anthropology, archaeology and classical studies, economics, folklore, geography, history, language and literature, music, philosophy, political science, religion and theology, sociology, theater arts and many other periodicals of general scholarly interest." Known as the *International Index* until June, 1965, its title was changed to reflect its coverage which, until June, 1955, had included about 175 English and foreign language periodicals in pure science, psychology, and the humanities. The *Social Sciences & Humanities Index* is issued quarterly, with permanent annual volumes. As most of the journals indexed are the leading learned journals in the fields covered, no college library should be without this. Since it augments the *Readers' Guide* so well, students should learn to use this as easily as they do the other, and its list of periodicals indexed can well be used as a subscription guide.

17-4969

UNITED NATIONS DOCUMENTS INDEX.   v. 1, 1950-

Monthly (except July/Aug. combined)   N.Y. $25.00

Prepared by the Documentation Division of the UN Headquarters Library, it "lists and indexes all documents and publications of the United Nations—except restricted material and internal papers—and all printed publications of the International Court of Justice." Each issue consists of three sections: 1) a checklist of UN documents and publications, arranged by symbol and with complete bibliographical details; 2) a list of all documents received at the Library (not just those listed in section 1), a list of republished mimeographed documents, and a list of sales publications; 3) a combined author-subject index to the documents listed in section 1. Before 1963, documents and publications of the specialized agencies (FAO, ILO, WHO, etc.) were listed; beginning in 1963, these were dropped and the monthly issues have been superseded (eventually—publication is slow) by two separate annual cumulations, the *Cumulative Checklist* and the *Cumulative Index,* each issued in parts.

Even though a library may not receive many UN publications, the index is an important bibliographical tool for borrowing materials and should be available where there is much work done in international affairs.

(Note: In 1970, a computer-assisted index to UN documents and publications, *UNDEX,* was begun on an experimental basis. It is expected that it, along with supplementary indexes, also computer-produced, will eventually supersede the *United Nations Documents Index.*)

51-5008

VERTICAL FILE INDEX.   v. 1, 1932-

Monthly (except Aug.)   N.Y. $8.00

Known as the *Vertical File Service Catalog* through 1933. "A subject and title index to selected [current] pamphlets considered to be of interest to general libraries. It is not intended to be a complete list of all pamphlet material, nor does inclusion of a pamphlet constitute recommendation." Covers all fields, and all levels of sophistication, but is especially valuable for the social sciences. Most federal documents are excluded; state and local publications are listed. Entries are arranged by subject, then by title. For each is given pagination, publisher, series, publication date, kinds of illustrations, and price or conditions under which it may be obtained. Brief descriptive notes for many titles are useful in determining their bias and usefulness. A title index follows the subject listings.

Useful for locating ephemeral materials; careful consideration should be given, however, to how much servicing of the collection is necessary and how much use is made of it—in other words, whether or not the vertical file collection is worth the time. Also, since pamphlet material is listed in many other sources, this index, which is primarily useful for smaller libraries, may not be appropriate for many college libraries. Through 1964, annual cumulations were published; their discontinuance reduced even further the publication's utility.

45-40505

WALL STREET JOURNAL MONTHLY INDEX.   v. 1, 1961-

Monthly.   Princeton, N.J. $75 (for monthly issues only)

The *Wall Street Journal* has long been widely read by businessmen, but it has grown enormously in general readership in the last decade. This is due to its reliable reporting of economic trends and developments, of individual firms and businessmen, and on political and social matters affecting business. Its four regional editions also add to its popularity. It should, consequently, be familiar to every student of business or economics, who should also know of the existence of this *Index*, which makes the *Journal's* contents accessible. Each monthly index is in 2 parts: corporate news (including municipal bond news), and general news. The annual bound volume (also $75—together they cost $125) is also arranged this way. Users should keep in mind that the index is for the final Eastern Edition; other regional editions vary to some extent in paging and content.

An essential item (along with the microfilm of the newspaper, costing $100) where there is much work done on business, and an important one for any academic library that emphasizes public affairs.

59-35162

AMERICAN ARCHIVIST.   v. 1, 1938-

Quarterly.   Lawrence, Kans. $15.00

Published by the Society of American Archivists, it is concerned with
every aspect, type and level of archival work. The articles, of which
almost all are short to medium length, are by practicing archivists, and
are on the theory and history of archives, the processing of materials,
including classification and mechanical preservation, storage, services, etc.
Case studies of individual collections, from the local to international level,
are frequently carried. Regular departments include: an annual classified
bibliography, *Writings on Archives, Current Records and Historical Manuscripts*; signed, critical reviews, about 12 per issue, averaging about 500
words each; abstracts of articles on archival matters from foreign periodicals; news of personnel, organizations and programs; technical notes
about new products, processes and equipment, sometimes based on careful experimentation. An important publication for the practicing archivist, it also has much useful information for librarians in general.

Indexed in: Lib.Lit.   40-8025 rev.*
           P.A.I.S.

*AMERICAN LIBRARIES.   v. 1, 1970-

Monthly (bi-monthly, July-Aug.)   Chicago, Ill.   Membership

The "Bulletin of the American Library Association," it was so titled
through 1969. The change in title was accompanied by an improved format—larger, easier to read, more interesting layouts—but the journal has
remained essentially the same; if there is any difference, it is a reflection
of the change in the Association itself—that is, a greater involvement with
the troubling social and political issues of the day and increasing concern
that librarians stand up and be counted when these issues are discussed.
There are many regular columns and features: "Of Note" consists of
news of individuals, libraries, institutions, or organizations—their activities, publications, projects, appointments, retirements, etc.; "Intellectual
Freedom" contains news of community action, library situations, court
decisions, legislative activity, publication notices, statements, etc. all relating to the fight against censorship; "Memo to Members" consists of
news and notices from the ALA offices about its activities and organizations; "Aware," a feature beginning in June, 1969, announces and comments on new programs, demonstration projects and experiments—at all
levels, by all types of libraries; "Publications Checklist" includes pamphlets, books, bibliographies and other publications about or by libraries—
all briefly annotated. There are several important regular annual features:
the annual listings of Notable Books and of Notable Children's Books;
plans for the annual conference, with a tentative program, then a lengthy
report on the conference; also a report on the annual mid-winter conference. The November or December issue has generally been devoted to
organizational units and services of ALA, plus background information on
the Association and its activities.

In addition to all these features, a number of which are important for all
librarians, there are many articles on all aspects of the profession—on
buildings, administration, social responsibilities, public relations, unions,
information networks, etc. These vary widely in length and significance,
but they should at least be looked at by all librarians who consider them-

selves professional. An essential publication for every library and every librarian.

Indexed in: Lib.Lit.   70-21767
           P.A.I.S.
           R.G.

*BULLETIN OF BIBLIOGRAPHY.   v. 1, 1897-

Quarterly.   Boston, Mass. $10.00

Published by the F.W. Faxon Co., it was established "as a medium for the publication of studies in bibliographies, research, bibliographies, reading lists and articles in fields of related interest." The bibliographies, compiled by librarians, professors and other specialists, are in many fields, though those in literature are greatly predominant. An issue in 1969, for example, included bibliographies on Dylan Thomas, *Mutiny on the Bounty*, Perry Miller and Alain Robbe-Grillet. The formats vary from simple listings to critical bibliographical essays. An important regular section is *Births Deaths and Magazine Notes*, a record of new and changed titles, price and address changes, notices of special issues, and discontinued titles in the world of periodicals.

From 1912 to 1953 it was known as the *Bulletin of Bibliography and Dramatic Index*, the latter portion of the title deriving from the regular feature which, starting in 1909, indexed reviews and articles about the drama, actors, actresses, playwrights, etc., including references even to illustrations and portraits.

An important item for the reference collection since the bibliographies are mostly up to date and often cover subjects for which there are no, or at least no recent, bibliographic compilations.

6-8140 rev 2*

*COLLEGE AND RESEARCH LIBRARIES.   v. 1, 1939-

Bi-monthly (plus 11 monthly News Issues)   Fulton, Mo. $10.00

Official journal of the Association of College and Research Libraries, a division of A.L.A., it contains usually 4 or 5 articles an issue—mostly brief and sometimes including a symposium—on all aspects of college and university libraries: administration, buildings, personnel, book selection, budgeting, services, cooperation, systems analysis, etc. There are articles reporting the results of research, surveys of practices, reports on particular experiences, histories of libraries or collections, essays on the theory of academic librarianship, etc., with a great emphasis on "practical" articles. A useful semi-annual feature which began in 1952 is *Selected Reference Books of 19— ,* describing and evaluating recent titles; *New Periodicals of 19— ,* with descriptions of new periodicals but with little evaluation also appeared semi-annually, but was discontinued in 1967. Abstracts of documents, based on those prepared by the ERIC Clearinghouse for Library and Information Sciences, have appeared regularly since 1969.

In 1966 certain types of material that had been included in *C&RL* began to be carried in a monthly (except for a combined July/August) bulletin, *ACRL News*. These include "News From the Field," containing news of important acquisitions, awards, grants and scholarships, new buildings announcements, meetings and workshope, miscellaneous publications, etc.; personnel changes; other timely news and announcements; the classified advertisements.

The basic journal for academic libraries, it should be circulated and discussed by all college librarians and their staffs. Back files are often useful in working on a particular administrative or service problem.

Indexed in: B.R.D.   42-16492 rev.
           Lib.Lit.
           P.A.I.S.

HORN BOOK MAGAZINE.   v. 1, 1924-

Bi-monthly.   Boston, Mass. $7.50

Begun as an 18-page sheet published by a children's bookshop, it has come to be perhaps the most highly regarded source of reviews of children's books. Each issue contains three or four articles, on all aspects of children's literature—authors, illustrators, history, publishing, bookmaking, criticism, etc.—with many of them by well-known figures. The booklist section contains reviews of around 60 or 70 recommended books. Each review is done by one of the panel of experts, and in 100-200 words summarizes the story and gives some evaluation. The annual section, "Fanfare," in the October issue, carries a listing of especially recommended books of the previous year. The section, "Views on Science Books," a column with general comments as well as brief evaluations of specific titles, began in 1961 and was done until 1967 by Isaac Asimov. "Outlook Tower" reviews a small number of adult books of interest to teenagers. "The Horn Book League" is a department for children's own writing and drawing. "The Hunt Breakfast" contains news and comments on authors, awards, festivals, and the children's book world in general. The August issue contains the acceptance speeches of the winners of the Newbery and Caldecott Medals along with their biographies. Contains poetry and an occasional story, and a large number of illustrations. An essential item where are courses in children's literature or book selection, or where the library does much buying in the area.

Indexed in: B.R.D.   30-5988
           Lib.Lit.
           R.G.

JOURNAL OF LIBRARY AUTOMATION.   v. 1, 1968-

Quarterly.   Chicago, Ill. $15.00 or membership in the A.L.A.

The official publication of the Information Science and Automation Division of the American Library Association. Publishes articles in all fields of "research and development in library automation, including inter-library communications; research in information science directly related to libraries." Also included are articles on the history and teaching of these subjects. Each article is preceded by an abstract of less than 100 words. 4 to 6 articles per issue averaging about 4000 words per article. 3 to 6 signed, critical book reviews range from about 200 to 500 words in length. Essential for libraries that are involved (or thinking about involvement) with automation, it is important for librarians who want to keep up with developments and theory in the field.

Indexed in: Lib.Lit.   68-6437
           P.A.I.S.

JOURNAL OF THE AMERICAN SOCIETY FOR INFORMATION SCIENCE.
v. 1, 1950-

Bi-monthly.   Washington, D.C. $35.00

Titled originally *American Documentation*, its publisher, the American Documentation Institute, changed its name in 1968 to the American Society for Information Science, and the journal followed the change in 1970. During its first 10 years, most of the journal was devoted to techniques and information rather than to research, critical reviewing or state-of-the-art papers. With a new format in 1961, and the rapid growth of ADI, the journal became much more useful, and is now perhaps the leading journal in the field.

It contains articles on all aspects of the theory and practice of information science, from education for the field or its social implications to highly technical case studies and theoretical analyses, all written by specialists. Each article is preceded by an abstract. Also carries proceeding of the Society's annual meeting, and usually 4 to 6 book reviews, mostly 500-1000 words in length, but occasionally much longer.

An important journal for those interested in the information sciences and particularly systems analysis and other aspects relating to the use of computers; useful for all libraries since it frequently treats matters of everyday concern, such as filing, reference service and cataloging.

Indexed in: Lib. Lit.   A 51-10381

LIBRARY-COLLEGE JOURNAL.   v. 1, 1968-

Quarterly.   Norman, Okla. $10.00

Subtitled "a magazine of educational innovation," it is published by the Library-College Associates, a group devoted to promoting the idea of integrating the library and its resources into the process of higher education. This admirable objective may not be new, but the group's unique contribution is its willingness to suggest new and different, even radical, ways of promoting this end. Much of what is published in it is, in the view of many college librarians, impractical or trite, but there are frequently provocative suggestions and observations that are interesting and useful. Articles, by librarians, library science instructors, and college professors and administrators, are mostly brief, and are on all aspects of teaching and learning through the library. Regular sections include: "Innovations," news and descriptions of college programs and activities that are new and different, not just related to the library; "New Learning Resources," descriptions of materials, equipment and articles useful for educational innovation. One or two book reviews, usually 500-700 words long.

In 1971, *Omnibus*, a tabloid supplement to the *Library-College Journal*, becan publication. To be issued 4 times a year, it contains news items and stories about innovations and miscellaneous developments in higher education, much of it unrelated to libraries.

Every college librarian should at least look through the journal; while much of it is pedestrian, there is enough that is interesting and/or useful.

Indexed in: Lib.Lit.

NOTE: With the Fall, 1971 issue, the title was changed to *Learning Today*, and subtitled "an educational magazine of LIBRARY-COLLEGE thought."

*LIBRARY JOURNAL.   v. 1, 1876-

Semi-monthly (except monthly, July and Aug.)   N.Y. $10.00

Covers the entire field of library service. Articles are primarily on the practical aspects of librarianship though in recent years *LJ* has become more concerned with matters affecting the profession as a whole, with national programs and problems, and with controversial issues. In addition to the articles, there are a number of interesting and valuable regular features and departments. The "Calendar" lists national, regional, and state association meetings for the coming six months. News items on developments in the field—legislative, educational, major building and publication projects, etc. "People," listing major changes in position. "Professional Reading" contains signed, critical reviews, most from 300 to 400 words, of recent publications in library science. A "Checklist" describes recent free or inexpensive materials useful to library work. In 1967, the section "Magazines" began, listing and annotating new titles that are otherwise apt to be overlooked. "Buyers' Guide" describes new products and equipment. "On the Record" reviews new recordings, both spoken and musical. The classified "Book Reviews" section reviews a large number (over 5000 a year) of all types of books; the reviews, mostly by librarians, average about 200 words and evaluate the book for different types of libraries. Most are critical, but fewer are authoritative. An author-title index to the reviews appears bi-monthly. The want-ads are perhaps the most widely used job mart for librarians. Special numbers include the Spring, Summer and Fall Announcements issues, containing a classified listing of books to come, with brief descriptions. These numbers also contain biographical material and photographs of writers whose first novels are about to be published. There are also special issues on forthcoming Religious Books, Business, Technical and Scientific Books, Paperbacks, and Juveniles. One number carries articles on the A.L.A. convention city— its night life, restaurants, sights, etc., all very helpful; a number after the conference reports on its highlights. From September through May, the issue dated the 15th includes the *School Library Journal* (formerly *Junior Libraries*) which is also published and available separately. It is devoted to articles, features and reviews aimed at school and children's libraries.

The *Library Journal* is required professional reading. The wealth of news, features and articles—to say nothing of the many reviews and advertisements—make it the most useful single library publication, essential for even the smallest library.

Indexed in: B.R.D.   4-12654 rev.
          Lib.Lit.
          P.A.I.S.
          R.G.

LIBRARY Literature. *see* INDEXES

*LIBRARY RESOURCES & TECHNICAL SERVICES.   v. 1, 1957-

Quarterly.   Richmond, Va. $8.00

Formed by the union of the *Journal of Cataloging and Classification* and *Serial Slants, LRTS* is the official publication of A.L.A.'s Resources and Technical Services Division, which was also founded in 1957. It carries articles on all aspects of technical services—acquisitions, cataloging, serials, documents, binding, copying methods, etc., with staff members of university libraries the most frequent contributors. Many of the articles are practical presentations of recent developments or of descriptions of particular procedures. The Spring or Summer numbers review the year's work in the various fields, recapitulating trends and developments in each of the special areas. Contains news and reports of the Division. Beginning with the Summer, 1969 issue, carries ERIC/CLIS abstracts relating to technical services. The reviews evaluate books "on the basis of their meaning and contributions to the areas"of interest; there are generally 5 or 6 in most issues, signed and critical, usually from 600-1000 words. Though much of the information in *LRTS* is useful primarily to larger libraries, there is enough for the smaller library to make it essential reading for every librarian concerned with technical services.

Indexed in: B.R.D.   59-3198
            Lib.Lit.
            P.A.I.S.

*LIBRARY QUARTERLY.   v. 1, 1931-

Quarterly.   Chicago, Ill. $8.00

Established by, and still edited at the Graduate Library School of the University of Chicago, it contains generally 3 to 4 scholarly articles per issue with some emphasis on the historical, theoretical, and biographical aspects of bibliography and library service. One issue a year is devoted to proceedings of the annual conference of the Graduate Library School, each concerned with a theme of current concern—"Deterioration and Preservation of Library Materials," "Library Networks: Promise and Performance," and "Intellectual Foundations of Library Education" are a few recent ones. Since 1950, there has been an annual (recently, biennial) listing of *Theses and Reports Accepted by Graduate Library Schools in the United States and Canada.* Each issue contains an average of 20 or so excellent signed, critical reviews, mostly between 600 and 1000 words in length.

Though most of the articles are not "useful," there are enough that are; more important, perhaps, is the desirability of librarians being aware of the historical and theoretical underpinnings of their profession, and *LQ* is surely one of the best sources for this. An extensive backfile is not essential for most college libraries; a current subscription is.

Indexed in: B.R.D.   32-12448 (rev. '43)
            Lib.Lit.
            P.A.I.S.

*LIBRARY TRENDS.   v. 1, 1952-

Quarterly.   Urbana, Ill. $8.00

A publication of the University of Illinois Graduate School of Library Science, it "provides a medium for evaluative recapitulation of current thought and practice, searching for those ideas and procedures which hold the greatest potentialities for the future." Each issue, planned with an invited advisory editor, is devoted to one aspect of librarianship, ranging from "Manuscripts and Archives" to "Metropolitan Public Library Problems Around the World," from "Current Trends in Branch Libraries" to "Bibliography: Current State and Future Trends"—in other words, treating practical situations and theoretical issues, day-to-day operations and highly specialized materials. The invited articles, usually about 10 an issue, are by specialists, and almost all contain useful bibliographies or lists of references. Although many issues are not relevant to college libraries, a substantial number are; furthermore, the quality and content of the contributions make this of enough general interest to be required reading for any librarian who has more than just a journeyman's interest in the field.

Indexed in: Lib.Lit.   54-62638

LIBRARY OF CONGRESS INFORMATION BULLETIN.   v. 1, 1942-

Weekly.   Washington, D.C.   Free to educational or publicly-supported libraries.

Primarily a newsletter on the activities, public events, exhibits, publications, and personnel of the Library of Congress, it contains many items of interest to librarians in general. The listing and descriptions (often quite detailed) of LC's publications may suggest titles for purchase in reference or bibliography. Similarly, the section "Notes on Publications" describes selected recent works of reference and bibliography acquired by LC, many of which are not reviewed elsewhere for some time or not at all. "News in the Library World" reports on meetings, new buildings, collections, institutes and workshops, scholarships, special publications, etc., throughout the country. Finally, appendices report in detail the proceedings of meetings of national and international (and occasionally regional) organizations and associations of libraries, librarians, and related groups such as archivists, information scientists, area specialists, etc. These reports are often the best—indeed, sometimes the only—available.

A useful and inexpensive source for keeping up with a variety of activities and materials in the library world.

Indexed in: Lib.Lit.   51-3324

*NEWSLETTER ON INTELLECTUAL FREEDOM.   v. 1, 1952-

Bi-monthly.   Chicago, Ill. $5.00

Published by the Intellectual Freedom Committee of the American Library Association. Contains news and comments relating to "situations and incidents that threaten the freedom to read. More particularly, our reporting of news and comment on events will be directed mainly to matters affecting library policies and librarian's freedom of action," though this, of course, means it is also concerned with problems facing booksellers and educators. Most of the material consists of items from local newspapers, and reports and statements from individuals and groups. Since 1962, each issue contains a "Current Bibliography" of articles, pamphlets, and books on censorship and intellectual freedom. An inexpensive publication which every librarian should see, it also is useful in providing source material for papers on the subject.

Indexed in: Lib. Lit.   66-5042

QUARTERLY Journal of the Library of Congress. *see* GENERAL

*RQ.   v. 1, 1960-

Bi-monthly.   Chicago, Ill. $2.00

Official publication of the Reference Services Division of the American Library Association. According to a statement adopted by the Division in 1969, "The purpose of *RQ* is to disseminate materials of interest to reference librarians, bibliographers and others interested in the complexities of reference service, and to serve as a vehicle of communication with the Division's membership." Articles, mostly brief, on all aspects of the theory and practice of reference work, from the simple reference question to evaluation of bibliographical resources, including administration, public relations, government documents, service problems, etc. Features include: "The Exchange," contributors' reports on unsolved reference questions and—in later issues—their solutions; "Notes from RSD Headquarters," and a "Report by the RSD President"; "U.S. Government Documents," a column discussing problems in selecting and servicing documents, with frequent subject lists; "Research in Reference," commenting on articles, programs and reports; and short (100-200 words, usually) reviews or contents notes of about 40 reference books.

A slight publication before Fall, 1965, it now averages almost 100 pages per issue, and is essential reading for every reference librarian and for other librarians concerned with the development and improvement of reference services.

Indexed in: Lib.Lit.   77-23834

SPECIAL LIBRARIES.   v. 1, 1910-

Monthly (Bi-monthly May-Aug.)   N.Y. $12.50

Official journal of the Special Libraries Association. Contains general articles on the problems of development and organization of special libraries, on descriptions of types of libraries, and on library problems of particular interest to special librarians, but also of some general interest. Frequent bibliographies. Issues are occasionally devoted to a single topic. News of the Association, its chapters, and its membership is mostly in the regular section, "SLA News." "Vistas," a regular section, includes listings of publications of interest, a calendar of events, descriptions of institutes, information about new products, and other items of general interest. The September issue is devoted to the annual SLA convention and official reports. Book reviews now appear infrequently—at the most 2 or 3 per issue, usually 600-800 words; they are signed and critical.

The journal is of particular interest to libraries having specialized divisions or branches; but it is also useful to most academic libraries because of its concern with information technology and with the handling of special types of materials that many libraries have problems with acquiring and servicing, such as maps, scientific abstracts and indexes, government documents, etc. Because the authors of these articles do specialize in these materials, their opinions and practices are usually worth reading.

Indexed in: B.R.D.   11-25280
                Bus.Per.I.
                Lib.Lit.
                P.A.I.S.

UNESCO BULLETIN FOR LIBRARIES.   v. 1, 1947-

Bi-monthly.   N.Y. $4.00

"Originally conceived as a medium for helping war-damaged libraries to build up their collections. Gradually, however, it widened its scope to include articles and information on library development throughout the world. On the one hand, it has attempted to keep its readers abreast of the latest developments in library, bibliographical and related work; on the other hand, it has tried to assist newly developing countries in organizing their library services. The tremendous growth in importance of library and related services since the end of the Second World War can, to a certain extent, be traced in the pages of the first fifteen volumes of the *Bulletin*." Contains articles, most fairly brief, on libraries and on developments in library science throughout the world, with some emphasis on the work of Unesco and other international organizations and agencies in the fields of bibliography, publication, exchange, etc., and with particular attention to the problems and progress in the developing countries. Reports on conferences; notes of national bibliographies; news of important technical developments, special meetings and courses, services, etc. "New Publications" lists and annotates items on bibliography, librarianship, significant reference works, etc. Also a list of exchanges available (updating the latest edition of the *Handbook of the International Exchange of Publications* and a brief list of free materials. An important journal for institutions that have much interest in library and bibliographical information in foreign areas.

Indexed in: Lib.Lit.   49-48664 rev*
                P.A.I.S.

*WILSON LIBRARY BULLETIN.   v. 1, 1914-

Monthly (except July-Aug.)   N.Y. $5.00

For many years when its main purpose was "practicality," it contained numerous articles and features intended for all librarians, but in general was not highly regarded by college and university librarians. Beginning about 1960, however, its nature began to change. The former lacklustre cover became a display case for imaginative art work; articles, formerly fairly humdrum, with many "how-we-do-it" ones, were more original, sophisticated and forceful; issues formerly were without focus, but now most have special interesting, even unusual, themes; features such as authors' obituary notices, interviews with writers, and the departments on school and children's librarians, were dropped. Even "The Lighthouse," carrying news of the Wilson Company and the list of books analyzed in the *Essay and General Literature Index*, was discontinued in 1966.

The June issue is usually devoted to books, libraries and librarians abroad; the December issue, to children's literature; other issues frequently contain bibliographic essays on subjects ranging from physical anthropology to career guidance for youth. Regular features now include: a listing by Frances Neel Cheney of "Current Reference Books," with brief, somewhat evaluative annotations; "Selected Government Publications," by F. J. O'Hara, describing important recent U.S. documents or listing those in a particular area; "Overdue," a forum for guest expressions of opinion; and "ALA Washington Notes." Also, "The Month in Review," brief news items about people, libraries, books, legislation, special publications etc.; "Library Display" (reviving in 1969 in slightly different form a feature that had been dropped a few years before) carries photographs of successful exhibits and descriptions of display techniques; "Media," a listing of notable free or inexpensive materials; "Meetings," a calendar for the forthcoming few months.

The *Bulletin* has always been useful; it is now more readable and stimulating, and should be read by library staff members as well as made available to the public. Unlike a number of other professional journals, it may well be called for by non-librarians.

Indexed in: Lib.Lit.   30-9093 rev. 2*
            R.G.

*AMERICAN MATHEMATICAL MONTHLY. v. 1, 1894-

Monthly (bi-monthly June-Sept.)   Washington, D.C. $18.00

The official journal of the Mathematical Association of America since that organization was founded in 1915; the *Monthly*, however, was continued pretty much as it had been before then (though it was expanded) since its general aims and policies had coincided with those of the Association. Each issue now contains about 6 papers, of medium length, in "valid mathematics, of rather general interest, at a level intelligible to persons with two years of full-time graduate study." Occasional articles on the teaching or history of mathematics. Shorter contributions are in "Mathematical Notes," with others useful for or arising from the teaching of mathematics, in "Classroom Notes." "Mathematical Education" notes present news and developments—new courses, teachers' institutes, national programs, etc.; sections of problems and solutions, both elementary and advanced, sent in by readers, with solutions later sent in by other readers. In each issue there are a large number of reviews, since 1967 in two parts: the signed reviews, 10-15 per issue, are critical, vary in length, mostly 150-300 words, and only rarely are more than 500 words; the "Telegraphic Reviews" are succinct summaries of a much larger number of books, with indications of their levels and uses. Finally, there are personnel news and reports, news and notices of the Association, its sections, and their meetings.

Coverage of the *Monthly*—contributions and books reviewed—is from the junior through the second graduate year. It is, then, appropriate for all college libraries.

39-16866 rev*

AMERICAN MATHEMATICAL SOCIETY.   BULLETIN.   v. 1, 1891; ser. 2, v. 1, 1894-

Bi-monthly.   Washington, D.C. $12.00

The official organ of the Society. The largest section is devoted to "Research Announcements," which are mostly summaries of papers to be published elsewhere that demonstrate significant new results. "Research Problems" are sent in by readers. Some of the most important articles are those originally given as invited addresses to the Society, the Presidential and other special addresses, and the occasional lengthy "Survey Articles" covering the development of a particular theory or concept. Book reviews have become less and less frequent; now they are only of especially important works, and are very long. Carries reports of the various meetings of the Society, but abstracts of papers at the meetings, carried through 1957, now appear in the Society's *Notices*.

The Society also publishes its *Proceedings* (v. 1, 1950- $12.00) and *Transactions* (v. 1, 1900- $12.00). Both of these are devoted to research in pure and applied mathematics. The *Proceedings*, appearing bimonthly, carry papers of moderate length (not over 8 pages) and, beginning in 1961, "Shorter Notes"—papers not over a page in length, "of an unusually elegant and polished character, for which there is normally no other outlet." The *Transactions*, published 5 times a year, carry the longer contributions. The Society's *Notices* (v. 1, 1953- $12.00), published 8 times a year, contains announcements of meetings, items of all sorts of subjects of professional interest to mathematicians: visitors, grants, lectures, personnel, new publications, salary surveys, a listing of doctorates conferred during the year, etc. Since 1958, carries abstracts of all contributed papers presented to the Society. A Special Issue carries a list of assistantships and fellowships available in the U.S. and Canada, and an index to all the abstracts published during the year.

All publications of the Society are important, but necessary in colleges only where advanced work is done or where faculty members are involved in research.

15-1248 rev.

*AMERICAN STATISTICAL ASSOCIATION. JOURNAL. v. 1, 1888/89-

Quarterly. Washington, D.C. $25.00

Official journal of the Association, which was organized in 1839 and whose membership includes those in many disciplines and professions "who are seriously interested in the application of statistical methods to practical problems, in the development of more useful methods, and in the improvement of basic statistical data." Each issue contains a large number of articles (the number has been increasing—in 1969 there were about 35) of varied length; some are related to the social, behavioral, or natural sciences, but most are on statistical theory and methodology. About 15 book reviews per issue; the reviews are all signed and critical, and vary greatly in length from less than 100 to over 1000 words. Also a list of publications received. Summaries of papers delivered at the Association's annual meeting.

Indexed in: Bus.Per.I. 7-22199 rev. 3

AMERICAN STATISTICIAN. v. 1, 1947-

5 nos./yr. Washington, D.C. $5.00

Published by the American Statistical Association, it is devoted to articles on all areas of statistics and to news of the Association. The articles concern either new theory or new methodology, or the application of accepted theory or methodology to new areas; or they discuss or review topics of major significance in these fields. Most are fairly brief, and they relate to many areas of the social sciences, medicine, natural science and engineering. Professional news of conferences, meetings, courses, programs and other developments; news of members and of chapter activities. A "Questions and Answers" section is "devoted to discussions of conceptual and measurement problems." List of recent publications. Because of the growing importance of statistical studies in so many fields, the journal should be in libraries with strong mathematics or economics departments.

Indexed in: P.A.I.S. 59-28624

ANNALS OF MATHEMATICAL STATISTICS. v. 1, 1930-

Bi-monthly. Hayward, Calif. $30.00

Official journal of the Institute of Mathematical Statistics, it now contains "original contributions to theoretical statistics and to probability theory. The emphasis is on quality, not just on formal novelty and correctness of the contents." Now usually 20-30 articles per issue, varying in length from just a few pages to 30 or more, though most papers that are less than 5 pages appear as "Notes." Contains a few signed and critical reviews, personnel news and notes, reports of the Institute's officers and sections, and abstracts of papers presented at the national and regional meetings. An important journal where advanced statistics is taught.

31-33824 rev. 2

CANADIAN JOURNAL OF MATHEMATICS. v. 1, 1949-

Bi-monthly.   Toronto. $18.00

Supported by the major Canadian universities and by the American Mathematical Society, it is contributed to by mostly Canadian and American mathematicians. Almost all contributions are brief, and are in English, though occasionally in French. They are reports of research and range over all fields of mathematics. An important journal for advanced students and research.

53-20564

FIBONACCI QUARTERLY.   v. 1, 1963-

Quarterly.   St. Mary's College, Calif. $6.00

Official journal of the Fibonacci Association, which was "formed in order to exchange ideas and stimulate research in Fibonacci numbers and related topics." The first half of each issue, "Advanced," is devoted to mathematical developments and is primarily for the advanced student. The second half, "Elementary," is less difficult, more expository and can be read by those with a less serious interest in mathematics. Usually 4 to 7 articles, plus a section on problems and solutions from readers, in each part. Articles are mostly brief; an occasional special number contains longer contributions. Contributors are from colleges and universities here and abroad. An especially useful journal for undergraduates, since working with sequences requires no great mathematical sophistication and many of the articles are intended for the beginning mathematician.

68-126420

JOURNAL OF ALGEBRA.   v. 1, 1964-

Monthly.   N.Y. $104.00

Publishes papers reporting original research in abstract algebra and, occasionally, from related research areas. Issues contain usually 10 to 12 articles, contributed to by mathematicians from colleges and universities throughout the world. An important journal for advanced students and research.

JOURNAL OF RECREATIONAL MATHEMATICS. v. 1, 1968-

Quarterly. Westport, Conn. $10.00

Each issue consists of usually 5 to 7 articles on the light side of mathematics—mathematical constructions, number phenomena, problems and
puzzles, alphametics, chess problems, paper folding, and other mathematical diversions and curiosa. Contributors are laymen as well as professional mathematicians, and the substantial "Elementary Section" is
devoted to puzzles and problems appropriate for amateurs, as is the section "Problems and Conjectures." Occasional historical or biographical
articles and book reviews. A journal that will appeal to most mathematics
students and faculty, and will also be used by others with a casual interest
in the field.

JOURNAL OF RESEARCH OF THE NATIONAL BUREAU OF STANDARDS—
B. MATHEMATICAL SCIENCES. v. 63, 1959-

Quarterly. Washington, D.C. $5.00

The *Journal of Research* began in 1938; in July 1959, it divided into 4
sections, 3 of which are still published: A, Physics and Chemistry (q.v.);
B, Mathematical Sciences; and C, Engineering and Instrumentation.

This section, which is "designed mainly for the mathematician and the
theoretical physicist," includes "not only such applied fields as numerical
analysis and methods of numerical computation, compilation of mathematical tables, statistical experiment design, operations research, and the
classical theories of applied mathematics, but also topics in pure mathematics which have a bearing on these fields." The range of subjects, then,
is considerable; there are usually 7 to 10 articles per issue, almost all by
members of the Bureau's staff, but occasionally contributed by outsiders
on invitation. A depository item, it is primarily useful for advanced students and research.

Indexed in: A.S.T.I.   62-4414

JOURNAL of Symbolic Logic. *see* PHILOSOPHY

MATHEMATICAL GAZETTE. v. 1, 1894-

Quarterly. London. $9.80

The journal of the Mathematical Association, "an association of teachers and students of elementary mathematics." "Articles may be at any
level, with a preference for those that will help the teacher in the classroom. The work need not be new, though freshness of approach is desirable. There is no lower limit at the 'elementary' end, but articles will
not normally be accepted if the subject-matter goes beyond what a recent honours graduate may be expected to be within the experience of
readers most of whom are teachers in the schools." (Notes for Contributors) The articles vary in length, and many of them are of a descriptive, general nature. "Classroom Notes" and "Mathematical Notes"
are sent in by readers: the former giving odd or interesting problems
suitable for class presentation; the latter, more advanced proofs or odd

and interesting examples of primary interest to mathematicians. About 50 books are reviewed in each issue; they are signed and critical, review books at all levels, from elementary texts to esoteric monographs, and vary from a paragraph to 1000 words. Valuable for mathematics clubs, courses in the teaching of mathematics, as well as for supplementary reading for courses in regular mathematics.

65-7881/CD (for reprint)

MATHEMATICAL REVIEWS. v. 1, 1940-

Monthly. Providence, R.I. $320.00

An abstracting journal published by the American Mathematical Society, and sponsored by it and 27 other mathematical societies, foreign and domestic. Covers the research literature of mathematics throughout the world—over 1000 journals, plus hundreds of monographs and serials—amounting, in 1970, to over 16,000 entries. Each item to be abstracted is assigned to a specialist, many of whom are internationally outstanding contributors to their fields; their abstracts not only summarize the item, but frequently mention related works and comment critically on the conclusions or method; some of them are fairly long and are really reviews, rather than just abstracts. The abstracts are all signed, are usually in English but frequently in a foreign language (not necessarily the language of the article), and are arranged by subject. Monthly and semi-annual author indexes; no subject indexes. An expensive item, but necessary where any mathematical research is being done.

42-4221

*MATHEMATICS MAGAZINE. v. 1, 1926-

Bi-monthly (except July-Aug.) Washington, D.C. $4.00

Originally the *Mathematics News Letter*, then the *National Mathematics Magazine*, it assumed its present title in 1946. An independent publication for many years, supported by sponsoring subscriptions of individual mathematicians, it was taken over in 1962 by the American Mathematical Association. "A journal of collegiate mathematics," its level is somewhere between the *American Mathematical Monthly* and *Mathematics Teacher*. Each issue contains from 12 to 20 short articles—often only a page or two—with many appropriate for classroom use; covers all branches of mathematics, with some emphasis on calculus, algebra, and number theory. Contributors are from a wide variety of colleges, both here and abroad. A section of "Problems and Solutions," sent in by readers. "Quickies" contains problems chosen because they admit very brief solutions on proper analysis, and are popular with mathematicians. The book reviews in recent years were either very few or very brief—or both. In 1970, a new book reviewing policy was announced—reviews will be restricted "to longer critical reviews of publications of interest, with special attention to "textbooks and other publications at the general level of the first two years of college mathematics." These reviews have been between 500 and 1200 words.

A basic journal for all college libraries.

47-3192*

*MATHEMATICS TEACHER.   v. 1, 1908-

Monthly (except June-Sept.)   Washington, D.C. $10.00

A journal of the National Council of Teachers of Mathematics. Not for teachers of advanced courses, or for advanced mathematics majors, but important for teaching of lower level courses and for courses in the teaching of secondary school mathematics. Articles, mostly by college and university professors, are on techniques for presenting concepts, teaching practices and problems, trends in curriculum or method, course outlines, examples for class use, etc. There are a number of departments and regular features. "Experimental Programs" describes new courses, texts, research in teaching methods and effectiveness, etc.; "Classics in Mathematics Education (which began in 1966) reprints outstanding articles from past issues; "Historically Speaking" discusses some aspect of the history of mathematics; "Have You Read?" summarizes articles from popular and learned journals; "Reviews and Evaluations" of texts and treatises (mostly the former) containing signed, critical reviews, usually 400-500 words in length, appears in most issues. Listing of other publications. News of the NCTM, its chapters and committees.

Indexed in: Ed.I.   42-24844 rev.

PACIFIC JOURNAL OF MATHEMATICS.   v. 1, 1951-

Monthly.   Berkeley, Calif. $32.00

Contains research papers in all areas of mathematics, theoretical and applied, but primarily the former. Institutions supporting the journal include a number of West Coast universities, plus two in Japan, but contributors are from mathematics departments throughout the U.S. and occasionally from other countries. A leading general journal in the field, important for strong departments.

A 54-336

SIAM REVIEW.   v. 1, 1959-

Quarterly.   Philadelphia, Pa. $16.00

The purpose of the publishing program of the Society for Industrial and Applied Mathematics (SIAM) is "to further the application of mathematics to industry and science, promote basic research in mathematics leading to new techniques useful to industry and science, and provide media for the exchange of information and ideas between mathematicians and other scientific personnel." The *Review* contains expository and survey papers in applied mathematics, and essays of professional interest (on the teaching or history of mathematics, for example), each issue consisting of articles, short notes, problems and solutions, and reviews. The articles range from 6 or 7 up to 60 pages, with the median about 15. The "Short Notes" are no more than 4 pages. Supplements appear occasionally, the first (1970) was on "Graph Theory in the Soviet Union." The "Problems" and their "Solutions" are submitted by readers. An average of 9 or 10 signed and critical reviews per issue, mostly about 500 words. List of other books received. For advanced students and faculty.

The Society publishes several other journals, two of which should be considered by libraries where there are strong departments in mathematics. These are the bi-monthly *SIAM Journal on Applied Mathematics* (v. 1, 1953- $36.00) and the quarterly *SIAM Journal on Numerical Analysis* (v. 1, 1964- $18.00).

Indexed in: A.S.T.I.   64-39558

SCHOOL Science and Mathematics. *see* EDUCATION

SCRIPTA MATHEMATICA.   v. 1, 1932-

Quarterly.   N.Y. $4.00

Published by the Belfer Graduate School of Science, Yeshiva University, it is "devoted to the expository and research aspects of mathematics." Most articles are technical, but others not so are excellent for showing the relationships of mathematics to other fields, and for study in the history of science or mathematics. There are a large number of reviews—up to 40—per issue, of foreign and domestic books in all branches of mathematics, including even some textbooks and works in applied mathematics, but most are in fields of mathematical theory and history. The reviews are signed and critical, and vary greatly in length, from a paragraph to 1500 words. A lengthy listing of other books and pamphlets, with brief annotations. Since its founder and editor for 25 years, Dr. Jekuthiel Ginsburg, died in 1957, publication has been erratic. Recently, one volume has been spread over several years and many of the books reviewed have been published 5 or 6 years before their reviews appear; one article appearing in 1967 was received by the editors in 1955!—surely some sort of record.

34-41372

*FOREIGN LANGUAGE ANNALS.   v. 1, 1967-

4 nos./ yr.   N.Y. $10.00

Published by the American Council on the Teaching of Foreign Languages, it "is dedicated to advancing all phases of the profession of foreign language teaching. It seeks to serve as a chronicle of information
of current significance to the teacher, administrator, or researcher, whatever the educational level and the language with which he is concerned."
Issues consist of 5 or 6 articles on the purposes, techniques and evaluation of foreign language instruction, and on the training of teachers.
News of the ACTFL and its constituent and affiliate groups is in the section "ACTFL Affairs"; "FL Notes" contains items about programs, institutes, meetings, grants, publications, etc. "ERIC Clearinghouse on the
Teaching of Foreign Languages," in each issue, contains notes about the
Clearinghouse, a description of FL projects in progress and a list (once
or twice a year) of "ERIC Documents on the Teaching of Foreign Languages." Finally, there is the *ACTFL Annual Bibliography of Books and
Articles on Pedagogy in Foreign Languages,* covering about 300 journals
and various books. It includes not just modern foreign languages, but also
Latin and Greek and English as a second language.

A basic journal where there is much work done in foreign languages and
especially in the preparation of teachers.

73-9696

COMPARATIVE Literature. *see* ENGLISH

COMPARATIVE Literature Studies. *see* ENGLISH

CONTEMPORARY Literature. *see* ENGLISH

INTERNATIONAL JOURNAL OF AMERICAN LINGUISTICS.   v. 1, 1917-

Quarterly.   Bloomington, Ind. $8.00

Published by Indiana University under the auspices of the Linguistic Society
of America and the American Anthropological Association, with the cooperation of the Conference on American Indian Languages. Reflecting the
major intent of its founder, Franz Boas, for most of its history it was devoted to American Indian languages, with articles and notes contributed by
the leading scholars in that field. Only in the last few years has it been
announced that the journal "will also publish theoretically contributory
papers concerned with languages from other parts of the world," though
emphasis will continue to be given "to the languages of native America."
Because of its reputation and eminent associates, it will probably attract
many first-rate contributions. Subscribers receive two important series:
Indiana University. Publications in Anthropology and Linguistics. Memoirs

and *Indiana University. Research Center in Anthropology, Folklore and Linguistics. Publications,* both of which are issued as supplements. Abstracts of articles, books and papers appear irregularly. They are reported under general subject—e.g., "Abstracts from French Journals," "Abstracts on Primate Communication," etc.—but are numbered consecutively. The reviews vary greatly in length, and there are usually only a few in each issue. They are signed and, needless to say, very critical and scholarly. An important journal in a specialized field, it is for advanced students and faculty.

Indexed in: S.S.H.I.   22-9284

LANGUAGE.   v. 1, 1925-

Quarterly.   Baltimore, Md. $16.00

Journal of the Linguistic Society of America, each issue usually contains from 6 to 10 very scholarly articles, of brief to moderate length, on all aspects and families of languages: linguistic theory, syntax, etymology, structure, phonology, dialects, etc., but almost nothing on the teaching of languages. Each article is preceded by an abstract. A major portion of most issues is devoted to reviews; though there are never more than 25 per issue, many approach the length and depth of articles. (One, in the 1964 volume, was 63 pages and had 281 footnotes!) Needless to say, these reviews are signed and critical. Also a list of publications received. The "Notes" section includes items about members, meetings, new periodicals, etc. One issue each year has a second part which contains Proceedings of the LSA meetings and a list of its members. There is an index for every 5 volumes; in addition to the usual entries, it also indexes the articles and reviews by language and (beginning with the 1960-64 index) topic. The subscription cost (which entitles one to membership) includes the receipt of two series of occasional publications, *Language Monographs* and *Language Dissertations.* Both are important in the field, and many libraries class them as separate series. They may also be purchased separately. An important journal where there is any interest in linguistics, but primarily for advanced students and research.

27-11255

NOTE: Now available only by membership in Linguistic Soc. of America.

LANGUAGE LEARNING.   v. 1, 1948-

Semi-annually.   Ann Arbor, Mich. $5.00

"A journal of applied linguistics," it deals with descriptive linguistics, the teaching of general linguistics and specific languages, etc. Articles, by faculty members and others (in government or military research) interested in practical aspects of teaching languages, are mostly of moderate length and usually preceded by an abstract. Rarely more than 2 or 3 reviews per issue, but these are usually quite long, often several thousand words. List of publications received; news of conferences, meetings, new journals, educational programs, etc.; Newsletter of the English Language Institute, the University of Michigan. Before 1969 the journal was a quarterly, but for some years had been issued in double numbers and appeared just twice a year; on the other hand, special numbers, containing the proceedings of a conference or institute, have appeared fairly often. An important journal where there is interest in the theory of the teaching of foreign languages or teaching English as a second language.

Indexed in: Ed.I.   52-44910

MODERN Fiction Studies. *see* ENGLISH

*MODERN LANGUAGE JOURNAL.   v. 1, 1916-

Monthly (except June-Sept.)   St. Louis, Mo. $5.00

Published by the National Federation of Modern Language Teachers Associations, it is devoted primarily to methods, pedagogical research, and to topics of professional interest to all language teachers—in both schools and colleges. Includes teaching of Russian, Hebrew, Arabic and other "exotic" languages, and even the teaching of English as a second language—although, of course, most emphasis is on French, Spanish and German. Occasional articles on the literature of these areas, but these are fairly general—such as "The New Reality of the Continental Novel"—rather than critical studies. Frequent articles listing available materials—films, programmed materials, etc. News of national and regional meetings. A number of regular features: an annual listing of *American Doctoral Degrees Granted in the Field of Modern Languages,* carried since the one for 1934/35; the *Annual Annotated Bibliography of Language Teaching Methods* was carried until 1961; beginning in 1966, there have been annual listings of coordinators or supervisors of foreign languages in public school systems of the United States and of the NDEA institutes and programs; the section, "Also Noted" briefly notes articles of interest that have appeared in recent issues of popular and professional journals; "Notes and News" carries all sorts of information useful or interesting to language teachers—developments in particular states, notices of meetings, news of grants and awards, new periodicals, special opportunities, new programs, etc. The number of book reviews has increased: in 1954, only about 60 were reviewed during the entire year; now there are 30-40 per issue. On literary and critical studies as well as language studies and texts, the reviews are excellent, mostly between 500 and 1000 words. Includes reviews of tapes and programmed instruction. Occasional, but lengthy, lists of books received. An essential journal for present and future modern language teachers.

Indexed in: B.R.D.   37-24312
              Ed.I.

*MODERN LANGUAGE NOTES.   v. 1, 1886-

6 nos./yr.   Baltimore, Md. $15.00

For its first 76 years, *MLN* was issued monthly (except June-October), and carried scholarly, specialized, brief articles (rarely more than 5 pages long, and frequently just 2 or 3) and notes on all modern western languages and literatures, with most attention given to English literature. There were also a large number of book reviews.

In 1962 its policy changed. Of the five numbers published, each of the first 4 was "given over to articles and notes on one of the major languages and its literature—Italian, Spanish, French, German respectively." The fifth issue was a General Issue, with articles and notes on these languages, or on others in the Germanic and Romance groups, or on general subjects. In 1968 the policy changed again—but only slightly— when the 5 numbers were increased to 6. There are now 2 numbers devoted to German, and one each to French, Hispanic and Italian, and the final number is now designated "Comparative Literature." There are, then, no contributions at all on English or American subjects.Each issue contains an average of 5 or 6 scholarly articles of moderate length—mostly on literature and criticism—plus some shorter "Notes." Reviews of books published in any of the four languages treated appear in all issues. The number of reviews varies greatly—from 1 to 15 per issue; they are excellent, signed and critical, almost all at least 700-800 words, and frequently several times that. Articles and reviews in foreign languages and English. Contributors number some of the most eminent names in comparative literature, and the journal should be in every library where there is any emphasis on the literatures covered.

Indexed in: S.S.H.I.   10-32833 rev.

MODERN Language Quarterly. *see* ENGLISH

MODERN LANGUAGE REVIEW.   v. 1, 1905-

Quarterly.   London. $20.00

Published by the Modern Humanities Research Association, London. Contains scholarly articles, from 2000 to 10,000 words usually (before 1962 shorter contributions were listed separately), on English, Romance and Germanic languages and literature with literature greatly predominant. English authors receive most attention, though (for an English publication, certainly) the spread among French, English and German authors is fairly even, with much lesser attention to the other languages. A major portion is devoted to reviews, about 90 per issue currently. Signed and critical, these are mostly 600-1000 words long, but occasionally much longer. An important journal for advanced students and faculty.

Indexed in: Br.Hum.I.   7-37503 rev. 2
            S.S.H.I.

*PMLA.   v. 1, 1884-

6 nos./yr.   N.Y. $20.00

As the official journal of the Modern Language Association of America, the largest and most prestigious organization of scholars teaching or studying the modern languages, "*PMLA* endeavors to represent the most distinguished contemporary scholarship and criticism in the modern languages and literatures. It welcomes either new or traditional approaches by either young or established scholars, providing only that whatever it publishes is well written and likely to be of permanent value. The distribution of papers in *PMLA* should reflect work of distinction actually being done from year to year, regardless of periods or languages . . . . *PMLA* is reluctant to publish minor articles or highly technical studies addressed to specialists in limited fields. Nor does it encourage brief notes or unduly long papers." For many years the only scholarly periodical in this country devoted to modern languages, it remains perhaps the most important. Its emphasis has shifted from the philological to the critical, and it is now confined almost exclusively to literature, with a strong emphasis on English literature.

Usually 10-12 articles per issue, mostly of moderate length (7500-15,000 words); an abstract for each is on the contents pages. Shorter notes, documents and critical comments on earlier articles. The regular section "Professional News and Comment" (before 1970 called "For Members Only") carries items of interest to the profession—new programs and curricula, awards, institutes—and often some important for librarians, such as descriptions of new periodicals and other notable bibliographical developments.

The *MLA International Bibliography,* the most comprehensive bibliography in the field, was carried as part of the journal through 1969 (i.e., the *Bibliography* for 1968). From its beginning in 1921 through 1955 it was known as the *American Bibliography* as it covered books and articles by Americans only. It expanded continually, so that by 1969 it listed publications from all over the world on the literature and languages of all continents, covering about 1300 periodicals and including all the books, and analyzing the *Festschriften*—a total of some 24,000 items. Beginning with the *Bibliography* for 1969, libraries must subscribe to it separately; the prediction is that it will include about 35,000 items, so that the cost—$15.00 in addition to a subscription to *PMLA*—is certainly reasonable. Since many libraries purchased an extra copy of the *Bibliography* for their Reference Collections, this merely formalizes that decision.

The September issue used to include some articles on teaching and other professional matters, but now it is devoted to reports of the regional meetings and to various lists: MLA committees and statistics, English and foreign-language department chairmen, and a complete roster of MLA members—all 30,000 of them. This number is a useful reference tool also. There are no book reviews.

An essential journal for every academic library.

Indexed in: S.S.H.I.   12-32040 rev. 2

ROMANCE PHILOLOGY. v. 1, 1947-

Quarterly.   Berkeley, Calif. $12.00

Devoted to scholarly studies and reviews in all the romance languages. The number of long articles has declined, so that there is now usually just an article or two per issue, plus shorter scholarly notes; on the other hand, the number of review articles, which are almost invariably quite long, as much as 25-30 pages, has increased. In addition to these review articles, more than half of each issue is devoted to signed and critical book reviews, usually 10-15 an issue: the longer ones are at least 1000 words and often 3 or 4 times that; also a number of shorter ones, generally 500-1000 words. "Bibliographic Notes" contains news of new projects, critical comments, and other news of professional interest. Because of its specialized nature, with an emphasis on romance linguistics rather than literature, it is recommended only for those libraries with very strong departments.

Indexed in: S.S.H.I.   50-39994

ROMANIA.   v. 1, 1872-

Quarterly.   Paris. $13.00

Long regarded as one of the leading scholarly journals in the field of Romance philology and medieval studies, it is still important in that area, but its concentration on the early periods limits its usefulness for undergraduate studies. Very scholarly articles, of widely varying lengths, mostly relating to the medieval period. Contains corrections to editions of ancient French texts, and the full texts of newly discovered items. The final issue of each volume contains an index of the words analyzed or even mentioned in the year's articles and a list of the manuscripts cited. Some news of interest to romanticists; descriptions of contents of recent issues of a few other important journals of philology and medieval history. Primarily for advanced students and faculty.

10-32856*

*ROMANIC REVIEW.   v. 1, 1910-

Quarterly.   N.Y. $7.50

A publication of the Departments of Romance Languages of Columbia University. Though it declared it was "devoted to research in the romance languages and literatures," the contributions—articles and reviews—have always greatly emphasized French literature, or occasionally other aspects of French culture (of the 14 articles in a recent volume, to cite an extreme example, only one was not in the French area). All periods of literature are covered, though, as one might expect, recent or contemporary writers are treated less frequently. From 1938 through 1948 it carried the annual bibliography, *Anglo-French and Franco-American Studies*, listing and usually annotating books, articles and reviews on cultural and literary articles on important new works or on groups of works. The other book reviews, signed and critical, averaging about 15 or 20 per issue, range from several hundred to about 1000 words. Articles and reviews are in English or one of the Romance languages. A basic title for the study of Romance languages, especially French; an extensive backfile should also be available in most college libraries.

Indexed in: S.S.H.I.   12-20478

*SYMPOSIUM.   v. 1, 1946-

Quarterly.   Syracuse, N.Y. $8.00

Contains scholarly articles on all modern foreign literature of the Western world, with great emphasis on the romance languages. Articles vary greatly in length, though most are short to medium length. Contributors are scholars from American and European universities, and while research articles are stressed, essays on the creative and comparative aspects of literature often appear. From 1952 through 1965 it carried the annual bibliography, *Relations of Literature and Science*, a selected, mostly unannotated listing of books and articles. The number of book reviews, which are signed and critical, seldom exceeds 5 or 6, and they are mostly 1000-1500 words. List of books received. An important journal for all foreign language departments.

Indexed in: S.S.H.I.   51-23297

WORD.   v. 1, 1945-

3 nos./yr.   N.Y. $7.50

"Journal of the Linguistic Circle of New York," a group begun in 1943 by linguists from Paris and New York. The journal has been contributed to by leading linguistic scholars from many countries, including anthropologists, sociologists and philosophers. The articles vary greatly in length and number per issue and some are in French, but all are very scholarly, even highly technical, and cover all branches and schools of modern linguistics—semantics, phonology, structural linguistics, etymology, transformational grammar, etc. Subscription includes the Monograph series which supplement occasional numbers; 5 were issued through 1970. Publication of *Word* has been very late: the 1967 volume was issued in late 1969 when all three numbers were issued together. The number of reviews ranges from none to more than 20, and their length from several hundred to several thousand words. Some are in French. List of publications received in most issues. For advanced students and faculty only.

55-40019 rev

CRITIQUE. v. 1, 1946-

Monthly. Paris. $14.40

Subtitled "Revue générale des publications francaises et étrangères," it contains usually 5 or 6 review-essays on important books that have appeared recently, or on several works by the same author, or several works on the same subject by different authors. The term "review-essays" is not entirely accurate, since it implies less originality and significance than the essays in *Critique* contain—the books being discussed really serve more as springboards for the reviewers and are often longer than 10,000 words. They range over all fields of knowledge, and though the great majority are of works published in France, important books in the U.S., England and elsewhere on the continent are often discussed. Many important writers—Robbe-Grillet, Butor, among others—have contributed, and a number of the review-essays that appeared here served as the basis for books. Issues are occasionally devoted to single topics. A good publication for keeping up with intellectual currents in France.

49-19963*

*ESPRIT. Année 1, 1932-

Monthly. Paris. $14.90

One of the most respected general reviews, it treats all aspects of contemporary civilization, with some emphasis, of course, on France, and within France, on its literature and arts. Topics covered include economic and social questions (e.g., racism, educational reform, economic theory), political philosophy and movements, foreign affairs, religion, literature, and the arts. Frequently has special numbers (recent years have included Administration, The Press, The Architect, Urbanism and Society, Foreigners in France, The Student Revolt) which are highly regarded. Excellent signed and critical book reviews, of fiction, poetry and a variety of non-fiction, mostly 1000-2000 words each. An important journal for the study of all facets of contemporary French culture and society.

44-38107

*ESPRIT CRÉATEUR. v. 1, 1961-

Quarterly. Lawrence, Kans. $4.00

Founded because there was no American journal devoted to the critical study of French literature, it "presents critical analyses of different aspects of the literary production of one author or of a movement. All periods of French literature are reflected." Topics treated have ranged from Realism in the Literature of the Twelfth Century to New Directions in the French Novel and The Film and the Book; almost every standard French author has been treated, so that modern authors and topics are more frequently the subjects now. Each issue contains 5 or 6 scholarly articles, limited to 4000 words, contributed by faculty members from various universities. The book reviews are signed and critical; they have steadily increased in number—there are now usually between 6 and 10

per issue—and they range in length from 600 to 1200, but are mostly
about 750 words. In English and French. An important journal for French
majors and faculty.

64-51409

L'EXPRESS. *see* GENERAL

LE FRANÇAIS DANS LE MONDE   no. 1, 1961-

8 nos./yr.   Paris. $6.50

Published by Hachette and Larousse, it was begun on the initiative of
the French government to aid all teachers, both in and outside France,
who teach the French language as culture. Most issues contain 56 pages:
a few brief studies on modern language teaching, on the linguistics of
modern and spoken French and on French civilization, culture and—in
particular—literature; other articles are for classroom use and include prepared lessons, as well as analyses and explanations of texts and other aids
for study of French history and society; also information on developments
in the teaching of French—conferences, examinations, lectures, etc.—and
a few signed, critical reviews of texts or linguistic studies. 4 times a year
an LP record is mounted on the inside back cover; they contain songs,
examples of spoken French, phonetic exercises, model lessons, etc. Whole
numbers are occasionally devoted to single subjects—e.g., Guide Péda-
gogique pour le Professeur de Français, La Grammaire du Français Parle,
etc. The journal is well illustrated and among its contributors have been
some of the most eminent figures in French education and culture. An
important journal where there is much interest in French, especially for
the preparation of French teachers.

68-51103

*FRENCH REVIEW.   v. 1, 1927-

6 nos./yr.   Champaign, Ill. $8.00

Official journal of the American Association of Teachers of French. Its
articles generally fall into one of two categories: fairly scholarly ones on
French literature, philology, or criticism; or second, on the study of
teaching of French, from grade school through college. There are occasional articles on French life and culture, but these are not so numerous as
in the past. Articles are of moderate length, generally limited to 3600
words. Reports of the various officers; minutes of the annual meeting and
of chapter activities; other professional notes and news, and teaching
suggestions. *Dissertations in Progress* has appeared annually since 1963;
it is a classified listing that supplements lists of the previous years, listing
in full new projects only. "National Information Bureau News," a very
helpful listing of materials—posters, songs, reprints, books and pamphlets,
filmstrips, records, maps and periodicals—available to French teachers,
has appeared in most issues since October, 1954; before then it was separately published. "Review of Reviews," a critical survey of notable pieces

that have appeared in French literary journals,appeared twice a year from 1960 to 1967. About 40 or 45 reviews per issue, of textbooks, literary history and criticism, French civilization, a few works of fiction and poetry. The reviews are signed and critical, mostly around 700 words, but a few quite long. The last number of each volume contains a membership directory of the AATF. A substantial portion of the contents is in French. Because of the variety of useful and scholarly material contained in it, *FR* should be in every college library where French is taught.

Indexed in: Ed.I.   32-21964 rev.

NOUVEL Observateur. *see* GENERAL

NOUVELLE REVUE FRANÇAISE.   v. 1, 1953-

Monthly.   Paris. $17.50

Its predecessor of the same title (known familiarly as NRF) ran from 1909 to 1943, and was one of the world's leading literary reviews, introducing to France—and in many cases to the world—writers and critics who later became standard figures in the literary world. It was re-established in 1953 as *Nouvelle Nouvelle Revue Française,* then the first "nouvelle" was dropped in 1959. A general literary review, with a substantial amount of fiction and poetry, often by leading writers. Issues are frequently devoted to single subjects, especially literary figures. "Chroniques" provide reviews and commentaries on current cultural events and trends; "Notes" includes signed and critical reviews of recent books of poetry, fiction and criticism, and sometimes of the theatre, movies and concerts. Perhaps the leading French literary journal.

60-51571

NOUVELLES LITTÉRAIRES.   v. 1, 1922-

Weekly.   Paris. $25.00

Devoted to all aspects of contemporary French culture, with some emphasis on literature. Each issue carries a number of reviews and articles on recent books and authors, on literary and artistic festivals, prizes and other events, and on significant developments in the world of learning, including the natural and social sciences. There are regular reviews and listings of films, television, the theatre, and art exhibitions. Issues sometimes focus on an individual writer or artist, and interviews with persons important in contemporary French culture are a frequent and useful feature. Usually some 10 or 15 books are reviewed in an issue. These range over all subjects, from the most popular to the very scholarly; the reviews themselves may be from a few paragraphs to several thousand words.

Published in tabloid format, with many illustrations, it is a useful publication for keeping up with the current French cultural scene.

30-5499

PARIS Match. *see* GENERAL

RÉALITES. *see* GENERAL

REVUE; LITTÉRATURE, HISTOIRE, ARTS ET SCIENCES DES DEUX MONDES. 1948-

Monthly.   Paris. $16.40

Superseded *Revue des Deux Mondes*, one of the oldest, most respected and popular reviews, which had run from 1831 to 1944. Almost every well known French writer and critic of the nineteenth century contributed to it, and a lengthy backfile is invaluable for the study of all aspects of French life, literature and history. While the present *Revue* has not achieved the eminence of its namesake it is still perhaps the best known of the French general reviews, though not so important for the study of contemporary French literature as some other journals. Each issue contains 10-15 articles, mostly short, on a variety of topics relating to French society, culture and history. Some fiction and poetry. "Chronique du Mois" in each issue contains columns on books, the theatre, the arts, science and medicine, recordings, music, movies and television; "A l' Institut" reports news of events and personnel of the learned societies.

Useful for its rounded and reliable commentary on contemporary social, political and cultural developments.

50-15459

REVUE D'HISTOIRE LITTÉRAIRE DE LA FRANCE.   v. 1, 1894-

Quarterly.   Paris.   42F

Published by the Société d'Histoire Littéraire de la France, and boasting a long line of distinguished contributors, it is the most important periodical for the study of French literature, especially before 1900, though coverage of the modern period has increased. Most issues consist of 6 or 7 scholarly articles, on various periods and genres of French literature, but issues frequently are devoted to single topics—e.g., Littérature sous Louis XIV, Le Québec et sa Littérature, André Gide, etc. "Notes et Documents" contains shorter pieces, but especially recently discovered letters and texts. The "Bibliographie" in each issue, covering articles, books and theses, is compiled by René Rancoeur, and provides the basis for his annual *Bibliographie de la Litterature Française.* News of publications, meetings and personnel; proceedings of the Société. The book reviews are an important feature. Now 40 to 50 per issue, they vary widely in length, but are mostly 750-1000 words. An essential journal for strong French departments.

1-23484

REVUE DE LITTÉRATURE COMPARÉE.   v. 1, 1921-

Quarterly.   Paris.   45F

Certainly one of the Western world's leading journals of comparative literature, it is contributed to by scholars from many countries, with articles mostly in English and French, but occasionally in Italian or German. Usually 4 to 6 very scholarly articles per issue, ranging over genres, periods and geography. Shorter contributions in Notes and Documents. Occasional long essay-reviews; also an average of 7 or 8 shorter reviews per issue. Signed and critical, they vary from a few hundred to several thousand words, averaging about 1500. Written mostly in French, though covering books in many languages.

An important journal for comparative literature, but because of its emphasis, especially important where there is much work in French literature.

25-538 rev.

TEMPS MODERNES.   v. 1, 1945-

Monthly.   Paris. $12.75

Founded by Jean-Paul Sartre and directed by him until 1962, when a small committee, including Sartre and Simone de Beauvoir, was chosen to act in a director's capacity. Articles of varying length by leading French writers and scholars, on all aspects of society—politics, sociology, psychiatry, economics, literature, travel, etc.—with the assortment fairly well balanced and with as much attention (or more) to matters outside France as to within. Some poetry, but no fiction. Issues are occasionally devoted to a single subject—e.g., Japan, the Arab-Israeli conflict, Structuralism. No regular book review section; important new books are sometimes discussed as are certain films and plays. A leading journal of the French intellectuals on public affairs, reflecting Sartre's interests and social values.

49-19080*

*YALE FRENCH STUDIES.   no. 1, 1948-

Semi-annually.   New Haven, Conn. $2.00

Each number is devoted "to a special theme, a particular author, or important currents in contemporary French literature and life." Typical subjects have included: Shakespeare's France, Surrealism, The New Dramatists, Jean-Jacques Rousseau, Literature and Revolution, The Art of Cinema, Albert Camus, The Child's Part. The articles, usually 10 to 12 per issue, brief to moderate length, are by American and foreign scholars—many internationally known—but all are in English. The journal is, then, accessible for the general reader, and, because of the wide variety of topics treated, useful for other studies in the humanities as well as providing important material for the French major and professor. Along with its backfile, it should be in every college library where there is an interest in French society or culture.

Indexed in: S.S.H.I.   59-38386

AKZENTE. v. 1, 1954-

Bi-monthly. Munich, Germany. $5.90

Focusing on contemporary German literature, it has been perhaps the most important outlet for younger German writers, and was influential in introducing many of them who later became well known. In its early volumes, for instance, can be found contributions by Gunter Grass, Peter Weiss, Heinrich Böll and Nelly Sachs, to name some of the best known. Issues usually are concerned with a particular theme and these range over all areas of literature; recent ones, for example, have included New German Poetry, Poems from Seven Languages, Literature of the Working World, Prose and Poetry of Rumania. Drama as well as other forms of popular and traditional literature are treated. Well known writers from other countries are frequently represented in translation.

An important journal where there is an interest in recent and contemporary trends in German literature.

56-41571

AMERICAN-GERMAN REVIEW. v. 1, 1934-

Bi-monthly. Philadelphia, Pa. $5.00

Published by the National Carl Schurz Association, its aim is to promote "cultural relations between the United States and German-speaking peoples." Contains popularly-written and well-illustrated articles, by Americans and Europeans, on past and present aspects of German culture, society, and politics, and on personalities in these areas. Recent issues have emphasized the contemporary, and there are articles in almost every issue on contemporary German theatre, cinema, and literature, either in the form of reviews or discussions of developments. News of the Association, of the National Federation of Students of German, and of academic and cultural activities in Germany and the U.S. Lists books received and frequently reviews books about Germans, Germany and Germans in America. *Bibliography: Americana Germanica,* an important bibliography covering all aspects of German-American relationships, was carried from 1940 through 1967, when it was transferred to the *German Quarterly* (q.v.). The *Review* is an attractive publication and, for those interested in German culture or German-American relationships, worth reading. Many of the articles are translations from German publications; some appear in German.

36-29801

NOTE: In April, 1971 the *American-German Review* was replaced by *Rundschau,* "An American-German Review." In tabloid format, offset-produced with many illustrations and drawings, it is sort of a jazzed-up version of *AGR*, but devoting much more space to current educational, social and cultural news, and especially to news of students, student groups and activities. Published monthly, September through May, it costs $4.50 per year or is distributed free to all members of the National Carl Schurz Association of the National Federation of Students of German.

DIMENSION. v. 1, 1968-

3 nos./yr. Austin, Texas. $6.00

Published for the Department of German Languages of the University of Texas, its purpose is "to acquaint the inquisitive with the newest and most striking manifestations of poetic and literary creativeness in Germany without being partial to any particular direction, scheme or school." Each issue contains a substantial number of poems, stories, essays on contemporary affairs and developments and literary criticism in both the original German and the English translation, side by side. Poetry and poetry criticism is emphasized. Much of the material is original to this journal, some by well-known authors, but more by younger, experimental writers. "Letter from Germany," a regular feature, reports on the intellectual scene—books, politics, the arts, etc. An attractive, important journal for the study of contemporary German literature, it should also appeal to those interested in today's poetry and its criticism.

75-6622

GERMAN LIFE AND LETTERS.   v. 1, 1936;   n.s.v. 1, 1947-

Quarterly.   Oxford, Eng. $12.00

The only British periodical devoted exclusively to German studies, it greatly stresses literary studies, with only occasional articles on German intellectual history. Its earlier volumes were concerned with what was going on in German culture, and the Old Series contained many reports and correspondence from Germany, as well as scholarly articles on literature. These "Letters from Germany" were discontinued in 1955, but there were still reviews of current literature. Now, however, the articles and reviews treat literary history and criticism, though there are occasional reviews of important works on German history or culture. Reviews have occupied an increasing amount of space, with anywhere from 5 to 50 reviews per issue, ranging widely in length, but averaging 500-600 words. Contributors are mostly from British universities, though occasionally from American or German. Almost all articles are in English; the reviews are in English or German.

A scholarly journal of increasing importance.

Indexed in: Br.Hum.I.   A 39-585

*GERMAN QUARTERLY   v. 1, 1928-

Quarterly.   Philadelphia, Pa. $7.50

Published by the American Association of Teachers of German which is composed of secondary school and college teachers. The articles are divided between those on the content and method of teaching German, and scholarly articles on German literature and language. In earlier volumes the emphasis was on the former; now it is on the latter. Occasionally, issues are devoted to a single topic—e.g., Schiller, Advanced Placement Programs in German, but usually in the field of literature. Articles make up about half the journal; another quarter or so is devoted to professional matters: news of courses, programs, institutes, collections, etc., both foreign and domestic; "The Teacher's Forum," brief items on classroom practices; a section of news and notes for teachers of German in elementary schools; other professional news and notes and reports about the Association or of interest to its members. Book reviews comprise the final quarter or so of each issue. There are usually about 20 longer reviews—often several thousand words—divided between literature or linguistics and the teaching of German, plus a smaller number of brief reviews. All are signed and critical. The articles and reviews are in English or German. Since 1962, a Membership Issue has appeared between numbers 3 and 4. It contains a complete list of members and officers, and various other lists and reports of interest to members. In 1968, *GQ* took over from the *American-German Review* the annual feature, *Bibliography: Americana Germanica*. Sponsored by the Anglo-German Literary Relations Group of the Modern Language Association, it contains a large number of items from many sources on all aspects of German-American cultural relationships, with an appended list of published and in-progress theses in the same field.

A useful and important title, it should be available wherever German is taught.

Indexed in: Ed.I.   32-7760

GERMAN Tribune. *see* GENERAL

*GERMANIC REVIEW.   v. 1, 1926-

Quarterly.   N.Y. $7.50

"Devoted to studies dealing with the Germanic languages and literature." Articles, usually 4 or 5 per issue, are scholarly, of moderate length and treat all periods and genres of German literature; articles on linguistics appear only occasionally. The number of reviews has increased substantially and there are now usually 10-15 an issue, mostly of books on literature published in Germany. The reviews, which are signed and critical, vary in length, but are at least 650 words long, and many 2 or 3 times that. With few exceptions, the articles are in English; some of the book reviews are in German. From 1953 through 1960, it carried an annual bibliography *German Literature of the Nineteenth Century, 1830-1880*. A basic journal in the field.

Indexed in: S.S.H.I.   28-10218

MERKUR.   v. 1, 1947-

Monthly.   Stuttgart, Germany. $13.70

"A German magazine of European thought," it is of general interest and one of the most catholic of contemporary German periodicals. Contains some fiction and poetry, but it is best known for its articles and essays on literary, philosophical, historical, social and other general cultural subjects by noted German and foreign contributors. Each issue carries some 3 to 6 excellent book reviews, mostly 1500-2000 words in length, covering some scholarly works as well as important trade fiction and non-fiction titles. *Der Monat* (v. 1, 1948-   DM), founded by Melvin Lasky with the support of the Congress for Cultural Freedom, is the German equivalent of *Encounter* (q.v.) which is also supported by the Congress. It not only looks like *Encounter*, but uses some of the same writers, and like it, is known for thoughtful analyses of contemporary affairs and ideas, especially on the political and social scene. Thus, while *Merkur* is concerned with general matters—the humanities—*Monat*, while also treating literature and the arts, emphasizes the social sciences, and in particular their application to national and international affairs. Both journals are highly regarded and valuable for their coverage of current German social and cultural developments and thought.

50-57928

*MONATSHEFTE FÜR DEUTSCHEN UNTERRICHT, DEUTSCHE SPRACHE UND LITERATUR.   v. 1, 1899-

Quarterly.   Madison, Wis. $15.00

Went through several changes of title and frequency until 1928, when it came under the auspices of the University of Wisconsin's German Department, and was entitled *Monatshefte für deutschen Unterricht;* in 1946 the latter part of the present title was added. It appeared from 1919 through 1927 only as a *Jahrbuch,* and indeed, before 1928 it was primarily concerned with teaching news and practices, so that these early volumes are of primary interest to those concerned with the history of the teaching of German. Changed from a monthly to a quarterly in 1965. Issues now contain usually 4 or 5 scholarly articles, of moderate length, on German literature and—only very occasionally—on the German language. Symposia sometimes occupy a major portion of issues. An annual feature is "Personalia" that includes a directory (by institution) of personnel in German departments of American and Canadian colleges and universities; a list of promotions; and a listing of doctoral degrees granted. The number and length of reviews has varied greatly in recent volumes: as few as 3 per issue and as many as 20, with a tendency toward the larger number. Most reviews are 600-700 words in length, but a number are several times that; they are all signed and critical. In English and German.

E 104542 rev. 2

DER Spiegel. *see* GENERAL

WELT UND WORT. v. 1, 1946-

Monthly. Tübingen, Germany. $16.00

Covering the entire German literary and publishing scene, it contains news of books, publishers and authors, and reviews of a large number of books in all areas, fiction and non-fiction. Each issue contains several types of contributions: articles on literary trends and developments, on great publishers, past and present, on types of literature, on literature and society, etc.; biographical or autobiographical material about a contemporary German, Austrian or Swiss writer, frequently in the form of an interview; other authors, German and foreign, who have a special relevance for today's readers, are also treated; 70-80 brief (200-500 words) reviews, plus several longer review-essays on single works or on groups of works; frequently runs portions from recently published works.

Highly regarded in the German literary world, *Welt und Wort* is important for those German departments that put much stress on postwar writers and writing.

49-17163*

WESTERMANNS MONATSHEFTE. v. 1, 1856-

Monthly. Brunswick, Germany. $21.40

A standard item for the upper middle-class home throughout its lengthy history, it resumed publication in 1949 after a suspension of five years. Its format reflects the affluence of West Germany, with genteel novels and stories by leading writers, articles on travel, natural history, scientific advances and, except for politics, on many other subjects, all intended for the educated layman, the solid citizen of the world. It places special emphasis on the arts—painting, drama, music, design, architecture, etc.— and these are exceptionally well illustrated with photographs, drawings and paintings beautifully reproduced in color, black-and-white, and sepia. News of new films, art exhibits, the opera, theatre, etc., plus usually 10-15 book reviews, mostly 150-350 words in length, on a variety of trade books.

11-29520 rev 3*

AMÉRICAS. *see* AREA STUDIES/LATIN AMERICA

CUADERNOS Americanos. *see* AREA STUDIES/LATIN AMERICA

CUADERNOS Hispanoamericanos. *see* AREA STUDIES/LATIN AMERICA *under* Cuadernos Americanos

EL GRITO. *see* GENERAL

*HISPANIA.   v. 1, 1918-

   5 nos.   Wichita, Kans. $8.00

   Published by the American Association of Teachers of Spanish and Portuguese. Contains literary essays and articles, linguistic studies, bibliographies, and articles on teaching methods and practices. Contributions on
   literature and culture have steadily increased, while those on pedagogy
   have decreased. There are a number of features and departments—"Notes
   on Usage," "Shop-Talk," "Spanish in the Elementary Schools," "Foreign Language Currents"— devoted to suggestions for and discussions of
   teaching. "The Hispanic World," a lengthy regular section, carries all sorts
   of news from Spain, Portugal and Latin America, including political, but
   most of it is devoted to arts and letters—new journals, literary events and
   prizes, listings of articles in established journals, etc. Official announcements of the Association, minutes of its meetings, and news of its chapters; other notes and news of meetings, programs and projects, etc., of
   interest to the profession. One number annually is devoted to the membership list of AATSP and its structure. An annual listing of *Dissertations
   in the Hispanic Languages and Literatures,* both completed and in progress, at U.S. and Canadian universities. There are two book sections:
   "Books of the Hispanic World" contains reviews of books, foreign and
   domestic, all genres, on Hispanic subjects or by Spanish authors; the other
   section, "Reviews," contains reviews of texts, linguistic studies, grammars,
   etc.—that is, materials useful primarily for teaching purposes. About 35
   or 40 reviews per issue, averaging about 500 words each. They are all
   signed and critical. In September, 1971 will begin carrying short reviews
   of textbooks that have been in use for some time. Also a list of books received; occasional film reviews. Contributions are in English, Spanish and
   (rarely) Portuguese.

   Indexed in: Ed.I.   20-23701 rev.

HISPANIC REVIEW.   v. 1, 1933-

   Quarterly.   Philadelphia, Pa. $9.50

   Published by the Department of Romance Languages of the University of
   Pennsylvania, it is "devoted to research in the Hispanic languages and
   literature." Contains scholarly articles on all periods and in all areas, with
   much emphasis on literature, but rarely contemporary. Most issues contain just a few articles which are medium length to long; shorter contribu-

tions appear as Varia. A major portion of the journal is devoted to reviews: about half (generally 5 or 6 an issue) are long, usually at least 1000, and often several times that many words; the other half receive briefer mention, perhaps up to 500 words. All reviews are signed and critical. List of books received. Text in English and Spanish.

Indexed in: S.S.H.I.   34-28948 rev.*

REVISTA Iberoamericana. *see* AREA STUDIES/LATIN AMERICA

INSULA. *see* GENERAL

INTERAMERICAN Review of Bibliography; Revista Interamericana de Bibliografía *see* AREA STUDIES/LATIN AMERICA

VISIÓN. *see* AREA STUDIES/LATIN AMERICA

NOVYI MIR.   v. 1, 1925-

Monthly.   Moscow. $7.59

The official organ of the Writers Union of the USSR, it is the most important literary journal in Russia. Though its early volumes are important
for the study of Soviet literature, the journal became really significant
after Aleksandr Tvardovsky, an eminent poet, took over as editor in 1950.
Except for the period 1954 to 1958, he remained editor until February,
1970, when he resigned because of the dismissal of four members of the
editorial board. Under his editorship, *Novyi Mir* was, according to the *New
York Times,* "the leading liberal publication in the Soviet Union [and]
regarded by the intelligentsia as the country's most respected journal."
Time declared that it "earned the reputation of being one of the best
literary magazines published in any language."

Certainly the journal is important for its publication of non-conformist
writers—the memoirs of Ehrenburg, Solzhenitsyn, Yevtushenko and others—
but it is also important for the excellence of other contributions—the
poetry, essays, fiction and literary criticism. Its future as the organ of
the intellectuals, as a nonconformist outlet is in doubt, but there's not
much question that it will remain as the single most important literary
journal in Russia, and for a serious study of recent and contemporary
Russian literature, both a current subscription and backfile are essential.

50-17046

RUSSIANReview. *see* AREA STUDIES/SOVIET UNION AND EAST EUROPE

SLAVIC AND EAST EUROPEAN JOURNAL.   v. 1, 1943;   n.s.v. 1, 1957-

Quarterly.   Madison, Wis. $~~10.00~~ 17.50

Published for the American Association of Teachers of Slavic and East
European languages, it was originally its *Bulletin,* then the *AATSEL Journal,* assuming its present title in 1957. Devoted to articles, reviews and
other items related to the language and literature of East Europe (that
is, Poland, Hungary, Czechoslovakia, Bulgaria, Yugoslavia, Albania, Russia
and the Baltic states) and the teaching of them, both at the secondary
and college level. Each issue contains usually 5 to 7 articles, varying
greatly in length, on these subjects, with increasing attention paid to
literature and less to pedagogics. News and notes of the profession and
of the Association and its chapters, and an annual listing of its members.
A large number of signed and critical book reviews, between 30 and 50
per issue, of books related to all the subjects covered by the journal,
including textbooks. They vary greatly in length, from a few hundred
to a few thousand words. Frequent review articles; list of books received.

49-17078 rev 3*

AMERICAN MUSICOLOGICAL SOCIETY. JOURNAL. v. 1, 1948-

3 nos./yr. Denton, Texas. $8.00

Contains scholarly articles on music history, on composers and their works, on instruments, and on music theory, all concerned with analysis of the music itself rather than with its creation or performance. Covers all eras from ancient history on, but with special attention to the classic and pre-classic periods. There are a number of regular features: "Studies and Abstracts"contains shorter research articles (before 1960, Abstracts were from papers presented at sectional meetings); notices of Society's meetings and a list of papers read at them; an annual list of members; an annual *Supplement to Doctoral Dissertations in Musicology,* a classified listing with subject and author indexes. A list of publications received appears in most issues, and all numbers contain usually 5 to 10 signed, critical reviews of books and editions of musical works. Most of these are quite long, often approaching article length. A basic journal where music is a field of concentration.

Indexed in: Music. I.   50-12713

*AMERICAN RECORD GUIDE. v. 1, 1935-

Monthly. N.Y. $4.50

The oldest review of recorded music in this country, it was founded as the *American Music Lover,* assuming its present title in 1944. Contains two types of reviews: the long essay-review, several thousand words in length, which may discuss more than one recording; shorter reviews, from a paragraph or two to a page in length. All reviews are signed, and many of the reviewers are outstanding critics and musicologists. Both tape and record reviews give complete buying information and all details necessary for cataloging. According to the editor, every new issue of serious music is covered. There are book reviews, signed, often quite long, and critical; occasional subject bibliographies and discographies, columns devoted to reviews of equipment, to news for collectors, and to other types of recordings—jazz, folk music and the spoken word. The May (Anniversary) issue contains an expanded section of book reviews—some 20 in the latest one—that are excellent. All these reviews are, of course, of books of interest to the lay music lover rather than just to the musicologist. The quality and length of the reviews, which are often valuable for their comments on the music as well as the rendition, make this perhaps the most useful record reviewing medium for academic libraries.

Indexed in: Music I.   42-9739 rev.
                     R.G.

APERTURE. v. 1, 1952-

Quarterly. N.Y. $14.00

A journal devoted to photography as an art. In 1967, Minor White, the editor, wrote that its interest was in "work in the wide, broad, deep and significant world of photography outside of the precincts of photojournalism, advertising and technology . . .because the limited objectives of these branches dominate the present-day photographic environment and threaten to swamp civilization. We do so to help maintain in full the breadth and scope of photography and to keep it growing in humanness." Issues consist primarily of reproduction of the work of leading (and often lesser-known) photographers, past and present. Indeed, a number of recent issues have been catalogs of exhibitions, issued both as numbers of *Aperture* and in clothbound editions. The occasional article is generally on the philosophy or approach of photography, never on specific techniques or equipment.

A beautiful journal, especially important for the dedicated student and teacher of photography.

58-30845

DANCE MAGAZINE.   v. 1, 1927-

Monthly.   N.Y. $9.00

Began in Los Angeles as the *American Dancer* and primarily devoted to West Coast dance activities; in 1933 it moved to New York, and in 1941 combined with *Dance*, which had emphasized modern dance, to form the present journal. It is devoted to articles, features, and photographs on every aspect of the dance: history, training, teaching, analysis, design, current developments, etc. In addition to the articles, all of which are thoroughly illustrated, there are a number of regular features: "On the Boards" profiles each month one or several dancers or choreographers in show business; news of people, organizations, courses, conferences and meetings, both here and abroad; etc. "Looking at Television"; a "Brief Biography" of a dancer who is establishing a reputation; a continuing series of articles for dance teachers in local communities; brief reviews of records for dance teachers. The May issue contains the annual "Calendar of Summer International Dance Events." Reviews of special performances, concerts and premieres. A listing of schools, colleges, regional companies, and teachers in each issue. "The Dancer's Bookshelf," containing a few signed and critical reviews, appears in most issues. The leading journal in the field, it should be in every library where there is interest in the subject; because it contains so much general information it will also be used by general readers with even a casual interest in the dance.

Indexed in: R.G.   A41-1591

DANCE PERSPECTIVES.   v. 1, 1958 -

Quarterly.   N.Y. $8.00

Published by the Dance Perspectives Foundation, which was formed "to encourage awareness and understanding of the art of the dance as a great historical tradition and as a significant force in contemporary life." Issues are usually devoted to a single topic, but it may be historical or contemporary, anthropological or artistic, theory or practice. Some topics of issues have been Cine-Dance, Castanets, Trance Dance, translations of two 17th-century French texts on ballet, the dance lithographs of Currier and Ives. Handsomely produced, lavishly illustrated, it should be in libraries where there is a serious interest in the dance.

Indexed in: Music I.   62-3629

*THE DRAMA REVIEW.   v. 1, 1955/56-

Quarterly.   N.Y. $7.50

Publication actually began with number 3 of volume 1: the first two issues were published as the *Carleton Drama Review*. Then it became the *Tulane Drama Review* and, under the editorship of Richard Schechner,

grew rapidly in circulation and reputation. Its success was furthered by
a Rockefeller Foundation grant in 1965; in 1967 it moved to New York
under the auspices of New York University and adopted its present title.
(As the *Tulane Drama Review*, it had become known as *TDR*; those
initials still are its logo, though the T now stands for The.) Its contents
are difficult to categorize, but it is safe to say that it is very much concerned with the avant-garde (several playwrights, who later became fashionable, were introduced in *TDR*) and the controversial, especially the
social and political implications of theatre. It frequently carries tape-record-
ed interviews with playwrights, directors, and others and publishes texts of
of original short plays. There are critical articles and essays, original contributions to the theory of dramatic writing and production, and discussions of the relationship of the theatre to other arts and to various
segments of society. Issues are frequently devoted to single topics—e.g.,
Latin American Theatre, Bertolt Brecht, Politics and Performance. There
is no book review section any longer; important works occasionally receive special attention, and bibliographic articles sometimes are run as
part of the topic of a particular issue. Well illustrated, attractively produced, with stimulating contributions by theatre notables from here and
abroad, and controversial views on the role of the theatre emphasized,
TDR is an essential purchase for every academic library.

Indexed in: S.S.H.I.   59-16990

*EDUCATIONAL THEATRE JOURNAL. v. 1, 1949-

Quarterly.   Washington, D.C. $12.50

Published by the American Educational Theatre Association, Inc. to be
"the greatest possible use to students, workers, and teachers of the educational theatre and drama in all aspects and at all levels" (vol. 1, no. 1).
Its early emphasis was on "practical" articles on teaching drama, on production, and on the role of drama in education, but the articles have
more and more treated the drama from its biographical, historical, aesthetic, critical and comparative aspects. It still carries a number of articles about educational theatre (especially in colleges and universities) and
continues its annual survey of college and university theatre productions
and the annual listing of *Doctoral Projects in Progress in Theatre Arts*, but
it dropped in 1968 the section containing news and notices of developments, conventions, appointments, awards, etc., and the listing of plays
produced at members' theatres. Issues sometimes treat single topics —e.g.,
English-Irish Theatre, 20th Century French Theatre, etc,—and there have
been a number of special issues, usually containing the proceedings of a
conference on theatre research or education. There are 2 sections of reviews: "Theatre in Review" (formerly "Broadway in Review") reviews
productions in New York, but more on producing groups around the
country; "Books in Review" contains signed, critical reviews of 6 to 10
books, mostly 750-1000 words in length. Also a list of books received
with brief descriptive notes. An essential journal where there is any real
interest in the drama.

Indexed in: Ed.I.   52-794

ETHNOMUSICOLOGY.   v. 1,1953-

3 nos./yr.   Ann Arbor, Mich. $15.00

The journal of the Society for Ethnomusicology, it was known until
1957 as *Ethno-Musicology Newsletter*. It is devoted to the study of music
itself, but in its cultural context. Usually 5 to 7 scholarly articles per

issue, mostly on studies of particular ethnic groups—to give an idea of
the variety, one issue treated Urdu poetry chants, songs of the Amazonian
Indians, Javanese dance, Shona music of Rhodesia, a comparison of Plains
and Pueblo songs—or, occasionally, on the purposes and methods of ethno-
musicology. Bibliography is an important part of the journal. There are
frequent special bibliographies on particular aspects of folk music (e.g.,
"The Art Music of India") or on scholars in the field. Also, each issue
contains the important *Current Bibliography and Discography*, an extensive listing of books, pamphlets, periodical articles, recordings and
printed music, organized by geographical areas and topics. A substantial
number of book reviews and record reviews, all of them signed and critical,
and most of them well over 1000 words. Treating a topic that is of
rapidly growing interest, it is an important journal where there are strong
music departments or where there is much attention to non-Western culture.

Indexed in: Music I.   56-12963

FILM CULTURE. v. 1, 1955-

Quarterly. N.Y. $4.00

Founded and still edited by Jonas Mekas, who was also a founder of the
"underground film" movement and still is one of its leading figures, its
"chief objective" has always been "to help impart depth and vigour to
cinematic culture in our country by becoming a meeting ground for outspoken discussion and constructive analysis of ideas, achievements and
problems in the domain of the film." It is concerned mostly with the
experimental film rather than with commercial films, although it does of
course comment on some of the classic (and not-so-classic) commercial
films and their makers. Contains many interviews, discussions and essays
on the techniques and ideas of filmmaking, with numerous illustrations.
Its frequency and its format are hard to pin down (though from 1967
to 1970 its format has remained consistent, though only 3 numbers were
issued during that period.) Despite—or perhaps because of—its unorthodox
ways, it is one of the most perceptive commentators on the film, and
because of its contributors and interviews, will be looked at eagerly by film
buffs and amateur cinematographers. (A *Film Culture Reader*, selected
from the 1955-1970 issues, was published in August, 1970 by Praeger.)

Indexed in: Art.I.   59-37118

*FILM QUARTERLY. v. 1, 1945-

Quarterly. Berkeley, Calif. $6.00

Originally the *Hollywood Quarterly*, it changed to the *Quarterly of Film,
Radio and Television* in 1951, adopting its present title in 1958. Its coverage changed similarly: it began as a journal on the film, then expanded
to include radio and television, then retrenched (after suspending publication briefly) to cover only film. Each issue of (usually) 64 pages includes
brief articles by makers, critics, teachers and just devotees of the film on
its history, trends, and theory as well as on individual films and personalities, interviews with directors, producers, or critics; detailed reviews of a
few recent films, plus briefer reviews of less significant ones. Generally
several longer book reviews per issue; signed and critical, they are mostly
about 750 words; a few shorter reviews also. The periodical is well illustrated and should be of interest to the general reader as well as the student
of the film.

Indexed in: Art I.   A 45-5270 rev. 2*
R.G.

*HIGH FIDELITY AND MUSICAL AMERICA. v. 1, 1951-

Monthly (plus special Directory Issue in December)   Cincinnati, Ohio
$6.00

Musical America, which lasted from 1898 through 1964, was a periodical primarily for performing musicians or others connected with the profession, providing a thorough coverage of activities in the world of music, and was also, of course, interesting for undergraduates who aspired to the professional world of music. It was purchased in late 1964 by *High Fidelity Magazine*, which, since that time has had two editions: one, incorporating *Musical America* as an insert or a separate section; the other, available without it. It is the former that is recommended for libraries.

The *High Fidelity* portion covers three areas: (1) "Music and Musicians," containing articles and notes on composers and musicians, orchestras, music history and criticism, etc., and frequent discographies that are useful in building a collection; (2) "Audio and Video," evaluations of new equipment (these are lengthy and technical and highly regarded by hi-fi buffs) and articles and items of news and developments in music recording and reproduction; (3) "Recordings," including feature reviews in depth, plus shorter reviews, a paragraph or two in length, of other classical recordings, reissues, lighter music, folk music, jazz, cassettes and tape recordings. All reviews are by the staff, are signed, and are highly reliable. Complete buying information is given.

The *Musical America* section is, in number of pages anyway, a minor part of the periodical, and it carries less news than it used to as an independent publication. The articles and news of personalities and the professional world are still interesting, and subscribers may receive the invaluable *Special Directory Issue*. It is a directory of all U.S. and Canadian symphony orchestras, opera companies, concert series and managers, foundations and awards, professional and service and record companies, plus many of the same categories for foreign countries. It is an important reference tool and makes a subscription to the magazine worthwhile for every library.

Also contains a few signed and critical book reviews. The great interest by undergraduates in recorded music and hi-fi equipment, plus the many useful features for libraries, especially those that purchase hi-fi equipment or phonograph records (the frequent comparative evaluations, of both records and equipment are excellent) make it an essential purchase for every college library.

Indexed in: Music I.   56-3398 rev. 2
    R.G.

INSTRUMENTALIST. v. 1, 1946-

Monthly (except July) Evanston, Ill. $7.00

Intended for the music educator—the school or college teacher of music, the band or orchestra director, or the private teacher. Contains a large number of short, practical articles on all aspects of music history, theory, teaching and performance, but with great emphasis on such items as "Developing Good Clarinet Tone," or "Arranging for the Football Band." Sections appearing in most issues include: Brass Clinic, Conductor's Corner, Marching Band, National Bank Association Counterpoint, National School Orchestra Association Soundpost, Percussion Clinic, String Clinic, Wookwind Clinic. Each of these contains news of interest and teaching hints for those in the particular area. Brief reviews of new music, arranged by grade, with complete buying information. Brief reviews of a few new records and a few new books. The August issue contains the annual Football Music Guide, a listing of music arranged for field use, and the Buyer's Guide, a classified listing of companies supplying the needs of instrumental music. The annual Directory of Music Organizations is carried in it or the September issue.

An important journal for colleges where there is much work in music education or where the teaching of instrumental music is significant.

Indexed in: Music I.   51-32280

JOURNAL OF MUSIC THEORY.   v. 1, 1957-

Semi-annually.   New Haven, Conn. $6.00

Each issue contains usually 4 to 6 articles in all areas of music theory—history, structure, analysis, musical notation, bibliography—and on all periods, from ancient to computer-produced music. Occasionally carries translations of works important in the history of music theory. Contributors are professors of music from many universities, mostly American, but sometimes from abroad, and their articles are frequently quite technical. Usually 4 or 5 long signed book reviews, often running to several thousand works, in each issue; also a listing of recent books and articles. For advanced students and faculty.

Indexed in: Music I.   66-99830/MN

*MODERN DRAMA.   v. 1, 1958-

Quarterly.   Lawrence, Kans. $4.00

Covers the drama since Ibsen, with perhaps more attention quite appropriately paid to continental playwrights. The articles are scholarly, fairly brief (rarely more than 10 or 12 pages), and either biographical, historical, or critical. Technical matters of stagecraft and production are generally not treated. Issues are occasionally devoted to a single author or to a subject such as Classical Myth in Modern Drama, or German Drama since World War II. Bibliographies of individual playwrights appear frequently, and there is a useful bi-annual feature (originally annual), *Modern Drama: A Selective Bibliography of Works Published in English*, that covers a number of drama and philological periodicals as well as books, and is arranged by country and author. "Research in Modern Drama," reporting doctoral and post-doctoral research, was an annual feature from 1965 through 1968. There are a few book reviews, generally no more than 6 or 7; these are signed and critical, usually between 500 and 1000 words.

An important publication where there is any interest in drama, either its production or study.

Indexed in: S.S.H.I.   59-4524

MUSIC & LETTERS.   v. 1, 1920-

Quarterly.   London. $6.00

Contains scholarly articles on musical history, criticism, biography, etc. There is some musicology, but it is outweighed by the historical approach, as the journal is intended for the serious student or the well-informed layman, as well as the scholar. Because of this, there is no discussion of current developments in music and the classical composers receive by far the most attention. Some 15 to 20 book reviews appear in each issue; they are mostly 750-1000 words long, but some are longer, and all are signed and critical. "Reviews of Music" includes both new music and new editions of older works; the reviews, 30-35 an issue, vary greatly in length. There is also a list of "Books Received" and "Music Received."

Indexed in: Br.Hum.I.   63-24794/MN
            Music I.

MUSIC EDUCATORS' JOURNAL.   v. 1, 1914-

Monthly (except June-Aug.)   Washington, D.C. $6.00

Originally titled the *Music Supervisors' Journal*, it adopted its present title in 1934, when the name of its parent organization was changed to the Music Educators' National Conference. The Conference, which is a department of the N.E.A., represents "all phases of music education in schools, colleges, universities, and teacher-training institutions." Reflecting this interest, the articles are mostly of interest to teachers of music rather than to musicians or musicologists, but there are enough for the latter groups to make the journal important even when music education is not a major concern. There are frequent articles on aesthetics and on performing, but, again, mostly as they relate to music education. Many "practical" articles on equipment, curriculum, teaching methods, etc. Regular features include: news of the MENC and of music activities in schools and colleges; a listing of "Professional Materials," including catalogs and pamphlets, with descriptive notes; descriptions of summer festivals, workshops and schools; awards results and announcements of "Awards and Competitions"; news and descriptions of new "Instruments and Equipment." "Book Reviews" contains signed reviews, occasionally fairly long, on a variety of musical books, though again, mostly related to teaching music. An important journal for music departments, and especially where music teachers are being trained.

Indexed in: Ed.I.
            Music I.

MUSIC Index. *see* INDEXES

*MUSIC LIBRARY ASSOCIATION.   NOTES.   Second Series, v. 1, 1943-

Quarterly.   Ann Arbor, Mich. $15.00

Includes articles on the historical and general aspects of music, but emphasizing musical literature rather than the music itself; also articles on music bibliography and on the acquisition of music materials. A major portion of each issue is devoted to regular features. "Notes for *Notes*" reports news of interest to the membership of the Music Library Association. "Current Catalogs from the Music World" lists recently issued catalogs from music dealers and publishers, and record dealers and manufacturers, both domestic and foreign. The "Index to Record Reviews," begun in 1948, which lists reviews of recent recordings from 17 of the best periodical sources, with evaluation symbols, comprises a very handy guide for record selection. News of MLA and an annual listing of members. There are a large number of excellent signed book reviews (now usually 25-30 in each issue), some several pages long, others briefly noted with a few paragraphs. A list of foreign and domestic "Books Recently Published" also appears. "Music Reviews" are extensive and carefully written, and there are frequent surveys of music for a particular instrument or interest group—e.g., Piano Music for Children, Organ Music. Listings of newly-published music and forthcoming reprints of music and musical literature are also included. Because of these very useful bibliographical features, comprising perhaps the most comprehensive listing of current music literature available, *Notes* is an essential purchase for every college library.

Indexed in: B.R.D.   43-45299
             Lib.Lit.
             Music I.

MUSIC REVIEW .   v. 1, 1940-

Quarterly.   Cambridge, Eng. $14.40

Edited since its inception by Geoffrey Sharp, it is devoted to scholarly studies of music—its history, theory, analysis, biography, etc., with each issue containing an average of 6 articles, mostly brief to moderate length, on these topics. Contributors include leading musical scholars from all over the world. A good book review section; the number of reviews varies widely, from one to perhaps 15, though usually there are fewer than 5; the length also varies, but many are several thousand words. All, however, are signed and critical and are excellently done, though *Grove's Dictionary* feels they "are sometimes rather unnecessarily polemical and didactic in tone." Reviews of some new music; lengthy reviews of a few important recent recordings, though not in every issue. An important journal for the serious music student.

Indexed in: Br.Hum.I.   56-29749
             Music I.

*MUSICAL   QUARTERLY.   v. 1, 1915-

Quarterly.   N.Y. $9.00

Published by G. Schirmer, Inc., but granted absolute independence by that company, it has been edited since 1946 by Paul Henry Lang. From 1929 to 1944 it was edited by Carl Engel, the eminent musicographer who made it really cosmopolitan and established it as the most important of American music periodicals. Contains scholarly articles on the historical, technical and biographical aspects of music by musicologists, composers and musicians. While it is primarily concerned with "standard music and composers," generally at least one article in each issue is, and several special issues have been, devoted to contemporary music, and there are occasional articles on "exotic" music. Regular features include: "Current Chronicle," containing comments on performances of new works both here and abroad; a few signed book reviews (rarely more than 4) that are quite long, done mostly by recognized scholars; "Reviews of Records"—again, only a few, with no attempt at comparative reviewing and little comment on technical matters, but compensated for by detailed, authoritative analysis of the music; a very valuable "Quarterly Book-List," classified by language, and giving complete bibliographical information. The basic music journal for academic libraries.

Indexed in: B.R.D.   16-24484
          Music I.
          R.G.

*OPERA NEWS.   v. 1, 1936-

27 nos./yr.   N.Y. $10.00

Published by the Metropolitan Opera Guild from September through June, irregularly at the beginning and end of the opera season, and weekly during the Metropolitan Opera broadcast season. Issues are received in time for the Saturday broadcast, and that week's opera is featured in the issue which covers the story of the opera, listing each aria, duet and chorus, illustrating the sets, plus a brief list of suggested readings. Other articles treat additional aspects of that opera, plus profiles and general discussions of composers, conductors, artists, opera houses, and opera news and history. Additional features include interviews with leading personalities, miscellaneous opera news including a "U.S. Calendar" of productions for the next few weeks of opera groups around the country, and reports of other operatic developments here and abroad. Both records and books are reviewed; these are signed reviews, many fairly brief, some of moderate length. *Opera News* is attractively produced, thoroughly illustrated, and generally well written. An important journal for the opera lover and for research where there is much interest in music because of its extensive coverage of the field and the first-hand information about its participants.

Indexed in: Music I.   CA 18-1142 unrev'd.
          R.G.

PERSPECTIVES OF NEW MUSIC.   v. 1, 1962-

2 nos./yr.   Princeton, N.J. $6.00

Dedicated to contemporary music, it was founded to encourage discussion of the fundamental issues in the field and to provide a forum for the orderly development of ideas and the presentation of problems. There are some scholarly historical and biographical articles, and thoughtful essays on the relationship of contemporary music to the profession and to society, but most of the journal is devoted to articles, discussions, analyses, and notes on composition, some written by musicologists, but frequently by the composers themselves. An important part of many of the contributions is controversy, and this is as it should be in a field that is just developing and has many strong and disparate personalities. "New Music" reviews one or a few new compositions; "New Books" covers— usually briefly, but occasionally at length—recent books with excellent reviews. There is also a list of publications received. The journal's Advisory and Editorial Boards consist of some of the most respected contemporary composers, and it is an essential title where there is much interest in new music, and an important one wherever music is taught.

Indexed in: Music I.   66-89176/MN

*POPULAR PHOTOGRAPHY.   v. 1, 1937-

Monthly.   N.Y. $7.00

Covers every aspect of photography: equipment and materials, process-ing, interviews with and biographies of well-known photographers with particular attention to their work, professional training, special techniques, recent developments, etc. Still photography is the main interest, but there are frequent articles, as well as a regular section on movies. Practical advice and reports are emphasized, with features describing, testing and comparing new equipment and devices and giving advice and instruction to help readers improve their work. Regular features include a description of competitions, a national calendar of exhibitions, reviews of shows, technical questions from readers, and many others. A large number of pages are devoted to advertising, an important feature for photographers, both amateur and pro-fessional. Issues are of course thoroughly illustrated, much of it in color.

A similar journal, with a somewhat smaller circulation, and perhaps more appealing to better photographers, is *Modern Photography* (v. 1, 1937- $6.00). Its annual "Camera and Accessory Buying Guide" is especially useful. It is also published monthly, and in addition to being indexed in the *Readers' Guide* is also in the *Applied Science and Technology Index*.

Both contain some book reviews, usually under 500 words. For most college libraries, the browsing value of these titles is more important than the reference value, and binding—or even keeping an extensive back-file—may not be necessary. But they will be looked through regularly by today's students, so many of whom are interested more or less seriously in photography.

Indexed in: R.G.   39-13623 rev. 2

*SCHWANN RECORD & TAPE GUIDE.   v. 1, 1949-

Monthly.   Boston, Mass.   Available from record distributors. $10.50

A listing of currently available stereo LP records, cartridge tapes and cassette tapes. Does not include records sold only by direct mail or those available only in a small number of outlets. Some 45,000 titles on 751 labels are now listed; they are mostly listed by compo-ser, giving for each the name of the composition, the artist, contents of the reverse side (if different), the label and number. (A price list for all labels is included in the back of each issue.) A number of categories are listed separately—collections of works, ballets, opera, current popular, jazz, etc.—all giving the same items of information.

brief listing of "Recent Books on Music." Since 1969, a *Supplementary Record Guide*, published twice a year, has listed certain categories of special and unusual records not as much in demand: imports, non-current, religious, spoken, Latin-American, international popular and folk, and children's records. Most of these were formerly listed in the monthly number. Libraries purchasing records will need both series for their order departments, but since many record collectors get copies of the Schwann catalog from the shops in which they buy records, it is probably not necessary to display it. Only libraries with extensive research music collections will want to keep back numbers.

58-28654

SIGHT AND SOUND. v. 1, 1932-

Quarterly. London. $5.00

"The international film quarterly," it is sponsored and published by the British Film Institute, though not necessarily expressing its views. Each issue contains a good balance of articles, features and reviews. The articles are on individuals—actors, directors, producers, etc.—often in the form of interviews, on the history of the film, on themes, methods, etc., relating mostly to English and American films. Written by staff members and others, they vary greatly in length. The features include news of the film world, of individual activities, coverage of film festivals, and a page of notes on 30 to 40 recent films of special interest. The reviews of films—usually about 10 in an issue—are carefully done; they are mostly on English-language films and usually 500-1000 words in length. One or two book reviews per issue; signed and critical, usually 1000 words or longer. Thoroughly illustrated. On the one hand, it has been criticized as conservative; on the other, it has been called "the world's most important film magazine." Whatever one's view, it is reliable and perceptive, and surely important where there is much interest in the film. It is, furthermore, an excellent buy.

Indexed in: Art I.
          Br.Hum.I.

SING OUT! v. 1, 1950-

Bi-monthly. N.Y. $5.00

Many folk music journals began in the post-World War II period, responding to the tremendous popular interest in the field, but only *Sing Out!* achieved any real stature; indeed, almost all the others were short-lived. The periodical was founded as part of an organization known as People's Artists, and financed by the success of Folkways Records; after the first few issues, Irwin Silber, who had worked with Folkways, became editor, a position he held until 1968.

Devoted to the creation, growth and distribution of "People's Music," which includes more formally composed music as well as traditional folk music and "has to do with the hopes and fears and lives of common people," it showed steady growth and ultimately reached a circulation of 25,000. Over the years, almost every well known person associated with American folk music—performers, composers and scholars—have contributed articles, reminiscences, columns, and songs. The last type of contribution has been one of *Sing Out!*'s important features, since it includes many songs that are unavailable elsewhere, and usually contains not just words and music, but also guitar chords. Also important and unique are the reminiscences and interviews with folk artists. Most articles and features have been well illustrated. Also contains news of the world of folk music and excellent record reviews.

The journal reached its peak in content and format in the middle 1960's. In 1968 its larger size (which it had adopted only 2 years before) was reduced, and in 1971 it was announced that it faced a severe financial crisis. Should it overcome this, college libraries where there is much interest in folk music—and where is there not?—should consider subscribing. A back file provides an extraordinary source of material for the history of American (and some other, though not nearly as much) folk music.

Indexed in: Music I.   61-45751

AMERICAN PHILOSOPHICAL QUARTERLY. v. 1, 1964-

Quarterly.   Oxford, Eng. $18.00

Each issue contains between 5 and 10 scholarly articles, varying in length from 2000 to 25,000 words, "on any aspect of philosophy, substantive or historical." Occasional list of books received, but no book reviews, news items, or discussion notes. Contributors are mostly from American universities, but other countries are frequently represented. Analytical and critical surveys of recent work in various areas of philosophy appear from time to time, covering work that appeared in journals as well as books.

ANALYSIS. v. 1, 1933-

Bi-monthly.   London. $4.80

Founded by a group of philosophers who had been influenced by Russell, Moore and Wittgenstein. The journal's intent always has been "to publish short articles on limited and precisely defined philosophical questions about the elucidation of known facts" and to foster the exchange of views and debate. Due to the war, it was discontinued between 1940 and 1946. Each issue consists of brief contributions, some less than a page long and almost never more than 3000 words, by British and American philosophers, stating a position, or taking issue with one previously stated. (Two supplements were issued in 1963 and 1964 to accommodate longer articles, but the practice was dropped.) An important journal in the fields of logic, philosophy of science and linguistic analysis.

Indexed in: Br.Hum.I.   52-20996

AUSTRALASIAN JOURNAL OF PHILOSOPHY. v. 1, 1923-

3 nos./yr.   Sydney, Australia. $8.00

Published by the Australasian Association of Philosophy, it was titled, until 1946, the *Australasian Journal of Psychology and Philosophy*. Since 1935, under the editorship of John Anderson and A. K. Stout (the latter's father was editor of *Mind*), the journal became increasingly well-known, and today it receives contributions from a wide assortment of British, Australian, Canadian and American scholars. The "asian" part of its title does not at all signify that it has any relationship with oriental philosophy; its contents—usually 6 to 8 articles per issue, of brief to moderate length, are in the standard Western topics, and on the standard figures, and most fall in the areas of logic, metaphysics and epistemology. Some "Discussions." The number of reviews varies from 4 to 10 or so; signed and critical, they are mostly at least 1500 words and often much more. List of books received and "Notes and News" of the Association and other organizations.

36-2061

BRITISH JOURNAL FOR THE PHILOSOPHY OF SCIENCE.   v. 1, 1950-

Quarterly.   London $9.50

Official organ of the British Society for the Philosophy of Science, whose purpose is "to study the logic, the method and the philosophy of science as well as those of the various special sciences, including the social sciences." Usually 3 to 5 scholarly articles in these areas, rarely exceeding 5000 words, plus 2 or 3 shorter "Discussions," which are usually responses to earlier articles, or observations on points made in recent books. Contributors have included the most eminent names in the field: L.L. Whyte, S.O. Wisdom, Karl Popper, Michael Polanyi, E.H. Hutten, and many others. An average of 6 to 8 reviews per issue; these are excellent, mostly 750-1000 words, but often several times that for especially important books. Alternate issues (annually) carry abstracts from recent numbers of *Philosophy of Science* and *Synthese*, the other two important journals in the field. and there are frequent lists of "Recent Publications." Because of the central position of the Society in this area, this is perhaps the most importa nt journal for the philosophy of science, and, considering the increased interest by philosophers in this subject, the journal should be available where there are strong departments of philosophy.

Indexed in: Br.Hum.I.   58-20562

DIOGENES. *see* GENERAL

*ETHICS.   v. 1, 1890-

Quarterly.   Chicago, Ill. $8.00

Originally the *International Journal of Ethics*, it changed to its present title in 1938. Subtitled "an international journal of social, political and legal philosophy," it is "devoted to the study of the ideas and principles which form the basis for individual and social action. It publishes articles in ethical theory, social science, and jurisprudence contributing to an understanding of the basic structure of civilization and society." One recent number, for example, contained pieces on the ethics of birth control, on moral commitments, on freedom in history and politics, on determinism, on inalienable rights and on the concept of obligation. Each issue contains 3 to 5 articles of moderate length, plus 4 or 5 pieces (usually shorter, but not necessarily) under the heading "Discussion." The "Discussion" items and the leading articles are not related; the latter are mostly original, speculative papers, while the former are responses to earlier articles, or to books published recently or long ago, or just to concepts or precepts with which the author takes issue. From 2 to 5 book reviews per issue, of works on politics, education and sociology as well as philosophy; they average 750-1000 words, but are frequently several times that. "Notes on New Books" annotates but does not evaluate a large number of titles; the section listing reprints, translations and textbooks also contains brief descriptive notes.

An interesting review, with material relevant to all disciplines; an important journal for all liberal arts education.

Indexed in: S.S.H.I.   10-22570

INQUIRY.   v. 1, 1958-

Quarterly.   Oslo, Norway. $7.50

"An interdisciplinary journal of philosophy and the social sciences, it is intended for philosophers who are interested in problems concerning the foundations of the sciences of man and society; it is intended for behavioral and social scientists who are concerned with problems of theory-building, with the logic of analysis and inquiry, and with the ethical assumptions and the practical implications of their research." Early numbers contained usually only 3 or 4 articles; the size has gradually increased (from about 60 to over 100 pages) so that there are now from 4 to 7 articles per issue, plus discussions of previous articles. Occasionally issues treat a single subject—e.g., Philosophy in Eastern Europe, Functionalism, Spinoza. Despite the original purposes of the journal, most of the articles are now in central areas of philosophy. Contributors are from many countries, but all articles are in English and each is preceded by an abstract. No book reviews, but frequent review-discussions.

Indexed in: Ment.Hlth.B.R.I.

INTERNATIONAL PHILOSOPHICAL Quarterly. *see* page 435.

JOURNAL of Aesthetic Education. *see* EDUCATION

*JOURNAL OF AESTHETICS AND ART CRITICISM.   v. 1, 1941-

Quarterly.   Cleveland, Ohio. $15.00

Published by the American Society for Aesthetics and the Cleveland Museum of Art. The Society's purpose is "to promote study, research, discussion and publication in aesthetics," which "includes all studies of the arts and related types of experience from a philosophic, scientific, or other theoretical standpoint, including those of psychology, sociology, anthropology, visual arts history, art criticism, and education. "The arts include the visual arts, literature, music, and theater arts." Issues, which are sometimes devoted to a single topic, now contain about 10 scholarly articles; also about 15 book reviews, signed and critical, varying from a few hundred to over 1000 words. Notes and news of interest, including news of the Society's members, of whom there is an annual listing. The *Selective Current Bibliography for Aesthetics and Related Fields,* including books, articles, and pamphlets, and portions of larger works, has appeared annually since 1945. An important journal where there is much interest in philosophy or music, art, or literary theory, or for the relationships between any of these areas.

Indexed in: Art I.   A 43-3205 rev.
            Music I.

*JOURNAL OF PHILOSOPHY.   v. 1, 1904-

Bi-weekly (every 4 weeks, July-Aug.)   N.Y. $9.00

Publishes scholarly articles, many fairly brief, on philosophical topics of current interest, especially in metaphysics, ethics, and aesthetics, generally representing a naturalistic viewpoint. Articles "that explore the borderlines between philosophy and the special disciplines" are encouraged. The book reviews are now few, but critical and quite long, sometimes article length. Proceedings of the annual meeting of the Eastern Division of the American Philosophical Association are reported fully—the program, texts of the symposium papers, and abstracts of other papers. Also reported, though not as fully or regularly, are other meetings' programs—the Society for Existential Philosophy and Phenomenology, the Southern Society for Philosophy and Psychology, among others. "Notes and News" contains items about individuals, meetings, promotions and appointments, new courses and programs, new periodicals, other special publishing projects, etc. Founded as the *Journal of Philosophy, Psychology and Scientific Method,* it assumed its present title in 1920 after the contributions on psychology had diminished. Since some of the most eminent figures in both fields were regular contributors, with the journal serving as an outlet for several new movements, the back files are important for both the history of American philosophy and psychology.

Indexed in: B.R.D.   6-973
               S.S.H.I.

JOURNAL OF SYMBOLIC LOGIC.   v. 1, 1936-

Quarterly.   Providence, R.I. $30.00

Official organ of the Association for Symbolic Logic. Includes original technical papers, expository papers, philosophical papers relating to or using symbolic logic, and studies in the history of logic. Almost all articles fall in the first two categories. Issues contain about 10 to 12 articles, though this number and the length of the articles may vary widely. Because it is the leading journal in this specialized area, its contributors are from all over the world; growing interest in this area may be inferred from the increased size—in the last few years the number of pages per volume has almost doubled. The reviews, all signed and critical, are of important articles as well as of books; it is an extensive section containing some long, almost article-length reviews, many shorter ones, and a listing of articles in other journals. Publishes official notices of the Association, and contains abstracts of papers presented at its meetings. There is an annual listing of the Association's officers and members. A specialized and scholarly journal, but essential where courses in symbolic logic are offered.

Indexed in: S.S.H.I.   41-486

JOURNAL of the History of Ideas. *see* HISTORY

*JOURNAL OF THE HISTORY OF PHILOSOPHY.   v. 1, 1963-

Quarterly.   La Jolla, Calif. $10.00

Sponsored by the Claremont Colleges, Stanford University, the University of California, and the Winchester Foundation, it contains scholarly articles, notes and discussions about the history of Western philosophy, broadly conceived. Almost all contributions are in English, but occasionally one appears in another major European language; contributors are international. The book reviews are all signed and critical, but vary in length and number per issue; while there have been as few as 5 and as many as 20 per issue, they are mostly over 1000 words long, and not infrequently run to 2500 or 3000 words. A few shorter book notes, and a listing of books received.

65-9310

*MIND. *see* page 435.

MONIST. v. 1, 1890-

Quarterly.   LaSalle, Ill. $8.00

After volume 46 (1936) the journal suspended publication for 25 years, resuming in September, 1962 under the sponsorship of the Edward C. Hegeler Foundation. The first 46 volumes were devoted to the philosophy of science and had as contributors some of the most eminent international scholars in this area—Dewey, Peirce, Bertrand Russell, Bosanquet, Paul Carus (who also was its editor, 1890-1919), and others. The revived publication is concerned with general philosophical inquiry, each issue being devoted to a single topic—e.g., Philosophical Implications of the New Cosmology, Metaphysics Today, British and American Realism, 1900-1930, Philosophy of John Duns Scotus. Each issue contains on the average 8 or 9 scholarly articles, mostly 5-10,000 words, by international contributors. Issues usually contain a list of books received, but there are no reviews. Not a ground-breaking or very influential journal, perhaps, but the topical approach, and the reliability of its contributions make it very useful for undergraduates.

8-22458

PHILOSOPHER'S INDEX.   v. 1, 1967-

Quarterly.   Bowling Green, Ohio. $20.00

A publication of the Philosophy Documentation Center at Bowling Green University, "an organization for the collection, storage and dissemination of bibliographic data in philosophy." The *Index* covers "all major American and British philosophical periodicals, selected journals in other languages, and related interdisciplinary publications," a total of about 150 titles. It consists of 4 major sections: 1) "Subject Index" (these are mostly one-word subjects—major fields or divisions of fields of philosophy, persons, periods, concepts); 2) "Author Index"; 3) "Bibliographic Information and Abstracts" of all the items indexed (most abstracts provided by the authors); 4) "Book Review Index." Despite its format (computer-produced, all upper case) and the problems of indexing ideas as mercurial as philosophical speculations, it is an important reference tool for faculty and students of philosophy and should be available wherever there is any serious interest in the field.

74-250928

PHILOSOPHICAL BOOKS.   v. 1, 1960-

3 nos./yr.   Leicester, Eng. $3.00 $2.40

Devoted solely to reviews of current books in the field. Each issue contains reviews of some 15 to 20 books, usually 750-1000 words, but
longer for more important works; each review is by an authority in
the field. Only books in English are included, though they range over
all areas of philosophy. Useful for book selection as well as for the astute analyses by the reviewers.

67-33484

PHILOSOPHICAL QUARTERLY.   v. 1, 1950

Quarterly.   St. Andrews, Scotland. $7.00

Published by the University of St. Andrews for the Scots Philosophical
Club. Contains scholarly articles in all branches of philosophy, with preference given to metaphysics, ethics, logic, and the history of philosophy.
About 5 articles, short to moderately long, per issue, plus one or two
shorter "Discussions" which are mostly responses or reactions to recent
or older books and articles. Contributors are primarily British. About 20
reviews per issue, all signed and critical, often bluntly so. Most are 500-
1000 words in length, but often they are much longer; under the heading "Critical Study" are reviews that are article length. List of books received.

Indexed in: Br.Hum.I.   59-39197

***PHILOSOPHICAL REVIEW.**   v. 1, 1892-

Quarterly.   Ithaca, N.Y. $6.00

Edited by the faculty of the Sage School of Philosophy in Cornell University. A relatively undistinguished journal for most of its life; in 1950
it changed from a bi-monthly to a quarterly and, under the editorship
of Max Black, became much more important, and is now regarded by
some as the most important philosophical periodical in the English-
speaking world. Its viewpoint is generally analytic. Proceedings of the
American Philosophical Association were carried annually through 1948-
49; a regular listing of articles in current philosophical periodicals was
discontinued after 1951. Each issue contains usually 3 or 4 scholarly,
moderately-long to lengthy articles, plus 2 or 3 shorter "Discussions,"
which are frequently extended comments on a previous article or on a
recently published book. Articles range over the entire field of philosophy, with perhaps some emphasis on metaphysics. Generally 10 or 12
reviews per issue, signed and critical, mostly 1000-1500 words in length;
lengthy list of books received. Should be in every library where philosophy is studied.

Indexed in: S.S.H.I.   13-6464 rev.

PHILOSOPHICAL STUDIES. v. 1, 1950-

6 nos./yr. Minneapolis, Minn. $27.82

Each issue is 16 pages, and contains usually 3 or 4 brief papers that are mostly responses to concepts or methods in recent books or articles, or extended footnotes to previously stated positions. Though ranging over all areas of philosophy, a high proportion are in logic or linguistic theory, and contributors are from colleges and universities here and abroad. No book reviews, but a list of books received in most issues. Useful in those institutions in which interest in philosophy is fairly well advanced.

52-62286

PHILOSOPHY. v. 1, 1926-

Quarterly. London. $10.50

The Journal of the Royal Institute of Philosophy, it was known as the *Journal of Philosophical Studies* until 1931. Intended as a medium "in which philosophical problems are discussed, and new books are reviewed, by writers whose care it is to make themselves understood by the public at large as well as by their professional colleagues." Issues usually contain 4 or 5 articles of moderate length, plus shorter pieces in the section, "Discussion."Contributors are mostly from British and American universities , but not all are philosophers. This is in keeping with the Institute's interpretation of philosophy, which is very broad indeed, though most of the articles fall within the traditional fields of ethics, metaphysics and political and social philosophy.

Indexed in: Br.Hum.I. 27-11362 (rev. '38)

*PHILOSOPHY AND PHENOMENOLOGICAL RESEARCH. v. 1, 1940-

Quarterly. Buffalo, N.Y. $9.00

Official organ of the International Phenomenological Society, and established by the Society shortly after the death of Edmund Husserl to further his inquiry into phenomenology. However, while his philosophy "is the point of departure for the publication, it represents no special school or sect. Its aim is to maintain philosophy in the ancient sense, as an exact, descriptive discipline, at the same time bringing it to bear on the problems of the modern world." Since its founding, its subject matter has broadened to include articles and discussions on general philosophical topics and it is now generally considered one of the more influential philosophical journals. Its backfile is also important during the 1940's and 1950's as it contained many significant articles. Usually 7 to 10 articles, of brief to moderate length, per issue, plus a fewer number of brief "Discussions" of ideas, concepts or statements on earlier articles or books. Contains an average of 15 or so signed, critical reviews per issue, mostly 400-500 words long. Professional notes and news; list of recent publications.

42-24850

PHILOSOPHY EAST AND WEST. v. 1, 1951-

Quarterly.   Honolulu. $6.00

"A quarterly of Asian and comparative thought." it contains scholarly articles, usually limited to 7500 words, "which seek to illuminate, in a comparative manner, the distinctive characteristics of the various philosophical traditions in the East and West" and especially "articles which exhibit the relevance of philosophy for the art, literature, science and social practice of Asian civilizations, and those original contributions to philosophy which work from an inter-cultural basis." Contributors, many of whom are foremost authorities on their subjects, are from universities and institutes in the U.S. and Asia. Articles are occasionally devoted to a single theme—e.g., On Violence and Nonviolence, East and West, Aesthetics East and West. The number of book reviews varies from just a few to 15 per issue; they are all signed and critical, and average about 750 words, though ranging widely. Also a list of books received. Many issues contain a brief listing of articles of interest from other current periodicals. "News and Notes" of personnel, programs, meetings, etc. An important periodical where there is much interest in Asian studies or in comparative philosophy.

53-16276

PHILOSOPHY OF SCIENCE. v. 1, 1934-

Quarterly.   Lansing, Mich. $15.00

Official journal of the Philosophy of Science Association. Attempts "to clarify, perhaps unify, the programs, methods and results of the disciplines of philosophy and of science." Contains scholarly articles and discussions of previous articles on the analysis of meaning; on the definition, symbolism and method in the nature and formulation of theoretical principles; on the structure, the function and significance of science, including the social sciences. Since 1959 each article has been preceded by an abstract; most issues contain a few pages of abstracts of articles that have appeared in a recent number of a related periodical, such as *Synthèse, British Journal for the Philosophy of Science, Dialectica, Inquiry*. The book reviews (usually 5 or 6 per issue) vary in length—usually between 500 and 1500 words; they are signed and quite critical. The list of members of the Association appears in the first number of each volume. An important journal where there is much work in philosophy; certainly essential where the philosophy of science is given, since so many important contributions to the field appeared here.

Indexed in: S.S.H.I.   35-14246

RELIGIOUS Studies. *see* **RELIGION**

*REVIEW OF METAPHYSICS. v. 1, 1947-

Quarterly. Washington, D.C. $10.00

Founded by Paul Weiss, and published by the Philosophy Education Society, it is "devoted to the promotion of technically competent, definitive contributions to philosophical knowledge." Issues contain an average of 3 scholarly articles of moderate length, mostly speculative in nature. Another major portion is devoted to "Critical Studies," which are review-articles of a single recent work, or of a number of works and articles on a single subject. "Explorations" provide another type of contribution. The "Discussions" section contains extended comments on previous articles or on statements of views in books. The annual listing of doctoral dissertations, arranged by institution, also provides information on the number of students, full and part-time, and the number of faculty members, in each graduate department. "Books Received" provides summaries and comments, often critical, on 75 to 100 titles. Also a list of other works received. The "Announcements" section contains news of conferences, colloquia, and seminars, appointments and promotions, new courses and programs, and other news of professional interest. Beginning in December, 1946, abstracts of articles from the leading philosophical journals, prepared by the authors, have appeared regularly. This issue also began the annual listing of "Visting Professors from Abroad." The many features and the quality of the main contributions make this a basic journal for all philosophy departments.

Indexed in: S.S.H.I.   50-38404

SYNTHESE. v. 1, 1936-

4nos./yr. Dortrecht, Netherlands. $17.00

Subtitled "an international journal for epistemology, methodology and philosophy of science." Publishes articles in all fields covered by these: "the theory of knowledge; the general methodological problems of science, such as the problems of scientific discovery and scientific inference, of induction and probability, of causation and of the role of mathematics, statistics and logic in science; the methodological and foundational problems of the different departmental sciences, insofar as they have philosophical interest; those aspects of symbolic logic and of the foundations of mathematics which are relevant to the philosophy and methodology of science; and those facets of the history and sociology of science which are important for contemporary topical pursuits. Special attention will be paid to the role of mathematical, logical and linguistic methods in the general methodology of science and in the foundations of the different sciences, be they physical, biological, behavioural or social." The number and length of articles varies greatly, the contributors are from universities of many countries. Issues are frequently in the form of symposia, and this is an increasing tendency. "Discussions" of previous articles and responses by authors to critics are common. Only a few reviews—sometimes none, almost never more than 5, but they are quite long, at least 1500 words. Abstracts of articles in *Philosophy of Science* or *British Journal for the Philosophy of Science* in one or two issues a year. List of books received in most issues. A difficult journal, but especially important in the philosophy of science; for advanced students and faculty only.

AMERICAN JOURNAL OF PUBLIC HEALTH AND THE NATION'S HEALTH.
v. 1, 1911-

Monthly. Washington, D.C. $20.00

Official publication of the American Public Health Association. Contains technical and general articles related to all aspects of public health—control, community programs, public and professional organization, the impact of governmental programs, related social problems, laboratory and field research reports, etc. Occasional supplements are usually devoted to papers presented at a conference or meeting on a subject of current interest or growing importance, e.g., Chronic Respiratory Diseases—An Emerging Public Health Problem, From Epidemiology to Ecology—Smoking and Health in Transition. Departments contain news of the Association, of affiliated associations and regional branches, employment notices, news of appointments and other developments, and a calendar of conferences and meetings. Each issue contains a "Selected Public Health Bibliography With Annotations" of articles from other journals, and generally about 10 signed reviews, mostly 300-500 words in length; also a list of books received.

The growth of interest in all aspects of this field make this an important journal for undergraduate libraries. An extensive backfile is not crucial.

Indexed in: B.R.D.   14-7152 rev. 3
           P.A.I.S.

*ATHLETIC JOURNAL.   v. 1, 1921-

Monthly (except July-Aug.)   Evanston, Ill. $4.00

Contains short, profusely illustrated articles by coaches and instructors on all aspects of physical education and training, but primarily on the actual playing of and preparation for sports—drills, plays and strategy. Football and basketball are emphasized, followed by track and field and baseball, with other sports receiving only minor attention. Features include: "Coaches' Clinic"; a "Coaching School Directory" for the summer months, appearing in the April and May issues; an annual listing of state basketball tournaments; "New Films," annotated rather than reviewed, "New Items"—a buying guide; "New Books," describing 5 to 10 titles, briefly and uncritically, and appearing in only a few issues.

A similar journal is *Scholastic Coach* (v. 1, 1931- $3.50). It has very much the same emphases, with some similar features plus an annual "Buyer's Guide to Sports Equipment and Services." Also useful is *Coach & Athlete* (v. 1, 1938- $3.00), which has a regional emphasis—the South—though it is not by any means confined to it. Neither of these latter two, however, is indexed. (*Scholastic Coach* was in *Education Index* but was dropped in 1969.)

All these would be important where there is some emphasis on training physical education teachers, and at every school with an athletic program any of them will be eagerly read by undergraduates.

Indexed in: Ed.I.   34-22334 rev. 2*

DANCE. *see* MUSIC, DRAMA, FILM, DANCE

DANCE Perspectives. *see* MUSIC, DRAMA, FILM, DANCE

FIELD and Stream. *see* GENERAL

HSMHA HEALTH REPORTS.   v. 1, 1878-

Monthly.   Washington, D.C. $10.75

Formerly titled *Public Health Reports* when it was issued by the U.S. Public Health Service, it changed to its present title in 1971 because of organizational changes within the Department of Health, Education and Welfare, specifically the creation of a Health Services and Mental Health Administration.

Each issue now contains three sections: one has about four feature articles on various aspects of health services—descriptions of new programs, public health education, reports of conferences, even personal experiences of health workers; the second consists of a number of brief items, "Programs, Practices, People," containing news of the department itself, technical developments of popular interest, findings of research programs, personnel, etc.; the third section contains about eight "Technical Reports." While many of the articles are intended primarily for public health workers and officials, enough of them are written in non-technical language and are of more general interest—to sociologists and social workers, educators, psychologists, biologists, and others—to make the journal useful in an undergraduate library, especially with the increased concern over topics such as population control, health conditions among underprivileged groups, the effects of chemical and other toxic agents, the role of nutrition, etc. The May or April issue has carried a topical and selective report of the annual American Public Health Association Conference, summarizing many of the papers given there. A synopsis for each technical article published. A depository item.

Indexed in: P.A.I.S.   6-25167

*JOURNAL OF HEALTH, PHYSICAL EDUCATION, RECREATION.
v. 1, 1930-

Monthly (except bi-monthly Nov.-Dec.; not publ. July-Aug.)   Washington, D.C. $25.00

Originally the *Journal of Health and Physical Education,* it changed to its present title in 1954. Official organ of the American Association for Health, Physical Education, and Recreation, an affiliate of N.E.A., and the most important physical education group. Contains a large number of illustrated articles, varying greatly in length, on all aspects of these subjects—physical education programs and facilities, health education, the dance, kinesiology, recreation, new products and equipment, professional education, governmental support and activities, etc.—in addition to outdoor education, safety and driver education, and to news of and from the AAHPER. Many regular features and departments, some on these same subjects; very brief, non-critical notices and listings of books, pamphlets, bulletins, and audio-visual materials. The May and June numbers report news and events of the annual convention. Serious articles relating to the purposes and methods of physical education—its place in the broader educational and social context—have become more frequent. This aspect, plus its wide readership, its emphasis on theory more than on the superficial aspects of sports, make it a basic journal for all libraries where there is any physical education program.

Indexed in: Ed.I.   56-59242

OUTDOOR Life. *see* GENERAL *under* Field and Stream

PARKS & RECREATION.   v. 1, 1907-

Monthly.   Washington, D.C. $7.50

The official publication of the National Recreation and Park Association, formed by the merger of several leading national park and recreation organizations in May, 1965. In January 1966, *Recreation* merged with 3 smaller journals, *American Recreation Journal*, *Parks and Recreation Magazine*, and *Planning and Civic Comment to* form the new journal. Concerned "with the full range of both natural and man-made beauty in America," the watchword of the periodical is "to make more abundant facilities for a more expressive life for all." Illustrated articles averaging 1500 words on conservation, the parks system, outdoor education, the recreational activities and facilities, with, of course, increasing attention to the environment. The January issue contains the annual buyer's guide, an extensive listing of supplies and equipment for parks, playgrounds, and recreational areas. Other regular features include a calendar of events, news from Washington, personnel notes, new products and news of the NRPA. Occasional book reviews, only a few hundred words long.

Indexed in: R.G.   77-13367

*QUEST.   no. 1, 1963-

Semi-annually.   St. Cloud, Minn. $8.00

Published by the National Association for Physical Education of College Women and the National College Physical Education Association for Men, organizations comprised of teachers of physical education (as opposed to coaches). The journal, then, is devoted to the history and objectives of physical education, and to its role in the academic program. With infrequent exceptions, issues are devoted to single topics—e.g., Psychology of Sport, The Physical Educator as Professor, Science and Physical Education. The articles, usually about 10 an issue, of brief to moderate length, are by physical educators from colleges and universities around the country; they are well written, and often scholarly. Most issues have a book review section, but never more than 3 titles: these are signed and critical, and usually 1000 words or more in length. An important journal where the education of physical educators is taken seriously.

SA 62-656

*RESEARCH QUARTERLY. v. 1, 1930-

Quarterly. Washington, D.C. $15.00

Published by the American Association for Health, Physical Education, and Recreation, a National Affiliate of the N.E.A. Contains usually 10 to 15 fairly short articles reporting the results of research studies, and occasionally reviewing research on a particular subject. Some of the subjects treated frequently include isometrics, physical fitness, motor learning and motor skills, reaction time, anthropometric measures, studies of the effects or methods of individual sports, traits contributing to physical skill and fitness. All articles are preceded by an abstract. The section of shorter "Notes" (limited to 500 words each) contains preliminary reports of research, critical comment on published research, and descriptions of new research apparatus or techniques. The section "Research Abstracts," discontinued in 1965, included abstracts of relevant articles from a variety of journals in education, psychology, etc., foreign and domestic. An important journal for physical education majors and faculty.

Indexed in: Ed.I. 64-56808

*SPORTS ILLUSTRATED. v. 1, 1954-

Weekly. Chicago, Ill. $12.00

Covers all sports, from angling to yachting, all over the world, but with an emphasis, as one would expect, on the major American spectator sports. There are previews as well as reports of major sports events. Also feature articles by and about major sports figures and occasional articles by major writers (notables in the past have included Ernest Hemingway and John Dos Passos; more recent ones have included Jack Kerouac and Budd Schulberg) who are sports devotees, and by major sports figures, whose contributions are often autobiographical as well as analytical. Articles and photographic features also on topics more or less related to sports, such as clothing, food and drink, resorts, travel and social practices. Features include short articles on various minor sports, weekly reports of baseball, and football when they're in season, on bridge throughout the year, and usually on golf and horse racing, and frequently on skiing, fishing, boating, horse shows, and other minor recreational sports, "For the Record" contains a record of the week's results. The occasional book reviews are excellent; portions of forthcoming books are sometimes published. Exceptionally well written and illustrated, often with original drawings or paintings in addition to the excellent color photographs, it is important for recreational reading more than for research, but files are worth keeping.

Indexed in: R.G. 55-41884

*TODAY'S HEALTH. v. 1, 1923-

Monthly. Chicago, Ill. $5.00

Published by the American Medical Association, it was titled *Hygeia* until March, 1950. As a "family magazine" it contains articles of general interest, and especially to parents—on infant care, understanding adolescents, child-parent relationships, diet and food (with recipes and menus), education, clothing, trips, hobbies, etc. Mostly, though, it is concerned with presenting the progress of medicine and the problems of health—physical and mental—to the public. Articles on medical history, on new discoveries, developments in treatment, on home and travel safety, on medical education and careers, hospital care, exposing quacks and fraudulent claims. The A.M.A.'s political views are not presented as openly as they used to be, but one still doesn't find very much on, say, government health insurance, though there is much more attention to social issues and problems related to health. There are a number of features and departments such as miscellaneous notes and tips, first aid hints, answering questions from readers. Reviews of books and films on health were dropped in 1958. Not at all scholarly, but most reliable, and containing much useful and interesting information.

Indexed in: R.G.   25-3503*

PHYSICS

ACOUSTICAL SOCIETY OF AMERICA. JOURNAL. v. 1, 1929-

Monthly. N.Y. $45.00

The basic journal covering all aspects of acoustics—its biology, physics and engineering. The monthly numbers beginning July, 1969 are divided into two parts issued separately. Part I includes news of the Society, Technical Notes and Research Briefs, Book Reviews (a few long signed and critical reviews), Patent Reviews, References to Contemporary Papers, and Programs of the Society's meetings. Also included are general articles on acoustics, acoustic instrumentation, noise and noise control, and signal processing, and Contemporary Literature, which is a classified list of articles on acoustics. Part II alternates subjects: one month, physical sciences (ultrasonics, radiation and scattering, mechanical vibrations and shock, underwater sound, aeroacoustics, and macrosonics); the next month, the biological sciences (physiological and psychological acoustics, music and musical instruments, and speech, communication and bioacoustics). This part contains research reports and technical papers from government scientists, engineers, and university and industrial scientists. This journal will be useful primarily in colleges with engineering programs or strong physics departments. Others need subscribe only when they have faculty interested in acoustics.

Indexed in: A.S.T.I.   NUC66-63905

*AMERICAN JOURNAL OF PHYSICS. v. 1, 1933-

Monthly. N.Y. $18.00

Published by the American Institute of Physics for the American Association of Physics Teachers, it is "devoted to the instructional and cultural aspects of physical science." Up to 1940 it was titled the *American Physics Teacher*. Issues contain usually about 15 or 20 articles, short to moderate length, plus a number of notes and letters; if they report the results of original research, it appears in this journal because it is of special concern to teachers rather than to research workers. Contributions also on equipment, curriculum, new experiments, instructional techniques, the history and philosophy of physics—many of these relating to specific areas or principles of physics. "Apparatus Notes" contains very brief descriptions of new equipment, techniques and materials; the notes are supplied by manufacturers. Usually about 8 or 10 book reviews per issue; many are just a few hundred words, but some are many times longer; all are signed and critical. Since 1962 has also carried reviews of films. Contains programs, and abstracts of papers presented at state and regional meetings and proceedings of the annual meeting of the AATP. Much of the journal is intelligible and interesting to beginning students and even to laymen, as well as useful to the faculty.

Indexed in: A.S.T.I.   36-11639

AMERICAN PHYSICAL SOCIETY. BULLETIN. ser. 1, v. 1, 1956-

Monthly. N.Y. $16.00

Contains notes on the Council meetings and various other matters relating to the Society, but mostly it is devoted to minutes and programs of local, regional, and national meetings of the Society, including titles of invited papers and abstracts of all contributed papers. Important only where faculty are actively engaged in research or need notice of new developments which are presented at recent meetings.

28-13344 rev.

APPLIED OPTICS.   v. 1, 1962-

Monthly.   N.Y. $45.00

A publication of the Optical Society of America, it is its outlet for papers "on the applications of facts, principles, and methods of optics." (Theoretical and experimental articles appear in the Society's *Journal*.) Each issue consists of 25-30 articles, averaging 5 or 6 pages, illustrated with photographs and drawings, on a wide variety of subjects—lasers, holography, interferometry, photography, spectrosocopy, astronomical instruments, etc. Issues often emphasize special topics—e.g., Optics and Meteorology, Eclipse Optics—with a number of papers on that topic and frequently a review article as one of them. "Letters to the Editor" contain very short contributions, including comments on earlier articles. Regular features include: "Meetings Calendar"; educational activities and announcements; "Meeting Reports" summarizing papers, reports and discussions at meetings around the world; "Patents," describing recently issued patents in the field; personnel and other professional news. An average of 5 signed book reviews per issue, mostly 300-500 words.

Indexed in: A.S.T.I.   64-2221

ASSOCIATION FOR COMPUTING MACHINERY.   **JOURNAL.**   v. 1, 1954-

Quarterly.   N.Y. $25.00

The Association's purpose is the advancement of the science and art of information processing and the free interchange of information both for the specialist and the public. Its *Journal* is one of the foremost journals on mathematical modeling and numerical analysis. Research articles on these topics and on programming theory and languages, logical design, etc., are contributed by university and industry scientists throughout the world. Other publications of the Association include the monthly *ACM Communications* (v.1, 1958- $25.00), *Computing Reviews* (v. 1, 1960- $25.00), also a monthly, and the quarterly *Computing Surveys* (v. 1, 1969- $40.00). *ACM Communications* carries technical review articles of wide interest as well as news of developments in the field, official reports of the Association, and other technical news. Its coverage and features change as rapidly as the field itself. Includes a brief list of recently published and forthcoming books on computers and its applications. *Computing Reviews* furnishes critical abstracts of all current books, periodical articles, and chapters in multi-authored books and a-v materials. Over 200 serials are regularly covered. *Computing Surveys,* the survey and tutorial journal of the Association, provides reviews and summaries of new developments. These articles are intentionally written at a level suitable for the beginning student. The *Reviews* should be available on campuses promoting computer-assisted instruction; the *Surveys* and *ACM*

Communications where there is some course work on computers; and the *Journal* only where there are departments of computer science or where faculty are involved in computer research.

Indexed in: A.S.T.I.   57-23489

BELL SYSTEM TECHNICAL JOURNAL.   v. 1, 1922-

10 nos./yr.   N.Y. $10.00

"Devoted to the scientific and engineering aspects of electrical communi-cation." The articles are almost all by scientists of the Bell Telephone Laboratories. They are experimental or practical rather than theoretical in nature, and pertain to those aspects of physics related to electrical communications, in particular those areas where the company has present or future commercial development interest. Thus, subjects such as elec-tronic switching systems, device photolithography, microwave radio relay systems, receive the major attention, with entire issues, or a large portion of them, frequently devoted to topics such as these, and the individual articles treating specific aspects of the topics. The articles vary greatly in length, from just a few to 50 or more pages, but all are highly technical and reliable. Primarily useful for advanced students and faculty, it is es-pecially important where much work is done in the engineering aspects of computers and electrical communications.

Also published by Bell Telephone Laboratories, but intended for a much more general audience, is the monthly *Bell Laboratories Record* (v. 1, 1925- $5.00). Thoroughly illustrated articles, written by scientists and engineers connected with the company, describe and explain developments and problems relating to their work, in particular the practical applications and possibilities. Since the company is engaged in so many areas, the vari-ety of subjects is considerable. An interesting journal for the non-scientist or for the beginning student, it is most useful for browsing, and an exten-sive backfile is probably not necessary.

Indexed in: A.S.T.I.   29-29519 rev. 3*

*CONTEMPORARY PHYSICS.   v. 1, 1959-

Bi-monthly.   London. $35.65

Its purpose is to permit experts "to present the whole field in perspective to a wider circle of their scientific colleagues." There are reports of orig-inal research, but its major importance lies in the general reviews, the histories of important developments, articles treating "the philosophical foundations of current ideas," and "the general consequences of impor-tant discoveries." Usually from 3 to 5 articles per issue, averaging about 20 pages each, contributed mostly by British physicists and scientists in related areas. From 10 to 15 book reviews in most issues, though there have been as many as 40; all are signed and critical, mostly 200-400 words though, again, occasionally much longer. Also list of books received.

An important journal, especially useful for undergraduates as well as for the research scientist.

61-59792

ELECTRONICS.   v. 1, 1930-

Bi-weekly.   N.Y. $8.00

One of the many expertly edited McGraw-Hill trade journals, it provides thorough, authoritative up-to-date coverage of the applied electronics field. Areas covered include product development, new technology, management and business aspects, marketing, foreign activities, professional and educational concerns, etc. Articles are well illustrated and interestingly presented. Special reports on developments or trends—in particular those with social or economic implications—are particularly useful for students. A number of regular features treat personnel movements, calendar of meetings, governmental actions and activities affecting the industry, descriptions of new products, listing and brief descriptions of recent literature. The annual Buyers' Guide and Material Section appearing in June contains a useful directory of products and manufacturers. Although intended for the trade, its breadth and interesting presentation make it useful for undergraduate use.

Indexed in: A.S.T.I.   36-15856 (rev. '43)

FRANKLIN INSTITUTE.   JOURNAL.   v. 1, 1826-

Monthly.   Elmsford, N.Y. $40.00

The second oldest extant scientific journal in this country, it was an important source of information on engineering and mechanics in its early years, one of its specialties being a list and description of patents filed in the patent Office. Also the transactions of the Institute were carried. The early files, then, are important in the history of science and technology.

Published by the Franklin Institute of the State of Pennsylvania until 1970, when the Pergamon Press took it over for the Institute, which is an industrial research organization engaged in basic and applied research in chemistry, engineering and technology, with an emphasis on materials science. The *Journal* contains lengthy articles in these areas, both of a research and historical nature. Includes reports on work done at the Institute and addresses given there. Lengthy, signed, critical book reviews

Indexed in: A.S.T.I.   19-5307-10 (rev.'35)

IEEE PROCEEDINGS.   v. 1, 1913-

Monthly.   N.Y. $40.00

Published by the Institute of Electrical and Electronics Engineers (originally the Institute of Radio Engineers), the largest professional organization in the field. The IEEE is now composed of 31 special interest groups, each with its own journal; the *Proceedings* carry papers which are "broad enough to span the interests of several IEEE Groups" or treat a subject not covered by one of the existing journals.

Now, almost every other issue focuses on a specific topic such as Air Traffic Control, Optical Communication, Technology and Health Services, Computers in Industrial Process Control, with a number of articles on that topic. A substantial portion of all issues is devoted to "Proceedings

Letters," which are brief reports on new research results, published as quickly as possible. Calendar of meetings; news of new products.

Because of the wide variety of topics covered, from discussions of communications theory to descriptions of electronic devices, and because so many of these are useful to scientists in fields other than engineering, the journal is an important one where there is much interest in physics, scientific instrumentation, and computers.

Indexed in: A.S.T.I. 29-10857 rev 2*

*JOURNAL OF APPLIED PHYSICS. v. 1, 1931-

Monthly. Lancaster, Pa. $52.00

Published by the American Institute of Physics, a federation of professional societies in physics, it is "devoted to general physics and its applications to other sciences, to engineering, and to industry." Before 1937, was titled *Physics*. From 50 to 70 articles—mostly short—per issue, describing either "significant new results in experimental or theoretical physics related to applied physics" or "important new applications of physics to other branches of science and engineering." Since 1955, a special number has been devoted annually to the *Proceedings of the Conference on Magnetism and Magnetic Materials*. Review articles appear only infrequently. "Communications" carries very short contributions.

The basic journal in the area, it should be available wherever there is a major in physics.

Indexed in: A.S.T.I. 33-23425

*JOURNAL OF CHEMICAL PHYSICS. v. 1, 1933-

Semi-monthly. N.Y. $105.00

Published by the American Institute of Physics, "its purpose is to bridge the gap between journals of physics and journals of chemistry. The artificial boundary between physics and chemistry has now been in actual fact completely eliminated, and a large and active group is engaged in research which is as much the one as the other. It is to this group that the Journal is rendering its principal service and makes its greatest appeal..." Issues contain an average of about 60 fairly short (3 to 10 pages) articles reporting the results of research from laboratories in universities, institutes and industry, both domestic and foreign. The section "Letters to the Editor" consists of four categories: Communications, Notes, Comments, and Errata. Each letter is limited to 950 words (less where there are figures or equations).

A journal of basic importance for both physics and chemistry departments.

35-14250

JOURNAL OF RESEARCH OF THE NATIONAL BUREAU OF STANDARDS— SECTION A. PHYSICS AND CHEMISTRY. v. 63, 1959-

Bi-monthly. Washington, D.C. $9.50

In 1928, the NBS began its *Journal of Research* to report its scientific findings. As the Bureau's program developed, it seemed desirable to separate the fields, and in July, 1959, it was divided into 4 sections: A, Physics and Chemistry; B, Mathematical Science (q.v.); and C, Engineering and Instrumentation; D, Radio Propagation (now defunct).

The Bureau "is concerned primarily with standards, methods of measurement, fundamental constants, and the properties of materials," but does conduct basic and applied research in most areas of chemistry and physics. The papers in Section A emphasize the science of measurement, fundamental constants, and properties of matter, review articles, critical tables, and compilations of information. The articles, which vary from just a few to many pages, are mostly by members of the Bureau's staff, but occasionally are invited contributions.

Because of the importance of the Bureau's work to the entire scientific community, the journal should be available wherever there is advanced work in physics or chemistry.

Indexed in: A.S.T.I.   62-37059

*OPTICAL SOCIETY OF AMERICA.   JOURNAL.   v. 1, 1917-

Monthly.   N.Y. $40.00

Official journal of the Society, "it is devoted to concise accounts of experimental or theoretical investigations which contribute new knowledge or understanding of any optical phenomena, principle or method including spectroscopy, physiological optics, color vision, and colorimetry." Issues consist of about 20 articles, averaging 5-6 pages, in these areas, plus a smaller number of very brief "Letters to the Editor." Also includes official reports and announcements, personnel and other professional news, calendars of meetings, and abstracts of papers delivered at the annual meeting. Usually 5 to 10 book reviews per issue, mostly 250-500 words, signed and critical.

Indexed in: A.S.T.I.   24-4175*

PHILOSOPHICAL MAGAZINE.   v. 1, 1798-

Monthly.   London. $108.75

Has gone through a number of title variations, and from 1840 through 1944 was known as the *London, Edinburgh and Dublin Philosophical Magazine and Journal of Science.* It was founded by Alexander Tilloch, the inventor of stereotyping, "to diffuse Philosophical [i.e., scientific] Knowledge among every Class of Society, and to give the Public as early an Account as possible of everything new or curious in the scientific World, both at Home and on the Continent." The early files are particularly important for the publication of new discoveries and inventions and for the many scientific papers of some significance, most of which were taken from the publications of various scientific societies.

Its scope gradually narrowed and for some years it has been one of the leading journals of theoretical, experimental and applied physics, chiefly the physics of solid materials. It contains mostly reports of current research in articles and some briefer ones in "Correspondence." Since January, 1971 book reviews are no longer published, and articles in French or German are carried.

An important journal for where there is much work in physics, the back files—especially before 1900—are invaluable as a source for the history of modern science.

19-4495 rev. 2

*PHYSICAL REVIEW.   v. 1, 1893-

See below.   Lancaster, Pa. $240.00 (for all 4 sections)

The most important title for the physicist, it is now (beginning in 1970) published in 4 parts, each available separately. *Physical Review A: General Physics* and *Physical Review C: Nuclear Physics*, are published monthly, and are $40.00 per year each. *Physical Review B: Solid State* and *Physical Review D: Particles and Fields* are published semi-monthly, and cost $80.00 per year each. Cumulative semi-annual indexes are available separately for $7.00 a year.

The recent history of the *Physical Review* is one of rapid growth. The issues for 1950 totalled less than 2000 pages; those for 1960, about 10,000 pages; and, for 1970, about 25,000. In 1964 it changed from a semi-monthly to 5 numbers a month; even with this, by 1966 some issues were almost 500 pages, so that in 1967 each of the 5 numbers was devoted to a specific field, an arrangement that lasted until 1970. All sections contain short (averaging 7-8 pages) technical articles, contributed by physicists the world over.

Because of the journal's size, the cost of binding (which would amount to 20-30 volumes a year) may be prohibitive, but since it will be used primarily by advanced students and faculty, keeping it unbound may be satisfactory. In any case, it is an essential journal where there is any advanced work in physics.

Libraries that take it will also undoubtedly want the weekly *Physical Review Letters* (v. 1, 1958- $40.00) which contains "short communications dealing with important new discoveries or topics of high current interest in rapidly changing fields of research." It grew out of the "Letters to the Editor" section of the *Physical Review*, which had been the only means of prompt and concise reports of important new work. The 20 or so reports are never more than 3 or 4 pages, and are contributed by physicists all over the world.

75-21361
79-21362
77-21568
78-21394

*PHYSICS TEACHER.   v. 1, 1963-

Monthly (except Dec., June-Aug.)   N.Y. $8.00

Published by the American Association of Physics Teachers, it is "dedicated to the strengthening of the teaching of introductory physics at

all levels"—specifically, at the high school, junior college or college fresh-
man level. Articles, by research physicists and teachers of physics, mostly
on physics programs, courses, and demonstrations and teaching methods,
but also on the history, theory and recent developments in physics useful
for student reading or incorporating into lecture material. Announcements
and news of the AAPT, of materials, events and developments of interest
to the teacher or prospective physicist, and of the profession in general.
Two sections are aimed at the high school teacher: Apparatus for Teaching Physics, describing mostly fairly simple devices, and Notes, describing
experiments, demonstrations and classroom techniques. Reviews of books
and films (very few of the latter), about 5 per issue, signed and critical,
usually between 350 and 750 words. Useful, evaluative book lists on
specific subjects (optics, oceanography, collateral reading for physics
courses, for example) appear occasionally.

Indexed in: Ed.I.   66-84757

*PHYSICS TODAY.   v. 1, 1948-

Monthly.   Easton, Pa. $9.00

Published by the American Institute of Physics as its news organ, though
contents are pretty well divided between articles and news. The 40-50
articles per year are over all aspects of physics, with particular attention
to its history and philosophy and on education at the college and graduate level. Other articles describe development and trends in special fields,
but are not reports of research. All articles are well illustrated. Regular
departments include: Search and Discovery, news of projects, discoveries,
institutional developments, etc.; State and Society, news of governmental
and organizational activities; reports from recent meetings and a calendar
of forthcoming ones; news of personnel, awards, etc. Usually 15-20 book
reviews per issue, with especially good coverage of the history and phil-
osphy of physics and of textbooks. They are signed and critical, almost
all between 250 and 750 words. Also a list of books received. As the
principal means of informal communication among all physicists (it has
the highest circulation of any physics journal) it belongs in any library
where physics is taught.

Indexed in: A.S.T.I.   51-4195
            R.G.

*REVIEWS OF MODERN PHYSICS.   v. 1, 1929-

Quarterly.   N.Y. $12.00

Published for the American Physical Society by the American Institute
of Physics, it "seeks to provide comprehensive scholarly reviews and
thoughtful evaluations of significant topics in physics." "The best papers,"
the editorial policy states, "should be milestones of physics, embodying
the intellectual contributions of hundreds of others whose work appears
in the original literature." Contributions range from less than 10 to over
100 pages, and cover all of physics, "from the very abstract to the applied
and from the traditional to the newer interdisciplinary fields." Each begins with an introduction "with sufficiently complete references so that
an advanced graduate student has adequate guidance to master the entire

page." Occasionally, issues are devoted to proceedings of an important international conference. In 1969, a Supplement series was begun; it contains material "particularly useful to a substantial sector of the physics community" so that "its utility could be further enhanced by separate binding for easy, frequent access." The annual "Review of Particle Properties," published since 1964, will appear in this form. All physics departments should have the *Reviews* available in the library, though it will be used almost entirely by advanced students and faculty.

31-21290

SCIENCE ABSTRACTS.   SERIES A, PHYSICS ABSTRACTS.   v. 1, 1898-

Bi-weekly.   London. $290.00

Published by the Institution of Electrical Engineers in association with the American Institute of Physics, it is "devoted to the recording, summarizing, classifying, and indexing of original publications" in physics. Covers all forms of publications issued throughout the world, but all titles and abstracts are in English. Almost 80,000 abstracts appeared in 1970, a substantial increase over the previous year. Arrangement of each issue is by subject classification; subjects cover adjacent fields, such as biophysics, astrophysics and physical chemistry, as well as theoretical and applied physics. Each issue contains an author index, and indexes for bibliographic articles, for books, for conference papers, for patents and for primary reports. Semi-annual author and subject indexes, plus separately issued 5-year cumulative indexes.

Covering some 1500 journals, this is a most important abstracting service, and though expensive, should be available wherever there is any research done in the field.

11-34608 rev. 2*

*ADMINISTRATIVE SCIENCE QUARTERLY.   v. 1, 1956-

Quarterly.   Ithaca, N.Y. $20.00

Published by the Graduate School of Business and Public Administration, Cornell University, it is a multidisciplinary journal "dedicated to advancing the understanding of administration through empirical investigation and theoretical analyses." Each issue contains usually 5 or 6 moderately long to lengthy articles (rarely exceeding 5000 words) treating all types of organizations—business, governmental, social, educational, etc.—in a variety of cultural contexts. Contributors include professors, public administrators and research specialists in the fields of sociology, political science, economics, business administration, educational administration, industrial management, etc. Single issues are occasionally devoted to a single topic such as "Universities as Organizations." 5-10 book reviews per issue, signed and critical, ranging from 600 to 2000 words; also a section of descriptive abstracts of pertinent articles, books, documents and pamphlets. One of the more prestigious journals in this area, it is important for all social sciences.

Indexed in: Bus.Per.I.   57-59226
           P.A.I.S.

AFRICA Report. *see* AREA STUDIES/AFRICA

*AMERICAN ACADEMY OF POLITICAL AND SOCIAL SCIENCE.   ANNALS.
   v. 1, 1890-

Bi-monthly.   Philadelphia, Pa. $12.00—Paper Edition ($16.00-Cloth).

In its first few years the *Annals* was a mixed-content publication, but since 1902 each issue has been devoted to a single topic with usually some 10 or 12 articles, each by an authority in the field, on various aspects of that topic. Topics range over all the social sciences, with international affairs, government, and socio-economics predominating, though occasionally an issue will treat a topic such as *The Sixties: Radical Change in American Religion*. Each article is now preceded by an abstract, and there is a separate index for each issue. Since 1961 most issues have also carried an article or two summarizing developments within one of the social science areas, for example, "Trends in Historical Writing about Modern Western Europe in the Last Five Years," "Recent Trends in Political Theory and Political Philosophy" or "Social Indicators: Selected Readings." These surveys are extremely useful not only for the non-technical though professional manner in which they are presented, but also their extensive bibliographies provide a handy source for checking portions of library collections. In the review section, usually 400-500 books are reviewed each year. These signed reviews, arranged by discipline, are by specialists in their fields, and are about 600-700 words long. There is also a listing of other books. All issues may be obtained in clothbound form, so that libraries with special interests may purchase extra copies of particular issues to classify separately. In addition to the LC card for the periodical, there is a separate LC card for each issue. The *Annals'* broad coverage, reliability, and objectivity make it an essential purchase for even the smallest library.

Indexed in: B.R.D.   6-19013 rev.
            P.A.I.S.
            R.G.

*AMERICAN BEHAVIORAL SCIENTIST.   v. 1. 1957-

Bi-monthly.   Beverly Hills, Calif. $18.00

Beginning as *PROD* (Political Research, Organization and Design), it was founded and edited to 1965 by Alfred de Grazia and a distinguished group of political and other social scientists. After that, it was taken over by a private publisher, but its editorial board still includes some of the most distinguished names from all the social sciences. Its interest has correspondingly broadened: where it was first primarily on political science, it is now concerned with all the social and behavioral sciences. Each issue is devoted to a single topic—e.g., Sociology and Ecology, Urban Violence and Disorder, Group Therapy for Social Impact, Interdisciplinary Relationships in Political Science—treated usually by a group of separately-authored articles, but occasionally by a lengthy report resulting from joint authorship. A regular feature is the "New Studies" section, a selected, annotated bibliography of books, pamphlets, documents and articles from 360 periodicals in the social and behavioral sciences. Because of the wide range of topics covered, the quality of contributions, and the increased importance of the behavioral approach to the social sciences, this journal should be in all college libraries.

Indexed in: Ment.Hlth.B.R.I.   63-24254
            S.S.H.I.

AMERICAN CITY.   v. 1, 1909-

Monthly.   N.Y. $15.00

Contains brief articles, items and features on the everyday problems of local administration and maintenance: purchasing and record-keeping; street construction and maintenance; outdoor lighting; sewerage and sewage purification; traffic and transportation; refuse collection and disposal; public safety; water supply and treatment; planning, zoning and housing; parks and recreation; air pollution and others. Intended for, and mainly written by, local public officials, the articles are practical and well illustrated. Regular features include: "Legal Notes and Decisions"; a calendar of meetings and conventions; "Recent City Manager Appointments" and news of other individuals in the field; descriptions of new products and equipment; "Municipal and Civic Publications," with a few critically annotated. The annual index includes a subject index and a useful index to places.

Important only where there is much work done in local government.

Indexed in: R.G.   11-194

AMERICAN JOURNAL OF INTERNATIONAL LAW.   v. 1, 1907-

Quarterly.   Washington, D.C. $30.00

Published by the American Society of International Law, it contains articles and features by professors, jurists and government officials, mostly American but frequently from other nations. Issues generally have 3 to 5 scholarly articles, many rather technical, from moderately long to lengthy. Regular features include: "Editorial Comment" on current and theoretical questions; "Notes and Comments," on the Society, other organizations in the field, news of conferences, courses, and other miscellaneous matters; "Contemporary Practice of the United States Relating to International Law" presents developments and communications; "Judicial Decisions" gives the text of recent important cases and notes on others. The book review section is extensive: about 10 to 15 major reviews, from 500 to 1500 words each, plus about the same number of briefer reviews. The books reviewed are both foreign and English-language; all reviews are signed and critical. There is also a listing of other books received, both foreign and domestic. The bibliography, "Periodical Literature of International Law and Relations" carried in each issue, was discontinued in 1964. The latter portion of each issue (until 1959, this was a *Supplement* to each issue) consists of "Official Documents"—of the United Nations, of Conferences, agreements between nations or groups, diplomatic notes, etc. Institutions whose interest in this field is especially strong may also want the Society's bi-monthly *International Legal Materials: Current Documents* (v. 1, 1962- $25.00) which reproduces the texts of official documents—U.S., foreign governments and international organizations—including legislation, treaties, court decisions and reports. Many of these used to be carried in the *Journal*, but became too numerous, so that it now carries only the most important ones. A backfile of the *Journal* is indispensable for any research in the field. Along with current issues it should be available where there is much work done in international law.

Indexed in: P.A.I.S.   8-36306
          S.S.H.I.

AMERICAN OPINION.   v. 1, 1958-

Monthly (except Aug.)   Belmont, Mass. $10.00

The editor states that the journal is not the organ of the John Birch Society; however, he is the founder of that organization, and the journal may at least be said to reflect the attitudes and beliefs of the John Birch Society. It does, then, present ultra-conservative opinions on political, economic and social questions, and is particularly concerned with the threat of communism in national and international affairs, the influence of "liberals" on domestic national and local matters, and the breakdown in traditional values and virtues. Most articles are brief, but their length does vary widely and are often by well-known writers and public figures. Anecdotes, quotations, pithy sayings are used to lighten the message, and there is occasionally some poetry. A few books are reviewed in each issue; the reviews are signed, long (mostly over 1000 words) and critical. Because it represents a widely held viewpoint, and because it is generally well written, it should be in college libraries to fill out the range of political opinions.

60-23483

POLITICAL SCIENCE   357

*AMERICAN POLITICAL SCIENCE REVIEW.   v. 1, 1906-

Quarterly.   Washington, D.C. $35.00

Published by the American Political Science Association. During its for-
mative years much of it was devoted to minor items and news; what
articles there were tended to deal with contemporary matters, and in a
descriptive rather than analytical way. Even in 1944, only about one-fifth
of it consisted of articles, the remainder given over to current developments, departments, notes, etc. In the 1950's the *Review's* reputation
became more firmly established, and by 1963 a survey of political scientists could labet it as the most prestigious journal in the field.

It contains scholarly articles in all areas of political science, with a balance
among the different approaches. Ignoring the behavioral approach pretty
much until 1950, it then began to stress it, so that eventually there was a reaction against this emphasis; now there is some emphasis once again on analytical and descriptive studies. The articles, usually 10 or 15 an issue, are
scholarly and of varied length; "Research Notes" carry briefer contributions, preliminary reports of longer works, and methodological articles.
An extensive book review section in each issue. About 50 or 60 books
per issue are reviewed—10 or 12 major, long reviews; the others, arranged
by field, are called "Book Notes," but even these average about 1000
words. Through 1967 there was also an extensive listing of selected articles and documents; the annual list of *Doctoral Dissertations in Political
Science in the Universities of United States and Canada,* as well as news
and notes of the Association, annual meeting programs, etc., and personnel appointments and changes were also carried through 1967, but
these were transferred to *P.S.*, the APSA's newsletter founded in 1968. Discontinuance of these sections permitted a great expansion in the number
of articles, and the average has almost doubled between 1965 and 1970.

Generally considered the most important journal in the field, a backfile (at
least from 1945) and current subscription should be in all college libraries.

Indexed in: B.R.D.   8-9025 rev 2*
          S.S.H.I.

ASIAN Survey. *see* AREA STUDIES/ASIA

CANADIAN JOURNAL OF POLITICAL SCIENCE.   v. 1, 1968-

Quarterly.   Toronto. $15.00

The official organ of the Canadian Political Science Association, it is one
of the two successors to the *Canadian Journal of Economics and Political
Science,* which in its 33 years of publication (1935-1967) had become
one of the more important journals in the social sciences; however, with
the growth of productivity of Canadian scholars the need for separate
journals became obvious.

Usually 6 or 7 articles per issue, most of them relating specifically to
"Canadian problems analyzed within the framework of political science,"
though many articles are of more general interest. Contributors are mainly
from Canadian universities, with some from the U.S.

News of the Association and other professional notes. The book reviews are
confined to "publications about, or related to Canadian politics, and publi-

cations of major interest to political science." About 12 or 15 of these per issue, ranging from 250 to 1000 words, with most 500-700. Articles and reviews are in either English or French.

An important journal for strong departments or for those interested in Canada.

Indexed in: P.A.I.S.
          S.S.H.I.

CENTER Magazine. *see* GENERAL

CITY.   v. 1, 1967-

Bi-monthly.   Washington, D.C. $10.00

Subtitled "Magazine of Urban Life and Environment," it is published by the National Urban Coalition, a non-profit, non-partisan group comprised of leaders in all areas of American society, whose effort is "to increase and inform national discussion of urban issues." While *City* is its major publication, it is not a spokesman for the Coalition. Though focusing on cities, the journal is concerned with metropolitan areas rather than central cities only, and on the "national problems and phenomena that are also significant determinants of the quality of life for residents of urban areas: poverty, racial discrimination, the workings of the federal and state governments, population growth and movement." The process of urbanization—growth, planning (or lack of it), conservation—are also topics covered by it.

Originally published by Urban America, Inc., the journal began in a fairly modest way, but in the summer of 1970, after the National Urban Coalition was formed, it took on a new, attractive format, with many more illustrations and pages. Whereas articles were mostly written by staff members before, they are now also contributed by journalists, government officials and social scientists, many of whom are well known. Issues are occasionally devoted to single topics, such as The Suburbs: Frontiers of the 70's, with a number of articles treating them. "Chronicle of Urban Events and Ideas" reports items of interest; one or a few signed and critical book reviews, often several thousand words in length.

Well edited in content and appearance, it will be used much for browsing, but is also important for the study of current developments in urban affairs.

Indexed in: P.A.I.S.

*CONGRESSIONAL DIGEST.   v. 1, 1921-

Monthly (bi-monthly, June-Sept.)   Washington, D.C. $12.50

Each issue features one current major controversy—proposed legislation or a policy matter—before the Congress. First, the background is given: the proposed legislation or action and its status in Congress, a description of the existing activity or situation and the agencies involved, and a chronology of the conditions, previous legislation and other circumstances that led to the present controversy—each of these being spelled out in some detail. The second part, the pros and cons, contains the arguments presented by Congressmen and others who are involved—agencies, organizations, officials, private and public—taken from speeches, editorials, official reports, Congressional testimony, etc. While Congress is in session, there is usually a section on other major developments on the floor and in committees. A valuable compendium of information, useful for term papers, debating preparation and courses in current affairs.

Indexed in: P.A.I.S.   23-18526 rev.
R.G.

*CONGRESSIONAL QUARTERLY WEEKLY REPORT.   v. 1, 1945-

Weekly.   Washington, D.C. $144.00

An information service giving facts, figures and unbiased commentary on all aspects of current national political affairs. In its earlier years it concentrated on Congress, but has expanded to cover the whole of contemporary federal government and politics. The subscription price includes four services. (1) The *Weekly Report* digests Congressional and political activities for the week, and also includes: special reports on the week's major issues; a roundup of committee activities; news of floor action; summary of all bills, acted upon and introduced; the full text of Presidential press conferences, major statements, messages and speeches; political notes, on important state and local offices, as well as national; news of Supreme Court activities; and other news. Tabular information is used extensively. (2) Occasional *Special Supplements* providing in-depth information on issues of major importance. (3) A cumulative *Quarterly Index* indexes by names and subjects all the preceding *Weekly Reports* for the year. (4) An *Almanac*, published early in the year, which distills the information contained in the previous year's *Reports* (but does not by any means supercede them). A loose-leaf binder is provided for the *Reports* and *Indexes*. Expensive, but an invaluable reference tool for every academic library, since it is generally regarded as one of the most thorough and reliable information services, and ought to be heavily used by students working in all areas of national affairs.

Indexed in: P.A.I.S.   52-36903 rev.

*CONGRESSIONAL RECORD.   v. 1, 1873-

Daily.   Washington, D.C. $1.50 a month.

Issued daily while Congress is in session, it "contains the President's messages, Congressional speeches, debates in full and a record of votes." A separately paged "Appendix" in each number contains other speeches, newspaper editiorals, letters, or any other material Congressmen wish inserted. The "Daily Digest" section, also separately paginated, contains highlights of the day's sessions, actions by both houses, a summary of committee actions, notes of the next day's committee meetings, and bills signed by the President. There is a *Fortnightly Index*, in two sections: an alphabetical listing of names and subjects, and a history of bills and

and resolutions, by number. The index is not cumulative, but there is an inclusive one at the end of each session. Bound volumes of the *Record* are available separately and priced individually; they are somewhat revised and rearranged, and do not (since the 83rd Congress) include the Appendices.

The *Record* is vital material for all courses relating to the national government; the daily numbers, which can usually be obtained through the local Congressman, should certainly be available in every academic library, and most libraries should try to acquire the bound volumes as well. A backfile, extending even through its predecessors (i.e., *Annals of Congress, Register of Debates* and *Congressional Globe*) is most important for the study of almost any aspect of this country's past. Because they comprise so many hundreds of volumes, many libraries will want them in microform, but the index volumes should preferably be in the original.

12-36438

CURRENT. *see* GENERAL

CURRENT Digest of the Soviet Press. *see* AREA STUDIES/SOVIET UNION AND EAST EUROPE

DISSENT. *see* GENERAL

*CURRENT HISTORY.   v. 1, 1941-

Monthly.   Philadelphia, Pa. $9.50

Formed by the union of *Current History and Forum* and *Events,* it is concerned with all aspects of current affairs. Each issue focuses on one important topic, most frequently in international affairs, with some issues devoted to the year's developments in specific countries or areas. Each issue has from 6 to 8 articles on the topic, each treating it from a different vantage; though written by specialists, both academic and governmental, the articles are not technical. Most issues contain some maps. Valuable regular features include "Current Documents," containing the texts of major treaties, speeches and diplomatic notes; "Book Reviews," 8 to 10 brief (almost all between 50 and 150 words), descriptive rather than critical reviews of books relating to that issue's topic; "The Month in Review" provides a day-by-day summary of the month's important events in world affairs. A reliable, readable journal, especially useful for undergraduates.

Indexed in: P.A.I.S.   43-5162 rev.
            R.G.

*DEPARTMENT OF STATE BULLETIN.   v. 1, 1939-

Weekly.   Washington, D.C. $16.00

Issued by the Office of Media Services, Bureau of Public Affairs of the U.S. Department of State, it "provides the public and interested agencies of the Government with information on developments in the field of foreign relations and on the work of the Department of State and the Foreign Service." It includes "selected press releases on foreign policy, issued by the White Houses and the Department, and statements and addresses made by the President and by the Secretary of State and other officers of the Department, as well as special articles [usually by well-known authorities] on various phases of international affairs and the functions of the Department. Information is included concerning treaties and international agreements to which the United States is or may become a party and treaties to which the United States is or may become a party and treaties of general international interest. Publications of the Department, United Nations documents, and legislative material in the field of international relations are listed currently." Many of the selections are prefaced by summaries of their backgrounds.

It is an official publication presenting, of course, an official point of view. A most valuable source of primary materials, indispensable for the study of U.S. foreign policy and international affairs. A depository item.

Indexed in: P.A.I.S.   39-26945
          R.G.

*FOREIGN AFFAIRS.   v. 1, 1922-

Quarterly.   N.Y. $10.00

Published by the Council on Foreign Relations, a non-commercial and non-political organization that was founded "to create and stimulate international thought among the people of the United States" and has numbered among its members some of the most respected names in public affairs and scholarship. *Foreign Affairs* was started as "a really first-rate journal with the best contributions available in the United States and abroad," and has lived up to, or even exceeded that intent. It is perhaps the pre-eminent journal in the field of international affairs, read and contributed to by scholars, journalists and statesmen and frequently cited in the world's press. Probably no single periodical article has had the impact that one appearing here in 1947 did—the article by "X" (who was later identified as George Kennan) proposing the Soviet containment policy of this country.

Issues contain generally 10 to 12 articles of moderate length on all aspects of American foreign policy and on other political, social and economic developments over the world. Contains two useful bibliographies: *Recent Books on International Relations*, a lengthy, classified listing of English-language books with brief, descriptive annotations; *Source Material*, an extensive, classified listing of foreign and domestic documents and pamphlets. (The former serves as the basis for the Council's decennial publication, *Foreign Affairs Bibliography*.)

Indispensable, along with a backfile, for every academic library.

Indexed in: P.A.I.S.   24-9921 rev. 2
          R.G.

HUMAN EVENTS.   v. 1, 1944-

Weekly.   Washington, D.C. $15.00

Ever since it began as a typewritten, 4-page newsletter, it has been one of the major outlets for the strongly conservative; in its own words, "it looks at events through eyes that are biased in favor of limited constitutional government, local self-government, private enterprise and individual freedom." The first number was written by William Henry Chamberlin, the second by Felix Morley; both of these eminent and respected conservatives were mainstays for many years, and ever since, its contributors have included the best-known names of the conservative political, economic and social commentators—Russell Kirk, Max Rafferty, Victor Riesel, James J. Kilpatrick, Morrie Ryskind, etc. Today, it appears in tabloid format, with news items from Washington, reprints of appropriate newspaper columns, and original articles in line with its stated bias. With a circulation of over 100,000, it does warrant some attention, and is perhaps the most representative spokesman for this large segment of political opinion. As such, and also because of the continuity of its contributors, a backfile is especially useful in tracing the course of conservative thought since World War II.

47-5824*

I. F. STONE'S BI-WEEKLY.   v. 1, 1953-

Bi-weekly.   Washington, D.C. $5.00

Published for many years as a weekly, it changed frequency in 1968, not so much due to a lack of readership, but to the publisher's health. I.F. Stone, a "gadfly on the left," had been a newspaper reporter and columnist since the late 1920's; he began the *Weekly* with a relatively small circulation, and it grew very slowly until 1965 when, over the next 5 years it almost tripled to its present figure of about 60,000. Each issue, which is just 4 pages, is devoted to a single topic, or at the most 2 or 3, relating to the current political scene, especially to issues of war and peace and the economy. Stone's method is to examine very closely official documents, speeches and statements, point out inconsistencies, contradictions, mistakes or call attention to matters that have been overlooked. Stone's muckraking, which he does almost singlehandedly through prolific reading and a prodigious memory, is respectfully regarded even by those who disagree with him; as a responsible individual spokesman for a position popular with many college students, his newsletter will be read and used.

A54-6050

NOTE: I.F. Stone has announced that as of January, 1972, he is discontinuing the *Bi-weekly*. He will become a Contributing Editor of the *New York Review of Books*, but hopes to do the same kind of writing and reporting.

INTERCOM.   v. 1, 1959-

5 nos./yr.   N.Y. $6.00

Begun by the Foreign Policy Association, it was taken over in late 1968 by the Center for War/Peace Studies, though its emphasis and intent have remained very much the same. Its basic purpose has been to provide for "executives of national and local organizations, world affairs program planners, teachers in schools & colleges, librarians, directors of the public affairs activities of business companies, government officers and others interested in education and world affairs" a clearinghouse of information and activities in the area. Each issue contains news of new programs and services, listings of films, books and pamphlets, and a special section for teachers. In addition, a major portion of each issue is devoted to a single subject—e.g., Disarmament, Handbook of Latin America, Eastern Europe, the Atlantic Community, the U.S. and Foreign Economic Aid, Careers in World Affairs, etc.—containing general discussions on the subject and a variety of types of useful information, including a selective, annotated bibliography, frequently listing periodicals on the subject, with many references to other material available (often free or inexpensive material) and to organizations from which additional information and materials may be obtained. Although aimed more for discussion groups and high schools, because of the variety of information (especially bibliographical) in it, *Intercom* ought to be available in the college library.

Indexed in: P.A.I.S. 63-25823

*INTERNATIONAL AFFAIRS. v. 1, 1922-

Quarterly. London. $10.00

A journal of the Royal Institute of International Affairs, an unofficial, non-partisan, highly respected organization. Its purpose in earlier years was to provide an outlet for the lectures on international matters given at Chatham House (the home of the RIAA) by leading British and foreign authorities, as well as for articles on political and economic affairs. In recent years, the number of addresses published has been small, with a corresponding increase in original articles. There are usually 5 to 7 articles of moderate length (shorter articles are carried in *World Today* (q.v.)) contributed by scholars, present and ex-government officials, journalists, and other experts on aspects of international affairs, many of them well known. These articles tend to survey events, discover trends, and discuss basic causes and problems; they are generally not, in other words, studies for the specialist. Though polemical articles are occasionally published, they are almost always thoughtful and responsible. More than half of each issue now is devoted to reviews: first, an essay-review of a group of recent titles on a common subject; then about 150-200 reviews, from a paragraph to 1500 words, with most 600-700 words. All are signed and most, but not all, are critical. Also an extensive listing of books received. A highly regarded journal, useful bibliographically as well as for its articles.

Indexed in: Br.Hum.I. 39-18471
P.A.I.S.
S.S.H.I.

*INTERNATIONAL CONCILIATION. no. 1, 1907-

Bi-monthly (except July-Aug.) N.Y. $4.00

It began as a bulletin of the American Branch of the Association for International Conciliation, an organization later subsumed by the Carnegie Endowment for International Peace, which still publishes the periodical. For many years its primary purpose was to reproduce texts of official treaties and public documents as well as to present the views of distinguished scholars, statesmen and other leaders of opinion, on international problems. After 1947, the publication of documents mostly ceased, and it gradually developed its current format which is to present "factual

statements and analyses of problems in the field of international organization. Each issue is devoted to a single topic and is written by a specialist
[or specialists] in that field." Subjects include a variety of aspects of international problems; thus, some recent issues have been on: "The War-
saw Pact," "Regional Development Banks," "Challenge of Rhodesia,"
"Political Influence in the General Assembly." Issues are generally 60 or
70 pages, except for the much longer annual number (usually in September) devoted to *Issues Before the General Assembly,* a handy preview of
U.N. activities and developments. A reliable, readable—and inexpensive—
source of information on basic problems and issues in international affairs,
very useful for undergraduates.

Indexed in: P.A.I.S.   8-18491
           R.G.

*INTERNATIONAL ORGANIZATION.   v. 1, 1947-

Quarterly.   Madison, Wisc. $20.00

Published by the World Peace Foundation, it is devoted to the activities
and problems of international agencies. Most issues contain 4 or 5 articles
usually by professors of political science and international affairs, but also
by governmental officials, graduate students and members of international
agencies, on all aspects of international affairs, with of course some emphasis on problems and issues of the United Nations and its affiliated
agencies. Issues are occasionally devoted to a single topic—e.g., The United
States and International Organization: the Changing Setting. Beginning in
1969, a section "Notes on Theory and Method" contains brief contributions
that may help "promote the development of the concepts and techniques
used in the analysis of international organizations." A major portion of
most numbers is comprised of the extensively annotated factual summaries
of current activities of the U.N., the specialized agencies, and the principal
political, regional and functional international organizations, with foot-
note references to the pertinent documentary materials. No book reviews,
but frequent lengthy review-essays of groups of books on a similar topic
and an extensive "Selected Bibliography" of secondary material, including foreign and domestic books, articles and pamphlets, arranged by subject.
An essential journal for the study of contemporary international affairs.

Indexed in: P.A.I.S.
           S.S.H.I.   49-1752

INTERNATIONAL Social Science Journal. *see* GENERAL

INTERPLAY.   v. 1, 1967-

12 nos./yr.   Norwalk, Conn. $10.00

Now subtitled "The Magazine of International Affairs," it was originally
(and until 1969) known as *Interplay of European/American Affairs.* Its

coverage has expanded, then, but its format has remained very much the same: usually 8 to 10 articles per issue, with a few grouped around a topic or two, and the others on varied subjects, mostly current international political, economic or military affairs, but often (and increasingly) on other matters of current concern—education, pollution, changing mores, etc. Articles are of moderate length, and though not scholarly, are thoughtful and well written. Contributors include journalists, professors and officials or ex-officials of governmental and international organizations, many of whom are European and some quite well known. "International Cable: An Economic Newsletter" appears in each issue. A few (3 or 4, usually) long book reviews per issue, generally on international affairs, but often on literature, social concerns or the arts. They are almost always between one and two thousand words, often by eminent names, and are excellent.

Providing reliable background material and opinion on current affairs, *Interplay* is especially appropriate for undergraduate libraries.

Indexed in: P.A.I.S.

JOURNAL OF CONFLICT RESOLUTION. v. 1, 1957-

Quarterly.   Ann Arbor, Mich. $18.00

Published by the Center for Research on Conflict Resolution at the University of Michigan, it "is designed to stimulate and communicate systematic research and thinking on international processes, including the total international system, the interactions among governments and nationals of different states, and the processes by which governments make and execute their foreign policies." Concepts, data, and methods from all the social and behavioral sciences, not just at the international level but at other levels of social organization, are treated in "reports of empirical research (basic or applied), theoretical analyses, critical reviews, as well as speculative or programmatic papers with a systematic focus." Single issues are sometimes devoted to one theme and, on occasion, to just one monograph, but most issues contain usually 5 or 6 articles, a section on Gaming (because of the increased interest in game theory) and a section of discussions with usually 2 or 3 long review-essays on a single or a group of books. List of books received. Abstracts of all articles are included in the back pages so they can be clipped and filed. Useful in many fields, and unique in its emphasis, it should be in every library where there is much interest in the behavioral sciences.

Indexed in: Ment.Hlth.B.R.I.   59-62807
            S.S.H.I.

JOURNAL of Developing Areas. *see* AREA STUDIES/GENERAL

*JOURNAL OF INTERNATIONAL AFFAIRS.   v. 1, 1947-

Semi-annually.   N.Y. $4.50

Published by the School of International Affairs, Columbia University. Although edited by graduate students there, the contributors include some outstanding scholars from foreign and American universities, and well known public officials. During 1969 and 1970, for example, contributors included Hannah Arendt, Charles V. Hamilton, Max Beloff, Adam Yarmolinsky and Arnold Toynbee. Each issue is devoted to a single topic on some aspect of international affairs, from fairly specific ones such as "East Central Europe: Continuity and Change," to general ones like "Theory and Reality in International Relations," with generally 8 to 10 articles of moderate length. Through 1966, there were usually between 10 and 20-odd reviews per issue, mostly between 350 and 500 words, done by graduate students at Columbia. Beginning in 1967, there have been a smaller number of reviews—5 or 6 mostly—of over 2000 words, and done by authorities in their respective fields. A journal whose reputation has grown considerably since its early years.

Indexed in: S.S.H.I.   50-1537

JOURNAL of Modern African Studies. *see* AREA STUDIES/AFRICA

*JOURNAL OF POLITICS.   v. 1, 1939-

Quarterly.   Gainesville, Fla. $8.00

Published by the Southern Political Science Association, but regional in neither emphasis nor contributors. Usually about 6 to 8 scholarly articles, with a good balance over the various areas of political science, plus (beginning in 1969) shorter "Research Notes" which "report some interesting data, some unexpected findings, some useful research results." An average of 25 to 30 books are reviewed in each issue; signed and critical, they are mostly 600-900 words long, and 40 or 50 other titles are briefly annotated. "News and Notes" of the Association and its members and minutes of its business meetings. An important journal wherever political science is taught.

Indexed in: P.A.I.S.   41-16606
            S.S.H.I.

LAW AND CONTEMPORARY PROBLEMS.   v. 1, 1933-

Quarterly.   Durham, N.C. $10.00

Though published by the Duke University Law School, it is much more than a legal journal. The foreword to the first volume stated its purpose: "Our social order has entered a period of accelerating change. Law is at once a barrier to such change and a mechanism through which it may be effected. Its relation to the problems of today cannot be ignored by lawyers or laymen." So, while concerned with legal aspects of current social, economic and political problems, it also treats these problems from other vantages and its contributors are from all fields, with each issue devoted to a single topic. For example, an issue devoted to Anti-Poverty Progress contained several contributions discussing the legal aspects, but there were also articles by politicians, economists, political scientists as well as lawyers and professors of law. Other topics treated have ranged over all matters of public concern, from very specific ones such as Migratory Divorce or Combating the Loan Shark, to general ones such as Urban Renewal or Problems of the Aging. Unquestionably, a large portion of the topics treated relate to private or public law or issues related to them, but enough topics of more general interest are treated to make the journal important for college libraries, and it is useful for all the social sciences.

Indexed in: P.A.I.S.　　　　　　　　　　　　　　　34-40465
　　　　　　　S.S.H.I.

MIDWEST JOURNAL OF POLITICAL SCIENCE.　v. 1, 1957-

Quarterly.　　Detroit, Mich.　$6.00

Official publication of the Midwest Political Science Association. Contains scholarly articles in all areas of political science with some emphasis on political structure, behavior, and practical politics, but with no regional emphasis. Articles vary greatly in length, and each is preceded by an abstract. Usually 15 to 25 book reviews per issue; many are reviewed in groups in fairly long, signed and critical reviews. An important journal where there are strong departments of political science.

Indexed in: P.A.I.S.　　　　　　　　　　　　　　　A59-1327

MONTHLY Catalog of United States Government Publications. see INDEXES

MONTHLY Checklist of State Publications. see INDEXES

NATIONAL CIVIC REVIEW.　v. 1, 1911-

Monthly (except Aug.)　Worcester, Mass.　$7.50

Published by the National Municipal League, a non-profit, non-partisan association dedicated to the improvement of local, state and national government. Known as the *National Municipal Review* until 1959, its name was changed to reflect its wider interests. Each issue usually contains 3 fairly brief articles, by professors, government officials, and other concerned individuals in business and industry, on the problems and prospects of local governments. "News of the League" and related articles. The major portion of the journal is devoted to "News In Review," a roundup of comments, programs and developments in specific areas of government: "City, State and Nation"; "Representation"; "Metropolitan Areas"; "Taxation and Finance"; "Citizen Action"; "Researcher's

Digest"—a discussion of several significant recent official or semi-official publications. 3 or 4 very brief book reviews, plus a listing of other books, pamphlets and documents.

Indexed in: P.A.I.S.   14-4890 rev. 3*

NATIONAL Review. *see* GENERAL

NATION'S CITIES.   v. 1, 1963-

Monthly.   Washington, D.C. $6.00

Official publication of the National League of Cities, it is intended for all those having a part in municipal decision-making. Most issues contain 5 or 6 articles by government officials and experts in various fields on a wide range of concerns to city administrations and dwellers—safety, pollution, planning and zoning, traffic management, city-county consolidation, etc. Articles are well written and illustrated. Issues are occasionally devoted to special reports, such as those on urban riots, pollution, the property tax, small cities, fiscal reform, all presenting diverse viewpoints. Regular departments include: "Capital Report," news from Washington; "Municipal News," containing brief items from various cities; a calendar of meetings of interest. No book reviews, but usually some briefly annotated listings of a few recent publications.

Not a scholarly journal, but an authoritative one, and very useful for courses in public administration and for all libraries where urban affairs are of any interest.

Indexed in: P.A.I.S.   67-122855

NEW Left Review. *see* GENERAL

*ORBIS.   v. 1, 1957-

Quarterly.   Philadelphia, Pa. $9.50

Published by the Foreign Policy Research Institute of the University of Pennsylvania, it contains scholarly articles by authors "whose overriding concern is the preservation of Western civilization, its free and pluralistic societies, and its parliamentary institutions." The 10 to 15 articles in each issue deal with all aspects of international affairs, but especially with U.S. foreign policy and with developments and trends in other nations and areas as they affect the U.S. *Orbis* stresses discussions of armaments and military strategy more than other periodicals concerned with foreign policy. An occasional issue is devoted to a single topic, such as NATO and European Security or A Special Issue Devoted to Hans Kohn. The section "Reflections on the Quarter" examines important developments with background information. Although there are only 5 to 6 reviews in each issue, almost all are over 1000 words, and some review several books in one area; the list of "Books Received" is extensive, and each entry includes a brief annotation up to 100 words in length. An important periodical representing a particular school of thought in foreign affairs.

Indexed in: P.A.I.S. 58-4080
S.S.H.I.

PACIFIC Affairs. *see* AREA STUDIES/ASIA

PEKING Review. *see* AREA STUDIES/EAST ASIA

POLITICAL QUARTERLY. v. 1, 1930-

Quarterly. London. $7.20

Contains well written, scholarly articles, both research and essay, on mostly contemporary British, Commonwealth and international political life, but interpreting "political" in its broadest sense—that is, concerned with social and economic matters that affect or are affected by politics. Founded on the theory that in Britain new ideas or progressive policies begin with discussions or writing among a restricted circle of exceptionally able persons, it has always drawn its contributions from such a group. Among those founding it, for example, were Leonard Woolf, A. M. Carr-Saunders, Harold Laski, J.M. Keynes, T.E. Gregory, Kingsley Martin and W.A. Robson. The last two acted as co-editors, Martin only for a year or so, when he was replaced by Leonard Woolf, but Robson is still there. Its opening page declared that it would "discuss social and political questions from a progressive point of view," and it was very many years pro-Labour, but now it must be regarded as independent, though still a forum for the intellectual Left. Articles with dissenting viewpoints have, however, always been welcome. Usually 6 to 8 articles of moderate length per issue; issues are often devoted to special topics—e.g., The Future of the Social Services, Foreigners in Britain, etc. Most issues contain the texts of important recent documents, such as Committee or Commission reports. An average of 15 books per issue are reviewed; these may be in single reviews or in groups, but all reviews are lengthy (mostly over 1000 words), signed and critical. An essential journal for the study of recent and contemporary Britain.

Indexed in: Br.Hum.I. 32-5946
P.A.I.S.
S.S.H.I.

*POLITICAL SCIENCE QUARTERLY.   v. 1, 1886-

Quarterly.   N.Y. $8.00

Edited for the Academy of Political Science by the Faculty of Political Science of Columbia University, and contributed to by scholars from all over. The oldest extant journal in the field, its editors, contributors and members of its editorial boards included most of the great names in the history of American political science, and until 1910 at least, it was the major American journal in the field. Throughout its history, a major emphasis has been on current events; now issues generally contain 5 scholarly articles, mostly of moderate length, in all fields of political science with occasional excursions into economics, history or sociology; little attention is given to behavioral studies. It has always contained a large number of signed, critical book reviews, frequently by eminent authorities in their fields; this is still true, and there are now usually 30-40 reviews per issue, 600 or so words in length. There are also a few pages of book notes. Price includes the *Proceedings* of the Academy (v. 1, 1910-   ) which appeared semi-annually through May, 1957, but since then irregularly and infrequently. Each issue contains the addresses and papers presented to the Academy at its meeting or (recently) at a conference held by it, dealing with a major current problem of national or international affairs. Discussions or comments following the papers are also included. A well-rounded, basic journal for all college libraries.

Indexed in: B.R.D.   7-36315*
            P.A.I.S.
            S.S.H.I.

NOTE: Now available only by Membership in Academy of Political Science

POLITICAL STUDIES.   v. 1, 1953-

3 nos./yr.   London. $12.00

The Journal of the Political Studies Association of the United Kingdom, a counterpart of the American Political Science Association. Each issue contains usually 4 or 5 scholarly articles, of moderate to substantial length, well distributed over the various areas of political science with perhaps some emphasis on British concerns and with some attention to the study or content of political science. A section is devoted to "Notes" (responses to earlier articles and other comments) and "Review Articles" which treat one or a group of books at length. Also "Notes and News" of the Association and an annual list of members. Almost always at least 50 titles, done singly or in small groups, are reviewed in the "Book Review" section. Signed and critical, these are mostly 600-700 words in length, but often much longer, and are well done.

Indexed in: Br.Hum.I.   55-28907
            P.A.I.S.
            S.S.H.I.

*PROBLEMS OF COMMUNISM.   v. 1, 1952-

Bi-monthly.   Washington, D.C. $3.00

Edited at the U.S. Information Agency (and the only USIA publication that may legally be sold in this country), "its purpose is to provide analyses and significant background information on various aspects of world communism today." Contains articles of varying length by scholars, journalists and government officials from this country and abroad on all aspects of current affairs relating to the Soviet Union, Communist China and other communist nations and to their relations with other countries. Occasional historical studies. "Documents," usually unofficial—that is, originally appearing clandestinely—are often run. Issues are sometimes devoted to a single theme—e.g., Nationalities and Nationalism in the U.S.S.R., China in Flux, The Russian Revolution: Some Historical Considerations. Most issues contain some reviews—almost 100 books were reviewed in 1969, many in small groups; they are all signed and critical, but vary greatly in length from a few hundred to several thousand words, with the majority around 500 words. One of the most authoritative and respected journals on the study of Communism, from East Europe to China, but especially the U.S.S.R., it should be in all academic libraries. A depository item.

Indexed in: P.A.I.S.   54-61675 rev.
            S.S.H.I.

PUBLIC ADMINISTRATION REVIEW.   v. 1, 1940-

Bi-monthly.   Washington, D.C. $25.00

Published by the American Society for Public Administration, its aim is "to advance the science, processes, and art of public administration . . .by communication among practitioners, teachers, researchers, and students. . . ." Usually about 5 articles, mostly about 3000 words (and limited by editorial policy to 4000), on all aspects of public administration—theory, history, case studies, teaching, training, etc. Each article is accompanied by an abstract. With increasing frequency, symposia contributions replace the articles (or some of them) in particular issues. These consist of papers actually delivered at meetings or contributions around a theme suggested by the editor. "From the Professional Stream" includes shorter articles, statements of opinion, developments in the field, both for the practitioner and the academic. About 10 or 12 books are reviewed at length in each issue. The single reviews are usually at least 1000 words, but most of the books are reviewed in groups, in fairly long review-essays. Also up to 25 shorter, uncritical and unsigned book notes, mostly 75-150 words. The most important journal in the field, it should be available wherever there is much interest in the study of local, state and national government; certainly it should be in any library where administration is taught—and not necessarily *public* administration, since many of the articles are useful for other areas of administration.

Indexed in: P.A.I.S.   A 42-2901 rev. 2
            S.S.H.I.

PUBLIC Interest. *see* GENERAL

PUBLIC MANAGEMENT.   v. 1, 1919-

Monthly.   Washington, D.C. $6.00

Originally titled *City Manager Bulletin* (1919-1922), then *City Manager Magazine* (1923-1926), it is published by the International City Managers' Association. Its focus for most of its history was, of course, municipal government, but in 1968, undoubtedly reflecting a realization of the need for wider action, it dropped from the masthead the phrase, "devoted to the art and science of municipal administration." It still, however, is mostly concerned with cities, and with the many and varied problems and practices related to their administration and with the preparation and improvement of city administrators and employees. Usually 4 or 5 fairly brief articles, mostly 1000-2500 words, written by local administrators, teachers of administration, or public officials. Since 1967 each issue has focused on a single topic. News of developments in city governments around the world; annotated list of recent publications. A backfile is useful in tracing the history of the development of municipal government in this country; for any institution where there are courses or much interest in local government, a current subscription is essential.

Indexed in: P.A.I.S.

*PUBLIC OPINION QUARTERLY.   v. 1, 1937-

Quarterly.   N.Y. $8.50

Organ of the American Association for Public Opinion Research. Treats the theory, methods and applications of public opinion analysis and related subjects—the mass media and communications techniques, content analysis, voting behavior, propaganda, etc. Usually from 5 to 7 scholarly articles of moderate length on these subjects, plus a section, "Current Research," that contains "brief reports of research in progress, discussions of unsolved problems, methodological studies, and public opinion data not extensively analyzed or interpreted." It also carries the results of individual polls: from 1937 to 1951 "The Quarter's Polls" reported the results of all available major polls in this country and sometimes from abroad; this was discontinued until 1961, but the section since then has rather presented the results of specific polls, mostly on topics of contemporary concern, e.g., Morality and Sex, Negro Employment, the Domestic Economy, etc. The Fall number includes the "Proceedings" of AAPOR's annual conference, with abstracts of papers and summaries of some discussions. "News and Notes" of professional and individual activities. Issues usually contain 7 to 10 signed, critical reviews, mostly 500-750 words in length, plus a small number of "Book Notes," 100-200 words long. The leading journal in its field, its usefulness and interest extends beyond just courses in public opinion to other areas of political science, as well as to journalism, social psychology and sociology. A backfile is important for all of these.

Indexed in: P.A.I.S.   38-5902
               S.S.H.I.

PUBLIC POLICY.   v. 18, 1969-

Quarterly.   Cambridge, Mass. $9.00

Published for the John Fitzgerald Kennedy School of Government, Harvard University, it appeared as an annual through 1968. Carries articles of moderate length to lengthy, on all topics of current public concern—not so much those relating to international affairs, but rather internal problems, and especially those that have more general application—e.g., law and violence, air and water pollution, political parties, agricultural development, public works, etc. The articles, which are scholarly and non-partisan, are by eminent faculty members from many universities, as well as researchers with public and private agencies, and government officials. No book reviews, but occasional review articles.

An important journal for all political science collections, it is useful for the other social sciences as well.

Indexed in: P.A.I.S.

REVIEW OF POLITICS.   v. 1, 1939-

Quarterly.   Notre Dame, Ind. $5.00

Published by the University of Notre Dame, it is a journal which, "without neglecting the analysis of institutions and techniques, is primarily interested in the philosophical and historical approach to political realities." Usually about 6 scholarly articles of moderate length in each issue, contributed by professors of political science from many American colleges and universities, and ranging over the entire field of political science, with some emphasis on international affairs and political theory. There have generally been 10-15 reviews per issue, signed and critical, almost always at least 1000 words, and sometimes much longer.

Indexed in: S.S.H.I.   40-29523

ROUND TABLE.   v. 1, 1910-

Quarterly.   London. $8.00

Concerned with the British Commonwealth, its purpose is "to provide, on the best authority, a current picture both of the Commonwealth and of the world as seen from a Commonwealth point of view." Each issue contains about 7 articles, usually fairly brief, on matters relating to the Commonwealth as a whole, or to individual Commonwealth countries or, less often, to other countries. Authors are professors, journalists, government officials, and other knowledgeable persons, with well known names appearing often (before July 1966, contributors were anonymous). The articles are not research articles, but generally rather keen analyses. There are also reports from various areas of the Commonwealth. Occasional review articles. A useful journal for students of international affairs or for those interested in any portion of the Commonwealth.

Indexed in: S.S.H.I.   CA 15-389 unrev'd

SOCIAL Science Quarterly. *see* SOCIOLOGY AND ANTHROPOLOGY

STATE GOVERNMENT.   v. 1, 1926-

Quarterly.   Chicago, Ill. $7.00

Published by the Council of State Governments, a joint agency of the various states which "conducts research on state programs and problems; maintains an information service available to state agencies, officials and legislators; issues a variety of publications; assists in federal-state liaison; promotes regional and state-local cooperation and provides staff for affiliated organizations." Contains non-technical analyses and discussions of state governmental problems, developments and accomplishments, written by scholars, by administrative officers in public and private organizations that are concerned with state activities, and often by governors. One issue each year is devoted to the Governors' Conference, and there are regular summaries of action by the state legislators, of state budgets, and of trends in state government as indicated by the governors' messages. Essential for courses on local and state government.

Institutions in which there is strong interest in this area may also want to take *State Government News* (v. 1, 1958- $5.00), the monthly newsletter of the Council of State Governments. It goes to all members of every state leglislature and to many other public officials and carries news of important developments in individual state governments, roundups of action in various states on key subjects, and a regular section on developments in Washington affecting the states. It replaced the section "Among the States" that formerly appeared in *State Government*, permitting it to change from a monthly to a quarterly in 1958, and to increase the number of articles by reducing the space devoted to news items.

Indexed in: P.A.I.S.   29-25399 rev. 2*

SURVEY. *see* AREA STUDIES/SOVIET UNION AND EAST EUROPE

SURVIVAL.   v. 1, 1959-

Monthly.   London. $7.50

Published by the Institute for Strategic Studies, a highly respected organization supported mostly by American, British and German foundations for the purpose of studying the problems of defense and international security. This journal is fairly slight in size (issues contain 30-35 pages), but it contains a choice selection of articles reprinted from periodicals and newspapers, and sometimes speeches or summaries of documents, from all over the world, relating to international security. Issues are sometimes devoted to a single country, area, or theme. The book reviews, usually about 4 or 5 per issue, are excellent; generally 500-1000 words in length, they are written by authorities from many countries. Also a list of books received. Since few college libraries receive many of the journals or newspapers from which the articles are taken, as an expert selection from the world's press *Survival* provides excellent source material.

64-5423

*UN MONTHLY CHRONICLE.   v. 1, 1964-

Monthly (bi-monthly, Aug./Sept.)   N.Y. $9.50

Successor to the *United Nations Review,* it is published by the UN's Office of Public Information. "It is designed to advance public understanding of the work of the United Nations by providing an objective, comprehensive and documented account of the Organization's activities as well as information on its related agencies." Issues, with some exceptions, are divided into 4 sections: (1) "Record of the Month," in which proceedings, decisions and resolutions of the main organs and committees of the UN are reported under relevant subheadings—political and security, economic and social, legal, etc.; (2) articles, consisting of significant statements by UN representatives, press conferences, texts of important documents, reports, and declarations, but occasionally original articles describing some aspect of the UN's work or organization; (3) "Notes of the Month," devoted to announcements and miscellaneous news of the UN and affiliated organizations, lists of forthcoming international meetings and events, notices of important UN publications and a selective listing of documents; (4) appearing infrequently, a picture section, generally related to a project or report. A very handy and helpful publication for keeping up with UN activities, it should be available for students in international relations courses.

Indexed in: R.G.   64-9411

UNITED Nations Documents Index. *see* INDEXES

URBAN AFFAIRS QUARTERLY.   v. 1, 1965-

Quarterly.   Beverly Hills, Calif. $15.00

Sponsored by the City University of New York, its editorial policy is guided by three purposes: "to provide a forum for an interdisciplinary approach to urban affairs"; to cater "to the need for an interchange of ideas and information between the academic community and policy-makers"; and to encourage comparative analysis in urban studies. Each issue contains 4 to 6 moderately lengthy to lengthy articles, mostly by professors in the social sciences, both here and abroad, but also by city planners and public administrators, on all aspects and problems of cities and urban life, practical and theoretical, present and future. Occasional issues on a single topic—e.g., The Urban Conflict, The Urban Negro. There were a few book reviews per issue, signed and critical, averaging 600-700 words; but since the Fall, 1969 issue, the book review section is "devoted to topical symposia in which the material reviewed provides the occasion for the examination of some critical issue in, or related to, urban affairs." The 2 or 3 contributions to these symposia are usually 2000-3000 words each. With some of the most eminent names in urban studies on the editorial board, it is an important journal in a field that has received and will receive growing attention.

Indexed in: Ment.Hlth.B.R.I.   65-9957
            P.A.I.S.

WAR/PEACE REPORT.   v. 1, 1961-

Monthly (bi-monthly June-Sept.)   N.Y. $5.00

Published by the Center for War/Peace Studies of the New York Friends Group, it contains articles, interviews, news and opinion "on progress toward a world of peace with justice." Non-partisan, its major thrusts are on disarmament, support of the United Nations, the growth of world law, and the settlement of current and potential crisis areas. Contributors include academicians, leading public figures from the U.S., the U.N., and foreign nations, and journalists. It has been open to dialogue on many touchy issues including the admission of Mainland China to the U.N. and the recognition of the NLF, with reports from and interviews with individuals not generally found elsewhere. Regular features are "On the Peace Front," containing news items relating to peace activities, and "Listening Post," which contains a few signed book reviews, usually by authorities in their fields, ranging from 200 to 1000 words in length. Because of its many outstanding contributors, and because it is one of the most reliable spokesmen for its viewpoint, it should be available for all students of international affairs.

Indexed in: P.A.I.S.   68-126119

WEEKLY COMPILATION OF PRESIDENTIAL DOCUMENTS.   v. 1, 1965-

Weekly.   Washington, D.C. $9.00

Published every Monday by the Office of the Federal Register, it contains Presidential materials released by the White House up to 5 p.m. Friday. Includes addresses and remarks, announcements, appointments and nominations, communications to Congress, directives, texts of news conferences, public letters and memoranda, proclamations, and other statements and messages. There is also a checklist of press releases and a digest of other announcements not carried in this publication. Each issue is thoroughly indexed, cumulating for the quarter, with separate semi-annual and annual indexes. An important source of primary material for undergraduate research and for reference purposes. A depository item.

65-9929

WESTERN POLITICAL QUARTERLY.   v. 1, 1948-

Quarterly.   Salt Lake City, Utah. $12.00

The official journal of the Western Political Science Association, the Pacific Northwest Political Science Association, and the Southern California Political Science Association, it contains 10-15 articles ranging over all areas of political science. It retains a regional emphasis insofar as it carries "Notes and News" of the sponsoring organizations, as the contributors are mostly from the area, as it contains a biennial analysis of election returns in the western states, now including Hawaii and Alaska, and finally, as it contains *Proceedings* of the sponsoring associations' meetings. But other than these, and occasional articles on regional politics or political history, it is of interest to political scientists in general, and is regarded nationally as one of the leading scholarly journals in the field. Each issue contains a large number (anywhere from 20 to 60) signed and critical book reviews, averaging 600-700 words. List of books received. An important journal for strong departments of political science.

Indexed in: P.A.I.S.   51-30582
           S.S.H.I.

WORLD MARXIST REVIEW.   v. 1, 1958-

Monthly.   Toronto. $5.00

The North American edition of *Problems of Peace and Socialism,* which is published in Prague and appears in 17 language editions, it is the "theoretical and information journal of Communist and Workers' parties, the "official" spokesman for the international Communist movement. Its object is "to contribute to the dissemination and elaboration of Marxist—Leninist theory and to facilitate unity of the Communist and anti-imperialist movements." Each issue contains articles by leading Marxist theorists and Communist officials throughout the world on the problems and activities of the Communist movement and on the theory and practice of socialism; news of meetings, political developments around the world; interviews with leading Communist figures; official documents, speeches and statements. 2 or 3 books are reviewed in each issue, in long signed reviews. An important journal for the insight it gives into the party line, for the articles on Communist history and Marxist theory, it should be available wherever there is serious study of Communism and Marxism.

62-27041

*WORLD POLITICS.   v. 1, 1948-

Quarterly.   Princeton, N.J. $9.00

"A quarterly journal of international relations," it is published under the editorial sponsorship of the Center of International Studies, Princeton University. Each issue usually contains 4 or 5 articles, moderately long to lengthy, on a wide variety of subjects in the general area of international relations, mostly concerned with the current or recent scene. "Research Notes," generally one or two an issue, are bibliographical surveys, methodological studies, or preliminary comments toward a more thorough study. There are no book reviews as such, but each of the 2 to 5 review articles sometimes covers only a single book each even though the articles are all over 2000 words, and many more than 5000. These review articles have always been a feature of the journal, and are outstanding. Contributors are political and social scientists from many universities. An important and prestigious journal, it should be in all libraries where there are courses in international affairs.

Indexed in: B.R.D.   50-3829
           P.A.I.S.
           S.S.H.I.

WORLD TODAY.   v. 1, 1945-

Monthly.   London. $10.00

A journal of the Royal Institute of International Affairs, an unofficial, non-partisan, highly-respected organization. Longer papers of the Institute are published in *International Affairs* (q.v.); this journal contains the texts of talks given at Chatham House (the Institute's headquarters) and shorter articles; 4 or 5 contributions per issue; almost all are under 5000 words. Written by scholars, journalists, present and ex-government officials from various countries, and ranging over all aspects of current international problems and national political and economic conditions, they are authoritative (though not necessarily impartial) and well written. The regular feature, "Note of the Month," contains short, more personal observations on recent developments. Along with its supplement, *Chronology of International Events and Documents,* which appeared through 1955, *World Today* superseded the Institute's *Bulletin of International News.* Provides excellent source material for undergraduates.

Indexed in: P.A.I.S.   47-29664*
              S.S.H.I.

PSYCHOLOGY

AMERICAN Behavioral Scientist. *see* POLITICAL SCIENCE

AMERICAN Imago. *see* GENERAL

AMERICAN JOURNAL OF PSYCHIATRY.   v. 1, 1844-

Monthly.   Washington, D.C. $12.50

Known as the *American Journal of Insanity* until 1921, it is the official journal of the American Psychiatric Association, the largest and most influential group in American psychiatry, with (in 1969) 17,000 members of the estimated 23,000 psychiatrists in the U.S. Contains articles, mostly brief to moderate length, and a number of features, on all aspects of theoretical and applied psychiatry and psychotherapy. Each issue contains a special section (sometimes published as a *Supplement*) devoted to a particular problem, issue or method, e.g., Impressions of Soviet Psychiatry, Some Contemporary Urban Problems, College Students and Mental Health, History of Psychiatry. "Brief Communications" contains case studies, descriptions of method and research reports. Contains news of the Association, its official actions and reports. Usually 10 to 15 book reviews, signed and critical, mostly 500-1000 words. List of books received. A highly professional journal, but containing enough on the lay level to make it useful for undergraduates, especially where psychology departments have strong offerings in personality and abnormal psychology. A backfile is important for tracing the historical development of psychiatry in the U.S., but for most institutions, a file beginning with 1950 is sufficient.

Indexed in: Ment.Hlth.B.R.I.   22-24537

*AMERICAN JOURNAL OF PSYCHOLOGY.   v. 1, 1887-

Quarterly.   Urbana, Ill. $10.00

Founded by G. Stanley Hall of Johns Hopkins University, its objective throughout its existence has been "to record the psychological work of a scientific as distinct from a speculative character." Though it is open "to all fields of scientific psychology," by far the largest number of articles are in the experimental field, with particular attention to learning and perception, especially in human subjects. About 10 or 12 articles per issue, mostly of moderate length; though there are no abstracts, each report of research concludes with a summary. A second section is made up of notes and discussions, including biography, replies to and comments on previously published papers, and reports of meetings of regional psychological associations and national groups whose work is related to psychology; third, there are book reviews, from 10 to 20 per issue, varying in length from a paragraph or two to 2000 words for the more significant works; all reviews are signed and critical. Finally there is a list of books received. Through 1968, there was a section devoted to descriptions of experimental apparatus, from very small pieces of equipment to entire laboratory arrangements. An important journal in experimental psychology.

Indexed in: Ment.Hlth.B.R.I.   5-35765

*AMERICAN PSYCHOLOGIST.   v. 1, 1946-

Monthly.   Washington, D.C. $10.00

The official organ of the American Psychological Association, it was
basically a vehicle for minutes of the annual business meetings, the call for
papers and the scientific program of the annual meeting, official reports of
the Association, a listing of officers and committees, and reports of various
meetings and congresses in which psychologists are interested. Now it
serves a much broader purpose. In addition to the official contents, it
contains articles on the place of psychology in society and the impact of
each on the other (a topic receiving more and more attention), articles on
the development of psychology, on methodology—both ends and means
—and on aspects of the psychological profession—teaching, training,
licensing, informational techniques, etc. Occasionally, the articles focus on
a single theme—e.g., Instrumentation in Psychology, The Place of
Psychology in the University. There are also notes and news of individuals,
of new academic curricula and programs, of project awards and developments, etc. The section "Comment" contains responses and rejoinders to
previous articles, plus opinions addressed to the profession generally. All
aspiring psychologists should read this journal if they have an interest in
the profession itself—its trends, prospects, personnel and programs. It is
also useful for librarians who want to keep up with the field insofar as
developments in it might affect the curriculum and the nature of the
library collection. Should be in every college library.

Indexed in: Ment.Hlth.B.R.I.   49-5284*

*BEHAVIORAL SCIENCE.   v. 1, 1956-

Bi-monthly.   Ann Arbor, Mich. $30.00

Co-sponsored by the Fund for the Behavioral Sciences, and the Institute of
Management Sciences, it "contains articles on general theories of behavior
and on empirical research specifically oriented toward such theories. An
interdisciplinary approach to problems of behavior is stressed. Although
the scope of the journal includes all aspects of behavior which can be
subsumed under broadly general interdisciplinary theory, special emphasis
in the field of application is placed on contributions relating to research in
mental health and disease." Usually 3 to 5 articles per issue, varying
greatly in length, contributed by scholars in all fields of the social sciences
as well as psychiatry and psychology. Issues occasionally focus on a single
topic. "Computers in Behavioral Science," a regular section since 1959,
includes news items about installations, programs or courses, brief papers
describing certain systems and longer papers on the theory and practice of
computer use in behavioral research; it also includes "Computer Program
Abstracts," describing briefly new programs of general interest. "Abstracts
of Literature with Interdisciplinary Implications," a regular feature, was
discontinued in 1966. Uusually 1 to 3 book reviews; signed and critical,
they are often very long and are excellent. One of the most important
interdisciplinary journals in the behavioral sciences, with an impressive
group of contributors, it should be in every institution where there is
interest in the area.

Indexed in: Ment.Hlth.B.R.I.   A 58-1607

PSYCHOLOGY 381

CHILD DEVELOPMENT. v. 1, 1930-

Quarterly. Chicago, Ill. $25.00

A publication of the Society for Research in Child Development. Consists almost solely of scholarly articles, now usually 20-30 per issue, brief to moderately long, mostly reporting the results of original research into aspects of children's psychological, social and educational development. Each article is preceded by an abstract. Both field and laboratory studies are included, representing both correlational and experimental designs; there are occasional theoretical and review papers, but experimental reports comprise the majority by far. A basic journal for courses in child and developmental psychology.

Indexed in: Ed.I. E 34-503

CHILD Development Abstracts and Bibliography. *see* HOME ECONOMICS

*CONTEMPORARY PSYCHOLOGY. v. 1, 1956-

Monthly. Washington, D.C. $10.00

Subtitled "A Journal of Reviews," it is published by the American Psychological Association and serves as its reviewing medium. (The APA's other journals do not contain reviews.) Each issue contains usually 25 to 30 reviews, but sometimes as many as 50. The reviews are signed and critical—their purpose is "not merely to abstract books but to criticize them both negatively and positively, to put them in perspective, and to suggest their significance to modern psychology." Extensive information is always given about the authors and the reviewers, thus providing a useful reference source. The reviews are generally lengthy, usually at least 1000 words, and frequently several times that. Rebuttals of criticisms are given prominence in the section "On the Other Hand." "Briefly Noted" gives a paragraph on a number of other books; there is also a list of "Books Received.

As an aid to book selection, as well as for its critical material and biographical information, it should be in every academic library.

Indexed in: Ment.Hlth.B.R.I. 59-38175

EDUCATIONAL AND PSYCHOLOGICAL MEASUREMENT. v. 1, 1941-

Quarterly. Durham, N.C. $14.00

"Devoted to the development and application of measures of individual differences," it contains: "1) discussions of problems in the field of the measurement of individual differences, 2) reports of research on the development and use of tests and measurements in education, industry, and government, 3) descriptions of testing programs being used for various purposes, and 4) new types of items or improved methods of treating test data." A portion of the Summer and Winter issues is devoted to a "Validity Studies Section," containing short reports on studies of validity relating to academic achievement; this section began in 1953. Beginning in 1960, the Spring and Autumn issues have contained a section "Electronic Computer

Programs and Accounting Machine Procedures," devoted to the publication of programs appropriate to psychometric procedures. For many years, there were a large number of book reviews, from 15 to 25 per issue; in the last few years, the number has declined, and there are now generally 5 to 15. They are still lengthy, however—mostly 750-1500 words.

Indexed in: Ed.I.   43-15039
            Ment.Hlth.B.R.I.

EXCEPTIONAL Children. *see* EDUCATION

GENETIC PSYCHOLOGY MONOGRAPHS.   v. 1, 1926-

Quarterly.   Provincetown, Mass. $26.00

Its subtitle declares that it is concerned with "developmental, comparative, and clinical psychology," but studies in other psychological fields also are published. Each number contains one or several complete research studies, experimental, statistical, theoretical, even historical. In its earlier volumes, a single study filled a whole number (sometimes even extending over two numbers), but recent issues have usually included 2, 3 or even 5 studies. A complete listing of studies published from 1926 through 1963 appears in the first half of each volume (there are two volumes per year); monographs published after 1963 are listed in the second half. Since publication costs are shared by authors, the time between submission and publication of articles is supposedly shortened, though the waiting period for many articles is still almost two years.

                                                                         54-4353

HUMAN INQUIRIES.   v. 1, 1961-

3 nos./yr.   Washington, D.C. $9.00

Subtitled the "Review of Existential Psychology and Psychiatry," which was its title until 1970. Published by the Association of Existential Psychology and Psychiatry whose purpose is "to advance the understanding of human existence by encouraging the dialogue between the human sciences and the phenomenology of man, and to point toward the integration of the theories and data of psychology and psychiatry into a science of man based on increasing knowledge of his essential nature." Each issue contains 4 to 6 articles, some of which are papers delivered at the AEPP's annual meeting. Of widely varied length and ranging over psychology, psychiatry, literature, the arts and philosophy, and the interrelationships among them. Many of its contributors are well known: Carl Rogers, Rollo May, Viktor Frankl, Leslie Farber, Maurice Friedman and others. Some book reviews—at the most 1 or 2 an issue—but they are usually fairly long. Not important for traditional psychologists, but because of the increased attention to the existential school, it should be available where there is a strong interest in humanistic psychology.

Indexed in: Ment.Hlth.B.R.I.

HUMANRelations. *see* SOCIOLOGY AND ANTHROPOLOGY

*JOURNAL OF ABNORMAL PSYCHOLOGY.   v. 1, 1906-

Bi-monthly.   Washington, D.C. $20.00

Its original title was the same as the present one, but with volume 16, 1921, it became the *Journal of Abnormal Psychology and Social Psychology,* which was shortened in 1925 to the *Journal of Abnormal and Social Psychology,* a title lasting through 1964. In 1965, because of increasing specialization of its readers, it was split, the older portion remaining, and social psychology going into a new journal, the *Journal of Personality and Social Psychology* (q.v.). Consequently, beginning in 1965, the *Journal of Abnormal Psychology* has been "devoted to basic research and theory in the broad field of abnormal behavior, its determinants, and its correlates. The following general topics fall within its area of major focus: (a) psychopathology—its development, treatment or remission, and its symptomatology, and course; (b) normal processes in abnormal individuals; (c) pathological or atypical features of the behavior of normal persons; (d) experimental studies, with human or animal subjects, relating to emotional behavior or pathology; (e) social or group effects on adjustment and pathological processes; (f) tests of hypotheses from psychoanalytic or other psychological theory. Thus, case histories, experiments on hypnosis, theoretical papers of scholarly substance on personality of emotional abnormality, studies of patient populations, analyses of abnormal behavior and motivation in terms of modern behavior theories, studies of therapy and behavior change, to cite a few illustrative items, all would fall within the boundaries of the Journal's interests." There are now generally 20-25 articles per issue, most of them fairly short, and each preceded by an abstract. The journal has been an official publication of the American Psychological Association since 1926.

51-5748 rev. 2

JOURNAL OF APPLIED BEHAVIORAL SCIENCE.   v. 1, 1965-

Bi-monthly.   Washington, D.C. $15.00

Published by the National Training Laboratories Institute for Applied Behavioral Science, which is associated with the National Education Association. Founded in 1947, NTL has had a powerful influence on the development of the interdisciplinary approach to the study of personal and group processes. The purpose of the journal is "to improve communication between research workers in fields such as anthropology, economics, political science, psychiatry, psychology, or sociology, and leaders in groups, organizations and communities. It focuses upon the processes by which individuals and institutions are changed." Articles, varying greatly in length, report the results of empirical research, explain a theory, or analyze problems. Case studies, either showing how the behavioral sciences have been used or misused to affect the working of a social system, are often reported, usually with comments and reactions from other practitioners. Each contribution is preceded by a lengthy abstract. A regular column, "The Biblioscene," critically discusses in detail a few recent publications in the field. The typography is exemplary. An important journal for the study of human and group relations, it will be useful for advanced undergraduates in sociology and psychology.

Indexed in: Ed.I.   65-9877
             Ment.Hlth.B.R.I.

JOURNAL OF APPLIED PSYCHOLOGY.   v. 1, 1917-

Bi-monthly.   Washington, D.C. $10.00

A publication of the American Psychological Association, it "gives primary consideration to original investigations in any field of applied psychology except clinical psychology. . . ." Includes quantitative investigations in personnel research, engineering psychology, working conditions, opinion and moral factors, marketing and advertising research, educational guidance and diagnosis. The 20-25 articles per issue are very brief—just a few pages—and each is preceded by an abstract. Useful for courses in personnel administration and other social sciences that use the methods or results of psychological experimentation.

Indexed in: Bio.Ag.I.   19-12586 rev.*
             Ed.I.
             Ment.Hlth.B.R.I.

JOURNAL OF BIOLOGICAL PSYCHOLOGY/WORM RUNNER'S DIGEST.
   v. 1, 1959-

Semi-annually.   Ann Arbor, Mich. $4.00

Published at the Mental Health Research Institute of the University of Michigan, it was originally called just the *Worm Runner's Digest,* assuming its present title in 1967. The editor, James V. McConnell, began it as a whimsy, not even, as a matter of fact, intending to go beyond volume 1, number 1, but the response to his humor was such that he felt forced to continue. Interested primarily in the study of Planarians, and through them the biology of memory, issues contained a few serious contributions on these topics, but mostly humor—cartoons, spoofs, parodies, limericks, etc.—written by scientists. The number of serious contributions grew, so that in 1967 it became necessary to give the journal academic respecta-bility; the *JBP* portion was added, and it was decided to publish both serious and humorous contributions within the same covers—the front half being the *JBP,* and the back half, the *WRD,* printed upside down. Its serious interest is still in Planarians and memory transfer, but it also publishes other studies in the area of conditioning. In addition to the articles, the *JBP* portion has carried regularly an "Annotated Bibliography of Research on Planarians." Occasional book reviews, signed and critical.

An excellent journal for undergraduate libraries. Many of the serious articles are by authorities in their fields, yet are clearly written, and the subjects treated are of general interest to psychologists interested in learning, as well as to developmental biologists. The *WRD* portion makes delightful reading, and proves that scientists *do* have a sense of humor, even about science.

JOURNAL OF CLINICAL PSYCHOLOGY.   v. 1, 1945-

Quarterly.   Brandon, Vt.

Contains mostly brief articles (30-40 per issue), many just one or two pages, and almost none over 10, reporting the results of research in all areas of clinical psychology — psychopathology, psychodiagnosis, testing, hospital treatments, therapy and counseling, etc. Occasional longer articles, called Monographic Supplements (though rarely more than 30 pages in length), are also available separately. Contributors are faculty and staff members from universities, hospitals and research institutes throughout the country.

Indexed in: Ment.Hlth.B.R.I.   Med 47-1542

JOURNAL of Communication. *see* GENERAL

JOURNAL OF COMPARATIVE AND PHYSIOLOGICAL PSYCHOLOGY.
   v. 1, 1921-

Monthly.   Washington, D.C. $40.00

Published by the American Psychological Association, its present title dates from v. 40, 1947, before which it was known as the *Journal of Comparative Psychology*, which, in turn, was formed by a union of *Psychobiology* and the *Journal of Animal Behavior.* It contains articles reporting original research on the behavior and mental functioning of living organisms with much attention to rodent learning. Theoretical discussions are permitted only when they bear on an empirical study being reported. There are generally about 20-25 short (5-10 pages) articles; even briefer supplementary reports (limited to 2½ pages) appeared from 1964 through 1969. *Monograph Supplements,* issued separately as part 2 of regular issues, began in 1968 and now appear with most issues. They are usually 20-25 pages in length. All articles and monographs are preceded by abstracts.

22-21128*

JOURNAL OF CONSULTING AND CLINICAL PSYCHOLOGY.   v. 1, 1937-

Bi-monthly.   Washington, D.C. $20.00

The American Psychological Association's publication "in the area of clinical psychology (child and adult), it was titled the *Journal of Consulting Psychology* to 1968. Its range of content reflects the many facets of this area including such topics as: personality assessment and diagnosis, theories and techniques of behavior modification, community mental health concepts and techniques, etiology of behavior, structure and dynamics of personality, clinical psychopathology, etc." Articles, mostly fairly brief, on these topics include original research reports, "major formulations of clinical theory or concepts," and "significant applications of psychological principles to clinical practice, including case reports."

Each article is preceded by an abstract. Includes also "Notes and Comment" on these topics. The section "Brief Reports" describes research studies recently completed but not yet written up fully in published form. An important journal in the field of clinical psychology, especially in the areas of testing, projective techniques and psychotherapeutic processes.

Indexed in: Ment.Hlth.B.R.I.   39-13843 rev.

*JOURNAL OF COUNSELING PSYCHOLOGY.   v. 1, 1954-

Bi-monthly.   Washington, D.C. $10.00

Published by the American Psychological Association, it carries articles of short to moderate length (about 20 per issue) in theory and research on counseling and related activities. Topics covered include counseling and personality theory, the counseling process, studies of students, vocational and rehabilitation counseling, and professional growth, with particular attention to "the developmental aspects of counseling as well as to diagnostic, remedial, and therapeutic approaches." Other topics covered include reviews of research, other systematic surveys, measurement studies and basic theoretical contributions. Each article is preceded by an abstract. Tests appropriate for counseling use are frequently reviewed. An important journal where there is much work done in psychology, particularly counseling and personnel psychology, and the greatly increased interest in this area should be considered.

Indexed in: Ed.I.   61-35988
            Ment.Hlth.B.R.I.

JOURNAL of Creative Behavior. *see* EDUCATION

*JOURNAL OF EDUCATIONAL PSYCHOLOGY.   v. 1, 1910-

Bi-monthly.   Washington, D.C. $10.00

An American Psychological Association publication, it "publishes original investigations and theoretical papers dealing with the problems of learning, teaching, and the psychological development, relationships, and adjustment of the individual. Preference is given to studies of the more complex types of behavior, especially in or relating to educational settings. Papers concern all levels of education and all age groups," but the ratio of "applied" to "basic" articles has been about 15 to 1. There are generally 10-15 articles per issue, most fairly brief, averaging 6-7 pages, each preceded by an abstract. Important for education departments as well as psychology, and the frequent articles concerning college students make it especially appropriate for academic libraries.

Indexed in: Ed.I.   E 14-803
            Ment.Hlth.B.R.I.

JOURNAL OF EXPERIMENTAL CHILD PSYCHOLOGY.   v. 1, 1964-

Bi-monthly.   N.Y. $56.00

Publishes "papers in which the behavior and development of children is clearly related to its determining variables. Typically (not always) this would mean that a variable has been manipulated in an experimental manner." The 10 to 15 articles per issue are from moderate length to lengthy, averaging 5-6,000 words; occasional notes on new apparatus or techniques. Though specialized, it will be useful to advanced undergraduates and faculty in experimental psychology.

Indexed in: Ed.I.   64-9409

JOURNAL OF EXPERIMENTAL PSYCHOLOGY.   v. 1, 1916-

Monthly.   Washington, D.C. $50.00

Published by the American Psychological Association, its stated aim is to include "original experimental investigations which are intended to contribute toward the development of psychology as an experimental science. Studies with normal human subjects are favored over studies involving abnormal or animal subjects, except when the latter are specifically oriented toward the extension of psychological theory. Experimental psychometric studies and studies in applied experimental psychology or engineering psychology [appear] . . .if they have broad implications for experimental and theoretical psychology." Actually, the contents are not as wide-ranging as might be supposed, and it has emphasized learning, motor processes and sensory psychology. The 20-30 articles per issue are usually less than 10 pages, and none are more than 20; supplementary reports of 1 to 2 pages are also published. Each contribution is preceded by an abstract. Since almost all studies contain technical data, the journal offers little for most undergraduates, but it is essential for better students and faculty.

17-30350*

JOURNAL OF EXPERIMENTAL SOCIAL PSYCHOLOGY.   v. 1, 1965-

Quarterly.   N.Y. $32.00

"Dedicated to scientific investigations of social interactions and related phenomena." Preference is "given to experimental studies and to theoretical analyses closely related to empirical data." Usually about 10 articles per issue, mostly of moderate length, in all areas of social psychology. Each article is preceded by an abstract. An important research journal, it is especially useful for advanced students and faculty.

65-9866

JOURNAL OF GENERAL PSYCHOLOGY.   v. 1, 1928-

Quarterly.   Provincetown, Mass. $26.00

Articles concerned with "experimental, theoretical, clinical, and historical psychology." The 15 or so articles per issue vary in length, but average about 8 pages. No abstracts, but a summary at the end of each article. Publication costs are shared by the authors, presumably to speed publication time, but there is a lapse of a year or more between receipt and publication of manuscripts. The section "Replication, Refinements and Comments" contains summaries of less than 500 words providing "useful data substantiating, not substantiating, or refining what we think we know." These are published soon after receipt. There have been no book reviews since about 1960; there is a list of books recently received.

Indexed in: Ment.Hlth.B.R.I.   17-30350 rev.

JOURNAL OF GENETIC PSYCHOLOGY.   v. 1, 1891-

Quarterly.   Provincetown, Mass. $26.00

Its original title was *Pedagogical Seminary*; in 1924 it was changed to *Pedagogical Seminary and the Journal of Genetic Psychology,* and it assumed its present title in 1954. Its changing emphasis from child psychology to developmental studies is reflected by changes in subtitles. For many years, it was subtitled "Child Behavior, Animal Behavior, and Comparative Psychology," but in 1959, "Problems of Aging" replaced "Comparative Psychology," and in 1969 the entire subtitle was changed to "Developmental, Comparative, and Clinical Psychology." Each issue generally contains about 15 articles, averaging around 8 or 9 pages. Publication costs are shared by the authors; there is still a lapse of 18 months to two years between submission and publication of articles. Book reviews have not appeared since 1960; before then, there were not many, but they were lengthy. There is a list of books recently received.

Indexed in: Ment.Hlth.B.R.I.   6-12252 rev.2

JOURNAL OF HUMANISTIC PSYCHOLOGY.   v. 1, 1961-

Semi-annual.   San Francisco, Calif. $6.50

"Concerned with the publication of theoretical and applied research, original contributions, papers, articles and studies in values, autonomy, being, self, love, creativity, identity, growth, psychological health, organism, self-actualization, basic need-gratification and related concepts." Emphasis is on the experiencing person, especially on "such distinctively human qualities as choice, creativity, valuation and self-realization, as opposed to thinking about human beings in mechanistic and reductionistic terms." Contributors are psychologists, psychiatrists and others in the behavioral sciences, many of them well known. Articles are mostly brief, but occasionally quite long and are more frequently expressions of personal attitudes or beliefs than are articles found in most other psychology journals. It is not, then, primarily a research journal, but because of the great interest of undergraduates in the humanistic approach to psychology, it should be considered by libraries. From 2 to 5 book reviews per issue; these are signed and critical, and usually quite long, at least 1000 words.

Indexed in: Ment.Hlth.B.R.I.   66-98467

JOURNAL OF PERSONALITY. v. 1, 1932-

Quarterly.   Durham, N.C. $8.00

"Stress is on experimental studies of behavior dynamics and character structure, personality-related consistencies in cognitive processes, and the development of personality in its cultural context." The 10 or so articles per issue, of brief to moderate length, mostly report empirical research, but there are also some methodological, theoretical and historical investigations. No abstracts, but each article concludes with a summary.

Indexed in: Ed.I.   34-9089 rev.

*JOURNAL OF PERSONALITY AND SOCIAL PSYCHOLOGY.   v. 1, 1965-

Monthly.   Washington, D.C. $40.00

Published by the American Psychological Association, it was formed when the coverage of the *Journal of Abnormal and Social Psychology* was divided between two journals. It "is devoted to basic research and theory relevant to social process and personality dynamics. Among the relevant subareas are: (a) social interaction and group processes, (b) social factors in perception, (c) attitude change and social influence, (d) psychological aspects of social systems, (e) collective phenomena (e.g., public opinion, mass movements, etc.), (f) psychological analyses of cultural forms and products (e.g., language, esthetics, style, etc.), (g) the socialization process both at the child and adult levels, (h) social motivation, (i) personality dynamics, (j) personality structure and (k) the relation of personality to social factors. Methodological articles and studies primarily concerned with the development of measuring instruments are marginal unless presented as part of a substantive piece. On the other hand, the methodological tactics or strategy employed in a study will not ordinarily be a criterion for exclusion. Hence, laboratory manipulational studies employing human subjects will be appropriate, as will also studies using nonhuman subjects, natural settings, cross-cultural comparisons, correlational methods, case histories, computer simulations, etc., provided they are appropriate on substantive grounds. It is anticipated that most manuscripts accepted will report results of hypothesis testing research that advances specific personality and social theorizing, but broader theoretical analyses will also be considered." Each issue consists of 10-15 articles, generally less than 10 pages long. *Monograph Supplements,* as little as 15 pages each, but usually 25-30, have been frequently issued—up to 6 a year. Finally, there is a list of the manuscripts accepted for late publication.

The basic journal in the field.

65-9855

JOURNAL OF PSYCHOLOGY.   v. 1, 1935/36—

Bi-monthly.   Provincetown, Mass. $39.00

Established to provide a medium for immediate publication (some appear less than 2 months after receipt) of articles. The 15 to 20 articles per issue vary in length from just 3 or 4 to more than 20 pages, averaging 8 or 9. Some are theoretical, but most report the results of research, and range over all branches of psychology—social, physiological, clinical, animal, developmental, etc. Immediate appearance is possible since the author bears the cost of publication.

38-3075

JOURNAL of Social Issues. *see* SOCIOLOGY AND ANTHROPOLOGY

JOURNAL OF SOCIAL PSYCHOLOGY.   v. 1, 1930-

Bi-monthly.   Provincetown, Mass. $39.00

Founded by John Dewey and Carl Murchison, it is devoted to reports of research and experiments in the fields of national, group, cultural, racial, and differential psychology. There are between 10 and 15 articles per issue, averaging about 8 to 10 pages, plus a few shorter contributions in the two sections containing summaries (under 500 words) of studies: "Cross-Cultural Notes" provides "comparable data from two or more societies through the use of standard measuring instruments"; "Replications and Refinements" provides "useful data substantiating, not substantiating, or refining what we think we know." There are no abstracts, but a summary at the end of almost all articles serves the same purpose. To speed publication, publishing costs are shared by the authors, but there is still a lapse of a year or more, except that articles reporting cross-cultural research receive priority. Until the formation of the *Journal of Social Issues* in 1945, the *Bulletin* of the Society for the Psychological Study of Social Issues was carried in the *Journal of Social Psychology*. Carried usually one or two lengthy book reviews per number up to 1960, but almost none since then; there is a list of books received.

Indexed in: Ment.Hlth.B.R.I.   33-21284

JOURNAL OF THE EXPERIMENTAL ANALYSIS OF BEHAVIOR.   v. 1,1958-

Bi-monthly.   Bloomington, Ind. $16.00

Published by the Society for the Experimental Analysis of Behavior, it is "primarily for the original publication of experiments relevant to the behavior of individual organisms," though review articles or theoretical papers appear on occasion. The experimental reports are mostly of moderate length; the review articles much longer. Also contains some brief technical notes or special articles describing new apparatus or methods. An important journal for advanced students and faculty in experimental psychology; the quality of the articles is very high.

The Society also publishes the quarterly *Journal of Applied Behavioral Analysis* (v. 1, 1968- $16.00) which reports "experimental research involving analysis of behavior to problems of social importance." Issues contain between 6 and 10 articles of moderate length, plus a few "Technical Articles" that apply techniques, an occasional "Discussion Article" on the theory or objectives of the field, and a "Technical Note" describing some experimental apparatus or procedures. Much attention is given to child and educational psychology and to the behavior of retardates. An important journal for advanced students and faculty.

61-1694

JOURNAL OF VERBAL LEARNING AND VERBAL BEHAVIOR.   v. 1, 1962-

Bi-monthly.   N.Y. $32.00

Publishes original experimental and theoretical articles dealing with problems of verbal learning, human memory and psycholinguistics and other closely related verbal processes—learning and remembering, attention and forgetting, recall and recognition, production and comprehension of language, etc. Usually 15 to 20 articles, averaging about 6 or 7 pages, appear in each issue, each preceded by an abstract. A journal of growing importance due to the increased interest in the study of language as a key to psychological issues. For advanced students.

66-93737

MENNINGER CLINIC.   BULLETIN.   v. 1, 1936-

Bi-monthly.   Topeka, Kans. $10.00

Published by The Menninger Foundation, it is "a scientific journal which publishes original articles on psychiatry, neurology, psychology, psychoanalysis, child psychiatry and related subjects." Generally 5 articles per issue; in some issues, a few or all of them treat a single topic, e.g., Youth in the Psychiatric Hospital, the Psychiatrist's Identity Crisis. The authors are mostly psychiatrists, either from the Clinic, or from universities or hospitals elsewhere. While reports of experiments are published frequently, a much more important aspect of the journal are the general articles on aspects of psychiatry and psychoanalysis, usually resulting from many years' experience and observation. Regular features include: "Reading Notes," by Karl Menninger—his personal reactions to articles, books and other publications recently read, and comments, more or less relevant to these materials, but always interesting; in alternate issues, an annotated listing of "Publications by Members of the Staff"; "Transactions of the Topeka Psychoanalytic Society"; and a book review section, containing at the most 3 longer reviews (but often none at all) from 400 to 1200 words, and from 10 to 15 brief reviews (50-300 words). All are signed and critical. For undergraduates interested in psychiatry and psychoanalysis, it is an especially useful journal because of its clarity and brevity, and the reputation of Dr. Karl and his clinic.

Indexed in: Ment.Hlth.B.R.I.   A 70-2517*

*MENTAL HYGIENE.   v. 1, 1917-

Quarterly.   Albany, N.Y. $10.00

Published by the National Association for Mental Health, it is an interdisciplinary journal containing "original papers about human behavior, with emphasis on the treatment and prevention of mental illness, research in human behavior, emotional and learning difficulties, social and cultural factors that contribute to mental health or mental illness, legislation relative to the emotionally ill, and the role of the voluntary agency and of volunteers in improving the care of the mentally ill." There are generally 15-20 short articles (averaging 5-6 pages), by psychiatrists, public health officers, hospital administrators, clinicians, etc., most of them related to the theme of the issue, such as: Focus on the Young; Politics, Extremism, and Mental Health; Death and Bereavement. Even where the issue has no theme, articles are grouped under categories such as The Community, The Hospital, The Family, Therapy, Education, etc. Also some shorter "Notes" and a section of opinions, "Points of View." Usually about 10 book reviews, signed and critical, mostly less than 500 words; summaries of selected other publications and occasional film reviews. Appropriate for clinical and abnormal psychology, and also for courses in areas of sociology, it is interesting for the casual reader as well as the student.

Indexed in: Ment.Hlth.B.R.I.   19-3844
          P.A.I.S.
          R.G.

MERRILL-PALMER QUARTERLY OF BEHAVIOR AND DEVELOPMENT.
v. 1, 1954-

Quarterly.   Detroit, Mich. $8.00

Published by the Merrill-Palmer Institute of Human Development and Family Life, it is "broad in scope, publishing papers representing the various disciplines bearing on human development," and in particular those areas of psychology relating to child development. There are usually 3 to 6 contributions per issue, mostly short to moderate length, including "results of exploratory studies and illustrative case material, as well as completed research reports." These are often in the form of papers given at the Institute's conferences and symposia, or at institutes throughout the U.S., and occasionally from abroad. Usually 1 or 2 book reviews; these are signed and critical, and quite lengthy, mostly over 1500 words.

Highly regarded in the field, it is a very useful journal where there is much interest in developmental psychology or training students to work with children.

Indexed in: Ment.Hlth.B.R.I.   58-34677

PERCEPTUAL AND MOTOR SKILLS. v. 1, 1949-

Bi-monthly. Missoula, Mont. $40.00

Carries a large number (more than 50) of brief (1 to 10 pages) notes, articles and reports in these fields: "experimental or theoretical dealing with perception or motor skills, especially as affected by experience; articles on general methodology." It attempts "to make the approach interdisciplinary, including such fields as anthropology, physical education, physical therapy, orthopedics, and time and motion study." Articles of more than 20 pages are included in the occasional monograph supplements. A few very brief book reviews and a listing of recently published materials in all areas of psychology. Two bibliographies, derived either from recent or older issues of *Psychological Abstracts* and from its predecessor, the *Psychological Index,* appear regularly: one on motor skills and the other on perception. Other bibliographies on special subjets (e.g., Flicker Fusion, Looking Time) covering a longer period of publishing, appear occasionally, and are useful.

Indexed in: Ment. Hlth.B.R.I.   58-32642

PSYCHIATRY.   v. 1, 1938-

Quarterly.   Washington, D.C. $12.50

Subtitled "Journal for the Study of Interpersonal Processes," and published by the William Alanson White Psychiatric Foundation, it "seeks to provide a medium for effective communication between psychiatry, the social sciences, and all other branches of the study of man and his individual and collective problems in living." Usually 6 to 9 articles, mostly by psychiatrists, on a variety of current socio-psychological issues, such as drug use, black identity, suicide, psychodrama, with many of the articles discussing these in terms of their interrelationship with psychiatry. Usually about 4 book reviews per issue, signed and critical, mostly 500-1000 words. A useful journal where there is much interest in the concerns of clinical and social psychology.

Indexed in: Ment.Hlth.B.R.I.   40-7255

PSYCHIATRY & SOCIAL SCIENCE REVIEW.   v. 1, 1967-

Tri-weekly. N.Y. Free, with book club membership.

Devoted solely to books in psychiatry, psychology, and allied fields. Each issue contains a few lengthy review-essays or articles about books plus several shorter reviews. The review-essays may be on works of fiction with psychiatric overtones, a marriage or parents' manual, a group of books on a common topic, or the works of an outstanding social scientist. The contributors include some of the most eminent writer-scholars-e.g., Paul Goodman, Karl Menninger, Bruno Bettelheim, George Steiner-and their essays usually are several thousand words and are not only excellent reviews of the book(s) at hand, but often important statements on the topic of the book(s). The short reviews-"Capsule Commentaries"-are extracted from longer reviews that appeared earlier in other professional journals. About one-third of each issue (i.e., 10 pages or so) is devoted to descriptions of and comments on recent selections and listings of past selections of the Psychiatry and Social Science Book Club, which publishes the magazine.

Indexed in: Ment.Hlth.B.R.I.   70-207492

*PSYCHOLOGICAL ABSTRACTS.   v. 1, 1927-

Monthly.   Washington, D.C. $130.00

Published by the American Psychological Association, it is the leading abstracting medium in the field. Issued monthly through 1953, then bi-monthly, it again became a monthly beginning in 1966. The 1970 volume contained some 21,700 abstracts from literature in psychology and allied subjects of interest to psychologists. Coverage includes books, reviews and discussion papers as well as articles and reports in over 600 domestic and foreign journals. (Abstracts of dissertations were discontinued in 1965.) Though many languages are covered, abstracts are all in English. Abstracts of research literature give briefly the problem, method, subjects used and principal results and conclusions. Abstracts of books, reviews and discussion papers give the principal topics and points of view presented. The abstracts are signed, but are non-critical; the time lag between the publication of an article and the appearance of its abstract is about a year. Author and a Brief Subject Index in each issue, with an annual author and more detailed subject index for each bound volume. Except for the most elementary courses, it is essential to all work in psychology.

29-23479

*PSYCHOLOGICAL BULLETIN.   v. 1, 1904-

Monthly.   Washington, D.C. $20.00

Published by the American Psychological Association, it contains "evaluative reviews of research literature in psychology. It includes reviews and interpretations of substantive and methodological issues." It does not publish original theoretical articles, and reports of original research appear only when they are "used to illustrate some methodological problem or issue," which "should be aimed at the solution of some particular research problem in psychology, but these issues should be of sufficient breadth to interest a wide readership among psychologists." There are generally 5 or 6 articles per issue, mostly 10-15 pages each, and each preceded by an abstract. Since almost all articles have extensive lists of references, the journal is very useful bibliographically, and, because of its emphasis on review, evaluation, interpretation and methodology, it is essential for the prospective psychologist as well as for the researcher, and should be in all college libraries.

Indexed in: Ment.Hlth.B.R.I.   5-19164 rev. 2

PSYCHOLOGICAL RECORD.   v. 1, 1937-

Quarterly.   Granville, Ohio $10.00

"Publishes both theoretical and experimental articles, commentary on current developments in psychology and descriptions of research planned or in progress. The journal is designed to serve a *critical function in psychology*. It therefore favors the publication of papers that develop new approaches to the study of behavior and new methodologies, and which undertake critiques of existing approaches and methods." Each issue contains about 15 articles, of brief to moderate length, in the above areas, and 30 or so signed and critical book reviews and book notes, ranging from just a paragraph to 600 words. List of books received.

Indexed in: Ment.Hlth.B.R.I.   39-25424

PSYCHOLOGICAL REPORTS.   v. 1, 1955-

Bi-monthly.   Missoula, Mont. $40.00   (2 vols. per year)

"The purpose of this journal is to encourage scientific originality and creativity, in the field of general psychology, for the person who is first a psychologist, then a specialist. It carries experimental, theoretical, and speculative articles." In recent years there have been about 60 to 80 reports per issue, averaging 4 or 5 pages each, though a number are really just notes, 1 or 2 pages long. Though all fields of psychology are represented, clinical and social psychology receive the most attention. Each report is preceded by a summary. There is a lapse of only a few months between acceptance and publication of articles. The book reviews are not important—there are only a few very brief, unsigned, uncritical reviews; a lengthy checklist of recently published materials is also included.

Indexed in: Ment.Hlth.B.R.I.   56-405

*PSYCHOLOGICAL REVIEW.   v. 1, 1894-

Bi-monthly.   Washington, D.C. $10.00

Founded by J. McQ. Cattell and J. Mark Baldwin because of their dissatisfaction with the *American Journal of Psychology*. Its ownership changed from time to time until 1925 when the American Psychological Association purchased it. Important articles by most of the leading American psychologists (with only a few individuals excepted) have frequently appeared, and a number of these may be regarded as landmark contributions to psychology. Since 1916, when the Journal of *Experimental Psychology* was founded, papers on experimental topics have appeared less often, so that today it is "devoted to articles of theoretical significance to any area of scientific endeavor in psychology." An average issue contains 5 or 6 articles, 15 or so pages in length each, plus a number of shorter theoretical notes which may be original contributions or critiques of others' works.

A journal basic to the field; should be in all academic libraries.

15-1953 rev. 3

*PSYCHOLOGY TODAY.   v. 1, 1967-

Monthly.   Boulder, Colo. $10.00

Contains articles on all aspects of psychology written mostly by professional psychologists and psychiatrists—many, indeed, of national and international repute—for the intelligent layman. The articles, then, are not only scientifically accurate, but, since they are edited by the periodical's staff, also readable, and they treat recent developments of significance, issues of current concern, and topics of perennial interest. Moreover, they are exceptionally well illustrated, often in color, with charts, diagrams and photographs. Each issue contains about six articles, plus (usually) an interview with an eminent figure in contemporary psychology—e.g., Kenneth Keniston, Jean Piaget, Abraham Maslow—or, on occasion, with individuals whose accomplishments have some bearing on psychological issues—e.g., Ray Bradbury, Peter Drucker, Charles Schulz. A listing of additional readings for each article is provided. These, incidentally, provide brief but useful introductory bibliographies for the subjects treated. A few good signed and critical reviews, usually 600-700 words, but often 2 or 3 times that, on popular, semi-popular and scholarly works in psychology or relating to a psychological concern. A well-edited, attractive, reliable periodical that should be in every library and will almost certainly be used heavily.

Indexed in: Ment.Hlth.B.R.I.

SOCIOMETRY. *see* SOCIOLOGY AND ANTHROPOLOGY

NOTE: In the last edition of this list, it was stated that "libraries in institutions with strong psychology departments should probably sub-scribe to at least one journal of psychoanalysis, a subject covered not much or at all by psychological journals." In this last regard, the situation has improved—articles about psychoanalysis are not as difficult to find. Of the titles listed above, for example, *American Imago*, *American Journal of Psychiatry, Human Inquiries, Menninger Clinic Bulletin* and *Mental Hygiene,* carry articles on psychoanalysis. *Still*, there may be libraries where there is a special interest in psychoanlysis, and because of the continuing fragmentation of the field into specific (and often competing) schools, the following are suggested as possibilities.

The *American Journal of Orthopsychiatry* (v. 1, 1930- $16.00), subtitled "A Journal of Human Behavior" is the official journal of the American Orthopsychiatric Association, which was founded in 1924 by a group of psychiatrists, among whom was Karl Menninger. The AOA promotes a multi-disciplinary approach to mental illness and its major thrust is preventive psychiatry and the dynamics of interpersonal relationships. As such, its journal is of wider interest than most others in the field. It appears 5 times yearly; one number is devoted to the proceedings and papers of the Association's annual meeting. The *American Journal of Psychoanalysis* (v. 1, 1941- $8.00) published semi-annually by the Association for the Advancement of Psychoanalysis, was founded by Karen Horney and is "devoted to the presentation of articles dealing with modern concepts of psychoanalytic theory and practice," but in particular with the theories and approach of Horney, one of the most influential of

American psychoanalysts. The quarterly *American Journal of Psycho-therapy* (v. 1, 1946- $12.00) is published by the Association for the Advancement of Psychotherapy. It is an eclectic psychoanalytic journal, not committed to any one school. Also, its main features, which include book reviews, abstracts of articles in other journals, notes and comments on news and developments in the field general-ly, make it of some general interest. The *American Psychoanalytic Association. Journal* (v. 1, 1953- $12.00) is the official quarterly of the Association, a federation of about 50 training institutions and local or regional societies. A fairly conservative organization in professional terms, almost all its members are M.D.'s. Since the Association is central to the whole psychoanalytic movement (it was founded in 1911 and two of its early presidents were A.A. Brill and William Alanson White), the journal is an especially important one, with many notable contributors. *Contem-porary Psychoanalysis* (v. 1, 1964- $8.00), appearing semi-annually, is the journal of the William Alanson White Psychoanalytic Society and the William Alanson White Institute of Psychiatry, Psychoanalysis and Psychology, which was founded in 1942-43 by analysts who believed that non-M.D.'s could be trained as psychoanalysts. It contains many contribu-tions on the relationship of psychoanalysis to the arts as well as on psychoanalytic theory and the processes of psychotherapy. The *Psych-oanalytic Quarterly* (v. 1, 1932- $12.00), which is devoted to theoretical, clinical and applied psychoanalysis, was established "to fill the need for a strictly psychoanalytic organ in America" and to represent an orthodox Freudian approach—which it still does. It usually contains 15 to 20 book reviews, ranging from a few hundred to several thousand words, and averaging about 500; list of books received. Also carries abstracts of articles from other psychoanalytic journals, and notes on various meetings. The *Psychoanalytic Review* (v. 1, 1913- $12.00) is publishedquarterly by the National Psychological Association for Psychoanalysis. In 1958 it absorbed *Psychoanalysis* and for the next four years was known as *Psychoanalysis and the Psychoanalytic Review,* resuming its present title in 1962. It contains fairly long articles, usually stressing the psychoanalytic explanation of human behavior or the interpretation of the arts, so that it is of more general interest than might be inferred. Also carries good book reviews and professional notes.

AMERICA. *see* GENERAL

---

*AMERICAN ACADEMY OF RELIGION. JOURNAL. v. 1, 1933-

Quarterly. Philadelphia, Pa. $7.50

Originally the *National Association of Biblical Instructors Journal,* its title was changed in 1937 to the *Journal of Bible and Religion.* It assumed its present title in 1967, following by three years the change of name of its parent organization from the National Association of Biblical Instructors to the American Academy of Religion. Early volumes were mostly concerned with the study and teaching of the Bible; while increasingly less attention was paid to this, there was still some emphasis on questions of Biblical interpretation and history, but as the change in the organization's name indicates, its scholarly articles now treat the phenomena, scriptures, philosophy and institutions of every known religion, including the teaching of them in colleges and universities. There is, naturally, an emphasis on Christianity.

Review articles and critical bibliographies have long been an important feature of the journal. In addition to these there are usually 15-25 signed and critical book reviews, ranging from just a few hundred to over 1000 words, averaging 500-700 words. Also a list of books received. The *American Academy of Religion. Bulletin* is issued as a supplement to the *Journal.* Appearing 3 times a year, it contains news of programs, organizations, grants, etc., and announcements and reports of meetings of the Academy as well as placement notices of persons wanting teaching positions.

Because of its eclectic approach to religion, and the sound scholarship of the articles, it belongs—with a substantial backfile—in all college libraries where religion is taught. Colleges in which there is much Biblical study may also want to consider the *Journal of Biblical Literature* (v. 1, 1881- $7.00) and *Interpretation* (v. 1, 1947- $18.00), the latter intended primarily for ministers and pre-ministerial students.

Indexed in: In.Rel.Per.Lit. 36-30418

CATHOLIC WORLD. v. 1, 1865-

Monthly. Paramus, N.J. $8.00

Published by the Paulist Fathers, it is the oldest Catholic magazine in the U.S. Its founder, Rev. Isaac Hecker, was also one of the founders of the Society, and saw its purpose as the conversion of America—"in the union of Catholic faith and American civilization a new birth and future for the Church brighter than any past." Its proselytizing role has long since disappeared and it is not at all parochial, being concerned with topical matters—world tensions, civil rights, youth, women's liberation, the Middle East, poverty, religion and the ghetto, the Church and violence, etc. These are discussed usually in terms of implications for the Church (or religion more generally) but often there are no religious overtones whatever. Articles are thoughtful and usually present a "liberal" (or even radical) point of view. Issues are occasionally devoted to single topics—e.g., Luther and the Church Today—but most contain 6 to 8 assorted articles.

Contributors are priests, faculty members from Catholic colleges and universities, and laymen. Some poetry. The book reviews are good. Signed and critical, there are usually 10-15 an issue, most 500-1000 words in length, on both fiction and non-fiction, in all areas.

A well edited and provocative journal, its coverage of contemporary issues makes it useful in all college libraries, and especially those where contemporary religion is a major concern.

Indexed in: R.G.   17-24439

*CHRISTIAN CENTURY.   v. 1, 1884-

Weekly.   Chicago, Ill. $12.00

"An ecumenical weekly" of religious news and opinion. Religious affairs are a main concern, but just as important are its educational and cultural concerns, discussions of national and international affairs, scientific thought and developments, and a variety of social and racial and intellectual problems as they affect and are affected by religion and religious organizations and personalities, and more specifically, by practical Christianity. Articles are frequently grouped around a single topic, and the contributors include eminent clergy, theologians, and men in public affairs. Takes a "liberal" viewpoint in secular and religious matters, and has been one of the leading spokesmen in the ecumenical movement. (Its subtitle through 1962 was "An undenominational weekly.") In 1964 it appointed a group of Editors-at-Large, from various faiths, who contribute occasional editorials; the editorials, as well as the articles, range widely and are often provocative and controversial. In June, 1970, it merged with the *New Christian,* an English ecumenical journal that began in 1965. The words "continuing *New Christian*" are now carried on the *Christian Century's* masthead, and the former editor of *New Christian* is now European editor of *Christian Century.* There is not yet much change in the magazine's content or appearance, and it will probably mean only that there will be somewhat more attention to European religious developments. "The World Around Us" section contains news, features and special reports on religious matters from all over. Frequent poetry selections. The number of book reviews has declined; there are now 3 or 4 in most issues, with a large number of them secular titles. The reviews are all signed and critical, vary in length, with most between 500 and 1000 words. A Fall Book Issue treats a larger number of titles, along with articles on trends in religious publishing. Also a listing, with annotations, of other books received. Good movie and theater reviews; occasional record reviews.

Because of its growing concern with public and social affairs, and the quality of contributions on these as well as on religious matters, *Christian Century* should be in every college library, along with a substantial backfile.

Indexed in:B.R.D.   4-19837 rev.
        R.G.

*CHRISTIANITY & CRISIS.   v. 1, 1941-

Bi-weekly   N.Y. $7.00

This Protestant journal of news and opinion has been strongly influenced by Reinhold Niebuhr, who was for many years chairman of the editorial board. Because of its wide and devoted readership, it has been more influential than its small size—about 12 pages—would indicate. Begun during the Nazi tyranny (which gave the "Crisis" to its title) it took on the task of making "Christian responsibility relevant to the political order . . . by preaching love more persuasively and by expressing Christian ideals politically through a mild socialism and an idealistic pacifism." It has taken an extremely liberal (even radical) position on most political and social issues since then—McCarthyism, militarism, race relations, U.S. policy toward Latin America, reception of Communist China, etc., and its contributors include many of the best known theological activists as well as others from academic and public life. Occasional lengthy book or movie reviews.

An important journal for anyone interested in the social responsibilities of religion.

Indexed in: In.Rel.Per.Lit.   47-35293
              P.A.I.S.

CHRISTIANITY TODAY.   v. 1, 1956-

Bi-weekly. Washington, D.C. $7.50

The major journal of evangelical Protestantism. The founders included Billy Graham, a frequent contributor, and Carl F.H. Henry, its editor from the beginning until July 1968. Conservative in both theology and social, economic and political issues, *Time* called its stance "literate highbrow fundamentalism." Main sections for articles—5 to 7 per issue—editorials and news. Occasional issues focus on a topic, such as evangelism. Features include:"Eutychus and his Kin," which are letters to the editor, including one letter by the pseudonymous Eutychus; "A Layman and his Faith," containing comments on scripture and modern life by the executive editor, L. Nelson Bell; "The Minister's Workshop," beginning in November, 1965, which dealt originally with preaching but now with pastoral counselling; "Current Religious Thought," one-page comment on articles, books or other topics, by various authors; "Books in Review," signed critical book reviews, about 10 per issue, from about 100 to 800 words; "Book Briefs," about 15-word annotations of approximately 15 books per issue. One issue in February is devoted to surveys of the past year's religious publishing. An important journal where there is much interest in religion, since it represents the viewpoint of a large segment of contemporary Protestantism, one that is frequently overlooked by many students.

Indexed in: In.Rel.Per.Lit.   58-40620
              R.G.

CHURCH HISTORY.   v. 1, 1932-

Quarterly. Oreland, Pa. $10.00

The official organ of the American Society of Church History, "it aims to represent the best scholarship which America affords in the history of Christianity." Issues carry 10 to 20 scholarly articles averaging 15 to 20 pages each, covering all periods and geographical areas, with perhaps some emphasis on American church history. Signed, critical book reviews, an important feature, have increased in number; there are now about 20-25 per issue, averaging 500 words per review. A few French and German titles are reviewed along with the English. Reports the affairs of the Society, including minutes, treasurer's reports, activities and projects, and carries (but not every year) a list of members. Though *Church History* carries a large proportion of specialized articles and is probably more useful to faculty than to most undergraduates, there is enough of general interest to make it useful where the study of religious history is given much attention.

Indexed in: S.S.H.I.   36-5757

COMMENTARY. *see* GENERAL

COMMONWEAL. *see* GENERAL

ECUMENICAL REVIEW.   v. 1, 1948-

Quarterly.   N.Y. $6.00

Issued by the World Council of Churches and edited by its General Secretary. Scholarly articles on the ecumenical movement and the task of the church in the contemporary world. Occasional issues explore a topic, such as conversion, evangelism, or developing nations, within the ecumenical context. Each issue carries: "Ecumenical Chronicle," giving texts of documents, addresses, messages and other papers; "Ecumenical Diary," primarily reporting on meetings, but also including editorials, obituaries, and reports of activities. Usually 5 to 7 book reviews, signed and critical, usually 750-1500 words. Beginning in July 1967, issues contain 2 useful bibliographical features: "Bibliography of Significant Current Ecumenical Books and Pamphlets," and a "Table of Contents of Significant Ecumenical Journals." A useful journal for the study of contemporary religious movements.

Indexed in: S.S.H.I.   51-32992

HISTORY OF RELIGIONS.   v. 1, 1961-

Quarterly.   Chicago, Ill. $8.00

"Devoted to the study of historical religious phenomena," it contains articles on "the central themes of the history of religion, such as the meaning and function of myth and ritual, the structure of religious symbolism, the problem of the high god, of mana, of totemism, and others." Edited by three leading scholars in the field—Mircea Eliade, Joseph Kitagawa and Charles Long, it is the first American journal to be devoted to the subject. The articles range over all periods and places; they are very scholarly and most are quite lengthy. Contributors include the most eminent authorities, both here and abroad, but all articles appear in

English. Usually a book review or two per issue—they are quite long, frequently several thousand words.

An important, specialized journal, for advanced students and faculty.

Indexed in: In.Rel.Per.Lit.   64-1081

ISLAMIC Studies. *see* AREA STUDIES/MIDDLE EAST

JEWISH SOCIAL STUDIES.   v. 1, 1939-

Quarterly.   N.Y. $15.00

"Devoted to contemporary and historical aspects of Jewish life," it is published by the Conference on Jewish Social Studies, an organization founded in 1933 to continue the work of the important centers of Jewish studies in Europe that were in danger of being destroyed. About 3 articles per issue, short to medium length, in the areas of politics, sociology or history, with a strong emphasis on studies of the twentieth century. Contributors are from colleges and universities in U.S., Britain and Israel. Frequent review articles, plus usually 10-15 signed and critical reviews per issue. The reviews vary greatly in length, but average about 1000 words. List of books received.

Its distinguished editorial board insures the quality of contributions, it is, then, an important journal where there is serious interest in Jewish history, the problems of prejudice, or the development of Israel.

Where there is much interest in contemporary Judaism, especially American Judaism, libraries should consider the quarterly *Judaism* (v. 1, 1952-   ), published by the American Jewish Congress, an organization representing a number of affiliated national groups which has been instrumental in the support of Israel and defending civil liberties in the U.S.

Indexed in: P.A.I.S.   42-47218
            S.S.H.I.

*JOURNAL FOR THE SCIENTIFIC STUDY OF RELIGION.   v. 1, 1961-

Semi-annually.   Philadelphia, Pa. $15.00

Official organ of the Society for the Scientific Study of Religion, whose members "represent practically all the intellectual disciplines concerned with the dynamics of modern culture: works in the sciences of man and nature, especially as these involve religion as ideal and as fact." A large number of the contributors are from sociology and psychology, and many of their contributions are empirical or methodological with interpretive reports preferred to descriptive ones. Usually about 10 articles per issue, of brief to moderate length, plus some brief notes. Each article is preceded by an abstract. Some 15-20 excellent book reviews per issue, from 750-1500 words in length.

An important journal for the study of religion outside its doctrinal aspects, especially useful for courses interrelating psychology or sociology and religion.

Indexed in: In.Rel.Per.Lit.   65-4004
            Ment.Hlth.B.R.I.

*JOURNAL OF RELIGION.   v. 1, 1921-

Quarterly.   Chicago, Ill. $8.00

Formed by a merger of *American Journal of Theology* (1897-1920) and *Biblical World* (1882-1920), it is issued by the Divinity School of the University of Chicago. Concerned primarily with Christian theology and philosophy of religion, with occasional articles on religion and literature, psychology of religion, and church history. Emphasis of the journal's content has moved along with shifts in the Divinity School: in the 1940's emphasis "veered toward a more theological and philosophical discussion of religious problems, reflecting the existential concern in theological study itself"; in the 50's, there were more contributions outside of these, though the philosophy of religion and the history of religious thought remained prominent. In recent years it has been much concerned with contemporary theologians and theological questions, with attention also to religious history and sociology. 3 or 4 articles per issue, medium length to lengthy. Signed, critical book reviews on a wide range of religious topics are an important feature. The number of reviews has dropped—there are now usually just 3 or 4 an issue, but they are article length, and many of them cover a number of books on a common topic. The "Book Notes," usually 6-8 an issue, are really reviews—signed and critical, they are 200-500 words in length.

An important journal, contributed to by the country's leading religious scholars, it should be in every library where the study of religion is taken seriously.

Indexed in: B.R.D.   27-10421 rev.
            In.Rel.Per.Lit.
            S.S.H.I.

*MOTIVE.   v. 1, 1941-

Bi-monthly.   Nashville, Tenn. $4.00

Published by the Division of Higher Education of the Board of Education of the United Methodist, it is surely one of the most interesting, attractive and imaginative publications put out by a denominational affiliate. Even in its earlier history it published contributions that were—for that time—unusual for a journal intended for the University Christian Movement, with such names as Viktor Frankl, Anna Seaton, Frank Lloyd Wright and other well known writers, artists and intellectuals. Under the editorship of B.J. Stiles, who took over in 1961, it developed into what *Newsweek* called "the most creative and unfettered magazine sponsored by any U.S. denomination." Stiles declared that *Motive* had "to reflect the concerns, language and style of life of the younger generation," and did this with excellent poetry and fiction, articles and features, and, with imaginative use of photographs, art work, typography and layout, a stunning graphic design. It was outspokenly liberal on the questions of race, peace, student rights and American ideals, and was anathema to many Methodists. Finally in 1969, when one issue devoted to Women's Liberation, and another containing an interview with San Francisco State strike leaders used a number of four-letter words, the May issue was suspended and a new editor selected.

Despite this controversy, the magazine has continued very much as before, calling the shots pretty much as it sees them, attacking inequities, injustices and hypocrisy, yet maintaining its basic religious thrust. A magazine that is interesting to read and a delight to see, it should be in every college library, along with an extensive backfile.

(Note: The April/May, 1971 issue carries an announcement that "*Motive* will be independent of the United Methodist Church as of July 1, 1971.")

Indexed in: Alt.Pr.I.   44-51695
               P.A.I.S.

NOTE: *Motive* was discontinued in January, 1972.

RELIGION IN COMMUNIST DOMINATED AREAS.   v. 1, 1962-

Semi-monthly.   N.Y. $10.00

Published by the National Council of Churches, its purpose is "to make available authentic information on the attitudes and practices of Communist parties with respect to the life, work and vital concerns of Christians and peoples of other religions in Communist dominated countries." Contains translations of articles and documents or excerpts from them that appeared in periodicals and newspapers or were distributed by other means in any of the Communist countries, but especially in Russia and East Europe. The selections relate to all aspects of religion and all religions, though they do, of course, stress the Christian denominations. Useful for courses concerned with politics and life in Communist areas as well as for the study of religion in today's world.

RELIGION IN LIFE.   v. 1, 1932-

Quarterly.   Nashville, Tenn. $5.00

"A Christian quarterly of opinion and discussion," each issue usually contains about 10 articles on theology, Biblical studies, Christian social concerns, and related fields. Generally the first 3 to 6 articles focus on a theme, such as the Death of God theology, Modern Art and Relgion, or Liturgy Today. Most contributors are from the large Protestant seminaries, and though it is one of the better scholarly journals in religion, much of it is appropriate for interested undergraduates. 25 or 30 excellent signed reviews per issue, averaging about 600 words. An important journal in the field, especially useful where there are strong departments of religion.

Indexed in: S.S.H.I.   34-5237

*RELIGIOUS EDUCATION.   v. 1, 1906-

Bi-monthly.   N.Y. $12.50

Official publication of the Religious Education Association, its subtitle is "A platform for the free discussion of issues in the field of religion and their bearing on education." Members of the Association include educators, seminarians and clergymen of varying faiths, professors of religion and philosophy, and laymen interested in its purposes. Articles, most fairly brief, on many aspects of religion with great emphasis, of course, on its functional and theoretical relationship with education. Almost every issue since the early 1940's has some or all of its articles around a symposium or discussion, e.g., "The Religious Education of the Retarded," "The Ecumenical Revolution and Religious Education," "Linguistic Philosophy and Christian Education," etc. Many articles are of interest to those in secular higher education, but most of the journal is of primary interest to seminarians and the clergy. There was an annual (now biennial) listing of *Abstracts of Doctoral Dissertations in Religious Education.* Now about 20 signed, critical book reviews per issue, varying widely in length from a few hundred to over 1000 words; most, however, are around 500 words. Other books are very briefly noted, also a listing of new paperbacks. An essential journal for departments of religion, but of more use to the faculty than undergraduates.

Colleges with a strong interest in Christian education should also consider the bi-monthly *Spectrum* (v. 1, 1924- $), which was titled the *International Journal of Religious Education* through 1968. It is less theoretically and philosophically oriented, but has helpful resources for the practicing teacher.

Indexed in: Ed.I.   9-7225 rev.

RELIGIOUS STUDIES.   v. 1, 1965-

Semi-annually.   London. $13.50

"*Religious Studies* is concerned with the main problems that present themselves in various fields of religious study. It provides a means of sustained discussion of the issues that have been sharpened by the course of recent philosophy and by the new findings of the historical and comparative study of religions. The psychology and sociology of religion, as they bear on major religious questions, come also within our scope." 8 or 10 scholarly articles per issue by members of British and American colleges and universities. At least one review article in each issue plus from 10 to 20 single reviews that are excellent, mostly 750-1500 words. An important journal for advanced students and faculty, especially those interested in the philosophical aspects of religion.

Indexed in: In.Rel.Per.Lit.   65-9981

SOUNDINGS. *see* GENERAL

THEOLOGY TODAY.   v. 1, 1944-

Quarterly.   Princeton, N.J. $5.00

Presbyterians at Princeton Theological Seminary founded and continue to control this widely-read quarterly. Its orientation is "the tradition of Protestantism usually called Reformed," but it is closer to being ecumenical than narrowly denominational. Usually 5 or 6 articles per issue, frequently in the form of symposia, concerned with theology in its widest dimensions, including not only Christian doctrine, but also Biblical studies, Christian ethics, the church and the world, Christianity and the arts, etc. Features include "Theological Table-Talk," which is news and editorials; "The Church in the World," editorial comment on the relations of the church to society, culture and the state; "Critic's Corner," containing discussion of previous articles, as well as comments on books, films, and church documents. Signed, critical reviews, about 10 to 20 reviews per issue and from 700 to 1200 words per review. Intended primarily for seminary students and faculty members, its concerns and style make it appropriate for undergraduates.

Indexed in: In.Rel.Per.Lit.   47-20879

ZYGON.   v. 1, 1966-

Quarterly.   Chicago, Ill. $8.50

"Journal of Religion and Culture" is its subtitle, and it is published by the Joint Publication Board of the Institute on Religion in an Age of Science and Meadville Theological School of Lombard College, The University of Chicago. It was founded "as a medium through which modern religions can seek and promote human values with full cognizance and acceptance of the scientific pictures of reality." Each issue has an opening editorial and usually 5 to 7 articles averaging about 8000 words, many by eminent scientists, philosophers and theologians. Useful for courses in philosophy of religion and philosophy of science. 2 to 5 signed critical reviews, mostly 500-1000 words. "In the Periodicals" is a regular features summarizing a number of articles on religion and science in other journals.

An important journal in a field that is somewhat recondite but of growing interest. Recent issues have appeared quite late.

Indexed in: In.Rel.Per.Lit.   74-1729
            Ment.Hlth.B.R.I.

ACADÉMIE DES SCIENCES. COMPTES RENDUS HEBDOMADAIRES DES SÉANCES. v. 1, 1835-

Weekly. Paris. $325.00 (for all sections; see below)

The Academy has long been one of the world's more important scientific groups, and its proceedings corresponds somewhat to those of our National Academy of Sciences, except that the *ComptesRendus* covers a broader spectrum of scientific research, and represents a more basic source for reports on all of French research. Contains brief articles, entitled "Notes" and limited to 4 pages, reporting the results of original research presented to the Academy in all the mathematical, physical and natural sciences. Since 1966, has been published in 3 separate parts, each of which is available separately. Part 1, Series A and B, covering mathematics and physics, costs $150 per year. Part 2, Series C, chemistry, costs $132; Part 3, Series D, the natural sciences, covers all of geology and biology, including some medicine, and costs $148. Another section, "Vie Academique," appears occasionally, and includes proceedings, reports, announcements, prizes and other business of the Academy.

An important journal for research in the fields covered, but because of its subscription and binding expense, necessary only where there is much research.

67-52730

*AMERICAN SCIENTIST. v. 1, 1913-

Bi-monthly. New Haven, Conn. $9.00

Official publication of Sigma Xi, the national science society, and covering all branches of science. Some articles are reports of research, but most are of more general interest, such as those on scientific, educational or the social implications of science, the history and philosophy of science, relationships between the sciences and the humanities, and introductory articles on new developments written for scientists in other fields. Articles are sometimes based on Sigma Xi—RESA (Research Society of America) National Lectures, or on other addresses, or on articles that have appeared elsewhere or on parts of books that are about to appear, and among the contributors are some of the most eminent names in all fields of science, education and the social sciences. In addition to the articles, each issue contains news of Sigma Xi, its committees and chapters; reports of the officers. "Scientists' Bookshelf" contains reviews of books in all scientific fields, at levels from those for the general reader to technical monographs. Except for occasional review-articles, before 1943 the journal never had reviews, but then it began carrying fairly long ones, all done by one book reviewer; the number of reviews has gradually increased, and the length of individual reviews decreased, so that now there are about 50 per issue, mostly from 100-300 words, and only rarely over 1000 words. Each issue also contains a listing of books received for review, arranged by publisher.

The journal has always contained important, readable material, useful not just for scientists, but also for the generalist. Redesigned completely in 1970, it is much more attractive and pleasant to read, and with the increasing attention to the social sciences, it becomes an even more important title for the college library, both a subscription and an extensive backfile.

Indexed in: A.S.T.I. 43-20253*

APPLIED Science and Technology Index. *see* INDEXES

AVIATION WEEK & SPACE TECHNOLOGY.   v. 1, 1916-

Weekly.   N.Y. $30.00

Founded as *Aviation and Aeronautical Engineering,* it had many subsequent changes in title, adopting its present one in 1958.

The largest and, generally acknowledged as the most proficient journal of the aerospace industry, it "is edited for persons with active, professional, functional responsibility in aerospace and advanced technologies." Thus it is primarily a trade journal, but it is far from beholden to the industry, and both its reporting and editorial policy have sometimes embarrassingly questioned the ethics and practices of manufacturers and the military. Its staff consists of trained engineers and knowledgeable reporters, so that because of its reputation for technical accuracy and readability, it has a significant influence on the industry.

The articles are mostly brief, but well illustrated and well written, and treat all aspects of the field—technology, business, management, engineering, safety, equipment, trends, etc. Regular features include: "Industry Observer," developments related to or of interest to the industry; "Who's Where," personnel items; "Washington Roundup," news items; "Aerospace Calendar," an international listing of meetings, conferences, seminars, expositions, symposia, etc. Special issues, on topics such as The Technical Revolution of the 1970's, appear occasionally; Special Reports (e.g., Layoffs Hit Seattle, European Joint Projects, etc.) frequently. There are two regular special numbers: a Forecast & Inventory Issue, covering trends in each of the areas of interest; a Marketing Directory issue, listing products and services available to the industry.

A journal that will be used heavily by browsers, it is also important for undergraduate courses in economics and political science—the many charts and graphs provide good information regarding the military and industrial scenes. Because of the cost of binding and the fact that so much of the contents are mainly of contemporary interest, an extensive backfile is not necessary, and college libraries may want to keep just a few recent years.

Indexed in: A.S.T.I.   18-14054 rev. 2
            Bus.Per.I.
            R.G.

BRITISH Journal for the Philosophy of Science. *see* PHILOSOPHY

BULLETIN of the Atomic Scientists. *see* GENERAL

ELECTRONICS WORLD.   v. 1, 1919-

Monthly.   Chicago, Ill. $6.00

Formerly *Radio News,* then *Radio and TV News,* it assumed its present title in 1959. Covers all sorts of electronics—radio, TV, high fidelity, marine and aviation, industrial, radio astronomy, computers, test equipment, etc., in news reports, features, and a large number of fairly brief, but thoroughly illustrated and diagrammed articles. Authors are mostly technicians and engineers in laboratories and industries. A special section is frequently given over to one item of equipment; there are tabular comparisons of products in many issues and, depending on the product, these are of value and interest to hi-fi buffs, radio hams, a-v personnel and others electronically inclined. Significant new products are tested and reported. Book reviews are brief and merely descriptive. The articles, news of new products and the advertisements make this useful where there is work done with complex electronic equipment, either in laboratories or audiovisual centers. It will also be in demand by hi-fi enthusiasts and students in physics or electrical engineering. Most liberal arts college libraries should receive currently and keep some back numbers; those where electrical engineering is taught or where there is much work done with electronic equipment may want an extensive backfile.

Where there is much interest in this type of material, libraries should also consider *Radio-Electronics* (v. 1, 1929- $7.00) or *Popular Electronics* (v. 1, 1954- $6.00). Both appear monthly, contain some of the same type of material as *Electronics World*, are indexed in the *Readers' Guide* but are somewhat less professional and wide-ranging.

Indexed in: R.G.   23-4771 rev 4*

NOTE: In January, 1972, *Electronics World* was taken over by *Popular Electronics,* making the latter much more useful.

ENDEAVOUR.   v. 1, 1942-

3 nos./yr.   London.   Free

Published by Imperial Chemical Industries, it presents "for scientists throughout the world, a regular review of the progress of science. While the emphasis is on British science, contributions are regularly commissioned from all parts of the world; the principal considerations are the intrinsic interest and importance of the subject and the authority of the writer." Articles are in all fields of science; they are brief and scholarly but well written and well illustrated. While many report the results of original research, there is an emphasis on reports of progress in particular fields and articles on the history or philosophy of science. Each issue contains about 20 book reviews; though brief (averaging around 200 words) they are signed and critical; also some even briefer, descriptive book notices and a listing of books received. Editions appear also in French, German, Italian and Spanish.

A useful, readable journal, contributed to by some of the world's leading scientists, it is certainly worth adding to the library.

44-5904*

*ENVIRONMENT.   v. 1, 1959-

Monthly.   St. Louis, Mo. $10.00

Containing "information about the effects of technology on the environment and about the peaceful and military uses of nuclear energy," it is
published by the Committee for Environmental Information, an organization dedicated to providing "scientific information relevant to political
and social issues without bias or prejudgment, in the belief that the
dissemination of such information is necessary for a democratic society in
a technological age." It is also an official publication of the Scientists'
Institute for Public Information, a national organization concerned with
all science-related public issues. Begun as *Nuclear Information,* and
published by the Greater St. Louis Citizens' Committee for Nuclear
Information, it was originally concerned only with the problems created
by nuclear weapons and civil defense, nuclear fallout, and related
questions. It changed its title to *Scientist and Citizen* in 1964 as its
coverage had gradually broadened to include other subject matter, and it
assumed its present title in 1969.

Well illustrated articles, mostly by research scientists and engineers, but
also by physicians and public officials, on the range of environmental
problems created by developments in science and technology: air and
water pollution, fallout, noise, poisoning by pesticides and other chemicals, etc. Issues are occasionally devoted to a single topic—e.g., the test ban
treaty, land poisoning. The book reviews, usually 2 or 3 an issue, are
signed and critical and mostly over 1000 words in length. As a source of
reliable information on controversial and crucial issues this is an important
journal for academic libraries; a backfile is useful for tracing the
development of interest in the area.

Indexed in: R.G.

68-1803

IMPACT OF SCIENCE ON SOCIETY.   v. 1, 1950-

Quarterly.   Paris. $4.00

Published by UNESCO, it is concerned with the social aspects of science
and technology, with the application of science to economic and social
development, with relations between science and governments, and with
the problems of scientific organizations and research. Each issue consists
of 5 to 8 fairly short articles on these subjects and on specific
developments in science and technology; though written by outstanding
authorities from all over the world, the articles are keyed to the intelligent
layman rather than to the specialist. Issues had only occasionally been
devoted to a single topic, but beginning in 1968, almost all issues are
focused on a particular theme—e.g., Women in the Age of Science and
Technology, the Scientific Basis of Peace, Science in a Changing Asia.
Because of the eminence of the contributors, the lucid style of their
presentations, and because the topics on which they write are important
and provocative, the journal is a valuable addition to any academic library.

Indexed in: P.A.I.S.   56-1335

JOURNAL of Research in Science Teaching. *see* EDUCATION

*ISIS.   v. 1, 1913-

Quarterly.   Bellsville, Md. $12.00

George Sarton, the eminent historian of science, founded *Isis* in Belgium, brought it with him to the United States in 1915, and remained editor until 1953. In 1926 it became (and still is) the official journal of the History of Science Society, which had been founded two years earlier. The annual *Critical Bibliography of the History of Science and Its Cultural Influences,* which now appears as an extra number, was an important part of *Isis* from its beginning; indeed, it was perhaps the most important reason for the founding of the journal.

The 93rd *Critical Bibliography,* for 1968, appeared in mid-1970. It includes 3345 citations to articles, books, essays and pamphlets, published throughout the world. These are arranged by subject and chronology, beginning with the 1968 number there is a separate listing of book reviews; an author index is provided for all entries. There are several useful features in addition to the usual bibliographical data: books containing a number of separate contributions have those contributions listed; other books have brief descriptions and sometimes critical comments.

The other numbers consist of scholarly articles, usually 5 or 6 an issue, in all areas of the history of science, in western and non-western cultures, plus briefer notes, translations and documents, and correspondence. Generally 20-25 book reviews per issue, varying greatly in length, but almost all at least 600 words and frequently several times that. Each, of course, is signed and done by an authority in the area.

The most important journal in the history of science, along with a substantial backfile it should be in every college library. Not only is there a growing interest in the field, but it is relevant for many disciplines in the social sciences and the humanities.

Indexed in: S.S.H.I.   14-20981 rev. 2*

NATIONAL ACADEMY OF SCIENCES.   PROCEEDINGS.   v. 1, 1915-

Monthly.   Washington, D.C. $35.00

Official organ of the National Academy of Sciences, it publishes "brief first announcements of the results of original research by members of the Academy or others. Articles are limited to 8 printed pages." The only exceptions are the texts of lectures delivered to the Academy and the papers given at its symposia or other meetings. As for the contributed articles, issues contain anywhere from 30 to 60 of them, ranging over all sciences; including a few in engineering; the largest number by far are in the biological sciences, with those in biochemistry heavily predominant. The shift in the concentration of articles is interesting (in 1957, mathematics and genetics were favored), and is some indication of national trends. Because all articles are by members of the prestigious Academy, or submitted through them, some of the most important research being done is first reported here; for this reason it is especially useful where there is some emphasis on research, but it is not essential for most college libraries.

16-10069*

*NATURAL HISTORY.   v. 1, 1900-

Monthly (bi-monthly, June-Sept.)   N.Y. $8.00

The official journal of the American Museum of Natural History and American Museum—Haydn Planetarium (and known as the *American Museum Journal* through 1918), it absorbed *Nature Magazine* in 1960. Contains popularly-presented articles and features on exploration, archae-ology, anthropology, geography and geology, animal, marine, insect and bird life, astronomy, etc.—all subjects that are related to natural history and several to social history. In many cases, the articles are by highly respected names in their fields—members of the Museum staff, academ-icians, research scientists, etc.; and all articles are profusely, often outstandingly, illustrated. Suggested additional readings are listed for all articles. Special supplements, treating a single topic—e.g., The Unforeseen International Ecologic Boomerang," "The State of the Species"—appear occasionally. Up until recently there were several regular features—"A Naturalist's Diary," "The Camera and Nature," "Washington Newsletter," the "Backyard Astronomer," but these have been discontinued except for the "Sky Reporter" and "Celestial Events," which discuss and illustrate astronomic phenomena for the coming month. Good book reviews: signed and critical, by experts in their fields, most are only a few hundred words, but some are very long. The November or December issue carries the annual "Survey of Science Books for Young People," a lengthy but incisive roundup. Though aimed at the general reader, its breadth and authoritativeness make it useful for undergraduate courses, and it is superb browsing material.

Indexed in: B.R.D.   20-20046
            R.G.

*NATURE.   v. 1, 1869-

3 times a week.   Hampshire, England. $108.00 (but see below)

In 1969, its subtitle changed from "A Weekly Journal of Science" to "International Journal of Science." This change did little more than formalize its status, since it is generally regarded as the world's foremost scientific journal.

It began when Sir Norman Lockyer, a civil servant in the War Office, and a scientist of some repute, suggested the idea of a scientific journal to Macmillan Ltd. and received its support (it is still the publisher), along with many eminent scientists. Lockyer remained editor for 50 years, and throughout the 19th century *Nature* was closely related to the great figures in science. Because of this, it has published first reports of some of the most important scientific achievements—e.g., the discovery of x-rays, synthesis of penicillin, the nature of the genetic code, etc.

Research reports, while providing the primary basis for *Nature's* reputa-tion, have not been its only important feature. Also important have been its articles and editorials on education, science and national affairs, social aspects of science, industrial development and other matters. Indeed, in 1930, Arnold Bennett wrote that it was "perhaps the most important weekly printed in English, far more important than any political weekly." An exaggeration, undoubtedly, but still it pointed up *Nature's* reputation for commentary on matters outside pure science. This is still an important part of the journal. In 1967, issues began to be sent to the U.S. by air and then surface-distributed here; in 1970, a Washington office was established to permit better coverage of North American developments, and a regular section now is devoted to the "New World." The aspect for which it is most important in the world of science, its reports on research, appear in both articles and letters and come from all over. Their extent, in number and source, is indicated by the statistic that in 1962 there were 3295 research reports from 71 countries. These covered all the sciences, fairly well divided between the physical and biological, with some attention to psychology.

Beginning in 1971 *Nature* appears three times a week, on Monday, Wednesday and Friday. The editions appearing on Mondays and Wednesdays are devoted respectively to the physical and biological sciences and carry important but specialized research articles in these fields. They are known accordingly as *Nature-Physical Science* and *Nature-New Biology*. The issue published on Fridays is simply *Nature* and is broader in scope and content and of more general appeal, but continues to publish original research articles, in many ways similar to the weekly journal that appeared before 1971. In the weekend edition readers are informed of important articles appearing in the Monday and Wednesday issues by means of notices in advance of publication, or through reviews and appraisals of articles which have already appeared.

This change to 3 numbers a week was "to allow more space for the publication of original research, to provide a fuller chronicle of events and to make it possible to deal with important matters now unwillingly neglected. A further important advantage of the several editions is that it will now be possible to bring together articles on work in related fields of study more effectively than has been possible in the past."

Subscriptions may now be of 3 kinds: 1) the Friday edition only ($48); 2) Friday's *Nature* and either *Nature-Physical Science* or *Nature-New Biology* ($83); or 3) all three editions ($108). *Nature-Physical Science* and *Nature-New Biology* are not available on separate subscriptions.

The book reviews, which appear in the Friday edition only, have long been noteworthy. There are now almost 1000 a year: 10-15 in each issue, plus 50-75 in the periodic review supplements. All are signed and critical; most are 300-500 words, but occasionally much longer. They are on the history and philosophy of science, biography, education, even non-scientific topics, as well as on specific technical works. Many other features, including announcements of meetings, appointments, international conferences, educational programs, plus listings of governmental reports and documents.

A lengthy backfile of *Nature* is important where there is much emphasis on the history of science; a smaller but substantial backfile is important where there is much research; every library supporting a decent science program should receive it currently.

12-37118 rev.

***NEW SCIENTIST AND SCIENCE JOURNAL.   v. 1, 1956-**

Weekly.   London. $16.00

An independently published journal covering the field of science, but not containing origianl research papers. Its purpose is to report scientific news and developments in a lively but authoritative way. The contents fall into 4 categories. First, the notes and comments, consisting of editorials on various scientific and technological events and developments, and especially those in Britain, plus items on important recent discoveries, and scientific and technological announcements, often reported in other journals, and frequently illustrated with photographs and drawings. Second, is the major part of the journal—usually 5 to 7 articles that may be on any aspect of the scientific world: science and government; science education; the future of particular areas of science; a review of a rapidly developing topic; an explanation of a highly technical but important subject; the philosophy or history of science; development in a foreign country, etc. These articles, which are usually less than 3000 words, are mostly by eminent British (and occasionally other) scientists, and are not only authoritatively, but gracefully written. Third, the miscellaneous features: "Tantalizer," a weekly brain-teaser; "Westminster Science," government actions affecting science; "People," brief biographies of scientists in the news; "Ariadne," a column of personal, often whimsical comment, on scientific events, personalities and developments—delightful reading.

Finally, the book reviews. Usually between 7 and 10 an issue, done by specialists in their fields, and though fairly brief, mostly 300-500 words in length, they are excellent. Some are reviews of technical monographs, but mostly they are on works of more general interest.

New Scientist began in 1956; *Science Journal* in 1965. Both were highly regarded, and in early 1971 they merged, with the *New Scientist's* format retained, but with significant trends covered in depth and with more attention to individuals through interviews and profiles. With the merger, the journal became even more useful than before.

An important, though neglected journal for American students and scientists. Similar in some respects to *Scientific American*, in others to *Science* or *Nature*, it combines their best characteristics for its own purposes, and should be in every library where there is an interest in science. It is particularly useful for non-scientists who want to keep up with the field in general, or for specialists who want to keep up with what other specialists are doing.

59-30638

NUCLEAR SCIENCE ABSTRACTS.   v. 1, 1948-

Semi-monthly.   Washington, D.C. $42.00

A publication of the U.S. Atomic Energy Commission, Division of Technical Information, it "provides the only comprehensive abstracting and indexing coverage of international nuclear science literature." Covers reports of the AEC and its contractors, other government agencies, universities, other governments and industrial and research organizations. "In addition, books, conference proceedings, individual conference papers, patents, and journal literature on a worldwide basis are abstracted and indexed." Popular works are not included. A number of official foreign atomic energy commissions contribute abstracts, and many organizations provide advance page proofs of their publications. Over 50,000 abstracts per year have appeared in each of the past four years, covering some 3000 journals and serials.

All titles and abstracts are in English, and the contents are arranged by subject. Each issue includes 4 indexes: subject, personal author, corporate author, and report number; semi-annual and annual cumulative indexes are available separately ($34.50), but are essential for using the service satisfactorily.

Essential where there is any advanced work related to nuclear research.

50-4390 rev.

QST.   v. 1, 1915-

Monthly.   Newington, Conn. $7.50

"Devoted entirely to amateur radio," it is the official publication of the American Radio Relay League, and is also the official organ of the International Amateur Radio Union. While most of the articles are fairly technical, there is a regular section for the "Beginner and Novice" and the amount of space given to news events, happenings, items of general interest, and even some fiction, make it appropriate for the reader with a general interest in ham radio as well as for the licensed operator. Contains news of both organizations, items on federal and international rules and regulations, descriptions of new equipment, and activities of individual stations. Occasional book reviews, mostly of manuals, handbooks and technical guides. Thoroughly illustrated with photographs, drawings and diagrams.

Similar in content, especially insofar as equipment and apparatus are concerned, is *CQ* (v. 1, 1945- $6.00). The major difference is the latter's lack of news of organizations.

Binding or an extensive backfile is probably not necessary for most college libraries, whichever title is taken.

Indexed in: A.S.T.I.   21-9421*

REVIEW OF SCIENTIFIC INSTRUMENTS.   v. 1, 1930-

Monthly.   N.Y. $22.00

Published by the American Institute of Physics, it was preceded by a section on scientific instruments that appeared in the *Optical Society of America Journal* from 1922 to 1929. Each issue consists of from 15 to 30 mostly brief (averaging 3 or 4 pages) articles, each describing a new instrument, piece of apparatus or technique used primarily in physics, chemistry and engineering, with lesser attention to the life and earth sciences. A smaller number of "Notes" describes even more specific instrumentation or techniques. Two additional sections, "New Instruments" and "New Materials and Components," contain descriptions of the items provided by the manufacturers. There is only an occasional review, but every issue carries a brief listing of new books. An important journal for any institution with well-equipped physics or electronic laboratories.

Indexed in: A.S.T.I.   17-24346 rev.

SCHOOL Science and Mathematics. *see* EDUCATION

SCHOOL Science and Science World. *see* EDUCATION

*SCIENCE. v. 1, 1883-

Weekly. Washington, D.C. $20.00

Actually begun in 1880, *Science* went through two false starts -- from 1880 until 1882, and from 1883 until 1894. Its editorial board as well as its contributors in these years contained some distinguished names, but it was not until James McQueen Cattell, head of Columbia's psychology department, took it over in 1895 that it began its uninterrupted publication. In 1900, the American Association for the Advancement of Science agreed to make it the official journal of the organization, and it is now sent to all members, numbering about 110,000. In 1958, *Science* absorbed the AAAS's other publication, *Scientific Monthly*.

Its "Letters" section and editorials permit airing of opinions and controversial matters. The "Reports" section contains brief research pieces (under .2000 words) of somewhat more specialized nature, in all areas of science, each preceded by an abstract; comments on previously published reports are also in this section. "News and Comment" discusses, among other things, major institutional developments and governmental activities and programs as well as announcements of grants, fellowships, awards, and new courses. A "Meetings" section describes the events and papers at some of the more important meetings, frequently in some detail, and contains a thorough listing of meetings to come during the next month. Beginning in 1963, an annual *Guide to Scientific Instruments* has appeared in November or December (from 1964 on, it has been a separate supplementary issue), containing comprehensive information on scientific instruments, equipment and their manufacturers. The signed book reviews, usually 6 to 10 an issue, vary in length,but are mostly 400-500 words. They are clear and critical, and cover as wide a range of subjects as the leading articles. There is also a listing of new books.

Aside from all these features, there are two aspects of *Science* that make it essential for every academic library. First, the lengthy feature articles reporting the results of research, some of great scientific import, ranging over all areas of the sciences, including an increasing number in the social sciences. Second are the readable, knowledgeable articles by its staff members on matters concerning the scientists' professional world -- in relation to education, social problems, politics, international relations, etc. -- that are of interest not just to scientists but to the intelligent layman and certainly to educators.

No library can be without it, and most libraries should have an extensive backfile.

17-24346 rev.

Indexed in: R.G.
A.S.T.I.
B.R.D.

*SCIENCE NEWS. v. 1, 1921-

Weekly. Washington, D.C. $7.50

Starting as *Science News Bulletin*, it became *Science News Letter* in 1922, retaining that title until 1966. Published by Science Service, a non-profit organization devoted to the popularization of science and with a board of distinguished scientists and journalists, it presents news, developments and discoveries in scientific research and technology, including news of government activities and individuals relating to them. Articles are well illustrated and usually less than 1500 words, most much shorter, though in recent years the number of longer articles has been increasing. In addition to the articles, there are now single pages devoted to brief items on the physical sciences, information sciences, life sciences, social sciences (psychology, psychiatry, archaeology, and sociology), environmental sciences and aerospace -- though not all of these in every issue. There is also a monthly page on astronomy, discussing phenomena for the coming month, with a celestial timetable. Weekly features include annotated, extensive listings of new books and films, and once a month New Products -- now fairly technical items of equipment -- are described.

Not only are there longer articles, but recent volumes have seen increasing attention to the social sciences and to the social role of science, the state of science in other countries, science in government, the education of scientists, and various other trends and developments of professional concern.

Concise, yet providing substantial coverage interestingly and accurately, it provides an excellent way of keeping up with science, and should be in every library.

Indexed in: R.G.   37-18541

*SCIENTIFIC AMERICAN. v. 1, 1845-; n.s.v. 1, 1859-

Monthly. N.Y. $10.00

One of the oldest continuing magazines, it began as a weekly, emphasizing "practical information" -- industry, science, invention and mechanics, replete with drawings, diagrams and (later) photographs. In 1876 the publishers began a *Scientific American Supplement* which carried more technical articles; this weekly *Supplement* was succeeded by the *Scientific American Monthly* which contained longer and more "serious" articles, in many cases translating important articles from leading foreign science journals. This lasted less than two years, and in November, 1921, it combined with the *Scientific American*, which then became a monthly. It still emphasized the "practical," but in May, 1948, having recognized the need for a journal somewhere between the very specialized and the very popular, it took on its present policy and, except for technical innovations, appearance.

Usually contains about 8 articles of moderate length, well illustrated with photographs, drawings and diagrams, by specialists in their fields, but written for the intelligent layman to explain important new concepts, to summarize recent developments, or to present interesting but informative aspects of their studies. Subjects range over all of science and technology, with frequent articles in the history or philosophy of science, in psychology, sociology and archaeology. An occasional issue, usually extra large, is devoted to a single subject -- e.g., The Ocean. Regular features include: "Science and the Citizen," scientific notes and news affecting the individual; "Mathematical Games" – puzzles, oddities, etc., – begun in 1957; "The Amateur Scientist," describing experiments, illustrating a scientific principle, that can be undertaken at home, begun in 1952. The book reviews are excellent: there is generally one signed essay-review, sometimes several thousand words long. Also a few -- usually 5 to 10 -- from 100 to 300 words done by the book review editor. Ranging over as many fields as the articles, they are all critical. The December issue contains short reviews of books about science for younger readers. A bibliography for each issue lists further readings for the articles contained.

A superbly edited journal, providing thoughtful, interesting and reliable material for students and faculty, it should be in every library, along with a substantial backfile.

Indexed in: A.S.T.I.   4-17574 rev.*
            B.R.D.
            R.G.

SEA FRONTIERS.   v. 1, 1954-

Bi-monthly.   Miami, Fla. $7.50

Begun as the *Bulletin of the International Oceanographic Foundation*, it assumed its present title in 1957. The Foundation's purpose is to encourage "scientific study and exploration of the oceans in all their aspects, including the study of game fishes, food fishes, ocean currents, the geology, chemistry and physics of the sea and the sea floor." Each issue contains a few—usually 4 or 5—short articles, on topics relating to the Foundation's purpose. They range from very specific studies of particular forms of sea life to accounts of exploration or general presentations of problems and developments. The authors are almost always authorities in their fields, and the articles are very well illustrated, frequently in color.

A book review section contains usually 10-15 short (20-250 words), not critical reviews of books on the seas and sea life at all levels—children's, general and technical, with a brief listing of other books received.

A reliable, interesting publication, with good material for undergraduate papers and recreational reading.

Indexed in: R.G.   59-52943

TECHNOLOGY and Culture. *see* HISTORY

ADMINISTRATIVE Science Quarterly. *see* POLITICAL SCIENCE

AFRICA. *see* AREA STUDIES/AFRICA

*AMERICAN ANTHROPOLOGIST.   v. 1, 1888;   n.s.v. 1, 1899-

Bi-monthly.   Washington, D.C. $30.00

The official organ of the American Anthropological Association and affiliated societies, containing scholarly articles in all branches of anthropology -- theory, ethnology, cultural and physical anthropology, linguistics, archaeology, etc. In addition to the major 4 to 6 articles, there are "Brief Communications" consisting of very specialized original studies or those illustrating or expanding on major studies, "Discussion and Debate" (formerly "Letters to the Editor") and, finally, book reviews and film reviews. The Association's *Memoirs* (which were also available separately) were issued irregularly as Part 2 of many numbers, but in 1964, they were replaced by a *Special Publication* series, issued only as Part 2 of numbers of the *American Anthropologist*. These *Special Publications* brought together papers "representing explorations at the frontiers of anthropology," but none have appeared since 1968.

In its earlier years, emphasis of the research tended to be on the United States, but this changed fairly quickly. Every major American anthropologist (and many important foreign ones) have contributed to the journal, so that a backfile is important. There are generally 50-60 book reviews per issue, averaging 700 words or so each. They are signed and critical. Beginning in 1965, a few films have been reviewed in each issue. These reviews, which give all necessary purchasing information, are signed, critical and fairly detailed. There is also a list of "New Publications Received" -- books, monographs and initial issues of new journals, with thorough bibliographical information.

The basic journal in the field, both a current subscription and an extensive backfile should be in all academic libraries where anthropology or sociology is offered. Libraries with strong departments of anthropology should probably also take the Association's 3-times-a-year *Bulletin*, (v.1, 1968- $5.00) which carries official news and reports, notices and abstracts of papers given at its meetings and the useful "Guide to Departments of Anthropology."

Indexed in: Ment.Hlth.B.R.I.
              B.R.D.   17-15424
              S.S.H.I.

NOTE: Available now only by Membership in American Anthropological Assoc.

AMERICAN Behavioral Scientist. *see* POLITICAL SCIENCE

*AMERICAN JOURNAL OF SOCIOLOGY.   v. 1, 1895-

Bi-monthly.   Chicago, Ill. $15.00

The oldest sociological journal in the world; it was the official journal of the American Sociological Society (now the American Sociological Association) to 1936, when the Association began its own journal. Contains scholarly articles on all fields of sociology, with some attention to theory, but more to the results of field work, research into special problems, and methodology. In addition to the articles, each of which is preceded by an abstract, there are shorter "Research Notes," a section "Commentary and Debate" which began in 1964 and contains responses to earlier articles or opinions on theory or on "the state of the art." Annual listings of doctoral degrees granted and of doctoral dissertations newly started began in 1920 and was discontinued in 1965; it carried both doctoral and masters degrees granted until the listing for 1961, when the masters' listing was dropped. The number of reviews has decreased in recent years: they had been steadily growing in number, and by the early 1960's there were about 50 signed, critical reviews per issue, each generally about 500 words in length; beginning in 1966, the number dropped sharply, and there are now 10 to 15 per issue, still averaging about 500 words. There is also an extensive listing of "Books Received."

The wide variety of articles, and the eminence of the contributors make it, along with its backfile, an essential journal for every academic library.

Indexed in: B.R.D.   5-31884
           Ment.Hlth.B.R.I.
           S.S.H.I.

*AMERICAN SOCIOLOGICAL REVIEW.   v. 1, 1936-

Bi-monthly.   Washington, D.C. $20.00

Official journal of the American Sociological Association. Contains about 10 research articles per issue, 10-20 pages in length each, on theory, methodology, case studies and field work in all branches of sociology. Each article is preceded by an abstract. Until 1966 it also served as the outlet for the publication of official reports and proceedings, news and notes, obituaries and other matters of interest to those in the Association. From 1958 through 1965 it also began to carry more discussions of problems of the profession, both within the organization as well as its relation to non-sociologists. Beginning in 1966, however, with the publication of the *American Sociologist* (q.v.) the *Review* no longer carried matters relating to the profession, but only articles, communications about previous articles or about methodology, book reviews, and a review symposium containing 3 or 4 individual reviews of a recent important work. The number of book reviews has increased greatly, even during the past few years. There are now usually 70 to 80 signed, critical reviews per issue, generally 450 to 700 words in length. Also a listing of books received.

The basic journal in the field, especially for more advanced students and faculty, all academic libraries should have a complete file.

Indexed in: B.R.D.   37-10449
           Ment.Hlth.B.R.I.
           S.S.H.I.

AMERICAN SOCIOLOGIST. v. 1, 1965-

Quarterly.   Washington, D.C. $10.00

An official publication of the American Sociological Association. Because the pressures on the *American Sociological Review* had grown so, it was decided to split its two main publishing functions: (1) scientific and scholarly output would remain with the *Review* and, (2) a publication would be started to serve "as an organ of information and discussion for the professional concerns of sociologists as a social collectivity". Articles in all areas of sociology as a profession: education for it, teaching it, its purposes and foundations, social responsibilities, theory and methodology, composition of its personnel, etc., with titles such as "Current Soviet Work in Sociology," "Status of Women in Graduate Departments of Sociology," "An Innovative Course in Urban Sociology." In the last few years much attention of course has been given to the issue of whether or not sociologists should take social or political stands. Other sections include: "Communications to the Editor"; news and announcements -- of grants, fellowships and awards, of news from other associations, of new publications, of departmental personnel in colleges and universities; a calendar of meetings; official reports and proceedings, and lists of officers; "In Memoriam" carries lengthy obituaries of recently deceased ASA members. Finally, there is an "Employment Bulletin," listing positions open and applicants available.

Though of primary interest to faculty, it will also be useful for the more advanced undergraduate who is thinking about sociology as a profession or who is interested in its approaches and trends.

65-9976

BRITISH JOURNAL OF SOCIOLOGY.   v. 1, 1950-

Quarterly.   London. $7.20

Each issue contains generally about 6 or 7 scholarly articles, mostly of moderate length, in all areas of sociology. Contributors are mainly faculty members from various universities, with a large proportion now from America. Early volumes contained some key articles by leading sociologists and other social scientists from many countries. The number and length of reviews varies widely, with as few as 5 or 6 and as many as 25 or 30, in length from a few hundred to over 2000 words, but averaging 700-800. They are all signed and critical, and are excellent.

The frequency of articles relevant to American society and the emphasis on sociological theory make this an important journal for college libraries, more so than the title might indicate.

Indexed in: Br.Hum.I.   54-36111
            Ment.Hlth.B.R.I.
            S.S.H.I.

CIVIL Rights Digest. *see* GENERAL

CRIME AND DELINQUENCY ABSTRACTS.   v. 1, 1963-

Bi-monthly.   Washington, D.C. $4.50

Published by the National Clearinghouse for Mental Health Information of the National Institute of Mental Health, and titled into 1966 *International Bibliography of Crime and Delinquency*. Under that title it was primarily a bibliography, with annotated listings, but no abstracts. The 1969 volume contained about 3800 abstracts, including books, reports of research projects, and articles in some 140 journals, primarily in the fields of criminology and law. Author index and subject index based on the keywords from the titles and abstracts; beginning in 1971 the index will be cumulative.

Even though it is not comprehensive, since it does not cover many basic sociological journals, its low price (also it is a depository item) means that it should be considered wherever there is much interest in a topic which is of growing concern and attention.

66-3911

CURRENT ANTHROPOLOGY.   v. 1, 1960-

5 nos./yr.   Glasgow, Scotland. $21.00

Sponsored by the Wenner-Gren Foundation for Anthropological Research, it is a central source for many kinds of information relating to anthropology. It includes, first of all, articles and research reports on a variety of anthropological concerns: field research and site reports, historical and theoretical and methodological articles, etc. It also contains long review articles of recent important books. Both the articles and reviews are submitted to a large number of readers whose comments also appear, along with the author's response. There are many departmental items appearing more or less regularly: a calendar of events, list of conferences and research grants, notices of items for sale, descriptions of free materials, and other items of professional interest. A *Directory Issue*, listing anthropologists and organizations or institutions concerned with anthropology, has been issued every few years. Each issue also includes a listing of recent books, pamphlets, and serials, plus a listing of the main articles in the more important anthropological journals and selected articles from other journals. An interesting and useful *mélange* of up-to-date anthropological material and information and contributed to by leading anthropologists from many countries, *Current Anthropology* is an essential journal where there is serious interest in the field.

Indexed in: Ment.Hlth.B.R.I.   A63-576 rev.
        S.S.H.I.

CURRENT SOCIOLOGY.   v. 1, 1952-

3 nos./yr.   The Hague, Netherlands.   Bill Later.

Begun by Unesco, then published by Blackwell and now by Mouton with Unesco's financial support, its early issues alternated a world bibliography of sociology with trend reports on major topics. With the separate publication of the *International Bibliography of Sociology* beginning in 1955, the journal took on its present form: issues are devoted to the study of research trends in individual areas of sociology (e.g., Sociology of Sport, Military Sociology, 1963-1969, Sociologie de la Jeunesse) done by recognized authorities, along with an extensive bibliography (up to 2500 items) of articles, theses, books, etc., on the topic.

Though the trend reports are really only important for advanced students and faculty, the bibliographies are generally useful enough to warrant consideration wherever there is much work done in sociology.

Publication has been slow. The last number of the 1968 volume was received in late 1970, and the 3 numbers for 1969, appearing as a combined issue, were received in mid-1971.

55-57288

ETHNOLOGY. v. 1, 1962-

Quarterly.   Pittsburgh, Pa. $8.00

"An international journal of cultural and social anthropology" it contains research articles mostly resulting from field studies, and theoretical or methodological discussions appear "only if they specifically relate to some body of substantive data," "Ethnology" is defined in its "broadest sense to embrace, for example, technology, pre-industrial economics, primitive or comparative art and religion, pre-scientific medicine and psychotherapy, social and political organization, value systems, culture and personality, and culture change." Contributions range from just a few up to 50 pages, and are on societies all over the world; authors are faculty members here and abroad. Frequent attention is given to additions and refinements to Murdock's *Ethnographic Atlas*. An important journal for advanced students and faculty in anthropology.

Indexed in: S.S.H.I.   64-5713

HUMAN Biology. *see* BIOLOGY

*HUMAN ORGANIZATION.   v. 1, 1941-

Quarterly.   Washington, D.C. $18.00

Subtitled "A Scientific Quarterly for the Study of Developmental Change", it is published by the Society for Applied Anthropology (and titled *Applied Anthropology* for its first 7 volumes). It is "devoted to the application of social science to practical problems" in the fields of community organization, economic development, industrial relations, mental health, culture change, political behavior, field methods and techniques, etc. It is, then, of interest to scholars in all the social sciences. Issues carry an average of 9-10 articles, mostly 5000-7500 words, with occasional shorter contributions on methodology. A few issues have been devoted to single topics -- e.g., Human Adaptation to Disaster, Dimensions of Cultural Change in the Middle East, Poverty and Social Disorder. No book reviews (there were a few in volumes up to 1957). An important journal for sociology and anthropology, its emphasis on problems and situations about which many students are concerned makes it especially useful for college libraries.

Indexed in: Ment.Hlth.B.R.I.   47-33317 rev.
                 S.S.H.I.

HUMAN RELATIONS.   v. 1, 1947-

Bi-monthly.   London. $24.00

"A quarterly journal of studies toward the integration of the social sciences." Originally under the joint editorial auspices of the Tavistock Institution of Human Relations, London, and the Research Center for Group Dynamics of the University of Michigan, its editorial committee gradually broadened in both institutional and professional affiliations. A "Restatement of Editorial Policy" in 1965 indicated that while there had not been as much integration of the social sciences as originally anticipated, a revival of interdisciplinary interest—particularly in relation to major social problems and social action—seemed imminent, and the journal would continue to reflect these developments. It is, then, still primarily devoted to studies on aspects of group processes, interpersonal relations and other problems of social structure at all levels, from the family to international societies, as well as methodology in the social sciences. From 5 to 7 articles per issue, mostly 5-8,000 words, by contributors from mostly American and British universities and research institutes. No book reviews. A useful journal in social psychology as well as sociology.

Indexed in: Br.Hum.I.   50-57567
           Ment.Hlth.B.R.I.
           S.S.H.I.

INTERNATIONAL Social Science Journal. *see* GENERAL

*JOURNAL OF AMERICAN FOLKLORE.   v. 1, 1888-

Quarterly.   Austin, Texas. $12.00

Official publication of the American Folklore Society. While founded to explore the folklore of the Americas, and especially this country, in its first few years it did treat other areas, but after the beginning of this century was concerned solely with the folklore and mythology of the American continent; then in the early 1940's, it again extended its interest to folklore of all peoples, though the emphasis has been on American, and especially U.S. folklore. The number and length of articles, all of which are scholarly, vary considerably: usually there are about 5, of moderate length. Shorter contributions, including responses to previously published reviews and articles, are contained in the "Notes and Queries" section. The number of book reviews has steadily increased; their length has decreased. There are now about 15-20 reviews per issue, averaging about 700 words; they are signed and critical, often outspokenly so. Also reviews of recordings, not only of traditional folk music, but also of popularized folk music such as jazz, blues, country music, etc. Beginning in 1954, a separately paged supplement has appeared carrying the reports of the officers and committees of the Society, programs of meetings, list of members, professional news and notes; it also carried the *Annual Bibliography of Folklore*, a list of books and periodical articles from the world over, with most entries described very briefly. This bibliography continued *Folklore in Periodical Literature*, which appeared from 1949 to 1953, and was superseded in 1963 by *Abstracts of Folklore Studies*, a separate publication of the Society. However, it still does carry the annual listing of work in progress.

An important, interesting publication for all academic libraries, one that is useful to a number of areas in American studies.

Indexed in: Music I.   63-24221
         S.S.H.I.

JOURNAL of Applied Behavioral Science. *see* PSYCHOLOGY

JOURNAL of Communication. *see* GENERAL

JOURNAL of Conflict Resolution. *see* POLITICAL SCIENCE

JOURNAL OF CRIMINAL LAW, CRIMINOLOGY AND POLICE SCIENCE.
    v. 1, 1910-

    Bi-monthly.   Baltimore, Md. $15.00

    Published for the Northwestern University School of Law, it is the official publication of the National District Attorneys' Association and the National Association of Defense Lawyers in Criminal Cases. The first English-language periodical devoted to criminology, it was originally the *Journal of the American Institute of Criminal Law and Criminology*. In 1931 it became the *Journal of Criminal Law and Criminology*, adding *Police Science* in 1951. It has always recognized the interrelationship of the social and political sciences along with law in the study of criminology, and among its contributors over the years have been the most eminent names in criminology and allied fields. The Police Science section of each issue is of interest only to professional law officers and attorneys, but the section on Criminal Law and Criminology (at least half of each issue) contains much that is important for sociology and, occasionally, for political science. In addition to the 3 to 5 articles in this area, there are regular sections of notes and abstracts of recent cases and research projects. Usually 5 to 10 reviews, signed and critical, mostly 500-1000 words, per issue, with the reviews in the Police Science section shorter and less numerous than those in the Criminal Law and Criminology section. Also list of books received.

    Particularly useful where there are courses in criminology or penology.

    Indexed in: Ment.Hlth.B.R.I.   12-27508 rev. 2

JOURNAL of Marriage and the Family. *see* ECONOMICS

*JOURNAL OF SOCIAL ISSUES.   v. 1, 1945-

    Quarterly.   Ann Arbor, Mich. $15.00

    Published by the Society for the Psychological Study of Social Issues, a division of the American Psychological Association. "The Society seeks to bring theory and practice into focus on human problems of the group, the community, and the nation as well as the increasingly important ones that have no national boundaries. This journal has as its goal the communication of scientific findings and interpretations in a non-technical manner but without the sacrifice of professional standards." Almost all issues are on a single topic—e.g., Urbanization and Social Change in the South, Alienated Youth, Problems of Bilingualism, Impacts of Studying Abroad, etc.—with guest editors, and with as few as 4 or 5, and as many as 12 or 13 separate contributions. Abstracts of articles in each issue have appeared since 1963; these are arranged in 3 x 5 strips at the end of the issue. Supplements—fairly brief—appeared from time to time, but none since 1959. In 1968, the regular section "The Activists' 'Corner' " began; edited by two outstanding social scientists, David Krech and Nevitt Sanford, it consists of informal comments and suggestions for making the study of social issues more relevant to those issues.

Contributed to by some of the country's most eminent social scientists, and treating relevant social problems in authoritative articles, it is a journal that, along with a backfile, belongs in every academic library.

Indexed in: S.S.H.I.   48-23297*

JOURNAL OF THE FOLKLORE INSTITUTE.   v. 1, 1964-

3 nos./yr.   The Hague, Holland. $4.00

Edited by the fellows of the Folklore Institute, Indiana University, its predecessors were, first, the mimeographed sheet, the "Hoosier Folklore Bulletin," which began in 1942; this then became in 1946 a printed quarterly, *Hoosier Folklore*, which in turn became *Midwest Folklore* in 1951. The *Journal's* original intention was to maintain some continuity with midwestern folklore, but it has gotten almost completely away from that area (indeed, it treats American folklore only sparingly) and has turned to an emphasis on the international scene and comparative studies in folklore. Issues are often devoted to single topics such as Folklore and Culture, or the proceedings of the African Oral Data Conference, but other issues usually contain 5 or 6 articles by professors from universities here and abroad on various aspects of folklore, including methodology, and on a variety of culture areas. The articles are scholarly, but generally not technical.

An important journal in the field of comparative folklore.

Indexed in: Music I.   68-130162

OCEANIA.   v. 1, 1930-

Quarterly.   Sydney, N.S.W., Australia. $11.25

"A journal devoted to the study of the native peoples of Australia, New Guinea and the islands of the Pacific Ocean," it is published by the University of Sydney. Contributors are from universities and institutes from many countries; their contributions vary greatly in length, from just a few pages to almost an entire issue and are very scholarly, mostly reporting the results of field research in various types of anthropological studies. Archaeology and physical anthropology, to which much attention was paid, are no longer included, since a journal covering these areas of Oceania research was begun in 1966; special linguistic studies were not carried after 1956, when a monographic series devoted to that subject was established. The number and length of book reviews also vary considerably, from one to 15 per issue, and from a few hundred to over 1000 words. They are, however, all signed and critical. An important journal in anthropology.

Indexed in: S.S.H.I.   38-17490

*PHYLON.   v. 1, 1940-

Quarterly.   Atlanta, Ga. $4.50

"The Atlanta University review of race and culture," it was first edited by W.E.B. Du Bois, and carries articles mostly in sociology, politics, history and anthropology, but also in religious studies, literature and the arts. Almost all these are relevant to the study of Negroes as a cultural group, and usually on aspects of their relationships to a predominately white society, though inter-racial problems of other groups are occasionally treated. There is usually some poetry, and an occasional short story. Between 1960 and 1964, it carried an annual listing of doctoral dissertations and master's theses on race and culture completed the previous year. Signed, critical reviews of books—fiction and non-fiction—that are concerned with the journal's interests in race and culture. These vary considerably in number and length. An essential journal for any college library, both for sociology departments and for the more general study of black culture and history.

Indexed in: In.Per.Negroes   42-16469 rev.2
            P.A.I.S.
            S.S.H.I.

POPULATION Bulletin. *see* GEOGRAPHY

RURAL SOCIOLOGY.   v. 1, 1936-

Quarterly.   Brookings, S.C. $12.00

Official journal of the Rural Sociological Society. Contains research articles, 4 or 5 an issue, relating to economic, cultural, and demographic sociology of rural areas, especially in the United States, though with increased attention recently to the developing areas. Each article is preceded by an abstract. Briefer, but just as scholarly articles along with less formal contributions of opinions and suggestions, appear in "Brief Articles and Commentary." There are two sections devoted to reviews: the first contains about 25-30 book reviews which are signed, critical, and averaging about 500 words in length; the second, the *Bulletin Index*, is an annotated listing of bulletins related to rural affairs that are issued by federal, state, local, or international agencies, and other research organizations. There are also lists of books and other publications received. Finally, there is a section of news and announcements of interest to those in the field, and minutes and reports of the Society. An important journal for a field in which there is a renewed interest.

Indexed in: Bio.Ag.I.   37-10448
           Ment.Hlth.B.R.I.
           P.A.I.S.

SMITH COLLEGE STUDIES IN SOCIAL WORK.   v. 1,1930-

3 nos./yr.   Northampton, Mass. $4.00

Published by the Smith College School for Social Work, it contains articles in all areas of social work plus social psychiatry, sociology, child development and clinical psychology. The articles, which range from moderately long to lengthy, are rarely written specifically for the journal, but rather result from lectures given at the School or before other groups, or are based on papers, theses and dissertations of graduate students at the School. One issue a year contains abstracts of doctoral dissertations and master's theses accepted by the school. An important journal in the field, it is especially useful where there is a strong interest in social work or clinical psychology.

Indexed in: P.A.I.S.   34-10866

SOCIAL BIOLOGY.   v. 1, 1954-

Quarterly.   Chicago, Ill. $16.00

Titled *Eugenics Quarterly* through 1968, it is published by the University of Chicago Press for the American Eugenics Society, and "is devoted to furthering the discussion, advancement, and dissemination of knowledge concerning the biological and the socio-cultural forces which affect the structure and composition of human populations."

Each issue contains usually 5 to 7 articles of moderate length, plus a brief report or two, on demography, human genetics, family life, and other topics relating to the quality and characteristics of population, with comparative studies comprising a significant portion of the articles. Contributors include zoologists, sociologists, anthropologists, demographers, geneticists, and others from academic, governmental, and private research organizations from many countries "Communications" includes news of meetings, other major items of professional interest and responses to earlier articles. "Periodical Abstracts" in each issue carries abstracts from the fields of genetics and demography from periodicals and other serials in many languages. About 10-15 book reviews per issue, signed and critical, mostly under 500 words, but occasionally fairly long. Many articles are technical, but many are also appropriate for undergraduate use, so that the journal will be useful wherever there is much work done in demography or human genetics.

Indexed in: Ment.Hlth.B.R.I.   58-34868
           P.A.I.S.

SOCIAL CASEWORK.   v. 1, 1920-

Monthly. (except Aug.-Sept.)   N.Y. $9.00

Published by the Family Service Association of America, it was originally entitled *The Family*, changed to the *Journal of Social Casework* in 1946, and assumed its present title in 1950. It "is devoted primarily to the interests of social work practitioners and educators. Preference is given to articles that illuminate a facet of casework theory or practice, that report professional experimentation and research, or that are relevant to the social problems of the day and to the professional concerns of social workers." Usually 5 or 6 articles per issue, mostly 4-5000 words, relating to all areas of social welfare—mental health, child and family welfare, rehabilitation and correction, etc.—and on the administration, teaching and method of social casework. 4 to 8 book reviews per issue, mostly 500-600 words in length, signed and critical. An extensive listing of positions open. An essential journal for institutions with courses in social work, its increased attention to current social issues makes it useful in many areas of sociology and social psychology.

Indexed in: S.S.H.I.   22-5593

*SOCIAL FORCES.   v. 1, 1922-

Quarterly.   Chapel Hill, N.C. $10.00

Founded by Howard W. Odum of the University of North Carolina and still under the editorship of that university's eminent sociologists. "A scientific medium of social study and interpretation," it carries brief, scholarly articles and research notes reporting the results of research over the entire range of theoretical and applied sociology and related subjects—the family, social psychology, public opinion, methodology, group theory, social problems, etc. Each article is preceded by an abstract. Also the section, "Commentary" contains comments on earlier article and responses to the comments. During the 1920's and 1930's, it carried many articles on regionalism when that concept was of special interest, and it was an important source for the sociological study of the South, but it is no longer in any sense a regional journal. 40 to 50 signed, critical book reviews per issue, averaging 500-600 words. Also a list of new books. received.

One of the more important journals in the field, it should be in every library where there is a sociology major.

Indexed in: P.A.I.S.   24-31023
           S.S.H.I.

*SOCIAL PROBLEMS.   v. 1, 1953-

Quarterly.   South Bend, Ind. $15.00

Published by the Society for the Study of Social Problems, which is affiliated with the American and International Sociological Associations. Research articles, about 10 or 12 an issue, mostly 4-6000 words, on various aspects of social pathology, racial and ethnic behavior, delinquency, suicide, crime, alcoholism and drug addiction, marriage and family problems, etc., and on methodology and trends in research and writing in the field. Each article is preceded by an abstract. Issues in the past were frequently devoted to single topics, but this is no longer the case. Book reviews were discontinued in 1963, but there are occasional review-essays. Useful for papers and discussions in other social sciences as well as sociology, it is an important journal for academic libraries.

Indexed in: Ment.Hlth.B.R.I.   56-38132
          P.A.I.S.
          S.S.H.I.

SOCIAL RESEARCH.   v. 1, 1934-

Quarterly.   N.Y. $12.00

"An international quarterly of political and social science," it is published by the Graduate Faculty of Political and Social Science of the New School for Social Research. Issues consist usually of 6 articles, of moderate length, in all areas of the social sciences, with some emphasis on the interrelationship of areas, on social service methodology, or on the history or impact of ideas and theories, though studies reporting the results or research are not uncommon. In the last few years numbers have been about equally divided between those carrying a variety of articles, and those focusing on a theme such as Human Biology and the Social Sciences, Conservative Approaches in the Human Sciences, or The Future of Latin America. Most issues now contain a section, "The International Scene—Current Trends in the Social Sciences," containing lengthy reports on intellectual trends and developments abroad. Contributors are from many American and foreign universities, as well as from the New School. Signed book reviews appear in most issues; usually 4 to 6 in number, mostly over 1000 words, they are excellent.

A significant journal for social scientists, it is especially important where there is much concern with social or political theory.

Indexed in: P.A.I.S.   35-9665
          S.S.H.I.

SOCIAL SCIENCE QUARTERLY.   v. 1, 1920-

Quarterly.   Austin, Texas. $11.00

Published jointly by the Southwestern Social Science Association and the University of Texas, it was at first titled the *Southwestern Political Science Quarterly*, then (in 1923) the *Southwestern Political and Social Science Quarterly*, then (in 1933) the *Southwestern Social Science Quarterly*, and changed to its present title in 1968. The changes in title reflect the changes in emphasis. It was founded as a "medium of publication for articles and notes relating to the government and public affairs of the States of Texas, Louisiana, Arkansas, Oklahoma, Arizona, and New Mexico," but its coverage broadened early to include other social sciences and later other areas and nations. Though today the editors and many of the contributors are from the Southwest, many other contributors are not, and the subject matter is rarely just of regional interest. Many issues now are devoted to single topics such as Youth and Society, or Black America, with contributions by scholars from the various social sciences (excluding history). The general issues also include contributions from all the social sciences in articles that are short to medium length, rarely more than 5-6000 words. "News and Notes" of the Association, reports and minutes of its meetings. Usually 20-25 signed and critical book reviews, averaging about 500 words. Also list of other books received. A useful journal for all institutions, a backfile is essential for those with special interest in the Southwest.

Indexed in: P.A.I.S.   28-12245 Revised

SOCIAL SERVICE REVIEW.   v. 1, 1927-

Quarterly.   Chicago, Ill. $8.00

Edited by the Faculty of the School of Social Service Administration of the University of Chicago, it is "devoted to the scientific and professional interests of social work." Research articles on theory and practice of all aspects of social work, with much attention to the aims, methods and training in the field. "Notes and Comments" carries editorial interpretations of developments related to social welfare in addition to news items of interest to the profession. A "Source Materials" section appears occasionally, containing portions of reports, documents, proposals, etc., of special interest but not generally available. The September issue includes *Doctoral Dissertations in Social Work.* This section, which began in 1954, at first was just a listing of dissertations completed and in progress; in 1958 it added abstracts of the completed dissertations. Usually 10 to 15 signed, critical reviews, averaging 600-700 words in length, in each issue. Important government documents—mostly federal, but occasionally from a state, local or foreign government, or an international organization, are reviewed and commented upon, some of them quite extensively.

Indexed in: Ment.Hlth.B.R.I.   29-8588
           P.A.I.S.
           S.S.H.I.

SOCIOLOGICAL ABSTRACTS   v. 1, 1952-

7 nos./yr.   Brooklyn, N Y. $100.00

Co-sponsored by the American Sociological Association, the Eastern Sociological Society, the International Sociological Association, and the Midwest Sociological Society. The 1970 volume carried some 6,500 abstracts, classified into 54 sections and 26 areas. The abstracts are from journals and other serials in sociology and closely-related topics published throughout the world, though all abstracts are in English; they range in length from just a few lines to several hundred words, and for the more important articles, are quite substantial. They are, however, not evaluative or critical. There are subject, author and periodical indexes in each issue, with the seventh number of each volume comprised of the annual cumulative index (appearing late in the following year). In addition to the abstracts, issues of the last few years have begun carrying special articles—autobiographies of noted sociologists, "Sociology in Finland," annotated bibliographies, etc., and Supplements have carried abstracts of papers presented at certain professional meetings.

Most useful where there is a great deal of work in sociology, but for most colleges, it is a luxury.

58-46404

*SOCIOLOGICAL INQUIRY.   v. 1, 1925-

Semi-annually.   Haverford, Pa. $6.00

Official journal of Alpha Kappa Delta, the national sociology honor society, and known as the *Alpha Kappa Deltan* through volume 30, it is designed to implement its aims "by communicating and reviewing developments of sociological interest in the service of faculty, investigators, and students alike." Covers all areas of sociology, but is especially concerned with articles that relate to theory, especially those articulating theory and research. Most of the articles, which are brief to moderately long, are by faculty members, including some eminent sociologists, but contributions by graduate and undergraduate students also appear, and each article is preceded by an abstract. Most issues are devoted to a single topic, which are often on method or theory, and in 1969 a regular section, "Reports on Work in Progress," was added which describes research plans of active scholars. No book reviews. Having improved greatly in recent years, it is now a very useful journal for undergraduate sociology majors, not just because it is keyed to them, but because the contributions are relevant to their concerns and of excellent quality.

SOCIOLOGICAL QUARTERLY.   v. 1, 1960-

Quarterly.   Columbia, Mo. $7.00

Superseding the *Midwest Sociologist,* it is the official journal of the Midwest Sociological Society. Publishes scholarly articles in all areas of sociology, with some emphasis on reporting the results of empirical research. Usually 5 or 6 articles per issue, mostly 5000-6000 words in length. There are a few long reviews, about 750-1000 words and sometimes much longer, plus a larger number of briefer reviews, generally 300-500 words in length. They are all signed and critical. Occasional review articles; lists of publications received.

Indexed in: S.S.H.I.   64-5249

SOCIOLOGY.   v. 1, 1967-

3 nos./yr.   London. $12.00

The official journal of the British Sociological Association, it reflects the rapid growth of professionalism in British sociology in the 1960's. Each issue consists of 5 or 6 scholarly articles, mostly of moderate length, but on occasion quite long, and ranging over all areas of sociology, with some emphasis on theory and method. Each article is preceded by an abstract. Authors are mainly at British universities. "Notes and News" of the Association, of university departments, of research organizations and of conferences and meetings. There are a few (1 to 5) long book reviews (1000-2000 words) plus a large number (30 to 40) shorter ones (150-500 words). They are all signed and critical. Also a list of books received.

73-12649

SOCIOLOGY AND SOCIAL RESEARCH. v. 6, 1921-

Quarterly. Los Angeles, Calif. $6.00

Its original title was the *Journal of Applied Sociology,* formed by a combination of the former publications of the Southern California Sociological Society, primarily *Studies in Sociology.* This had been published from 1916 to 1921; then the *Journal of Applied Sociology* was formed and took over its numbering. The present title was adopted in 1927.

Contains 6 to 10 articles, usually 4-6000 words, mostly reporting the results of research on specific aspects of sociological problems and phenomena. Some attention to social theory and methodology. Each issue contains generally 10 to 15 signed reviews, mostly 400-500 words long. A smaller number of books are reviewed briefly (100-200 words) in "Book Notes," and there is a list of other publications received.

Indexed in: P.A.I.S.   24-21157 (rev. '32)
           S.S.H.I.

SOCIOLOGY of Education. *see* EDUCATION

SOCIOMETRY. v. 1, 1937-

Quarterly. Washington, D.C. $14.00

Founded and edited until 1956 by Dr. J.L. Moreno, its subtitle was "A journal of inter-personal relations." In that year it became an official publication of the American Sociological Association and its subtitle was changed to "a journal of research in social psychology." Its editorial policy states that it "is concerned with the entire range of interests and problems represented by research in social psychology . . . [which] has as its central focus the investigation of the processes and products of social interaction at the interpersonal, intrapersonal, intergroups, and intragroup levels and the development of significant generalizations therefrom. In keeping with the more general meaning of the name of the journal emphasis will be placed on measurement of social behavior." There are usually 7 to 10 articles per issue, on various aspects of social psychology, with a special emphasis on methodology. Each article is preceded by an abstract. An important journal for advanced students and faculty in both sociology and psychology.

Indexed in: Ment.Hlth.B.R.I.   39-25267 rev.

SOUTHERN FOLKLORE QUARTERLY. v. 1, 1937-

Quarterly. Gainesville, Fla. $5.50

Published by the University of Florida in cooperation with the South Atlantic Modern Language Association, it is "devoted to the historical and descriptive study of folklore and to the discussion of folk material as a living tradition." 3 of the 4 annual issues contain articles, of brief to moderate length, on all aspects of folklore—research, theory, texts, dance, music, drama, proverbs, material culture, etc.—written by scholars and devotees. It is not strictly a regional journal any longer; earlier vol-

umes were concerned almost solely with folklore of the South, but now
the articles cover all areas and periods, though there is still some emphasis on the South. The first number of each volume contains (since
1947 it has comprised the entire number) the annual *Folklore Bibliography for 19—* which now covers "with substantial completeness"
articles, essays and books on the folklore of the United States, Canada,
Latin America, and the rest of the Spanish and Portuguese-speaking world,
with many items annotated. Coverage and nature of the bibliography
have varied a bit over the years. A few signed and critical book reviews,
varying greatly in length, but mostly about 500 words. An important
journal wherever folklore is studied, and an interesting journal for browsing.

Indexed in: Music I.   38-17465
          S.S.H.I.

SOUTHWESTERN JOURNAL OF ANTHROPOLOGY.   v. 1, 1945-

Quarterly.   Albuquerque, N.M. $7.00

Published by the University of New Mexico, it is "designed to include articles in all branches of anthropology relating to people and cultures, past
and present, in any region. It is offered as a vehicle of expression for
anthropologists in all parts of the world." Each issue contains usually 5
or 6 scholarly articles, mostly of medium length, averaging 5-6000 words,
covering theory as well as field research, and primarily in social and cultural anthropology, though with some attention to archaeology and physical anthropology. Each article is preceded by an abstract. A basic journal
where there is any interest in anthropology.

Indexed in: S.S.H.I.   47-5758

TRANS-ACTION. *see* GENERAL

WELFARE IN REVIEW.   v. 1, 1963-

Bi-monthly.   Washington, D.C. $1.75

An official publication of the Social and Rehabilitation Service of the
HEW, though not necessarily reflecting official policies. Published monthly
until November, 1967, it contains articles and other information on all
aspects of public welfare—social work, education, federal, state and local
programs, proposed and recent legislation, research and evaluative studies,
etc., including matters in other disciplines affecting welfare programs, such
as housing, income and employment, health, delinquency, etc. Contributors
include officials of the HEW and other federal, state, local and private
agencies. Through February, 1970, the concluding section of each issue
was devoted to "Public Assistance Statistics," containing a number of the
various tables of data on public assistance programs for the latest month
and earlier periods. Since then, the section carries only reports of changes
in the programs. An annual *Statistical Supplement,* carrying more detailed
tables and covering, in some areas, data for earlier years as well, was published until 1968. Usually 1 or 2 book reviews, signed and critical, and
usually 1000-1500 words. These are often books of comparative or historical interest and not just on the current domestic welfare system. An annotated listing of recent publications, governmental and non-governmental.

An important journal for courses in social work and studies of the sociology
of poverty. A depository item.

                                                                65-62351

Philosophy

INTERNATIONAL PHILOSOPHICAL QUARTERLY.   v. 1, 1961-

Quarterly.   Bronx, N.Y. $8.00

Jointly edited by the Department of Philosophy, Fordham University, and by Berchmans Philosophicum, Haverlee-Louvain, Belgium, it was "founded to provide an international forum in English for the inter-change of basic philosophical ideas between the Americas and Europe and between East & West. Its primary orientation is to encourage vital contemporary expression – creative, critical and historical – in the intercultural tradition of theistic spiritualist, and personalist humanism, but without further restriction of school within these broad perspec-tives." Usually 5 or 6 scholarly articles contributed by faculty members from universities around the world (editorial policy states that each issue should have 3 original articles from European authors), with a range of topics just as wide. The section, "Contemporary Currents," appears in most issues and surveys recent literature on a contemporary movement, author, or problem. The book reviews consist of one or several long review-articles, plus 3 or 4 single reviews, signed and critical, usually 1000-1500 words. Though its contributors are not as eminent and the articles not as technical as those in the major journals, the journal will be very useful for undergraduate libraries.

Indexed in: S.S.H.I.

*MIND.   v. 1, 1876; n.s.v. 1, 1892-

Quarterly.   Oxford, England.   25/

Though still subtitled "a quarterly review of psychology and philos-ophy," since its early years it has not devoted much attention to psychology, and in recent years none at all. Published for the Mind Association since 1900, it has contained a large number of influential articles during its history – for example, G. E. Moore's and Bertrand Russell's earliest contributions appeared in it, and all the great turn-of-the-century figures in American and British psychology and philosophy can be found in the early volumes. Today it carries articles by contri-butors from universities in many countries, covering all branches of philosophy, though rarely historical studies. Usually under 7 articles, ranging from medium-length to lengthy, plus briefer "Discussion Notes" on previous articles. Also frequent "Critical Notices," a feature since the journal's beginning; these are really review articles occasioned by recent books. The number of reviews varies, but now averages about 7 or 8 per issue; they are excellent – mostly from 600 to 1000 words, with some several times that, all signed and critical. An extensive listing of other books received. There is an annual listing of all members of the Mind Association. It is today, according to William Gerber, "one of the dozen most influential journals of philosophy in the world," and both a backfile and a current subscription are essential where there is much work in philosophy.

Indexed in: Br. Hum. I.   15-1957*

Many titles are listed in more than one subject classification. They are, however, annotated in only one and this index refers to the page on which the annotation appears.